ARTILLERY

ARTILLERY

OVER 300 OF THE WORLD'S FINEST ARTILLERY PIECES FROM 1914 TO THE PRESENT DAY

CHRIS CHANT

amber
BOOKS

First published in 2005 by Amber Books Ltd

ISBN 1-904687-41-5

Published by
Amber Books Ltd
Bradley's Close
74–77 White Lion Street
London N1 9PF
United Kingdom
www.amberbooks.co.uk

Project Editor: Sarah Uttridge
Design: EQ Media

Printed in the United Arab Emirates

PICTURE CREDITS
All Aerospace Publishing except for p5 DOD

Contents

Introduction..8

World War I Field Guns...30

World War I Heavy Artillery...38

World War II Field Guns..50

World War II Heavy Artillery..70

World War II Railway Guns and Armoured Trains.....................82

World War II Self-Propelled Artillery....................................92

World War II Anti-Tank Guns...106

World War II Rocket Artillery...124

World War II Light Anti-Aircraft Guns..................................134

World War II Heavy Anti-Aircraft Guns.................................146

Post-War Towed Artillery..158

Cold War Self-Propelled Artillery..164

Short-Range Ballistic Missiles...172

Modern Towed artillery..180

Modern Self-Propelled Artillery..198

Modern Multiple Rocket Launchers......................................214

Modern Towed Anti-Aircraft Guns.......................................226

Modern Self-Propelled Anti-Aircraft Guns.............................232

Glossary..250

Index..251

Introduction

Artillery has been present on the battlefield for thousands of years – witness the fearsome ballistae of Ancient Rome, for example – but it is only in the last few hundred years that it has come to dominate the modern battlefield in a way that is only now being challenged by air-dropped 'smart' weapons. The Emperor Napoleon, a former gunner, was one of the first generals of modern times to use artillery offensively, but artillery first took centre stage in the great cataclysm that was World War I.

After the Battle of the Marne in 1914 and the stabilising of the Western Front, the establishment of defensive trenches gave the artillery of both sides a sitting target to bombard. Lined up almost wheel-to-wheel, heavy guns would pound a trench section with such force that the concussive effects of the rounds exploding around them would literally drive men mad. Most of the casualties suffered on the Western Front were caused not by bullets or disease, but by artillery shells.

World War II saw the development of specialist artillery alongside the regular field pieces. Anti-aircraft guns became faster-firing, while anti-tank guns became bigger and more penetrating. As infantry formations were mechanized to keep up with the tanks, self-propelled artillery was also developed to provide mobile fire support. Rocket artillery emerged as a means of delivering a powerful salvo in one swift blow, and this was particularly popular on the Eastern Front, the German Nebelwerfer taking on the Soviet Katyusha.

After 1945 the Cold War saw the increasing sophistication of rocket artillery, and the introduction of tactical nuclear weapons. Anti-tank guns were superseded by wire-guided missiles, but field and heavy artillery remained little changed from the weapons that had won World War II. In Vietnam one of the cornerstones of the American strategy were the firebases, placed throughout the Vietnamese countryside to give fire support to any troops in range – these were so successful they attracted many direct attacks from the Vietnamese in an attempt to knock them out.

On the modern battlefield the majority of artillery now seen is either self-propelled or ultralight and air-portable. Counter-battery fire has become so deadly that a modern artilleryman needs to fire three rounds, the last clearing the barrel before the first has landed, and then instantly move out, or risk instant retaliation. Despite this vulnerability, artillery remains a vital part of any general's toolkit.

In this book you will find a detailed directory of the various types of artillery pieces that either serve or have served in the world's armies.

Left: U.S. Army soldiers of Fox Battery, 7th Field Artillery, fire a 155mm M198 Towed Howitzer during an artillery training exercise near Khowst, Afghanistan, on 9 January 2005. The Fox battery soldiers are using the training opportunity to hone their ability to provide destructive, suppressive and protective indirect and direct field artillery fires with the howitzer.

Voice of the guns
World War I artillery

To the sentry standing on his pre-dawn duty in the trenches of the Western Front, the sight of a jagged line of light on the opposite horizon cannot have been comforting, for behind such a line lay the fire of the largest concentration of artillery pieces in history.

The image of World War I battle-fields which has been passed down through history is of lines of rifle-armed soldiers marching into a hail of gunfire and being cut down in swathes by machine-gun fire. But deadly though they were, machine-guns were not the worst killers, and more soldiers were killed on the Western Front by artillery than by any other type of weapon.

Artillery played a crucial role in shaping the course of World War I. The hail of shells produced by quick-fire field artillery forced the armies of 1914 to shelter in the trenches, where they remained until 1918.

Gun development

During World War I, field guns were the most numerous type of artillery in use. Light, mobile guns had been developed and produced to take part in the fluid type of warfare that had been the norm during the previous century, in which large armies wheeled about the battlefields of Europe with field artillery providing them with fire support.

The nature of warfare during World War I did not allow the use of such artillery in its customary mobile fashion. After a brief period of open warfare in 1914, the firepower of the new QF guns drove the infantry to take cover in trenches. Although it was the field artillery which had created the stalemate in the trenches, it was the trenches which then took away much of its importance.

Field artillery could not destroy earthworks. It was the heavy artillery

that ultimately won or lost battles. It was only the heavy artillery that had the shell power to destroy the earth or concrete protection upon which each side came to rely for survival in the front line, and it was only the heavy artillery that could smash a way through the lines of defences behind which each side sheltered.

Powerful weaponry

By 1914 most European powers had built up large gun parks that contained artillery of increasingly heavy calibres and power. These were necessary to demolish the rings of fortifications that all the major powers used to protect their frontier regions against the intrusions of others. That same heavy artillery was equally useful in the strange conditions of the Western Front, where the trench lines imposed their own peculiar method of warfare.

The 'Great War' was the heyday of heavy artillery. In the purely static conditions that existed along the Western Front, the heavy guns and howitzers could be carefully emplaced with few thoughts of dramatic or rapid moves, and they could be fed with their heavy projectiles for as long as the required logistic machinery remained in being. They had plenty of targets, as

A 38-cm (15-in) Schiffskanone L/45 'Max' Eisenbahn Gerüst, an adapted naval gun, is prepared for action. Rail guns were easier to move and could be readied for action more speedily.

Above: A 9.2-in (234-mm) howitzer of the 2nd Australian Siege Battery in action at Voormezeele, near Ypres, in September 1917. Such weapons lacked the mobility for use in a war of movement.

Above: German gunners prepare a 30.5-cm (12-in) howitzer. These weapons offered useful range with a devastatingly powerful shell that descended almost vertically to punch though overhead cover.

Below right: An Italian 300-mm (11.8-in) gun on the road at Sandrigo in northern Italy in June 1918. The Italians placed great reliance on such weapons, but these were too heavy and lacking in mobility to be saved when the Central Powers broke through.

Below: The Holt tractor was very successful in the task of hauling heavy artillery and equipment through the mud of the Western Front. It eventually led to the caterpillar-tracked fighting vehicle, or tank.

each side burrowed deep into the earth to survive the storm that daily flew over their heads. The only way to harm such burrows was by the use of heavy projectiles that could smash their way through this level of overhead protection, and these heavy projectiles could be delivered only by the heavy artillery.

The howitzer was the most effective form of heavy artillery: their fire at a high angle of elevation meant that the shells descended at a nearly vertical angle. Only howitzers could reach out into the enemy trenches, and only the heavy howitzers could be of any real use. Guns varied in size from the British 6-in (152-mm) howitzer through 8-in (203-mm), 9.2-in (234-mm) and 15-in (381-mm) guns to the massive German 42-cm (16.54-in) M-Gerät, or 'Big Bertha'.

Crucial role

The big guns played a key part in the offensives on the Western Front, firing millions of shells for up to a week before a major attack. Such was the intensity of the barrages that they could be heard in London, more than 240 km (150 miles) away. Once the infantry went 'over the top', the artillery switched to a creeping barrage, delivering a curtain of shells just in front of the advancing foot soldiers.

Even though lighter field artillery was less than effective against an entrenched enemy, all of the armies involved in the conflict maintained large numbers of such weapons. They could do little against even the most lightly protected defences, especially as during the early stages of the conflict most of their ammunition was Shrapnel, intended for use against an enemy in the open. Shrapnel could neither penetrate dug-outs nor cut barbed wire, so gradually it was replaced by High Explosive.

Field artillery

But commanders on both sides eventually expected some kind of strategic breakthrough into mobile warfare. Should that ever be achieved, the field guns would once more come into their own, while the static and heavy siege guns that had become so important could be left behind. It was also easier to manufacture lighter field artillery, while the production of heavier weapons took much more time and money.

But there were theatres in which mobile artillery played a major role. Not all World War I warfare was restricted to the trenches. In Russia, aggressive German artillery tactics were an important factor in establishing dominance over the large but poorly equipped Russian armies, while in the Middle East and in the Balkans the fluid warfare envisaged by the pre-1914 military planners did take place. Here, field artillery could play its proper role of supporting the other arms in the field.

But the main theatre of World War I was the Western Front, and there all the massed field artillery could achieve was the provision of support to the real killers, the heavy guns.

Heavy artillery in battle World War II big guns

Despite the tactical developments since 1918, heavy artillery still had a vital role to play in World War II. Many battles became siege-like slogging matches, horribly similar to those of 1914-18. From Leningrad to Cassino, from Sevastopol to the Siegfried Line, armies dug themselves in so deeply that only big guns could blast a way through.

The classic role of heavy artillery in warfare is the destruction or neutralisation of the enemy's fortifications and strongpoints, though in more recent times it has also included the destruction of the enemy's field and other artillery. In World War II both tasks were important. This may seem curious, for we have by now become used to the idea that World War II was a war of swift movement and armoured thrusts. But on many fronts this was not always the case: along many battlefronts campaigns often settled down into long periods of relative inactivity, and further advances and/or withdrawals were often prevented either by weather conditions or lack of resources on both sides. Under such conditions heavy artillery could once more resume its importance and make life as miserable and dangerous as possible for the enemy.

Fortifications
During World War II fortifications were still around. The best-known example is the French Maginot Line, but there were many others such as the old but nonetheless effective defences that ringed the port of Sevastopol and the ring of 19th century forts that defended Metz. These were still strong enough to stop the US 3rd Army in its tracks after Patton's rapid advances across France in 1944. It must not be forgotten that under modern conditions many large cities can become just as effective as fortifications in stopping the rapid advance of even armour-heavy forces. The examples of Stalingrad and Leningrad are still there for all to see, and under these conditions the only weapons that can be used to reduce such large-scale obstacles remain the heavy gun and the heavy howitzer.

Therefore, heavy artillery had a large part to play in many campaigns during World War II. Some

of the weapons were rather elderly (to put it mildly), but most combatant nations had deemed it worthwhile to invest heavily in large-calibre artillery of all kinds.

Counter-bombardment
One kind of heavy artillery that was relatively new was the specialised long-range counter-bombardment gun. Experience gained during World War I was that enemy batteries had to be silenced during critical periods such as large-scale attacks (to prevent harassing fire on sensitive rear areas, for example). During World War I this role was often assumed by railway artillery, but in World War II the specialised long-range guns often weighed in for this purpose. Typical of these long-range guns was the German 24-cm (9.45-in) Kanone 3, which was really a case of overkill for the targets against which weapons such as the American 155-mm (6.1-in) Gun M1 or the German 15-cm (5.9-in) Kanone 18 were more than adequate.

But among the heavy artillery types the howitzer tended to predominate over the gun, for with its higher projectile trajectory and flexible system of propellant charges, the howitzer was often a far more useful weapon than the gun. The gun certainly had the greater range, but it often had to use a flat trajectory at times when plunging fire would have far more effect on the types of target involved, such as strongpoints or bunkers. By 1945, artillery developments were such that the range discrepancy between guns and howitzers were not all that marked, the howitzer's shorter range being frequently offset by its heavier projectiles.

Gun-howitzer
Another World War II innovation was the introduction of the gun-howitzer in which a variable propellant system could be allied with the ability to use either direct

Above: Connected by field telephone to the gun battery, the Forward Observation Post reports the map reference of the target and will spot the fall of shot. These Soviets have dug themselves a deep trench to escape a German counter-offensive barrage designed to 'blind' the Soviet guns.

Below: Heavy guns were sited several miles behind the enemy lines to avoid the unwelcome attention of enemy field guns and mortars, so target information had to be relayed back to the gunners by forward observers, like the Afrika Korps team shown here.

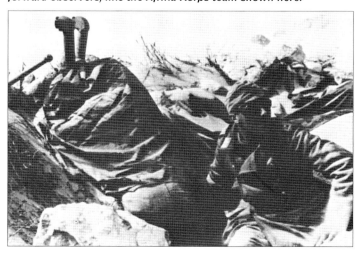

Left: The British 7.2-in howitzer could fling its 91.7-kg (202-lb) shell nearly 18 km (11 miles), but manoeuvring it the few yards to the breech was tricky. It had a vicious recoil, requiring blocks like the one in the foreground to be placed behind for the wheels to run up.

fire or fire in the upper register, i.e. at high angles of elevation to produce plunging fire. Typical of such weapons was the Soviet 152-mm (6-in) Model 137 gun-howitzer.

For all these technicalities the imagination is still attracted by the sheer scale of weapons such as the German 35.5-cm (14-in) H M.1 or intrigued by such technical freaks as the American 'Little David' with its huge 36-in (914-mm) calibre. No doubt it would be possible to formulate viable reasons why such oddities should exist in an era dominated by the tank and the heavy bomber, but it is still something of a challenge. Although such monsters survived until 1945 (and were even under further development at that time), the truth was that their day was well past. Perhaps the greatest indication that their era was over can be seen in the example of the greatest protagonist of heavy artillery during World War II, namely the Red Army. It used

nothing larger than the 203-mm (8-in) Model 1931 howitzer from the beginning to the end. Rather than relying on a few super-heavy weapons spread thinly (which was usually the case for most other combatants who had such weapons), the Red Army relied instead on the principle of mass, using large numbers of heavy artillery batteries to deliver streams of heavy projectiles, both against fortified areas and against the enemy's answering batteries – and the Red Army won.

The difference between gun and howitzer is seen by comparing this photograph of the US 155-mm howitzer with the pictures above. The 40-calibre barrel length of the 'Long Tom' helped give a range of 22000 km (24059 yards) compared to the 14000-m (15311-yard) range of the stubby-barreled howitzer.

'Long Tom': the 155-mm M1 at war

A 'Long Tom' fires at minimum elevation, the front of the weapon resting on a firing jack underneath the carriage with the bogies raised above the ground. When it was time to move off, the barrel would be pulled back and clamped to the trail.

The US Army's 155-mm M1 proved to be an immediate success and the weapon soon was assigned the nickname 'Long Tom'. This name was well deserved, for the M1 had a long slender 45-calibre barrel (L/45) that gave the gun a distinctive appearance. Gradually numbers of M1s crossed the Atlantic and moved into action in Italy. In the UK the type was prepared for the invasion of France, but back in the United States the M1s were already on active service. Like the earlier M1918, the M1 also assumed a coastal defence role and was used as part of a four-weapon defence system to cover the coasts of the mainland US. Largest of the four types of weapon involved were the 16-in (406-mm) coastal-defence guns that could shield large areas of coastline. Behind them were 6-in (152-mm) coast-defence guns and

numbers of 90-mm (3.54-in) guns in turrets. Finally the M1s were intended to cover the gaps in the coverage of the static weapons, and this they did using some of the old Panama Mounts but also numbers of the mobile metal 'Kelly Mounts' whose origins owed much to the basically similar mounts used by the German 15-cm Kanone 39. After the middle of 1944, the M1 was to be found in service everywhere from the Pacific to Germany. They at all times provided sterling service and were also used by the Royal Artillery long-range batteries of the British Army and for a time by the Free French forces.

Right: An imposing weapon even when on the move, the 'Long Tom' was developed from the excellent French 155-mm GPF gun supplied to the US Army in 1918. The heavy split-trail carriage provided a very stable firing platform.

Below: The carriage of the 155-mm M1 was required to accept an 8-in howitzer and was standardised in 1938, also under the designation M1. On operations the gun was normally towed by the M4 tractor rather than the truck shown here.

Gun versus howitzer Design and tactics

Guns and howitzers are both types of artillery that have been in widespread use for centuries. Yet there are significant differences in both design and use between the gun and howitzer, and World War II saw both types in extensive and often decisive action.

To the layman the gun and the howitzer are one and the same thing, but to the gunner they are very different beasts. They are not only constructed differently, but are even deployed in action in different ways and with different targets in mind.

The gun was for many hundreds of years the most common form of artillery piece. In artillery terms it fires only in the lower register (at low angles of barrel elevation), so that the fired projectile travels in a relatively straight line. To make matters more complicated the gun usually uses only one propellant charge contained in a fixed case (the projectile and the 'cartridge' case are one unit and are loaded into the breech as a single item).

This combination of a fixed charge and a relatively flat projectile trajectory makes the gun ideal for attacking, with a very high degree of accuracy, targets that stand well out in the open. Guns are usually long-barrelled devices.

Variable charge

In contrast, howitzers are usually short-barrelled devices. Developed from the ancient family of weapons known as 'mortars', howitzers are used primarily to fire in the upper register (at high angles of barrel elevation) so that the projectiles climb upward, peak and then fall to Earth at the end of a highly curved trajectory. By juggling with a variable-charge system, the howitzer can be used to fire on targets that are quite close to the firing point, and by elevating the barrel above about 45° (i.e. in the upper register) the projectile can be made to fall with great accuracy at ranges well below those possible using full

charge and fully 45° elevation. Thus the howitzer is said to have a variable charge system, and the projectile is loaded into the breech separately from the charge, which has traditionally been contained and loaded in fabric bags. The howitzer may thus be regarded as a more complicated artillery system than the gun, but it provides the gunner with a far greater operational flexibility than the gun. For a start, the curved trajectory enables the gunner to engage targets that may be behind some sort of protection (such as the curve of a hill), and it was the howitzer that spelled the demise of the classical fortification. The gunner can also use the variable-charge system to suit the target type and range. For instance, a protected target may be engaged by any number of charge and elevation angle combinations, both high and low angle and high or low charges.

Increased range

In practice a gun, having more range than the howitzer, can be placed well back from a front line for firing. The howitzer is generally placed well forward to give its variable charge system full rein.

To make optimum use of both types of weapon, many artillery organisations once had provision for both in their battle arrangements. In British practice up to the end of World War I, artillery regiments (battalions) had two batteries of field guns and one of field howitzers, but after the 'Great War' there was a definite tendency to produce new designs that combined the attributes of both the gun and the howitzer. The 25-pdr was one of the very first of these gun-

Above: This leFH 18 crew is about to experience the rigours of the first winter of the Russian campaign. Seen in action at Orel, the sturdy 105-mm (4.13-in) howitzer was too heavy to be easily handled in the endless mud and then ice of the autumn and winter in the USSR.

Below: The US 105-mm (4.13-in) M102, with its short barrel and high elevation, is a classic example of the field howitzer, firing a larger and heavier shell than a field gun of the same weight.

Above: The German K18 gun was long-barrelled and extremely heavy. Until the advent of the heavy halftrack it took two teams of horses to tow the weapon in two loads, so in the largely horse-drawn German army of 1939 the K18 was not a popular weapon.

All out attack: Soviet artillery

The 203-mm (8-in) B-4 M1931 (pictured) was the largest Soviet howitzer of the war. It was one of the weapons fielded by the Soviets' September 1944 'breakthrough artillery division'. This comprised an observation battalion and seven mortar/artillery brigades: a light brigade (two regiments each with 24 76-mm guns), a howitzer brigade (three regiments each with 28 122-mm howitzers), a heavy howitzer brigade (four battalions each with eight 152-mm howitzers/gun-howitzers), a BM howitzer brigade (four battalions each with six 203-mm howitzers), two mortar brigades (108 120-mm and 32 160-mm mortars), and a rocket brigade (36 300-mm rocket launch units).

howitzer compromises. The 25-pdr was often used with the barrel at low angles of elevation, but the charge system was variable and the propellant was loaded separately. Today the divisions between gun and howitzer are even less obvious. More recently, designs such as the 155-mm (6.1-in) FH-70, bought by eight countries, are termed howitzers but have very long barrels (to reach ranges of 31500 m/ 34,450 yards with a base-bleed projectile), and are frequently fired as guns once were.

German tactics

During World War II, however, the divisions between the gun and the howitzer were still quite marked. The Germans plumped almost universally for howitzers as the mainstay of their field batteries. They decided that the flexibility of the elevation and charge system of the howitzer outweighed the utility of guns, and there was one other factor involved. That is that the howitzer generally fires a larger projectile than the equivalent calibre of gun, for in most armies of the

period field guns tended to have a calibre of around 75 mm (2.95 in), while the equivalent calibre of howitzer to match these guns was 105 mm (4.13 in), and that meant a considerably heavier projectile.

Considered in terms of extremes, the two best examples of field guns and howitzer that can be quoted are the Red Army's 76.2-mm (3-in) Field Gun Model 1936 and the American 105-mm (4.13-in) M2A1: even a quick visual comparison emphasises the long slender barrel of the Soviet gun and the far stubbier barrel of the American howitzer. In between is the example of the hybrid British 25-pdr, using not only a calibre intermediate to both but the best points of both systems. Today such fine divisions have all but vanished from the battlefield.

Right: Superficially a howitzer, the classic British 25-pdr weapon was often used in gun roles (indeed, even as an anti-tank gun); it came to be known as a gun/howitzer and was used in both roles.

Though it favoured the medium howitzer over the gun for most tactical purposes, the German army did make considerable use of 150-mm (5.9-in) howitzers and guns for heavier, longer-range work.

Left: American M8 4.5-in rockets were fired from several types of launcher, including elevating units attached to the turrets of M4 Sherman medium tanks. These launchers were produced in several sizes.

Below: The best of the British rocket designs was the Hedgehog, which fired rocket-propelled depth charges against a U-boat on any bearing. The Hedgerow land-based system was used in Normandy.

Rockets of the West World War II Allied rockets

Britain had been the first Western nation to use rockets in action, Congreve rockets helping to burn Washington in 1812. But the introduction of modern rockets into British Army service took a long time. Despite starting from scratch, it was the Americans who produced the best Allied rocket, in the M8.

The first Allied nation of World War II to devote attention to war rockets was the UK. During the 1930s staff planners appreciated that the British armoury had fallen to the point at which the nation was wide open to air attack. The production of adequate numbers of anti-aircraft guns would be expensive to an extreme, so it was reasoned that the rocket might help to bridge the gap.

Thus British scientists started a major programme. Starting virtually from scratch and having only the technology derived from the old black-powder Congreve and similar designs of the previous century, they soon established basic principles. One was that the use of new propellants, based on extruded grains of cellulose-based compounds, was a viable proposition, and the production of such propellants on a large scale was established. They learned what could and could not be achieved by rockets using the new propellants, and at times the negative aspect seemed to be all too much in the ascendant.

Rail launchers

Together with the rocket research went investigation of launchers. The classic form of rocket launcher had been fixed decades earlier with the Congreve and Hale rockets. The rocket required only a simple frame or rail system for launching and, as mass production was the ultimate objective, the simpler the design the better. That is exactly what emerged. At the time two rockets were under consideration, namely 2- and 3-in (50.8- and 76.2-mm) weapons, and both used very simple rail launchers. In the event the 3-in rocket proved more useful and the intended anti-aircraft launcher for this was simple to an extreme. The first launcher for 3-in rockets, sometimes known as the Harvey projector, was simply two rails 3.66 m (12 ft) long with light metal sheets to protect the crew from blast at the moment of firing. These simple projectors were used in large closely grouped batteries all fired at the same instant, which was the only way that a target could be usefully engaged as for simplicity's sake the British rockets used fin stabilisation and were thus inherently inaccurate.

As the rockets left their launcher rails, any slight influence on their path from side winds or other factors made them veer off course, sometimes to an alarming degree. Mass production methods for the rockets introduced more variants,

and so poor was the accuracy of the first British rockets that the only way to use them effectively was in salvoes. Thus later projectors used a greater number of launcher rails until the ultimate was reached with no fewer than 20 rockets on a single launcher.

Once the anti-aircraft rocket was in service, it was appreciated that there could be other uses for so simple and relatively inexpensive a weapon. Various experimental applications for the rocket were trialled, these including what was perhaps the most bizarre of all, the Grand Panjandrum. This was a massive twin-wheel arrangement

propelled by rocket motors round the wheel rims. The idea was that the wheel could be launched from landing craft and allowed to move up a beach to any local defences, where the wheel would be exploded. The idea was sound, but did not work in practice. Far more successful was the Hedgehog, which was a cross between a spigot mortar and a rocket to hurl depth charges at submerged submarines. From the Hedgehog grew the Hedgerow used to fire racks of bombs at beach defences during the Normandy invasion. Also from the Hedgehog came the American 7.3-in (183-mm) T37 rocket.

Although British efforts before World War II to develop cheap yet effective anti-aircraft rockets were unsuccessful, they paved the way for test items such as this air-portable 24-pdr rocket projector.

The American effort

By the time the offshoots of the British rocket programme were underway the Americans were in the war. Starting from nothing they soon built up the entire industrial complex required for rocket production. The main US effort was directed to producing an all-purpose rocket, although in the event the weapon was used mainly for the artillery role. The Americans concentrated all their efforts on the 4.5-in (114.3-mm) M8 rocket, which proved to be an excellent decision. The M8 was produced in far greater numbers than any other solid-propellant rocket during World War II with the possible exception of the Soviet types, for which no precise figures are available. A bewildering array of launchers was developed to fire the M8 rocket. Few of them ever got into the hands of the troops, and the few

that did were usually unable to meet the strict safety and other standards normally required by the US forces. Thus many of the M8 projectors retained their T-series experimental designations although some were used in appreciable numbers. Some were even local or emergency improvisations, such as the Scorpion, improvised for island-invasion purpose in the Pacific. This was a multiple launcher that could be fitted into the cargo area of a DUKW amphibious cargo carrier, and could fire up to 144 M8 rockets.

By 1944 the rocket was well established as an airlaunched weapon, and was used for attacks on land and sea targets. But there was one role that the Allies had yet to explore, and that was the artillery rocket. In their haste to get rockets into production both the British and the Americans opted for the fin-stabilised rocket to speed production. But such a rocket was primarily an area-saturation weapon, a fact well demonstrated by the Soviet Katyushas, while the main protagonists of the artillery rocket were the Germans, who used spin-stabilised rockets in large numbers. Thus, if the Allies wished to counter the German rocket batteries on their own terms, they too had to adopt the spin-stabilised rocket with all the attendant production costs and perhaps even some loss in potential range since this weapon has to use some of its energy to produce the spin.

Spin stabilisation

In typically thorough fashion, the Americans set about producing a proper spinner and in time came up with the 4.5-in M16 rocket together with its multiple projector, the T66. However, only small numbers saw action before the war ended. The British tried a simpler system in which a finned rocket was spun by its launcher rails. This method, although rather crude in design terms and nowhere near as efficient as a proper spin-stabilised rocket, was efficient enough for artillery use. Thus, there appeared the Land Mattress system, but only in numbers insufficient to make any real impression when compared with the German artillery rocket batteries.

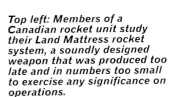

Top left: Members of a Canadian rocket unit study their Land Mattress rocket system, a soundly designed weapon that was produced too late and in numbers too small to exercise any significance on operations.

Above left: The British Land Mattress system was a compromise between the expense of the spin-stabilised rocket and the inaccuracy of the fin-stabilised rocket: the launcher itself imparted spin to the rocket.

Left: The only rocket of the Western Allies to be used in numbers approaching those of the Soviet Katyushas was the US M8, seen here in action in the Hurtgen forest of western Germany during November 1944.

Flak Artillerie German AA guns of World War II

Trained to operate closely with tactical aircraft, the German army was well aware of the value of an efficient anti-aircraft defence. In spite of the political interference endemic in the Third Reich, when war came German arms were more effectively shielded from air attack than any other.

This light halftrack mounts a 2-cm Flak 38, and was known as the leichte Selbstfahrlafette SdKfz 10/4, using the chassis of the 1-ton halftrack SdKfz 10 series. This example is seen during the German drive on Stalingrad in the summer of 1942, and is towing an ammunition trailer.

When the German forces began to re-equip in the early 1930s, the light flak arm was entirely new and had therefore to be built from scratch. But even as the army was creating a light AA capability, so too was the air force. There was supposed to be a division of responsibilities between the two services in that army light AA units were intended for the defence of the field armies, while those of the air force were supposed to defend the Reich. What actually happened was an overlap of responsibilities and therefore great confusion. Arguments reflected not only on the control of light AA organisations but even matters such as equipment procurement.

Despite the imposition of rigid quotas by higher command levels, new equipment was frequently the cause of inter-service squabbles, and these

grew in number and acrimony with the increase in the number of Waffen-SS formations with their wholly separate command structure. Many of these conflicts were never resolved, and as the German war situation deteriorated they generally grew in quantity and severity.

A unit bound for the field would often find its equipment 'hijacked' by another arm. In general the army tended to be at the bottom of the pile for equipment allocations, and thus although a certain army field unit was supposed to be equipped with halftrack tractors for its guns, it was frequently issued with impressed French civilian trucks or similar. Some Eastern Front units often had to use animals to tow their guns.

Parallel evolution

Despite many differences in policy and priorities, the army and air force

organised themselves along similar lines as far as light AA units were concerned. Later the Waffen-SS also organised itself along army lines.

In broad terms, German army light AA units were divided into motorised and non-motorised types, the latter intended mainly for defence of rear areas and static emplacements such as barracks and stores dumps. By contrast, motorised units were intended to operate with field formations and were equipped accordingly. The transport was meant to be halftracks, though in practice trucks of various kinds were more common.

The field unit most generally used at high levels of command was the Flakregiment. This took a number of forms, comprising either three mixed Flak-abteilungen (battalions) or a mix of two schwere Flakabteilungen (heavy battalions) and three leichte Flakabteilungen (light battalions). Mixed formations were more common as they provided commanders with greater flexibility and enhanced capability. Some mixed Abteilungen had as many as three heavy batteries armed with the 88-mm (3.46-in) Flak 18 or 36, and three light batteries (one with the Flakvierling 38). Such

A Luftwaffe crew mans a 2-cm Flak 38 in March 1945. The ring-type gun mounting was one of the main points that distinguished the Flak 38 from the earlier Flak 30, which did not have this feature although the guns could be mounted on either carriage if required. Note the simple sight in use by 1945.

Not all the German army units were able to move on wheels or tracks, and in winter the sledge came into its own, seen here towed by two sturdy little Russian ponies. Improvisations such as this were commonplace when Eastern Front winters set in, for the fighting did not cease even under extreme conditions.

Flakvierling 38: versatile anti-aircraft gun

Smaller-calibre AA weapons remained in use throughout World War II even though the only way they could ensure a target 'kill' was to increase the number of projectiles actually hitting the target. Since any increase in the rate of fire of most guns would in most cases have entailed a major redesign, the only way to boost the weight of fire was to increase the number of barrels firing from one mounting at any time. Perhaps the best example of this concept could be seen with the change of the single-barrel 2-cm Flak 38 to the four-barrel 2-cm Flakvierling 38, one of the weapons most feared by Allied tactical airmen. Although intended as an AA weapon, the Flak 38 was often used as an anti-tank weapon, and is shown here in such action with the Afrika Korps. Although of limited use against tanks, it was very effective against soft-skinned vehicles and light armoured vehicles such as armoured cars and artillery tractors (and their guns).

an Abteilung had a strength of 1,350 officers and men, 339 motor vehicles, 38 motorcycles, 12 searchlights, 12 88-mm weapons and 48 light flak weapons.

However, there were leichte Flakabteilungen made up entirely of light flak batteries. These were smaller than the mixed formations, with three light flak batteries and a manpower strength of 800. These light groupings were quite common and required far less logistic support than the larger formations, as they had their own integral supply system. Mixed Abteilungen also had this capability, but devoted mainly to the heavy batteries.

A leichte Flakabteilung was headed by a battalion HQ and command platoon. The HQ contained mainly the administrative staff, while the command platoon was the home of the battalion commander plus his immediate staff and sig-

nallers, and although responsible for its own defence, the platoon had no organic AA weapons.

Tactical organisation

Each of the three batteries had four sections. In theory, after 1941-42, one of the four sections was equipped with the Flakvierling 38 and the other three with the single-barrel Flak 30 or 38. Each of the sections had three guns. In manpower terms each battery in theory had six officers, 65 NCOs and 139 other ranks, but in practice such manpower levels were rarely achieved. The same went for equipment: each battery was supposed to have 58 motor vehicles and five motorcycles, but in practice had far less than this. The overall shortage of motor transport proved one of the army's major tactical and operational weaknesses.

The logistic supply system was

based on a column of vehicles that carried the battalion's ammunition reserves, spare parts, food and other day-to-day supplies. There were also workshop vehicles to keep the guns and vehicles functioning, and the supply column enabled the batteries to remain in the field for some days without support.

The men of the light AA units obtained their initial training at schools scattered around Germany. Many of the flak schools used somewhat ancient equipment, for more modern weapons were earmarked for front-line units. Thus many crews trained on the 2-cm Flak 28 or 29 purchased during the early days of German re-armament. The main accent was on teamwork, especially with the ammunition numbers who had to be adept at changing each gun's box magazines quickly. Filling empty magazines was another gun crew task. The

most skilled personnel on the gun were the aimer and rangefinder, but as time went on the latter, with a hand-held stereoscopic rangefinder, became less important. Aimers found that the tracer elements of the projectiles afforded them a much better indication of range than the rangefinder's shouted instructions, and by mid-1944 the rangefinder had been discarded.

Getting the guns into and out of action was a relatively easy task. Apart from their small size and low weight, the Flak 30 and 38 were carried in a tubular steel trailer designed to lower the gun to the ground and pick it up again with a minimum of physical effort from the crew. Once in place the gun rested on a low flat platform that could be accurately levelled by small adjustable feet.

Left: A mittlerer Zugkraftwagen 8t halftrack mounting a 3.7-cm (1.46-in) Flak 36 guards an Italian bridge in September 1943. Some of these Flak 36-armed halftracks had armoured cabs for the driver and towed a trailer with extra ammunition.

Below: This early example of a mittlerer Zugkraftwagen 8t carries a 2-cm Flakvierling 38 somewhere deep in the USSR some time late in 1941. This vehicle is towing a trailer that not only carried extra ammunition but also accommodated the crew's kit and day-to-day supplies, as well as extra fuel for the vehicle.

World War II AA fire control Aerial defence

It may seem strange considering the resources devoted to ground-based defences during World War II, but the chances of an aircraft actually being hit by a heavy anti-aircraft shell were remote. Strenuous efforts were made to alter this situation, notably in the areas of fire control and targeting.

One of the most difficult of all artillery targets to hit is an aircraft in flight. There are several reasons for this, not the least being that the pilot is free to move the aircraft in any one of three planes. Another is that projectiles fired from any gun take time to reach their destination and by the time they arrive at the point at which they are aimed the target may well have moved from its previous course in any direction. Thus the anti-aircraft gunner has to use a great deal of special equipment in order to stand a chance of hitting the target.

Much of what is contained here has now been rendered obsolete by the advent of radar, the guided missile and the silicon chip, but the gunner of World War II initially had none of these. In their place they had to rely on a number of mechanical contrivances, all of which relied on one basic precept: that for the guns to have any sort of a chance of hitting anything the target had to remain flying on a set course at a constant speed. It is very rare for aircraft to fly in this fashion and even massed bomber formations tended to leave some leeway for individual aircraft to bob and weave, but there was no alternative for the gunners but to make this 'constant path and speed' assumption.

Basic sighting

Nearly all but the largest anti-aircraft guns had some form of on-carriage fire-control system in the form of a simple 'cartwheel' sight for use when operating in isolation or in an emergency. Under such conditions range information was derived from a simple form of portable rangefinder. However, for useful accuracy the optical base of such an instrument had to be as wide as possible, so even in the early days range data was usually derived from a wide-base rangefinder located in the centre of a gun position and shouted or telephoned to the guns. Once this central position was an accepted fact it then became easier to conceive the idea of using this central position to derive other gun-control data. Thus in place of the on-carriage sight the predictor was developed. In the early days of World War II this was a purely mechanical device into which target information (range, heading, wind speeds etc.) was fed manually. The resultant fire-control data could then be read off from dials and fed to the guns by voice, either simple shouting or by telephone. As time went on the predictors became more complicated and cables were used to transmit the control data direct to the guns. There it was initially read off from dials and then applied to the gun controls, but even this was eventually bypassed, first by a system of 'follow-the-pointer' or the alignment of flashing lamps, and then by a fully automatic system in which the gun layers had little to do other than supervise the operation. Again, in time this data transmission was extended to other factors such

as fuse setting. Most anti-aircraft projectiles were HE shells that relied on a time fuse to set off the main charge when it was near the target, the chances of hitting an aircraft target being too remote for anything else. But in the time it took to set these time fuses manually the target information might well have changed, so the 'dead time' it took to set the fuse and to load and fire had to be as short as possible. In time this was reduced by the use of centrally-controlled or automatic fuse-setting machines first on the gun carriage and then actually on the loading tray so that the fuse was set only as the round was being fed into the gun breech.

The fuses themselves were small wonders of manufacturing skill and were expensive to make, even when mass produced. Early in the war most relied on some form of clockwork, but later some electrical and even electronic timers were in service. For real technological wonder the best of all the anti-aircraft fuses was the proximity fuse, for which the body of the shell acted as a miniature radar transmitter and signals reflected from the target were detected by the fuse itself. If these signals reached a certain level the target was in range and the shell detonated. By the use of such fuses the V-1 flying bombs were finally defeated, but even without such fuses the V-1s formed a perfect anti-aircraft gunner's target. They flew along a fixed course at a constant altitude and speed until the final moment before falling, and were thus ideal candidates for the well-

Above: The American 120-mm (3.94-in) M1 anti-aircraft gun had two gun aimers. One layer would be concerned with the elevation control (on the left in this photograph) and the other with the traverse (seen on the right). On some similar guns an additional layer would be controlling the fuse-setting machine.

Below: The simple wire sight, seen here on a French 75-mm (2.95-in) gun, was standard on most World War II anti-aircraft weapons, for use in emergency or when operating in isolation away from more sophisticated fire-control equipment.

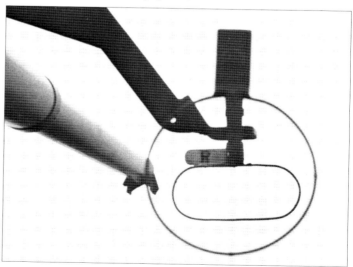

established predictor/rangefinder methods of fire control.

By the time the war ended both the Allies and the Germans were using various forms of radar for fire control. Radar took a lot of the guesswork out of target prediction

as it could accurately track both course and altitude, while the advent of what we now know as the electronic computer made prediction as accurate as it could be. However, by then the aircraft targets were flying higher and faster and no matter how

Fighting the flying bombs:
Britain versus the V-1

The first V-1 flying bombs were launched against targets in the UK on 12 June 1944 and by the end of the war some 2,419 of these weapons had hit London. The British response to the V-1 included four lines of defence: two coastal areas were covered by long-range interceptors, while an inner zone between London and the Channel was protected by AAA in conjunction with radar installations, together with high-speed interceptors under ground control. The final line of defence was offered by barrage balloons over the capital itself. Around 3,000 anti-aircraft guns were located in coastal positions between Dover and Hastings within a period of four days in July 1944 to tackle incoming V-1s. These guns mainly comprised 40-mm Bofors and 3.7-in Mk 1 and Mk 6 automatic weapons guided by US-built M9 radar, and using proximity-fused shells to engage their targets from within a range of 2000 m (2,187 yards) over the sea. The defences were at their most effective during 27 August 1944, when a total of 97 incoming missiles were detected by radar: of these, 62 were claimed by AAA, 19 by fighters and six by barrage balloons.

high the muzzle velocity of the gun became it still took an appreciable time for the shell to reach the target altitude. It was a problem that could only be overcome in the usual manner, the application of masses of fire and large projectiles that could carry as powerful an explosive payload as possible.

It was a problem that was not solved until the advent of the guided missile. By the time that the last anti-aircraft guns for large-scale defence were removed during the 1960s there were large-calibre guns that could fire massive shells to unprecedented heights at the rate of at least one per second, but somehow the attacker could still survive it

Above: Two gun layers are seen on a US Army anti-aircraft gun. The layer on the left of picture operated the traversing mechanism, while the layer on the right operated the elevation mechanism and fired the gun.

Right: Typical of many World War II rangefinders is this Japanese example. This would be used by one person, with another checking readings and transmitting them verbally to a central fire-control point. These expensive instruments were usually distributed on a basis of one to each battery.

Short Range Ballistic Missiles

Transforming the Cold War battlefield and giving an added punch to field artillery, the Short Range Ballistic Missile (SRBM) was a staple feature of Cold War land forces on both sides of the Iron Curtain.

Descending from the German A-4 (V-2) missile of World War II, the Short Range Ballistic Missile or SRBM is defined as a weapon with a range of between 100 km (62.1 miles) and 1000 km (621.4 miles). Developed as a battlefield nuclear weapon during the Cold War, it was designed to deliver nuclear warheads directly onto the rear areas of large armoured formations. SRBMs could also target high-value communications and logistics targets, such as bridges and rail junctions, as well as military airfields and key command centres.

The nuclear balance

During the Cold War, NATO saw SRBMs as essential for 'levelling the balance' with the Soviet-led Warsaw Pact (WARPAC). NATO SRBMs were introduced to counter the numerical superiority of the Red Army. For the Soviets, the SRBM was an enhancement of the prevailing Red Army doctrine of attacking NATO forces with overwhelming firepower. Soviet war-fighting plans envisaged hundreds of these weapons targeting NATO forward positions in central West Germany prior to a drive westwards by WARPAC armoured columns.

The deployment of SRBMs was instantly popular with NATO artillery commanders, who saw them as a prestigious addition to the battlefield artillery force. However, during the 1950s, as the US began to deploy its first SRBM, the 240 km (149.1 miles) Hermes, the Soviets were beginning to deploy the famous 'Scud' missile series, starting with the 'Scud-A' in 1957.

Soviet developments

The Soviets introduced many innovations with their SRBMs. US and NATO systems usually required large convoys of trucks to carry and prepare the missiles for launch,

which in itself would often require hours of preparation time. One US system, the 138-km (85.7-miles) Corporal, needed over seven hours before it was ready for launch. The Soviets, on the other hand, used a single Transporter-Erector-Launcher (TEL). TELs were highly mobile and designed for off-road travel. They moved rapidly to a predetermined location to launch their missiles, before moving to a new location to replenish. Several of the Soviet 'Scud' systems were also air portable in massive Antonov cargo aircraft.

The most numerous American SRBM developed was the Lance system. Although classed as a tactical weapon by the US Army, it had a range of 130 km (80.8 miles) and could carry a nuclear warhead with a variable yield of between 1 and 100 kilotons. It could also carry a 1-kT Enhanced Radiation warhead – more commonly known as a 'neutron bomb'. Lance's range enabled it to hit 'depth' targets, such as vehicle, supply or troop concentrations far behind the enemy's frontlines.

The end of the Cold War signalled the end of the battlefield SRBM in US, NATO and former Warsaw Pact inventories. The cessation of East-West confrontation in Europe had rendered it obsolete. Even when equipped with conventional warheads, the 'expeditionary' nature of most Western military operations have precluded their use. For example, low intensity conflicts in Somalia and the Balkans haven't required the massive firepower that an SRBM can deliver.

The 1987 Intermediate Nuclear Forces (INF) treaty sounded a death-knell for US and Soviet SRBMs. INF banned all nuclear-armed missiles that had a range of between 500 km (310.7 miles) and 5600 km (3,480 miles). By 1997, all Pershing missiles – one of the US's most potent and

Although developed from German World War II technology, the SRBM was a vital Cold War weapon and would go on to become a symbol of national prestige in the 'New World Order'.

accurate SRBM systems – had been decommissioned and destroyed.

Fortunately for the world, SRBMs were never used in anger during the Cold War. However, they were used in other conflicts.

SRBMs in action

Several hundred 'Scud-B' systems with a 300 km (186.4 miles) range were thought to have been sup-

plied to the communist government of Dr. Najibullah Khan in Afghanistan, following the Soviet withdrawal of 1989. Afghanistan is believed to have seen the most intense short-range missile combat since World War II, with over 1,000 SRBMs being fired.

The Iran-Iraq war during the 1980s saw about 900 missile firings of various types; many during the 'War of the Cities' in 1988,

Above: France was the only western European country to develop a nuclear-capable, battlefield SRBM system. The Pluton missile served with French forces in West Germany.

Left: With a range of only 19.3 km (12 miles), 'Honest John' was more an artillery piece than an SRBM – but it was the US Army's first operational tactical nuclear missile. First fired in 1951, it was deployed in 1954. It was declared obsolete in 1982.

when both sides attacked each other's principal urban centres.

The end of the Cold War has not meant the end of the SRBM proliferation. Several states in the Middle East and the developing world are believed to be actively pursuing SRBM programmes. As well as their destructive potential, SRBMs can be fastened together as 'stages' to make crude, longer-range systems. It is unlikely that SRBMs are deployed for solely conventional missions. Experts have commented that: "using missiles to merely dump a little high explosive somewhere near the target is

Left: The US Lance battlefield missile system served in large numbers with the US Army in Germany, and was also deployed by the UK, Germany, Holland, Italy, Belgium and Israel.

Below: Soviet 'Scud' systems were designed for rapid deployment across the battlefield. TEL vehicles were air portable, and missiles could be launched quickly once in position.

like buying a Ferrari to collect groceries". Moreover, many SRBM systems are highly inaccurate, as shown by Iraq's 'Scud' missile attacks during both the 1990-1991 Persian Gulf War and the 'War of the Cities'. A conventionally armed SRBM needs to hit a target more or less directly to destroy it. This is not so important for an SRBM armed with a Nuclear Biological or Chemical (NBC) warhead.

SRBM advantages

Used on their own, SRBMs can hit military and civilian targets at close ranges, possibly with NBC warheads. When connected together, they can be developed into longer-range systems, which can strike targets further away. It is these concerns that have prompted the United States and several other countries to develop Anti Ballistic Missile (ABM) systems for their own territory and to protect their troops deployed on missions abroad. For example, during the Persian Gulf War, Iraq fired several 'Scud' missiles at coalition military targets and civilian targets in Israel and Saudi Arabia.

Some experts now believe that the 'short-range' description for SRBMs is misleading. Many countries that are developing SRBM systems share borders with their adversaries. For example, India and Pakistan field their respective Prithvi and Hatf-2 SRBM systems, and although neither missile has a range over 500 km, they each have the capacity to hit major cities and military targets with conventional or even nuclear explosives.

SRBMs are also attractive to new proliferators on grounds of cost and performance. An SRBM travels at speeds well in excess of even the most advanced aircraft – Iraq's 'Scud' missiles travel over three times the speed of sound – making defence against such missiles much more difficult than defending against attack aircraft.

SRBMs are much more economical than aircraft, costing in the region of $1 million each, while a relatively non-advanced combat aircraft can cost up to $20 million. Also, combat aircraft production is concentrated in North America, Europe and Russia where strict export restrictions to 'countries of concern' often apply. Indeed, some of the countries believed to be pursuing SRBM programmes, such as North Korea, are less fussy about where they sell their wares.

Soviet air defence artillery Red Army defenders

In concert with regimental-level SAMs, anti-aircraft artillery (AAA) provided point defence for Warsaw Pact forces. Meanwhile, area coverage was dealt with by SAM brigades, with operations co-ordinated with those of the tactical air army.

Perhaps as a result of the virtual air supremacy they had enjoyed from around 1943 until the end of World War II, the Western Allies seriously neglected their air defences throughout much of the Cold War. Indeed NATO anti-aircraft units tended to rely upon World War II-era gun technology to meet their needs long into the 1950s. In contrast, the Soviet Union afforded its air defences continued high priority and followed a coherent plan of development.

The first self-propelled anti-aircraft guns (SPAAG) to enter service in the USSR during the immediate post-World War II period were the BTR-40A and the BTR-152A. These were both armed with a turret containing twin 14.5-mm (0.57-in) machine-guns.

The BTR-40A entered service in 1950 and was based on the BTR-40 (4x4) armoured personnel carrier (APC), while the BTR-152A which entered service two years later was based on the BTR-152 (6x6) APC. The original role of these systems was to provide suppressive fire to infantry units, with air defence being a secondary capability. Effective range against airborne targets was around 1500 m (4,920 ft) but they had limited capability against the jets that were being deployed in increasing numbers in the early 1950s.

Early equipment

The first purpose-built SPAAG to enter service with the Soviet army in 1955 was the ZSU-57-2. The numbers indicated the calibre of the cannon (57 mm) and the number of barrels (two).

The chassis of the ZSU-57-2 was based on the T-54 tank which was then in service in large numbers, but had much thinner armour as it was not expected to be deployed

Top: The ZSU-23-4 can also be used in the ground support role (often with radar removed) and as such has proven effective during Russia's conflicts in Afghanistan and Chechnya (pictured).

Right: The 2S6M Tunguska is a highly effective mobile air defence system combining guns and missiles. The initial 2S6 version entered Soviet service in 1986 with two rather than four SAM launchers.

Below: Versions of the BTR-152 wheeled APC were deployed in both the anti-tank and anti-aircraft roles by Warsaw Pact and other forces. The BTR-152A was armed with twin 14.5-mm machine-guns.

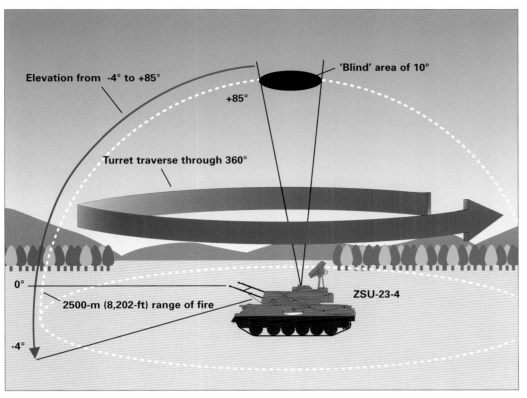

- Elevation from -4° to +85°
- 'Blind' area of 10°
- +85°
- Turret traverse through 360°
- 0°
- 2500-m (8,202-ft) range of fire
- ZSU-23-4
- -4°

ZSU-23-4: the 'awl' in action

The Shilka was developed to provide motorised rifle regiments with protection from low-level aerial threats, and systems normally operate as a pair. The system's RPK-2 'Gun Dish' radar can pick up targets 20 km (12 miles) out and a computer automatically bears the guns onto the intruder. Acquisition, lock-on and firing takes 20-30 seconds.

in the front line. The chassis had four well-spaced road wheels either side compared to the five of the T-54.

Mounted in the middle of the chassis was a larger open turret

The ZSU-57-2 was based on a modified T-54 tank chassis with four rather than five road wheels. The main drawback of the ZSU-57-2 was its slow rate of fire and lack of an onboard fire-control system.

armed with two 57-mm S-68 guns; these fired the same ammunition as the S-60 towed anti-aircraft gun, which entered service in 1950. Each of these 57-mm cannon had a cyclic rate of fire of over 100

rounds per minute, but normally much smaller bursts would be fired as only 300 rounds were carried on board.

The 57-mm weapons had a maximum vertical range of up to 8000 m (26,247 ft) although their effective range was less than half this and only optical sights were provided to lay the weapons on the target.

Significant quantities of ZSU-57-2 systems were built for the home and export markets, and China built a similar system called the Type 80 that was based on a Type 69-II tank chassis.

The ZSU-57-2 had a number of significant tactical drawbacks including a slow rate of fire, lack of onboard fire-control system (FCS) and no protection against NBC attack.

In the late 1950s development work commenced on two new SPAAG systems, the ZSU-23-4 and the ZSU-37-2. The former was armed with four 23-mm cannon and the latter with two 37-mm cannon. Following extensive trials the ZSU-23-4 was accepted for service with production starting in 1965.

Shilka production

The ZSU-23-4 is also commonly referred to as the Shilka (awl) and it is estimated that total production of the system amounted to between 7,000 and 8,000 systems and it is still used by some 30 countries.

The system is based on a new fully tracked chassis which is fitted with a power-operated turret armed with four 23-mm water-cooled can-

non with a cyclic rate of fire of 800 to 1,000 rounds per barrel per minute. Normally, bursts of up to 30 rounds per barrel are used, with maximum effective air defence range being about 2500 m (8,202 ft).

Mounted on the turret rear is the large radar that carries out a variety of functions including target detection and tracking. When not required this is lowered to the rear to reduce the overall height of the system.

The ZSU-23-4 has seen extensive combat use in the Middle East and has proved to be highly effective when used in combination with SAMs. The latter force aircraft to fly at much lower altitudes where they come within the effective range of the ZSU-23-4.

In recent years a number of companies have developed upgrades to the ZSU-23-4 to extend its operational life. This includes replacing the old electronics with new and more efficient digital subsystems and mounting pods of fire-and-forget SAMs. The latter are used to engage the targets at long range, with the guns being used to engage close-in targets.

While the ZSU-23-4 was a highly effective system, it did have a number of drawbacks including the short range of the 23-mm cannon.

In the 1970s development of a new SPAAG/missile system commenced and this finally entered service in the mid 1980s as the 2S6 Tunguska, with the latest version being the 2S6M. Owing to an acute shortage of funds, the 2S6M has not been deployed in large numbers within the Russian army and India is the only known export client to date.

The 2S6 is based on a new fully tracked chassis which is also used as the basis for the Buk (SA-11 'Gadfly') SAM. This is fitted with a new power-operated turret that is armed with two twin 30-mm cannon and two pods of four 9M311 SAMs.

The 30-mm cannon are water-cooled and have an effective range of 3000 to 4000 m (9,843 to 13,123 ft). The 9M311 (SA-19 'Grison') missiles have an effective range of about 8000 m (26,247 ft) up to an altitude of about 3500 m (11,483 ft) and are fitted with a HE fragmentation warhead.

Tunguska engagement

An advanced computerised FCS is provided for the 2S6M and this includes a surveillance radar mounted on the turret rear and a tracking radar mounted on the forward part of a turret. This is similar to the system fitted on the German Gepard SPAAG.

In a typical 2S6M target engagement the missiles would be used to engage aircraft and helicopters (including hovering rotorcraft) at long range, with the cannon engaging close-in targets.

The latest Russian system to be developed is the 96K6 Pantzyr-S1 containerised system which is normally carried on an 8x8 truck, although the United Arab Emirates has ordered a system on a tracked chassis. The 96K6 Pantzyr-S2 features two 30-mm cannon and a total of 12 9M335 SAMs (derived from the 9M311) with an advanced day/night computerised FCS installed.

On the ranges with the South African 155-mm G6 self-propelled artillery system. The turret of the G6 has been proposed as an add-on unit for tank chassis – a version developed for mounting on Indian Army T-72 tank chassis is known as the T6-52.

Hi-tech artillery

Modern developments

Artillery is in a constant state of change as gunners continue to demand ever-increasing on-target effectiveness, but perhaps the most pressing requirement is for advances in range.

The past few decades have witnessed some startling increases in the reach of modern artillery. Not so long ago 24000 m (26,250 yards) was accepted as the standard for 155-mm (6.1-in) field artillery. Guns and ammunition have now developed to the point where over 50000 m (54,680 yards) can be attained – but at a high financial cost.

Two factors have emerged where 155-mm artillery is concerned – longer barrels and improved ammunition design. The 24000-m ranges achieved by guns such as the US M198 were produced by barrels 39 calibres long. Many gun barrels are now 45 or 52 calibres long, with larger capacity chambers for more powerful propellant charges. Firing streamlined Extended Range Full Bore (ERFB) projectiles with add-on Base Bleed (BB) units that burn to reduce the effect of drag-inducing eddies behind the base of the projectile, 52-calibre barrels allow 40000 m (43,745 yards) to be reached. Over 50000 m is possible with further enhancements such as rocket assistance. Future trends can be seen by the development of the US XM987 Excalibur projectile which glides through part of its tra-

jectory to reach 57000 m (62,336 yards).

Not only projectiles have been improved. In place of the old cloth-bagged propellant charges there are now modular charges. These are standard-sized charges packed into rigid combustible containers that can be joined together to suit specific fire missions – a full charge could be formed by joining six modules while shorter ranges might need only two. This simplifies logistics and makes mechanical handing, loading and ramming much easier and faster.

Lightweight mobility

To date artillery mobility has been obtained mainly by tracked self-propelled equipments but these tend to be heavy. In an era where rapid

Mechanical handling allows this German army 155-mm PzH 2000 to fire three rounds in nine seconds. Once inside the armoured hull, all projectiles and modular charges are handled, selected and loaded mechanically so the entire system can be operated by just three gunners should the need arise – the usual crew is five.

reaction and equipment deployment are essential, many self-propelled equipments are too heavy for air transport in sufficient

numbers. Too much weight was one reason why the US Crusader 155-mm system was cancelled. Lighter alternatives are now being

Developed specifically for the export market, the Giat Industries 105-mm LG1 light gun is one of the lighter pieces of modern artillery and has a maximum possible range of 17,500 m (19,138 yards).

155-mm Caesar: wheeled mobility

The Giat Industries Caesar (*Camion equipe d'un système d'artillerie*, or truck-mounted artillery system) mounts a 52-calibre 155-mm barrel on a modified 6x6 Unimog cross-country truck chassis and is designed for rapid deployment. Caesar is intended to bridge the gap between heavy tracked or wheeled self-propelled artillery systems and 155-mm towed guns. After undertaking trials with the system in 1998, the French Army ordered a batch of five of these equipments for operational evaluation.

sought using truck-based mountings. Typical of these is the French air-portable Caesar. Other similar equipments are known to be under development, especially in South Africa.

South Africa continues to be in the vanguard of artillery development as shown by the 155-mm G5 towed and G6 self-propelled pieces, widely regarded as among the best artillery systems available. Sensing that mobility would be afforded increasing importance, South Africa decided to produce a light 105-mm (4.13-in) towed gun with a 155-mm performance, both in range and on-target effects. The result has been the Lightweight Experimental Ordnance (LEO), which has demonstrated it can achieve ranges of 30000 m (32,808 yards) with 105-mm BB projectiles. On-target effects of the 105-mm projectile are improved to the extent that it can exceed the

The combination of the South African 155-mm G5 towed gun-howitzer and its ERFB ammunition allow a range of up to 40000 m (43,745 yards). The G5 has seen combat in southern Angola and South West Africa.

area coverage created by conventional 155-mm projectiles. Specially developed proximity-fuzed air-burst projectiles use advanced high-fragmentation steels and an internal lining of small steel spheres to amplify the number of effective fragments produced on detonation. LEO is still in the technology development phase with the intention that the overall weight will be reduced to about 2.5 tonnes. A truck-mounted variant is forecast.

Other light 105-mm guns continue to find favour, especially with special forces. The Royal Ordnance 105-mm Light Gun has become a world leader in its class while the Giat Industries 105-mm LG1 has also been sold in significant numbers. Special 105-mm BB projectiles can provide a range of over 17500 m (19,138 yards) to be reached by both.

Self-propelled designs

Although wheeled, the South African G6 155-mm gun system now has the option of a 52-calibre barrel as well as the in-service 45-calibre barrel. Travelling on a special 6x6 carriage the G6 weighs over 40 tonnes.

Within Europe the lead in self-propelled numerical terms has been assumed by the German Panzerhaubitze 2000 (PzH 2000), a fully tracked and highly mobile design with many advanced features such as electrical gun drives and a land navigation and fire control suite that allows each vehicle to act as a self-contained fire unit. The gun is able to fire a salvo of projectiles at successive barrel elevation angles to permit all rounds fired to land on target simultaneously. This 'party trick' is now a standard artillery practice that can be accomplished by some other recent self-propelled artillery equipments such as the Royal Ordnance AS90 and its export model, the Braveheart. The AS90 is in service with the British Army, with a 52-calibre update scheduled, and the turret has been selected by Poland for mounting on a locally-developed tracked chassis.

Advanced projectiles

Mention must also be made of the increasing importance of electronics to artillery developments. Much of this can be seen in increasingly sophisticated fire-control systems and their associated communication links, yet electronics now

intrude into the projectiles themselves.

Proximity fuses have been around for decades but fuses can now include GPS elements that allow the trajectory of a projectile to be monitored throughout its flight. Using such data it becomes possible to alter the trajectory to ensure the projectile impacts within a selected confined area by erecting pop-out spoiler surfaces at the appropriate instant. This capability gains further significance when cargo projectiles become involved.

To date most cargo projectiles have carried payloads of multiple dual-purpose (anti-personnel/anti-armour) bomblets that free-fall from the airborne projectile to cover a wide area. Payloads have now been extended to include two autonomous anti-armour sub-projectiles that, once ejected from the cargo projectile body, fall to earth under drogue or parachute control while multiple sensors scan the terrain below for suitable targets, typically tanks or artillery positions. Once a target has been selected, at the appropriate height above the target the sub-projectile fires a self-forming fragment to penetrate the target's top protection.

Typical of these projectiles are the Bonus and the Rheinmetall DeTec SMArt 155 (Sensor-fuzed Munition for the Artillery 155 mm). Bonus is in service with the armies of Sweden and France while SMArt 155 is in production for the German army. The much heralded US XM898 SADARM (Sense And Destroy ARmor Munition) was finally cancelled after a prolonged development programme that cost millions of dollars, so Bonus and SMArt 155 now have the market to themselves. Their long-term success is likely to be compromised by their unit cost and the likelihood that the massed armoured attacks that these autonomous sub-munitions were developed to counter are increasingly unlikely to present themselves during future conflicts.

Primarily intended for the close-support role, the prototype South African 105-mm Lightweight Experimental Ordnance has demonstrated a combat range of up to 30000 m (32,808 yards).

Artillery rockets today

From the massed battles of the Eastern Front during World War II to the digital battlefields of Iraq, the artillery rocket seems set to continue its leading role in the delivery of indirect fire.

Over the last few decades, artillery rocket developments have followed those of conventional artillery. The emphasis has therefore been directed to improving the paramount artillery assets of more range, enhanced accuracy and more efficient warheads. Overall, the artillery rocket remains an area coverage rather than a point precision weapon so they are still almost always delivered in massed salvos from multiple launchers, although some of the larger examples are now deemed accurate enough to be launched individually.

Improved propellants

Most artillery rocket range enhancements have been achieved by the introduction of improved propellants. An example of this can been seen with what is now the most widely deployed of all current artillery rocket systems, namely the 122-mm (4.82-in) BM-21 Grad (hail), the Russian successor to their Great Patriotic War Katyusha series, and now licence produced or copied by many countries. When first introduced back in the 1960s Grad rockets could reach 12000 m (39,369 ft) or so, with lesser ranges induced by securing aerodynamic spoiler rings over the nose. The latest generation of 122-mm Grad rockets have their original solid single or double base rocket motors replaced by faster and more evenly burning propellants that increase the maximum range to 20000 m (65,616 ft). In 1994, the Splav Scientific Production Concern began work on a joint Russo-French solid propellant motor, involving the French company CELERG, but the project was abandoned.

Latest technology

Some recently introduced artillery rocket systems have taken advantage of the latest propellant technology by introducing Hydroxy-Terminated-Poly-Butadine, or HTBP. A typical example is with the rockets launched from the 227-mm (8.94-in) Multiple Launched Rocket System (MLRS), now the standard artillery rocket system employed by numerous armed forces. The exhaust from the HTBP motor is vented in a spectacular fashion through a single nozzle in the MLRS rocket tail, the result being that a standard MLRS rocket can achieve 32000 m (104,985 ft). Further enhancements in the development pipeline will increase this maximum range to 37000 m (121,389 ft) and eventually 45500 m (149,276 ft). The price to be paid for these range enhancements is that the HTBP exhaust is highly acidic and can corrode anything that comes into contact with it, so careful cleaning of the launch frame is necessary after launches.

Many current rocket launchers now have their rockets pre-loaded within sealed transport containers, or pods, that double as launchers when secured within a launching frame. This makes reloading between salvos much quicker and easier, especially

The spectacular launch of a 227-mm (8.9-in) MLRS rocket. It is used by Bahrain, Denmark, Egypt, France, Germany, Greece, Israel, Italy, Japan, South Korea, Netherlands, Norway, Turkey, the UK and the US.

A battery of Brazilian ASTROS II launchers delivering 180-mm (7.1-in) SS-40 rockets to a maximum of 30000 m (98,424 ft).

when suitable handling and lifting equipment is provided, as it is with MLRS. The time-consuming process of loading each rocket individually (and usually manually) is thus avoided. With the BM-21 Grad system, 40 rockets have to be loaded for every salvo, no mean task when the latest rockets weigh about 66 kg (145.5 lb) each. Accuracy enhancements have been introduced by several means. The most advanced of them make use of Global Positioning System (GPS) to plot the point of launch and the intended target location.

Computer control

As the rocket travels towards the target a small computer carried within the rocket monitors the position of the rocket in flight, again using GPS. Any necessary course corrections to ensure the target is hit are then introduced either by small vanes at the nose or by small gas generators that act as side thrusters to alter the trajectory. A refinement is to track the in-flight rocket by radar, again using GPS references to determine when course corrections are to be introduced. However, many nations do not favour the employment of radar for such purposes as it is too easily detected and jammed by the enemy, so it seems that GPS monitoring is the preferred trajectory correction option – as long as GPS is available under wartime conditions.

Another accuracy enhancement process relies on the use of laser target designators, either ground-based or airborne. This is a process already employed by some conventional artillery munitions in that the laser designator bathes the target with laser energy, some of which is reflected to be detected by sensors in the rocket nose. Flight correction systems within the rocket then automatically deliver trajectory corrections, usually by adjusting aerodynamic surfaces or sometimes by small explosive thruster units.

Warheads

Rocket warheads have been improved in many ways since 1945. As most rockets fired remain high explosive fragmentation (HE-FRAG), their fragmentation effects can be improved by the introduction of preformed fragments (usually small steel spheres) packed around the high explosive content. Lethal fragments can therefore be spread over a wider radius than for conventional warheads, especially when electronic proximity fuses are introduced to ensure the warhead detonates at a fixed altitude above the ground surface, shredding the soft-skinned vehicles – and personnel – below.

The potential array of rocket warheads has also been greatly enlarged. One example of the selection now available can be deduced from the Russian 300-mm (11.81-in) Smerch (Tornado), an advanced 12-round launcher system with a maximum range of no less than 70000 m (229,656 ft); some rockets within the system can reach 90000 m (295,275 ft). Apart from the usual HE-FRAG warhead, contents can include up to 646 (small) or 72 (large) dual-purpose (anti-personnel/anti-armour) bomblets to be dispensed over a wide area, anti-tank mines, thermobaric (fuel/air incendiary) or concrete penetrating warheads, or up to five autonomous self-homing submunitions that can detect and attack armoured targets as they descend under a drogue parachute after airborne ejection from the rocket.

One special Smerch rocket can carry and launch a remotely piloted vehicle during the rocket's flight. The vehicle can then fly over a pre-programmed course transmitting video images of potential targets to a control station up to 70000 m (229,656 ft) away.

Astros II: bombardment from Brazil

The 300-mm (11.81-in) variant of the Brazilian ASTROS II SS-60 rocket (pictured) has a range of 60000 m (196,848 ft) and a 212-kg (467.3-lb) warhead. The system includes an AV-LMU Universal Multiple Launcher (pictured) and an AV-RMD Ammunition Resupply Vehicle, which is fitted with a hydraulic crane for the resupply of ammunition to the AV-LMU. A command and control vehicle (AV-VCC) works with the AV-UCF Radar Fire Control Vehicle. In addition, several vehicles carrying electronic and mechanical maintenance workshops are also available. A typical battery for the ASTROS II would include one AV-UCF truck, six AV-LMU vehicles and six AV-RMD. At the battalion level there would be a single AV-VCC plus two mobile workshops. The AV-VCC truck can provide fire-control information for up to three ASTROS II batteries during combat operations.

Self-propelled AA artillery Development

Tied as it is to the evolution of combat aircraft capability, air defence has had to develop the capacity to combat all-weather and night attacks, greater target speeds and stand-off weaponry. This has led to a requirement for gun systems with longer range, increased accuracy and more assured lethality.

The M247 Sgt York, with its twin 40-mm cannon and radar-aided fire-control system, was intended as the replacement for the M42 Duster and as such to provide significant enhancement of the US Army's air defence capability. The system suffered intractable technical problems, however, and was therefore cancelled.

Self-propelled anti-aircraft gun (SPAAG) systems are by no means a new invention, armoured trucks fitted with guns having been developed before World War I to engage the balloons used for artillery spotting. One of the first such systems in 1906 was the German Panzer-kraftwagen Ehrhardt fitted with a turret-mounted 5-cm (1.97-in) gun.

Production

Although serious development of SPAAGs started in the 1920s, it was not until World War II that they appeared in quantity. During this conflict large numbers were built on wheeled, half-track and full-tracked chassis by the major powers, with Germany making the greatest effort as it rapidly lost air superiority over Europe. In the mid-1980s, well over 40 years after the type was first used, several countries were still using versions of American half-tracks with four 0.5-in (12.7-mm) machine-guns or two 20-mm cannon. The Israeli army has a halftrack version of the TCM-20 twin 20-mm

system, credited with shooting down no less than 60 per cent of the aircraft downed by ground-based systems (guns and missiles) during the 1973 Middle East war.
The systems developed during

Above: By the 1960s it was clear that the increased capabilities of tactical aircraft demanded some kind of blind-firing system allied to larger-calibre weapons. The ZSU-23-4 was one of the most successful of the generation of equipment stemming from that realisation.

Left: The impact of the armed battlefield helicopter, with its ability to deliver low-level stand-off attacks, has meant that the fire-control system must be able to detect and the guns to engage such targets at long ranges. The twin 35-mm guns and comprehensive fire-control system of the Gepard represent a typical but costly solution.

Right: The US adapted an aircraft weapon, developed in the 1950s for the Lockheed F-104 Starfighter, for its anti-aircraft needs. Of 20-mm calibre, the Vulcan offered a phenomenal rate of fire but was also handicapped by comparatively short range with a projectile of only modest lethality, requiring multiple hits on the target.

Below: The expense involved in acquiring a capable modern system is often beyond the means of smaller nations, and manufacturers have made efforts to cater for their needs by introducing simpler systems of modular construction. Such was the private-venture Wildcat from West Germany, but this did not enter production.

World War II were in a variety of calibres ranging from 7.62-mm (0.3-in) up to 88-mm (3.46-in), but were all essentially clear-weather systems with optical sights. Most had manual controls for turret/gun traverse and weapon elevation, even though these were often tiring for the crew and made it very difficult to engage fast, low-flying aircraft.

In the post-war period the Americans fielded the M42 SPAAG with two 40-mm guns, but this was only a new chassis with the turret of the older M19. More sophisticated fire controls were designed for the M42 but none of these entered production as they were complicated, expensive and unreliable. By the 1960s it was obvious that the M42 could not cope with the new generation of jet aircraft, so the 20-mm General Electric Vulcan cannon, as installed in US fighters of the time, was turret-mounted on a modified M113 APC with a naval gun sight and range-only radar. This was fielded as the M163, its towed counterpart for non-armoured and mechanised divisions being the M167.

GADES

In 1970 the US Army carried out the Gun Air Defense Effectiveness Study (GADES) and came to the conclusion that the Vulcan system was limited in range, accuracy and lethality: in fact its range and lethality are probably both a good deal less than those of the M42 that it replaced.

In 1973 a twin 25-mm Gun Low-Altitude Air Defense System (GLAADS) was built to the prototype stage, but this was essentially a technology (especially fire control) test-bed. In 1978 General Dynamics and Ford Aerospace were each contracted for the design, development and construction of two prototypes of their different Division Air Defense (DIVAD) gun systems. Following trials with the twin 35-mm General Dynamics and twin 40-mm Ford systems, the latter was selected for production, first deliveries of this M247 Sergeant York system being made late in 1983. There were major problems with the fire-control system and the low rate of turret traverse, however, and the programme was cancelled in December 1986 after the completion of no more than 50 systems.

Re-formed in the mid-1950s, the West German army took delivery of some 500 M42 SPAAGs from the US. The service realised that a new and more effective system was needed, though, and after many false starts prototypes of systems with twin 30- and 35-mm guns on a modified Leopard 1 MBT chassis were built. The variant with 35-mm guns was selected for production and by 1980 a total of 570 Gepard equipments had been delivered (420, 55 and 95 to West Germany, Belgium and the Netherlands respectively).

Soviet developments

The USSR followed a similar route, first fielding a clear-weather system (the ZSU-57-2 with two 57-mm/2.24-in guns) and then an all-weather system (the ZSU-23-4 Shilka with four 23-mm cannon). The latter was widely deployed, and proved to be one of the most effective systems of the 1973 Middle East war when used in conjunction with SAMs. In the late 1980s the Soviets developed a new system, the 2S6M Tunguska, as an advanced vehicle with the hybrid armament of two 30-mm cannon and eight SA-19 'Grison' short-range SAMs.

The UK has shown little recent interest in SPAAGs, relying instead on SAMs for the air defence of its army. France procured just 60 AMX-13 DCA SPAAGs, while Italy has none at all, although it has developed a quadruple 25-mm system.

While systems such as the Gepard can be highly effective weapons, they are expensive to procure, maintain and operate. So in recent years there have been several SPAAGs developed in Europe specifically for the export market. These range from complete systems such as the Swiss private-venture Oerlikon-Bührle twin 35-mm GDF series to turrets such as the Hispano-Suiza CNMP H 20 R/H 20 S unit with twin 20-mm cannon that can be fitted on a variety of tracked or wheeled chassis and provided with a surveillance radar if required.

Modular system

Another recent idea is the development of a modular system with options ranging from a simple clear-weather system right up to an all-weather system. Such a system was the West German private-venture Wildcat, which was evaluated from 1984 by the Canadian Armed Forces. All-weather SPAAGs normally have surveillance and tracking radars, computers and a laser rangefinder.

It was only after the mid-1970s that effective all-weather SPAAGs were developed, mainly due to rapid advances in electronics. In the 1950s electronics tended to be not only expensive, but also bulky and unreliable, especially in tracked and wheeled vehicles that are subjected to violent cross-country movement.

As well as SPAAGs, many self-propelled SAMs have been developed in the last 25 years, but most are so expensive that they can only be developed under government contract, a recent exception being the Oerlikon-Buhrle ADATS anti-tank/aircraft missile adopted by Canada.

World War II experience: modified armoured cars

During World War II, anti-aircraft weapons had to cope with attackers operating in reasonably clear air, so optical sighting and manual control allied to weapons of machine-gun calibre were therefore often sufficient to provide adequate protection against attack. This, for instance, is the US T17 light armoured car operated by the British with the name Staghound, fitted with an open-topped Fraser-Nash AA turret armed with two machine-guns aimed by means of a simple optical sight.

Skoda 149-mm Modell 14 and Modell 14/16 Field howitzer

The **Skoda 149-mm Modell 14** is the medium howitzer equivalent to the 100-mm (3.94-in) Model 1914. The 149-mm (5.87-in) weapon was much larger and heavier, however, and was intended for use at higher artillery command levels than the 100-mm howitzer: the 149-mm howitzer was used by regimental and corps artillery. The Modell 14 was intended for the destruction of major enemy emplacements and field works, and could be a very powerful weapon.

There was no facility to break the weapon down into loads as was the case with the smaller-calibre weapons. Instead the Modell 14 featured a large box trail, so heavy that a special trail lifting lever had to be fitted over the spades. This was used to effect large changes of traverse, and it required two men to lift the lever and move the carriage. The Modell 14 had a large shield (sometimes curved and sometimes straight), and the recoil mechanism under the barrel was large and heavy.

Heavy load

In fact, weight seemed to be the watchword of the Modell 14, and it required a large horse team to move the weapon. Despite all this weight the Modell 14 did not have a particularly good range: 6900 m (7,546 yards) was the maximum, although the HE shell it fired was quite destructive.

During 1916 a new version of the Modell 14 began

to appear on the Skoda production lines. This was the **Modell 14/16**, which featured a slightly longer barrel. To provide more range, it fired a shell that was lighter than that of the Modell 14. The original Modell 14 ammunition could still be fired, and the Modell 14/16 shell could be fired from the Modell 14 if required, but the shells had entirely different ballistic performance, requiring a change in range tables and extra training for the crews to handle the differing performance. As a result, this was rarely done.

Improved range

The new barrel and ammunition gave the howitzer a range increase to 8790 m (9,613 yards) which was a help, but these were not the only changes. The Modell 14/16 had a new carriage design which was stronger and more stable than the original, but it was heavier than the original.

Both the Modell 14 and Modell 14/16 were used throughout World War 1 by the Austro-Hungarian armies, and gave good service. Many passed into Italian use; so many in fact that they were still the standard Italian medium howitzers in 1940, with the designations **obice da 149/12 modello 14** and **obice da 149/13**. After 1918 the howitzers were used by the Austrian, Hungarian and Czech armies (as the **hruba houfnize vz 14 and vz 14/16** in the latter) for many years.

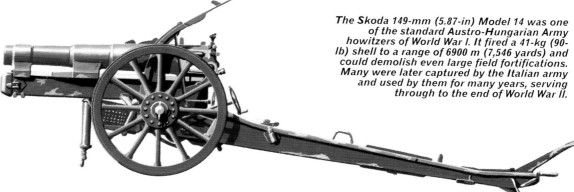

The Skoda 149-mm (5.87-in) Model 14 was one of the standard Austro-Hungarian Army howitzers of World War I. It fired a 41-kg (90-lb) shell to a range of 6900 m (7,546 yards) and could demolish even large field fortifications. Many were later captured by the Italian army and used by them for many years, serving through to the end of World War II.

Austro-Hungarian Skoda 149-mm (5.87-in) Model 1914 field howitzers in a battery position at Wolhynie. The difference from the heavily protected battery layouts of the Western Front are very apparent, although shelters for men and ammunition have been prepared near the guns.

Below: British and Italian transport passes captured Austro-Hungarian artillery on a road near the Val d'Assa in November 1918. The gun in the immediate foreground is a Skoda 149-mm (5.87-in) Model 1914 field howitzer, one of many that fell into Italian hands to become one of the standard Italian artillery weapons of World War II.

SPECIFICATION	
Modell 14 Medium Howitzer	**Modell 14/16**
Calibre: 149.1-mm (5.87-in)	**Calibre:** 149.1 mm (5.87 in)
Length of barrel: 2.09 m (82.3 in)	**Length of barrel:** 2.1 m (82.7 in)
Weights: in action 2344 kg (5,168 lb); travelling 3070 kg (6,769 lb)	**Weights:** in action 2765 kg (6,097 lb); travelling 3340 kg (7,365 lb)
Elevation: -5° to +43° **Traverse:** 5°	**Elevation:** -5° to +70° **Traverse:** 6°
Muzzle velocity: 300 m (984 ft) per second	**Muzzle velocity:** 350 m (1,148 ft) per second
Maximum range: 6900 m (7,546 yards)	**Maximum range:** 8790 m (9,613 yards)
Shell weight: 41 kg (90.4 lb)	**Shell weight:** 40.33 kg (88.9 lb)

Canon de 75 mle 1897 Field gun

The claim to being one of the most famous guns of all time can be truly made by the **French 75**, the well-known **'soixante-quinze'** or **Canon de 75 mle 1897**. Over the years this gun earned for itself an almost legendary reputation, but in historical terms it deserves fame as being one of the first true quick-firing guns.

This was achieved by the introduction of a novel hydraulic recoil system that rendered contemporary mechanisms (based upon the use of springs alone) virtually obsolete overnight. This mechanism, allied to the introduction of the Nordenfeld breech mechanism that could be opened and closed by the flick of a

lever, enabled the **'75'** to fire shells at rates up to 28 rounds per minute, which was truly revolutionary.

Original design

The '75' was a government design first produced at the Atelier de Bourges, but it was not long before the type was being made elsewhere, especially by

Schneider & Cie at Le Creusot. This company's production was so prolific that the design was sometimes attributed to Schneider. The first models appeared in 1897 (hence the 'mle 1897' designation) and were kept under wraps for a considerable time as they were regarded as highly secret weapons. Much was

expected of them, for they were seen as the main support weapons for the French doctrine of the attack, in which the offensive spirit was supposed to overcome any opposition. The high fire rate of the '75' was intended to overcome the relatively light weight of HE shell fired – 6.195 kg (13.66 lb). This doctrine was to cost

A 'Soixante-Quinze' in travelling configuration, with limber and carriage. French tactics in 1914 called for the weapons being used en masse, rate of fire compensating for the gun's lack of shell power. It did not work: well dug-in German howitzers proved more than a match for massed '75s'.

the French army dearly in 1914, but throughout the Great War the '75' remained the standard field piece of the French army.

Muzzle 'ears'
The hydraulic recoil system of the '75' produced a relatively long recoil action – so long, in fact, that two 'ears' were fitted under the muzzle to engage lugs on the recoil housing at full travel to take some of the barrel loads off the pistons. These ears provided the '75' with an easy recognition feature. The breech mechanism

used a simple lever and interrupted-thread action that was swiftly and easily operated to allow the one-piece ammunition to be fed into the chamber. A box-section pole trail was used, limiting the maximum angle of elevation and consequently the range. This undesirable feature was not rectified until well after World War I. Many '75s' had a fuse-setting machine fixed to the trail leg when in action.

The 'Soixante-quinze' was produced by the thousand during World War I, and it

was also issued to armies other than the French. The US Army adopted the type in 1917 and even commenced production of its own version.

Variants
So many '75s' were produced that the type was freely available for adaption to a variety of other purposes. The armament of the first French tanks was the '75'. The weapon was also used as an anti-aircraft gun, either mounted on some dreadful lash-ups involving metal frames, or on self-pro-

pelled mountings on de Dion lorries. Some were used as coastal defence weapons.

The '75' went on to a long post-war career after 1918 but it is as one of the most widely-used guns of World War I that the '75' will

be best remembered. Some examples used by the Germans in World War II were designated **7.5-cm Feldkanone 231(f)**, but the gun was more commonly known as the **7.5-cm FK97(f)**.

SPECIFICATION	
Canon de 75 mle 1897	
Calibre: 75 mm (2.95 in)	**Elevation:** -11° to +18°
Length of barrel: 2.587 m (101.85 in)	**Traverse:** 6°
Weights: in action 1140 kg (2,514 lb); travelling 1970 kg (4,343 lb)	**Muzzle velocity:** 575 m (1,886 ft) per second
	Maximum range: 11000 m (12,030 yards)
	Shell weight: 6.195 kg (13.66 lb)

Canon de 105 mle 1913 Schneider Field gun

During the early 1900s Schneider & Cie of France took over the assets of the Russian Putilov concern, including the latter's arsenal at St Petersburg. When Schneider officials looked around the works they discovered a rather large and handsome gun chambered for the standard Russian 107-mm (4.21-in) round.

Subsequent investigations demonstrated that this equipment fired a useful shell to a good range, and the Schneider representatives decided that it would be a good gun to offer the French army. The design was subsequently taken back to France and rechambered for the French 105-mm (4.134-in) calibre; few other changes were necessary.

Hard sell
Unfortunately for Schneider & Cie, the French army was not impressed. It already had large numbers of '75s' and according to French strategy there was no need for anything heavier, despite

the fact that the 105-mm gun was not being offered as a field gun alone but more as a medium support weapon. It took a great deal of lobbying and persuasion before the French army relented and purchased a relatively small batch in 1913; as a result, the gun became the **Canon de 105 mle 1913 Schneider**, or more commonly in the service abbreviation of the time, the **L 13 S**.

Schneider at war
The first batch was duly delivered, but the French army remained unenthusiastic until after the outbreak of war in 1914. After the Battle of the Frontiers and the arrival of trench warfare, the shortcomings of the '75' became painfully apparent: it lacked shell weight and had little significant effect on field fortifications, including trenches.

But the L 13 S fired a much heavier shell more able to damage such structures, and was soon in great demand. It was true that as

Above: This French battery near Amiens in April 1918 is armed with Schneider 105 mm mle 1913 medium field guns, also known as the L 13 S. Originally derived from a Russian Putilov design, they were among the best of the French artillery and were powerful enough to demolish German field works.

a high-velocity gun rather than a howitzer it fired its shell in a relatively flat trajectory that often prevented it from reaching down into trenches, but as a counter-battery weapon it was very useful. It was not long before Schneider was churning out the L 13 S as fast as it could.

In action the L 13 S was much more cumbersome than the handy '75'. The long box trail was rather heavy, but it kept the gun stable when firing for prolonged periods. The overall design had no frills, a carry-over from its Russian origins. The interrupted-screw breech was easy to operate but the ammunition

took a bit of handling, especially after a prolonged period in action: the HE shell weighed 15.74 kg (34.7 lb).

The L 13 S was often towed into action behind an eight-horse team with a small limber taking the weight of the trail, and in action the gun team could be as large as eight men, most of them handling the ammunition.

Numbers of L 13 S guns were handed over to the Belgian army during World War I and they were used in

the Belgian positions on the River Lys. After 1918 L 13 Ss were handed over or sold to Italy as the **Cannone da 105/28** and to Yugoslavia, and some ended up with the new Polish army. Most of these World War I veterans were still in use in 1939. Most of the French L 13 S guns ended up in German hands after 1940, and many were used for beach defence as part of the Atlantic Wall, with the designation **10.5-cm Kanone 331(f)** or **K 333(f)**.

Left: French gunners rest by their 105-mm (4.14-in) mle 1913 during a pause in the action in the Argonne. Ammunition limbers stand ready to the left of the gun, which has not yet been fired as the anti-recoil trail spade has not been dug into the ground.

SPECIFICATION	
Canon de 105 mle 1913	
Calibre: 105-mm (4.134-in)	**Traverse:** 6°
Barrel length: 2.987 m (117.6 in)	**Muzzle velocity:** 550 m (1,805 ft) per second
Weights: in action 2300 kg (5,071 lb); travelling 2650 kg (5,843 lb)	**Maximum range:** 12000 m (13,123 yards)
Elevation: -5° to +37°	**Shell weight:** 15.74 kg (34.7 lb)

Ehrhardt field guns 15-pdr field guns

Although less well known outside Germany, the Ehrhardt concern of Düsseldorf was one of the more important German steel and weapons manufacturers, although it was often overshadowed by the giant Krupp concern. In time it underwent a series of mergers and take-overs that resulted in the Rheinmetall-Borsig AG conglomerate that was to become as big and as important as Krupp, but during the early 1900s it had to struggle to get what orders it could. One of these early 1900 orders was from the UK, no less, which was at that time still enmeshed in the 2nd Boer War, a war in which the UK's farmer opponents were better off for modern field artillery than the British Army.

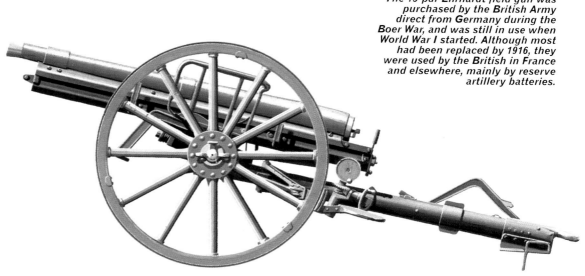

The 15-pdr Ehrhardt field gun was purchased by the British Army direct from Germany during the Boer War, and was still in use when World War I started. Although most had been replaced by 1916, they were used by the British in France and elsewhere, mainly by reserve artillery batteries.

New order

In 1901 the British ordered 108 Ehrhardt field guns that were known to the British as the **Ordnance, QF, 15-pdr**. These guns had a calibre of 76 mm (3 in) and were regarded very much as stopgap equipment until something better came along, when the Ehrhardt guns were handed over to the Territorial Army field batteries. Some of these TA batteries still had their 15-pdr guns when they were ordered to travel to France during 1915, and for a while these were used until enough 18-pdr guns were on hand to replace them in 1916. A few more batteries of 15-pdr guns were sent to

Egypt but these saw little, if any, action.

The 15-pdr guns were typical Ehrhardt designs as they prominently featured one of the main Ehrhardt trademarks, the pole trail carriage. Ehrhardt used the pole trail to enable the gun to be towed easily by horses as it combined strength with lightness. The company soon learned, however, that the pole trail restricted elevation (and thus maximum range) so later Ehrhardt guns featured what became known as the split pole trail. This had two tubular pole trail legs reaching back from the carriage cradle to a point well behind the breech at full recoil. A connecting tube then joined the two

poles at right angles and to this connecting piece the single pole trail ran back to the trail spade and towing eye. This combined the lightness of the pole trail with the ability of the barrel to elevate as much as required, and this feature became a virtual Ehrhardt trademark, being used on many Ehrhardt mountain gun designs.

The British 15-pdr guns had the ordinary pole trail, and the first versions even had two seats over the axle to carry two gun crew members on the move. These were later replaced by a shield, and the original gun wheels were replaced by British service items. The Royal Artillery was not very impressed with the

SPECIFICATION	
15-pdr	**Traverse:** 6°
Calibre: 76 mm (3 in)	**Muzzle velocity:** 510 m (1,674 ft)
Length: of barrel 2.286 m (90 in)	per second
Weight: in action 1030.5 kg	**Maximum range:** 5852 m
(2,272 lb)	(6,400 yards)
Elevation: -5° to +16°	**Shell weight:** 6.35 kg (14 lb)

15-pdr guns and, as already mentioned, they were replaced by 18-pdr guns as soon as possible.

Foreign trade

1901 was a good sales year for Ehrhardt, for in that same year it received an order for 132 field guns from the Norwegian army. These guns were of 75-mm (2.95-in) calibre and differed in many details from the British 15-pdr pieces.

Although Norway was not directly concerned with World War I, its **7.5-cm Feltkanon L631 M/01** Ehrhardt guns were kept in service throughout the war years and many of them were still in use when the Germans invaded Norway in 1940, whereupon they were designated **7.5-cm FK246(n)**.

Many other Ehrhardt guns were sold to South American nations.

7.7-cm field gun FK 96 and FK 16

During the 1890s the German army asked Krupp to produce a field gun with a calibre of 77 mm (3.03 in). This odd calibre was chosen as it was realised that most potential enemies used field guns with calibres of 75 mm (2.95 in), namely France or 76 mm (3 in), namely Russia. Thus, any captured

guns could be bored out to take German ammunition but an enemy would be unable to do the same with captured German guns: this is an early example of this nation's thorough approach to war. In order to save manufacturing potential the new gun was to be mounted on the howitzer

carriage of the day.

This gun was known as the **Feldkanone 96 n/A** (n/A for *neues Art*, or new model). It was the standard field gun of the German artillery arm when World War I began in 1914, and many served until 1918. The FK 96 n/A was a sound Krupp design, but the

Above: Gunners engaged in urban fighting against Bolshevik forces near Nariva, March 1918. The guns are 7.7-cm (3.03-in) FK 16s and the layer is aiming the gun over open sights. Note how the gun crew used the ammunition limber to obtain extra cover.

Left: German gunners train with 7.7-cm (3.03 in) C96 n/A field guns on ranges somewhere in Germany during World War I. These guns, although replaced by the FK 16 in the field batteries after 1916, were still in use for training or by reserve batteries until the war ended in 1918.

German gunners gradually came to appreciate that it lacked range and asked for improvements. New ammunition was introduced, but the main range increment came during 1916 with the introduction of a new and longer barrel; the carriage continued to be the original C/96 howitzer carriage and the breech mechanism of the FK 96 n/A was retained. This new field gun became known as the **7.7-cm Feldkanone 16** or **FK 16**, and it was rapidly adopted as the standard German field gun, replacing as many of the older models as possible.

Increase in range

The FK 16 introduced considerable range increase. With the old type ammunition the FK 96 n/A could manage only about 7000 m (7,655 yards) firing light shrapnel projectiles. The new FK 16 firing new streamlined shells could reach 10300 m (11,264 yards), which was a considerable increase. Some of this range increase had to be offset by an increase in overall weight but this price was borne willingly. The FK 16 could fire a wide range of ammunition types, all of

The 7.7-cm (3.03-in) Feldkanone C 96 n/A was the standard German field gun of the early war years. Built by Krupp, it was a rugged and very reliable gun but lacked range and was later replaced by the 7.7-cm FK 16, which had a longer barrel and some other small changes to the field carriage and shield.

them loaded separately, i.e. the shell and charge case were loaded as two items. As well as the usual shrapnel and high explosive (HE), the FK 16 was also used to fire various forms of gas shell. Compared with the earlier short projectiles, the improved ammunition for the FK 16 was much longer and more streamlined, offering less drag in flight. These shells were usually HE only; there were

also smoke and illuminating projectiles.

Into action

Ammunition for the FK 16 was carried into action on a gun limber. A six-horse team was used to pull the gun and limber into action, but late in the war other animals such as oxen had to be used. The normal gun crew was six or seven men but often less were used once the gun was emplaced in a forward

position; the rest then acted as ammunition handlers.

After 1918 the FK 16 was one of the few weapons allowed to the rump of the old German army. Others were handed out as war reparations to nations such as Belgium, and the Netherlands also received a number. Many of these FK

16s were converted to take 75-mm (2.95-in) barrels, including the German examples, so that when World War II came around there were virtually no 77-mm versions left other than a few training equipments, Many of the re-barrelled FK 16s were used throughout World War II.

Below: Detail of the breech of a captured FK 16 shows the sliding breech block, which was by 1916 a standard feature of German field artillery design.

Above left: A German army 7.7-cm (3.03-in) C 96 n/A field gun in action in Poland during the 1915 summer campaign. The gun sight can be seen above the lowered gun shield flap and some ammunition carriers lie in front of the gun muzzle.

Left: A German 7.7-cm Feldkanone (FK) C 96 n/A is shown in action in the Champagne region with the barrel at maximum recoil. As the loader stands by with a fresh round the soldier at the end of the carriage trail prepares to make any laying corrections the layer next to the shield might call for.

SPECIFICATION	
FK 16	
Calibre: 77 mm (3.03 in)	**Traverse:** 8°
Weights: in action 1422.5 kg (3,136 lb); travelling 2286 kg (5,040 lb)	**Muzzle velocity:** maximum 600 m (1,968 ft) per second
Length: of barrel 2.7 m (106.3 in)	**Maximum range:** 10300 m (11,264 yards)
Elevation: -9.5° to +38°	**Shell weight:** streamlined HE 5.9 kg (13 lb)

Cannone da 75/27 modello 11 75-mm field gun

Although the **Cannone da 75/27 modello 11** was designed by a Frenchman it was produced only in Italy and may thus qualify as an Italian weapon. The designer was named Deport, who conceived the idea of a recoil mechanism that could stay fixed in a horizontal plane while the barrel could be elevated to any angle desired. The advantages of this system are rather obscure, but the Italian army certainly took to the idea to the extent that they produced the modello 11 in large numbers.

The modello 11 was a relatively small field piece, as a result mainly of the fact that it was originally ordered for cavalry use. In time it was issued to other arms and became a standard field gun. Apart from the unusual (and uncopied) recoil system, the modello 11 also had one other novel feature for its day. This was split trail legs which gave the gun an unusually wide traverse by contemporary standards, and also enabled the barrel to be elevated to a maximum of 65° allowing the gun to be used in mountainous areas if required. In action the trails were spread and instead of the more usual trail spade the legs were held in place by stakes hammered through slots at the end of each. This certainly held the gun steady for firing, but there were two disadvantages to this system. One was that any large change of traverse could not be made until the stakes had been laboriously removed from the ground; the other was that on rocky or hard ground it took time to hammer in the stakes. For all these potential troubles the Italians used the stake securing method on

many of their artillery designs, large and small.

The modello 11 was a small but useful weapon with a good range: its 10240-m (11,200-yard) capability was well above that of many of its contemporaries. However, for its size it was rather heavy, which was no doubt a factor in its change from the cavalry to the field artillery. In action it had a crew of at least four men although a full detachment was six, the extra two looking after the horses.

Coastal defence

It is known that some of these guns were used by the Italian maritime artillery militia within the Italian coastal defence organisation. The modello 11s appear to have been used as light mobile batteries that could be used for close-in

Above: An example of Cannone 75/27 modello 11 field artillery lies abandoned by Italian forces along the roadside at Codroipo, near Udine, in October 1917.

beach defences of likely landing spots. Many of the modello 11s were still in use in this role after 1940, and many other modello 11s were in service with the field artillery. In fact so many were still on hand in 1943 that many came under German control, with the designation **7.5-cm Feldkanone 244(i)**, for use by the German occupation forces in Italy. By that time many modello 11s had been modified for powered traction by conversion of the old wooden-spoked wheels to new steel-spoked wheels and revised shields; these modernised equipments used pneumatic tyres.

The Cannone 75/27 modello 11 was not an ideal weapon for use by mountain troops: although relatively small it was heavy for its size, precluding its intended use by the cavalry arms.

SPECIFICATION	
Cannone da 75/27	**Traverse:** 52°
Calibre: 75 mm (2.95 in)	**Muzzle velocity:** 502 m (1,647 ft) per second
Length: of barrel 2.132 m (83.93 in)	**Maximum range:** 10240 m (11,200 yards)
Weights: in action 1076 kg (2,372 lb); travelling 1900 kg (4,189 lb)	**Shell weight:** 6.35 kg (14 lb)
Elevation: -15° to +65°	

Field Gun Model 00/02 76-mm light field gun

In 1914 the Russian army was desperately short of up-to-date field artillery, but this was not due to lack of production facilities or technological backwardness, as might be supposed. On the contrary, from 1906 vast sums of money were expended on artillery but were used to modernise the armament of the fortresses which protected the western frontiers of the Empire. These fortresses, which

absorbed so large a proportion of the defence budget, proved to be of little use when the German army finally invaded, while the lack of modern field guns in the armies was a serious handicap.

Since the 1860s Russia had used field artillery based on Krupp designs. Although unable at first to afford the steel barrel construction of the German weapons, Russia demonstrated to the

world the superiority of metal carriages over conventional wooden ones during the Russo-Turkish war in 1877. The campaign in Bulgaria revealed many shortcomings in the Russian army but probably saw the Tsarist army at the peak of its efficiency. Thereafter, its fortunes declined as vigorous officers like Skoboleff were passed over for political reasons.

Russian field artillery con-

tinued its reliance on Krupps, and its main field piece of World War I owed much to Krupp designs. The 76-mm Field Gun Model 00

was based on an older Krupp weapon, and had no recoil system other than a sprung spade under the axle. It had not been in

SPECIFICATION	
Field Gun Model 00/02	**Traverse:** 5.5°
Calibre: 76 mm (3 in)	**Muzzle velocity:** 588 m (1,929 ft) per second
Length: of barrel 2.286 m (90 in)	**Maximum range:** 6400 m (7,000 yards)
Weights: in action 1040 kg (2,293 lb); travelling 1965 kg (4,332 lb)	**Shell weight:** 6.5 kg (14.33 lb)
Elevation: -5° to +16°	

Russian Putilov 76-mm (3-in) Model 00 (1900) field guns were converted for the anti-aircraft role on modified garrison carriages and used by the Germans on the Western Front. This trio was captured at Chateau Thierry in July 1918.

service long before a more modern recoil system was fitted to produce the **Model 00/02**. This gun was produced at the Putilov arsenal at St Petersburg, which was the most modern facility in Russia at the time. Thus the Model 02 was very like many other Krupp designs of the period. The barrel was 30 calibres long and the

usual Krupp steel section trail was copied almost exactly. A shield was provided, but this was often removed and replaced by two seats over the axle. One small feature that was to become a virtual Putilov trademark was to be seen at the front of the recoil mechanism cylinder: this was a peculiar embossed

pattern that appeared on almost every subsequent Putilov product.

High demand
The quantities of field guns required by the massive Tsarist armies were so large that when World War I broke out many batteries were still using field guns that dated back to the

1870s. There were never enough Model 02s to go around, and the German victories of 1914 and after usually resulted in the guns that there were to hand being added to the pile of German war booty. All the Putilov workers could do was attempt to churn out as many Model 02s as they possibly could. Thus the

Model 02 was kept in production for long after 1917, and so many were still in use by 1930 that a programme to modernise them was instituted. Thus when 1941 arrived the Model 02 was still in service as the **Model 02/30**, and captured examples were designated **7.62-cm leFk 294(r)** by the Germans.

Field Gun Model 1910 107-mm field gun

Soon after production of the 76-mm (3-in) Model 00/02 got under way at the Putilov arsenal, the designers had an opportunity to assess what other artillery weapons would be needed by the Tsarist armies. At that time many of the heavy field batteries were equipped with a motley array of weapons, mainly of Krupp origins, and the Putilov designers decided to see what they could produce using their own talents. They soon demonstrated a real flair for designing modern artillery that was to come to full flower during World War II, for they produced a 107-mm (4.2-in) weapon known as the **Field Gun Model 1910**.

This Model 1910 was one of the best designs of its generation. It was well balanced and good-looking with an excellent all-round performance, and as time was to show it had a considerable amount of built-in growth potential. As only to be expected, features from existing weapons (especially from some Krupp sources) were evident in the design, but it was innovative and demonstrated a good balance of weight and performance. The shell weighed 16.4 kg (36.15 lb) and could be fired to a very useful 12500 m (13,670 yards). The gun was towed by eight horses.

It was at this stage, just after production of the

Model 1910 had commenced, that the Putilov concern got itself into severe financial difficulties. The state of the Russian economy was at best parlous, and the demands made upon it by rapidly expanding industries such as the defence concerns made it even shakier.

Financial input
The only way out the Tsarist officials could see was to attract foreign finance into such industries, and the French defence manufacturers descended on Russia like hawks. The massive Schneider & Cie concern soon took over the Putilov arsenal and poured in huge amounts of hard cash. In

return it took what it could to bolster its own sales efforts, and the Model 1910 caught the French eye. The result was the 105-mm (4.13-in) Model 1913, or L 13 S.

Red Army adoption
Even with the financial backing of Schneider, production of the Model 1910 at St Petersburg never got anywhere near meeting demand until well into the war years. But by 1917 Model 1910s were flowing off the lines in considerable numbers, so many in fact that when the line closed in the period after the revolution of 1917 there were many Model 1910s for the newly established Red Army to use during the civil war and for years after.

In 1930 the type was one of several chosen to be updated in an attempt to modernise the Red Army gun park. For the Model 1910 this meant a new and longer barrel and new ammunition; this produced the **Model 1910/30**. This gun was one that the Germans came to prize after the events of 1941, for it made an excellent weapon for use in the Atlantic Wall with the designation **10.7-cm K352(r)**. Thus the Model 1910/30 was used there alongside numbers of captured French L 13 S guns, and the two weapons that originated in St Petersburg many years before ended their service lives together.

SPECIFICATION	
Field Gun Model 1910	**Elevation:** -5° to +37°
Calibre: 107 mm (4.2 in)	**Traverse:** 6°
Length: of barrel about 2.99 m (117.7 in)	**Muzzle velocity:** 570 m (1,870 ft) per second
Weights: in action 2172 kg (4,788 lb); travelling 2486 kg (5,480 lb)	**Maximum range:** 12500 m (13,670 yards)
	Shell weight: 16.4 kg (36.15 lb)

A Russian army 107-mm (actually 4.2-in/106.7-mm) Field Gun Model 1910 in action with Armenian gunners in Mesopotamia. This gun was the originator for the Schneider 105-mm (4.13-in) L 13 S used by the French army, and a modernised version was used in World War II.

Ordnance, QF, 13-pdr Gun 3-in field gun

In the aftermath of the Boer War the Royal Artillery decided that its ageing gun park was in great need of overhaul, and so launched a search for replacements. Field guns were one new type of equipment sought, but the trial selection was difficult. The choice was between a design known as the **Ordnance, QF, 13-pdr Gun**, which was an amalgamation of the best features of Woolwich Arsenal and Vickers submissions, and the gun known as the Ordnance, QF, 18-pdr. Deliberations went on for some time before the decision was made to acquire the 13-pdr for the Royal Horse Artillery and the 18-pdr for the field regiments.

Into service

The first 13-pdr guns entered service in 1904. The numbers of these weapons were never as great as those of the 18-pdr, for the Royal Horse Artillery was much smaller than the rest of the Royal Artillery. Some 13-pdr guns were sent to India, but most stayed in the United Kingdom, ready to move to France in 1914. It was a 13-pdr gun that fired the first British shot of World War I, and almost as soon as they arrived these guns were involved in the epic gunner battle of Nery. Thereafter the 13-pdr weapons were gener-

ally overshadowed by the 18-pdr guns, to the extent that at one point some 13-pdr pieces were withdrawn to be converted to rudimentary anti-aircraft guns.

Shrapnel round

The 13-pdr had a calibre of 3 in (76 mm), and in the light of Boer War experience, much of the ammunition fired was shrapnel. This was not shrapnel as it is known today (fragments produced by the detonation of the shell) but rather a form of carrier shell which contained a small explosive charge (detonated when the shell was still in the air) to blow out from the front of the shell a large number of lead or steel balls that spread out to act as anti-personnel weapons. Against an enemy in the open, shrapnel was a very effective weapon, but against defended troops under cover it was virtually useless, and not much use at cutting through barbed wire. It took some time for appreciable amounts of high explosive shell to get to the gunners in France, so after the initial period of the war the 13-pdr guns were of only limited use in France. Instead many were sent to the Middle East where they were used in the various campaigns against the Turks.

Although not used in such large numbers as the 18-pdr, the 13-pdr was a good gun of

The Royal Horse Artillery began to re-equip with the 13-pdr from 1904. A necessarily robust weapon, the 13-pdr provided fire support for the cavalry, which meant that by the end of 1914 there was little role for it on the Western Front. Although many RHA batteries remained in Flanders, the weapon achieved its greatest success in the cavalry operations in the Middle East.

its type and well suited to the horse artillery tactics of the era before World War I. The problem for the 13-pdr was that those tactics did not last long under the trench warfare conditions of World War I. But the design was basically sound, so that apart from the departure of some for use as anti-aircraft guns, the 13-pdr remained virtually unchanged throughout its service life. That service life is still not over, for the 13-pdr is still used by the King's Troop of the Royal Horse Artillery for its well-known ceremonial and display duties in London and elsewhere.

Incidentally, the shell fired by the 13-pounder did not weigh 13 lb (5 9 kg), but rather 12.5 lb (5.67 kg).

The British 13-pdr was used by the Royal Horse Artillery and was produced in far fewer numbers than the 18-pdr field gun. The rope-bound tube over the barrel contained the hydro-spring recoil system.

Above: This photograph, taken near Inexent in June 1918, shows exactly how robust horse-towed field guns had to be. The 13-pdr was light enough to be towed at speed by a six-horse team, and to this day 13-pdrs can still be seen towed by the King's Troop, Royal Horse Artillery, during their dramatic displays.

SPECIFICATION	
Ordnance, QF, 13-pdr Gun	**Traverse:** 8°
Calibre: 3 in (76 mm)	**Muzzle velocity:** 511 m (1,675 ft) per second
Length: of barrel 186 m (73.25 in)	**Maximum range:** 5395 m (5,900 yards)
Weight: complete 1014 kg (2,236 lb)	**Shell weight:** 5.67 kg (12.5 lb)
Elevation: -5° to +16°	

Ordnance, QF, 15-pdr Gun 3-in field gun

The **Ordnance, QF, 15-pdr Gun** should not be confused with the Erhardt 15-pdr field gun, which was a much more modern weapon than the British 15-pdr. The original British 15-pdr was a pre-Boer War piece that used the old system of a spring-loaded spade to absorb much of the firing recoil. This spade was under the axle and the main 'springing' came from a rope connected to a spring contained in a tube on the trail spade. This system worked, but it was cumbersome and inefficient, demanding a lot of work from the gun team. So in the aftermath of the Boer War, rather than simply dispose of the large numbers of guns in service, they were converted to take a hydro-spring recoil system over the barrel. The old 15-pdr breech was modified to a more modern form and other alterations were made.

Once ready for use in 1907 they were issued to the Territorial Army batteries.

The 15-pdr was really too heavy for the field gun role and had an indifferent range capability, but it proved to be an excellent training weapon that could be provided at a relatively low cost. The new recoil system was efficient enough, but it was something of a fitter's headache as numerous marks of the old 15-pdr had been used for the conversions, and interchangeability of parts between guns was difficult.

Into action

The 15-pdr guns did not move to France until 1915, by which time the supply of 13-pdr and 18-pdr guns was becoming difficult. Only a few Territorial batteries took their 15-pdr equipments to France, but on arrival there was little they could do, for

the only ammunition they had was shrapnel, which was of little use against a well dug-in enemy under top cover, as was the case all along the Western Front by 1915. A few 15-pdr guns were present during the 1915 Battle of Loos, where

The 15-pdr field gun could trace its origins back to the 1890s, for it was an old field gun design altered to use a new hydro-spring recoil system plus some other changes. The result was heavy and cumbersome, and by 1914 most were used by the Territorial Army who took them over to France in 1915. They were replaced as soon as possible.

SPECIFICATION	
Ordnance, QF, 15-pdr Gun	**Traverse:** none
Calibre: 3 in (76 mm)	**Muzzle velocity:** 484 m (1,590 ft) per second
Length: of barrel 2.345 m (92.35 in)	**Maximum range:** 5258 m (5,750 yards)
Weight: complete 1339.5 kg (2,953 lb)	**Shell weight:** 6.35 kg (14 lb)
Elevation: -9° to +16°	

they could add little to the proceedings as a result mainly of their lack of suitable projectiles.

After that brief flurry of activity the 15-pdr was retired to act as a training gun once more. A few were sent to South Africa, where they were used during some of the campaigns against the Germans in East Africa, but most of the rest were used to fire off their large stocks of ammunition as burst-producing delivery systems for the training of artillery observers, both on the ground and in the air. They continued in this role for a remarkably long time, for some Royal Artillery batteries in India were still using 15-pdr guns for this same purpose as late as the mid-1930s.

The 15-pdr is still one of the lesser-known guns of World War I, but it had its small part to play. It was certainly distinctive enough. The recoil system added to the weapon during the conversion from the original sprung spade configuration gave the gun a very distinctive appearance, as it was contained in a metal shroud that covered the entire upper length of the barrel.

The original 15-pdr from which the World War I field gun evolved was still employed by the Indian Army in 1914, who used them in some of the early campaigns in German East Africa. This example is seen firing during a training camp exercise in India in July 1915.

Ordnance, QF, 18-pdr Gun 3.3-in field gun

The 18-pdr Mk I field gun entered service in 1904, and in 1914 was in widespread use by the British and some Commonwealth armies. It had a pole trail for horse traction and the original recoil system proved prone to breakage, but it was regarded as a good and sound gun design that was used throughout the war.

The first **Ordnance, QF, 18-pdr Gun Mk I** was issued to the Royal Artillery in 1904, and in the years after that it was also issued to many other armies of the Commonwealth, so that by 1914 the 18-pdr was the standard field gun of the British and Commonwealth armies; some were even being produced in India. The 18-pdr had no single parentage, but was an amalgam of design ideas produced by Woolwich Arsenal, the Elswick Works and Vickers. The barrel was wire-wound, had a simple single-action breech, and was mounted on a pole trail carriage. The usual shield was fitted, and as was common at that time the ammunition fired was almost entirely shrapnel.

Modifications

It was not long before the original design was being modified. The first change was to allow a barrel liner to be replaced when worn, but when the 18-pdr went to war in 1914 it was still basically the same as it was when first issued. The trials of battle soon highlighted what was to become known as the 18-pdr's weakest point: the recuperator springs, which returned the barrel back to the firing position after recoil, could not put up with the stresses that continued firing produced and broke under the strain, leaving the gun useless. At first all the gun fitters could do was to keep changing the springs, a hazardous and time-consuming operation until a modification that could be adopted in the field was developed. This was an entirely new hydro-pneumatic recoil system that fitted inside the existing spring housings this did the trick and the 18-pdr became much more reliable.

Redesigned version

However, the 18-pdr was to undergo one more major change during World War I. The original carriage used a pole trail which was useful enough for horse traction, but as it went right under the breech it limited elevation angles, and thus range. This led to what became known as the **18-pdr Gun Mk IV** (the other marks were development models, apart from the original Mk I). This was virtually a new design: for a start the Mk IV was fitted with a box trail which allowed the barrel to be elevated much further to provide the required range increase, the breech mechanism was changed to a new form known as the Asbury type, and the recoil system was moved to an entirely new position under the bar-

Right: An 18-pdr field gun is seen in action near St Leger aux Bois in the Oise region of France during August 1916. The pole trail is clearly visible, as is the one-piece round that was almost the same size as one of the old quart beer bottles.

rel. The new recoil system used a 'floating piston' that employed oil and compressed air to provide a much smoother and more reliable movement. The cradle was redesigned to take the loads imposed by these new features, and the result was a much better all-round gun. Not only did it have a far better range, but it was far more stable in action and proved to be capable of very high rates of fire: 30 rounds a minute in the hands of a well-trained team was not unusual.

The 18-pdr Mk IV was just getting into full production as the war ended, and it became the preferred weapon of the Royal Artillery in the inter-war years. By then the 18-pdr was in use outside the British and Commonwealth armies. The US Army had taken over large numbers commencing in 1917, and other nations that later used the 18-pdr were Ireland, some of the Baltic States and China. Many 18-pdr guns were used during World War II and the last of the type did not leave Irish service until the 1970s.

An 18-pdr field gun is manhandled from a waterlogged gun position near Zillebeke during the Flanders offensive of August 1917, providing a graphic indication of why that offensive failed to achieve anything and got bogged down.

SPECIFICATION	
Ordnance, QF, 18-pdr Gun Mk I	**Traverse:** 8°
Calibre: 3.3 in (83.8 mm)	**Muzzle velocity:** 492 m (1,615 ft) per second
Length: of barrel 2.463 m (96.96 in)	
Weight: complete 1280 kg (2,821 lb)	**Maximum range:** 5966 m (6,525 yards)
Elevation: -5° to +16°	**Shell weight:** 8.39 kg (18.5 lb)

Skoda Heavy howitzers

In the years before World War I the Skoda concern, based at Pilsen in what is now Czechoslovakia, was well to the fore in the development and manufacture of super-heavy artillery. Like so many other nations in Europe during that era, Austria-Hungary faced the prospect of having to smash through rings of massive fortifications that protected the main centres of the empire's potential foes, and as the fortifications grew heavier so did the weapons designed to defeat them. By 1911 Skoda had already produced a 305-mm (12-in) howitzer that was the equal of any comparable weapon in Europe, and this stubby howitzer fired a 382- or 287-kg (842- or 633-lb) shell able to penetrate the heaviest fortress defence.

Designed to move

This **Skoda Model 1911** was an important design: it was one of the first heavy howitzers to be designed from the start with motor traction in mind. Each of the howitzers could be broken down into three main loads: the barrel, the firing platform and the main carriage. The barrel and the main carriage could be towed by a massive Austro-Daimler tractor at a ponderous but steady pace over considerable distances.

By 1911 such tractors were not unusual, though designing a heavy howitzer to make use of them was novel and attracted much attention. The howitzers were organised into two-howitzer batteries with two gun-carriage tractor loads and another tractor pulling the two firing platforms.

Motorised support

Crew members sat on each towed load, primarily to operate the brakes, while further tractors pulled ammunition, assembly cranes, tools and even a special mobile workshop. More trucks carried fire control equipment, rations and administrative paraphernalia.

Mobile batteries such as these were used to crush the Belgian forts in 1914, where they served alongside the famous Krupp 42-cm (16.54-in) 'Big Berthas'. They were later used during the Verdun battles and in the campaign in Italy.

Once World War I was under way the need for even heavier artillery became apparent and Skoda went on to produce larger-calibre weapons. The first of these was ready in 1914, although it was not a field howitzer but a coastal artillery piece intended for use inside armoured turrets.

The Skoda Model 1911 305-mm howitzer was one of the first heavy artillery pieces to be designed with motor traction in mind. The equipment broke down into three parts, comprising barrel, gun carriage and firing platform.

The calibre of this **Skoda Model 1914** was 420 mm (16.54 in), the same as that of the Krupp howitzers, but despite the Model 1914's intended employment as a field piece the type was used on occasion as a weapon to demolish heavy fortifications during the campaigns along the border with northern Italy. Some survived as coastal artillery weapons until World War II.

Increased mobility

Moving the massive Model 1914 was a huge task, so in 1916 Skoda introduced a more conventional 420-mm (16.54-in) howitzer for field use. Even so, the **Skoda Model 16** was still a very

hefty piece that took days to emplace or to move, and it was not until 1917 that a 420-mm (16.54-in) design intended from the outset for relatively easy movement was ready. The **Skoda Model 1917** was in many ways the same piece as the Model 1916 but designed so that the individual loads could be towed by large wheeled tractors. The total weight of the emplaced Model 1917 was well over 100 tonnes, and on the road the combined loads came to far more than that.

The rate of fire was only about one or two rounds per hour, but the heaviest shell weighed 1000 kg (2,205 lb). The maximum range was

14600 m (15,965 yards).

380-mm howitzer

In 1916 Skoda also produced the **Model 1916 380-mm** (14.96-in) howitzer which was nicknamed 'Barbara'. It too was designed for motor traction, but few examples of the weapons were actually built.

After 1918 surviving 305-mm (12-in) howitzers were distributed among the new nations that had emerged from the old Austro-Hungarian Empire. Most went to Hungary and Czechoslovakia, but Italy also received some along with a few of the 420-mm (16.54-in) coastal howitzers.

SPECIFICATION	
Skoda Model 1911	**Muzzle velocity:** with heavy shell 340 m (1,115 ft) per second
Calibre: 305 mm (12 in)	**Maximum range:** with light shell
Length of barrel: 3.03 m (9 ft 11.3 in)	11300 m (12,360 yards) and with heavy shell 9600 m (10,500 yards)
Weight: 20830 kg (45,922 lb)	**Shell weight:** 287 or 382 kg (633 or 842 lb)
Elevation: +40° to +70°	
Traverse: on carriage 16°	

The Skoda Model 1914 was produced for coast defence, but during the campaigns in northern Italy the 420-mm piece was used as a fortress smasher. Rate of fire was only two shells per hour.

Canon de 220 L mle 1917 Schneider Heavy gun

At the beginning of the 20th century, the French military philosophers who dictated the nature of the French army training and tactics decided that fast attack was to be the main strength of the French army. As a result, there would be little need for heavy artillery, whose main roles were in defence or deliberate attack. The famous 75-mm (2.95-in) mle 1897 field gun was all that would be needed, they thought, as massed French infantry swept all before them. As a result, scant attention was given to the

provision of heavy weapons before the start of World War I. The 1914 Battle of the Frontiers demonstrated in a terrible fashion the fallacies behind such thinking, and after encountering well dug-in German machine gun nests and artillery positions, the battered French army withdrew behind the trench lines that were to be the trademark of World War I.

Heavy artillery was sorely needed behind the trenches. The concentration on the '75' as a weapon for all tasks proved to be a major blunder, for against

The Schneider Canon de 220 L mle 1917 was derived from a naval weapon. The long-barrelled gun was the first new design to enter French army service in place of the largely obsolete coastal artillery, which had been a stopgap in 1914.

protected earthworks light field guns were virtually useless.

Heavier-calibre weapons were needed to destroy trench lines and bunkers, and the French army had few. The only sources for such weapons were from coastal batteries and from the nation's ancient forts. Heavy guns were stripped from these locations and it was with these elderly weapons that the French army withstood the rigours of the dreadful Verdun battles of 1916.

Better weapons were demanded, but since the French designers had to work virtually from scratch, it took time for these to be produced. Developing and

manufacturing new heavy guns took years and it was not until 1917 that Schneider was able to deliver the first of its heavy offerings, a gun known as the **Canon de 220 L mle 1917** or the **Can 220 L 17 S**.

Long-range firepower

It had a calibre of 220 mm (8.66 in) and was a derivative of a naval gun design. It had a long slender barrel and was mounted on a long heavy carriage in such a way that the barrel slid in its cradle back along the length of the carriage when the gun was fired.

The L 17 S was a heavy weapon that had to be towed in two loads (the barrel and the carriage) but

it had a very good range, firing a shell weighing 104.75 kg (231 lb) out to a maximum distance of 28800 m (24,935 yards).

In action the L 17 S proved to be an excellent heavy weapon but it arrived late on the battlefields of France. By mid-1917 the French army was in such a state following the massive loss of life in the Verdun battles that the forces in large sectors mutinied and refused to fight further.

In many ways, the L 17 S was the gun which saved France in her hour of need. For some reason the Germans never got to hear of the mutinies, and for long periods were held at

bay only by the artillery. The French artillery arm was relatively untouched by the mutinies and fought on using the L 17 S and other such heavy weapons until the troubles were resolved and the French army once more settled down to face the enemy. The L 17 S was to go on to play its part during the decisive Western Front battles of 1918.

By 1918 the L 17 S was one of the better of the many types in the French artillery gun park, and it was retained until 1940, when the many examples still in service fel'l into the hands of the Germans, who used them as coastal guns emplaced in the Atlantic Wall. Some saw action again during the Normandy landings of June 1944.

SPECIFICATION	
Can 220 L 17 S	
Calibre: 220 mm (8.66 in)	**Traverse:** 20°
Length of barrel: 7.67 m (25 ft 2 in)	**Muzzle velocity:** 766 m (2,513 ft) per second
Weight: in action 25880 kg (57,055 lb)	**Maximum range:** 22800 m (24,935 yards)
Elevation: -10° to +37°	**Shell weight:** 104.75 kg (231 lb)

Canon de 240 L mle 84/17 St Chamond Heavy gun

The Canon de 240 L mle 84/17 St Chamond was originally a fortress weapon dating from 1884. First attempts at making the weapon mobile involved a railway mounting, but by 1917 a field mounting had been developed.

One of the early candidates considered for stripping from the French fortifications of an earlier era was a heavy gun known as the **mle 1884**. This was a St Chamond design with a calibre of 240 mm (9.4 in), but in the early part of 1915 the weapon was generally considered too heavy for field use by conventional means and was thus mounted on special railway gun carriages.

As such the weapons were as successful as any of the other extemporised French railway guns of the

period. But railway guns have a habit of not always being able to get to the locations where they are most needed, and this lesson was driven home during the Verdun battles of 1916, which settled down to a slogging match between the opposing artillery.

Heavy guns needed

Under such circumstances the heavier calibres were often of more use than the longer-ranged guns. Thus a call went out to mount the St Chamond 240-mm

(9.4-in) guns on to some form of field carriage.

The new carriage was delivered during 1917 and the gun and carriage combination became known as the **Canon de 240 L mle 84/17 St Chamond** or **Can 240 L 84/17 St Ch**. By that time there were few of the original mle 1884 guns available, so the guns were placed back in production – new equipment being designated **Can 240 L mle 1917 St Ch**.

The resulting weapon was a ponderous item, to say the least. The gun

barrel had to be towed separately from the carriage, and on the road both made for long and awkward loads. The usual towing vehicles appear to have been steam tractors; these meant that the St Chamond had a very limited cross-country capability, unless special roads were laid. The time allotted to assemble or dismantle the gun generally had to be considered in days.

Powerful shell

The ordnance fired a 161-kg (355-lb) shell of considerable power, though because of the age of the gun barrels, the range of the L 84/17 was limited to 17300 m (18,920 yards).

The numbers produced

during 1917 and after appear to have been limited, no doubt as a result of the time required to manufacture the large barrel and carriage. The new barrels produced in 1917 were slightly longer than the original but had the same performance, so they were still relatively unworn when the Armistice was signed in November 1918.

At least two or three batteries were retained up to 1940, but in that year the Germans demonstrated that the L 84/17 was a leftover from another era by destroying all the remaining weapons with Stuka dive-bombers, most of them while they were still on their road carriages.

SPECIFICATION	
Can 240 L St Ch	
Calibre: 240 mm (9. 45 in)	**Elevation:** 0' to + 38'
Length of barrel: mle 84/17 6.70 m (22 ft) and mle 19 17 7. 00 m (22 ft 11. 6 in)	**Traverse:** 10'
	Muzzle velocity: 575 m (1, 886 ft) per second
Weight: in action 3 1000 kg (68,343 lb)	**Maximum range:** 17300 m (18,920 yards)
	Shell weight: 161 kg (355 lb)

The barrel of the Canon de 240 L mle 84/17 was easily detachable from the carriage. Movable in two units, the great length of the equipment made for an extremely awkward load, and setting up a firing position could take several days.

Mortier de 280 mle 14/16 Schneider Heavy howitzer

The years up to 1914 were not entirely devoid of heavy artillery activity for the French armaments industry. The large Schneider concern continued with its full range of artillery development, mainly funded from internal sources in order to keep abreast of design influences elsewhere and to remain ready to seize upon any possible sales opportunities that might arise. Thus in 1914 it had ready to hand a design for the 280-mm (11-in) **Obusier de 280 mle 1914 Schneider** that was soon accepted for service by a French army eager to improve its heavy artillery holdings.

Designation change

It was two years before Schneider could deliver the first examples, however. By then the howitzer's designation had been decided as **Mortier de 280 mle 14/16 Schneider**, the term *mortier* (mortar) in place of *obusier* (howitzer) being a typical piece of European terminology as on the Continent heavy howitzers were frequently called mortars. As the type was ordered 'off the shelf', the French army had to take what they got and what they got was a very ponderous weapon. The original mle 1914 as produced by Schneider had been designed as a heavy artillery piece that would be used for siege warfare, in which plenty of time would be available for the move to the battlefield and more time for the emplacement. Thus the

mle 14/16 had to be broken down into no less than four loads for travelling and in position for firing rested on a heavy metal firing platform. Ammunition was delivered to the breech by means of a small crane which lifted the shell on to a small trolley that ran along a pair of rails to the breech. Ramming the shell into the breech was carried out by a chain-driven rammer.

Counter-bombardment

Once the assembly lines for the mle 14/16 had been established the units were churned out in relatively large numbers. Many suffered from enemy counter-bombardment as the range was only 10950 m (11,975 yards), putting the type well within the reach of many of the German long-range guns. The mle 14/16 was nonetheless a very useful weapon for destroying trench systems and underground installations, though it cannot have been a very popular weapon with the French gunners. Every move, however short, entailed the lengthy and involved job of breaking down the howitzer into four loads, and once on site a pit had to be dug for the heavy steel platform, together with a deeper pit to allow the barrel to recoil when the howitzer was fired at high angles of elevation.

After 1918 the mle 14/16 was one of the types selected to remain in service. Thus some were still around in 1940. By then they

belonged to a past generation and had no chance for effective use as the German Panzers rolled across France. Many mle 14/16s were captured intact and were added to the German army 'siege train', being used once again during the siege of Leningrad and later during the siege of Sevastopol, where their weight and bulk were no disadvantage. Thus the mle 14/16 ended up in the hands of the enemy it was originally procured to defeat.

The Mortier de 280 mle 14/16 was a ponderous piece designed for siege warfare. Range was limited, which placed the howitzer well within the range of German long-range guns. Indeed, many suffered from counter-bombardment.

SPECIFICATION	
Mortier de 280 mle 14/16 Schneider	**Traverse:** 20°
Calibre: 280 mm (11 in)	**Muzzle velocity:** 418 m (1,371 ft) per second
Length of barrel: 3.35 m (11 ft)	**Maximum range:** 10950 m (11,975 yards)
Weight: in action 16000 kg (35,274 lb)	**Shell weight:** 205 kg (452 lb)
Elevation: +10° to +60°	

Mortier de 370 Filloux Heavy howitzer

The **Mortier de 370 Filloux** had its origins in a requirement for a coastal artillery weapon capable of producing plunging fire to pierce the relatively thin protection of warship decks. By 1913 a number of these short howitzers that fired at high angles of elevation had been produced, but in 1913 the 370-mm (14.57-in) weapon was produced and this remained thereafter the largest of all these French specialist weapons.

Change of role

In appearance the Mortier de 370 Filloux was a deceptively small weapon. In fact it was a brute. It had originally been designed for use in static coastal emplacements where (in theory at least) it was to have been delivered, emplaced and thereafter left. What actually happened was that in the period following the early carnage of 1914, the French army rushed whatever it could find in the heavy artillery line to the areas behind the trenches

in order to have some trench-crushing capability, however limited.
Fortunately for the French, when the Mortier de 370 was delivered it came with special handling gear of two kinds. One was for use on railway trucks and the other for road transport and both had handling gantries, cranes and special rigs. The largest of these rigs was for the barrel, which was carried slung under a special wheeled gantry; the other loads were carried slung in a similar fashion. In all there were three main loads with more for the ammunition and the various accessories.

Preparation for fire

If moving the Mortier de 370 was not enough, emplacing the thing was worse. The preparation began with the digging of a large pit into which was lowered the main firing platform: this had a series of vertical spades on its underside which were intended to absorb some of the bar-

rel recoil. More of the recoil was taken by the heavy carriage, which was mounted on the platform and featured a rudimentary recoil cylinder system coupled to the trunnions of the barrel. The emplacement and assembly of all this took a considerable time and a great deal of labour, but it

Simple in appearance, the Mortier de 370 Filloux was a brute to handle, and its heaviest projectiles had a range of only 8100 m (8,858 yards). As was true of so many heavy artillery pieces of the period, the 370-mm was originally a coast defence weapon.

was a price the French had to pay in order to put some form of heavy artillery in the front line during 1915.
Once in the line the

ammunition for the howitzer was gradually changed from the original armour-piercing pattern to a heavy blast-producing type; the last of these projectiles was introduced into use during 1917. There were two of these 1917 type projectiles, the heavier weighing 489 kg (1,078 lb). But with this the range was only 8100 m (8,858 yards), which made all the labour involved rather a waste of potential. But for a considerable period it was all that there was to hand and the unfortunate French gunners just had to put up with it all.

After 1918 the Mortiers de 370 Filloux were placed into storage to be dragged out again during the

'Phoney War' of 1939-40. There then appears to have been some indecision as to exactly where they were to

be emplaced, and in the event most of them were apparently destroyed by Luftwaffe attacks.

A French 370-mm howitzer in position in the Ravin de la Baraquette west of Foucaucourt, seen in September 1916. The great battles of that year saw artillery become the great mankiller of an already murderous war.

SPECIFICATION

Mortier de 370 Filloux
Calibre: 370 mm (14.57 in)
Length of barrel: 3.31 m (10 ft 10½ in)
Weight: in action between 29000 and 30000 kg (63,934 and 66,139 lb)
Elevation: -6° to +65°
Traverse: 6°

Muzzle velocity: with light shell 370 m (1,214 ft) per second and with heavy shell 316 m (1,037 ft) per second
Maximum range: with light shell 10400 m (11,375 yards) and with heavy shell 8100 m (8,858 yards)
Shell weight: 413.5 or 489 kg (911.6 lb or 1,078 lb)

French self-propelled heavy guns Canon de 194 and M 280

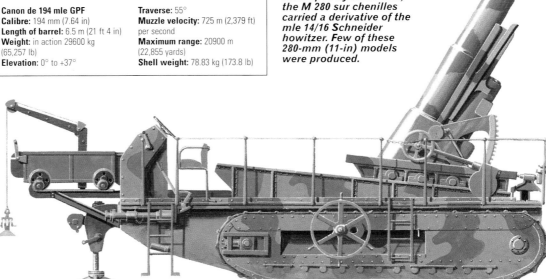

The Canon de 194 mle GPF used the same chassis as the 280-mm model. While elevation was limited, the vastly increased mobility was more than adequate compensation.

By 1917 one of the main problems suffered by the gunners of all nations engaged in the artillery war that by then prevailed, was the lack of mobility imposed upon them by the nature of the terrain and the ponderous weight of their charges. Whenever any sort of advance seemed likely opportunities were missed simply because the guns could not be moved up rapidly enough to positions from which they could provide the necessary support. All manner of experiments were conducted in efforts to remedy this state of affairs, but the only answer was soon seen to be caterpillar tracks; and if any emphasis were required it was provided by the advent of the tank.

Experimental work

Once the potential of the tracked carriage had been appreciated it was not long before the French were involved in a series of experiments to mount heavy gun barrels on to self-propelled tracked chassis. These experiments were carried out quite separately from the French tank programme, and involved a large tracked chassis developed by Schneider at its Le

Creusot works. Early trials involved a 155-mm (6.1-in) gun but this was later changed on production models to a long gun known as the **Canon de 194 mle GPF** (*Grand Puissance Filloux*, or High-Power Filloux). Another weapon carried by some of these carriages was the **Mortier de 280**, a derivative of the mle 14/16 Schneider, and

this was also known as the **M 280 sur chenilles**.

These two weapons shared a common carriage driven by a petrol engine installed at the rear of the chassis, below the elevating gear. The driver sat at the extreme front of the equipment with the barrel cradle almost immediately behind him. A small crane was provided to raise ammunition

to the level of the crew platform behind the breech. The design had one drawback, the installation so arranged that ordnance elevation was somewhat limited (preventing the full range of the piece from being reached), but the mobility that the carriage provided more than made up for this. Later models were redesigned to achieve increased elevations.

Limited availability

Not many of the 280-mm (11-in) models appear to have been made. Production was apparently concentrated on the 194-mm (7.64-in) model, but even so the main problem during the latter part of World War I was that there were never enough of them. Despite their bulk and weight they were able to cross terrain that no equivalent towed weapon could negotiate without difficulty, and the gun itself had a good range and a useful projectile weight.

After 1918 the 280-mm

carriages were either withdrawn from use or converted to take the 194-mm guns, and by 1939 there are few records of any remaining in service. The 194-mm model was still in use, and was fired in anger during the 1940 campaigns until overrun by the German Panzers. The survivors then joined the German ranks and were used for a while by garrison units of the German occupation forces based in France.

Pioneering weapon

For its day the French self-propelled carriage was a remarkable achievement. It now seems safe to say that it was the first true self-propelled artillery platform to be used operationally in any numbers, and it certainly had many features that were carried over to later designs. Apart from their caterpillar tracks these carriages had automatically-adjusting recoil mechanisms to suit all angles of elevation, hydraulic brakes and pneumatic recuperators.

SPECIFICATION

Canon de 194 mle GPF
Calibre: 194 mm (7.64 in)
Length of barrel: 6.5 m (21 ft 4 in)
Weight: in action 29600 kg (65,257 lb)
Elevation: 0° to +37°

Traverse: 55°
Muzzle velocity: 725 m (2,379 ft) per second
Maximum range: 20900 m (22,855 yards)
Shell weight: 78.83 kg (173.8 lb)

Based on a large chassis developed by Schneider, the M 280 sur chenilles carried a derivative of the mle 14/16 Schneider howitzer. Few of these 280-mm (11-in) models were produced.

15-cm Kanone 16 Heavy field gun

The inclusion of a gun with a calibre of only 150 mm (5.9 in) may seem out of place in a description of heavy artillery, but the German 15-cm guns were really in a class above that of normal field artillery. Quite apart from their size and weight, they were intended for use as corps artillery capable of long-range counter-battery and 'interdiction' employment, and thus came into the heavy artillery category.

Long-range artillery

By 1916 the long-range German artillery in use on the Western Front was mainly of a makeshift nature, being derived from a policy of placing coastal defence or naval gun barrels on to improvised field carriages. While this was adequate as a stopgap measure, the gunners needed something more suitable and manageable for their long-term equipment, and consequently the German general

staff made a special plea to its artillery designers for a world-beater. Both Krupp and Rheinmetall took up the challenge, and as things turned out their individual submissions were virtually identical. Both guns were named **15-cm Kanone 16** (otherwise **K 16**), but in the long term it was the Krupp **15-cm K 16 Kp** submission that was produced in the greater quantities. The Rheinmetall **15-cm K 16 Rh** was produced in some numbers as the demands from the front were so great, but never in the numbers that Krupp was able to churn out.

The 15-cm K 16 was a long and large gun. The overall design was entirely orthodox for the time apart from the fact that the barrel was extraordinarily long (L/42.7 in the Krupp design and L/42.9 in the Rheinmetall offering) for the size of the wheeled carriage. The carriage was a fairly simple box-trail design fitted with a large shield for the

gun crew. Heavy spoked wheels were fitted as the gun had to be towed by horse teams as motor traction was by that stage of the war (it was 1917 before appreciable numbers of the guns actually reached the front) at a premium and reserved mainly for the really heavy guns. The weights involved meant that the 15-cm K 16 had to be towed in two loads, the barrel and the carriage. The carriage was usually towed on a special four-wheeled limber which also had some seating for the crew members, who also operated the brakes.

Powerful weapon

On the Western Front the 15-cm K 16 became one of the most feared of all the German counter-battery guns. The long range (22000 m/24,060 yards) of the gun meant that it could reach well into the rear areas behind the Allied lines to destroy gun batteries, road and rail junctions and gener-

In contrast to most of the artillery involved in World War I, the German 15-cm pieces were not howitzers. With their long range, the weapons were feared in the counter-battery role, and could only be opposed by much larger and less mobile Allied weapons.

SPECIFICATION	
15-cm K 16	
Calibre: 149 mm (5.88 in)	**Traverse:** 8°
Weight: in action 10870 kg (23,964 lb)	**Muzzle velocity:** 757 m (2,484 ft) per second
Length of barrel: 6.41 m (21 ft ⅓ in)	**Maximum range:** 22000 m (24,060 yards)
Elevation: -3° to +42°	**Shell weight:** 51.4 kg (113.3 lb)

ally to lay down harassing fire that could not be countered by anything other than the heaviest and longest-ranged Allied guns (railway artillery or specially emplaced weapons). This entailed a great deal of effort on the part of the Allies, for despite its weight and bulk, the 15-cm K 16 was still more mobile than its potential opposition.

After 1918 numbers of 15-cm K 16 guns were handed out to various

nations as war reparations (Belgium was a major recipient) but the gun was one of the few allowed to remain on the strength of the small post-Versailles German army. Thus for nearly two decades it acted as a training weapon for a new generation of gunners who, re-equipped and with a new military philosophy, went to war once again. Even then the 15-cm K 16 was used during some of the early World War II campaigns.

Left: A 15-cm K 16 gun is prepared for firing early in World War II, perhaps during the Polish campaign. The gun crew hauled the barrel from the separate wheels which carried it into the cradle of the gun. Once prepared, the gun would could hurl its 51.4-kg (113.3-lb) shell at an enemy 22 km (132.7 miles) away.

Below: The 15-cm Kanone 16 was manufactured by both Krupp and Rheinmetall, the latter (as seen here) being made in smaller quantities. The equipments were still in limited use during the early campaigns of World War II, as it was one of the few military items permitted to Germany by the Versailles Treaty.

German 28-cm howitzers Heavy siege and coast-defence artillery

The massive foundation and turntable necessary for the 28-cm howitzers made moving them a considerable task, and yet the huge weapons were dragged up and down the Western Front throughout World War I and also saw Eastern Front service in World War II.

By 1914 the growth of the German navy in terms of ship numbers and naval importance had ensured a corresponding increase in the number and power of the coastal batteries that were built to defend the various German dockyards and harbours. Coastal defence was the responsibility of the German navy, and as a general rule it adapted naval guns to carry out the coast defence role. But following the general fashion elsewhere it also adopted the high-trajectory howitzer, and for this it had to turn to the army for advice.

By the beginning of the 20th century the German navy thus had an adaptation of an army 28-cm howitzer known as the **28-cm Küstenhaubitze** (coast howitzer). The army weapon on which this was based was the **28-cm Haubitze L/12**, and both of these heavy weapons were products of the prolific Krupp armament works at Essen in the Ruhr.

Static employment
Both howitzers were intended mainly for the static role: the army howitzer had been designed primarily for fortification-smashing, in which the lengthy emplacement period that was required was of no real importance. Thus the howitzer's squat barrel rested in a cradle mounted on a large and heavy carriage, which was in its turn located on a turntable connected to a heavy firing platform dug into the ground. Both howitzers had features from an earlier age: at the rear was a crane for raising ammunition to the level of the breech, while most of the recoil forces that resulted from the firing of the weapons were absorbed by their barrel and cradle assemblies sliding along short rails, the rest of the forces being absorbed by the mass and weight of the carriage.

Even by 1914 standards the 28-cm howitzers were obsolescent. Their weight and bulk rendered them virtually immovable, and the relatively short ranges possible with the weapons, something in the order of 11400 m (12,465 yards) made them uneconomic in terms of their manpower and travelling requirements. Moreover, each howitzer took three or four days to emplace and then as long to remove, and was extraordinarily difficult to move. For transport the howitzers were broken down into the usual loads: the army version travelled in four loads, while the coastal version had to be virtually dismantled and reassembled each time.

Bagged propellant
The most unusual feature of these howitzers was that they used bagged propellant charges: for many years German artillery designers had used some form of cartridge case allied to a sliding-block breech mechanism, but the 28-cm howitzers used bagged charges allied to a screw breech.

Western Front service
During World War I these howitzers were dragged up and down the length of the German lines in France whenever and to wherever there appeared worthwhile targets for their power. Both the army and navy versions were used at Verdun and during many of the other major German artillery battles, and most survived the war to be hidden away in some of Germany's secret stockpiles. Thus both models were to hand when 1939 came around. Once more they were pressed into service, this time somewhat modified for traction by halftrack vehicles, and they were used during the siege of Sevastopol in 1942 and later during the savage crushing of the Warsaw Uprising of 1944. Thereafter these wholly obsolete weapons faded from view. It was a wonder that they lasted so long.

SPECIFICATION	
28-cm Küstenhaubitze	**Traverse:** 360° on turntable
Calibre: 283 mm (11.14 in)	**Muzzle velocity:** 360-379 m
Weight: in action 63600 kg	(1,148 to 1,243 ft) per second
(140,214 lb)	**Maximum range:** 11400 m
Length of barrel: 3.4 m (11 ft 2 in)	(12,465 yards)
Elevation: 0° to +65°	**Shell weight:** 350 kg (771.6 kg)

The 28-cm Küstenhaubitze was an extremely unwieldy weapon, its weight and bulk fixing it to one location and its relatively short range made it uneconomical in terms of manpower and resources. In spite of this, many served throughout World War I.

M-Gerät 'Big Bertha'

The Schlieffen Plan that was intended to secure the German defeat of France, by wheeling armies through Belgium to take the French armies in flank, was conceived during the 1890s, and honed almost to perfection during the years up to 1914. It entailed the invasion of a neutral state (Belgium) and the rapid destruction of the forts at Liège and Namur, both of them among the most powerful in Europe. Heavy artillery was needed, so Krupp was involved.

Krupp developments

Throughout earlier years Krupp had been responsible for a long string of super-heavy guns and howitzers, but to defeat the Belgian forts it had to produce something special. It undertook a series of trials with heavy-calibre weapons that ultimately led to a 420-mm (16.54-in) howitzer known as **Gamma**, a prodigious beast that proved to be very accurate when firing a heavy projectile capable of destroying any fortification. But Gamma was a static weapon, designed to be taken apart for moves and reassembled piece by piece after rail transportation. While the German staff planners appreciated the power of Gamma, they asked for a weapon that could be towed on roads and the obliging Krupp designers looked to their research and came up with the answer. This was an enlarged and modified wheeled carriage originally intended for a 305-mm (12-in) howitzer. Thus was born the **M-Gerät** (*Gerät* means equipment).

All this development took place right at the last possible moment, and it was not until August 1914 that the huge howitzers moved off to war. The type was soon known as the *dicke Bertha* ('Fat Bertha', but more commonly translated 'Big

Bertha') to its crews and the name stuck. The crews belonged to a special unit known as kurz Marine Kanone 3, and initially only two howitzers went into action against the Belgian forts. They moved on the roads in a series of tractor-towed loads, five to each gun. The carriages had been designed to enable the howitzers to be assembled with a minimum of labour and time. Special AP projectiles as well as the conventional HE types were available.

Attack on Liège

The impact of these huge howitzers has now passed into history. Within a few

days the mighty Liège forts were smashed and forced to capitulate, soon to be followed by the Namur forts. The 420-mm (16.54-in) shells were able to plunge deep into the earth before exploding and the resultant shock waves shook the forts to their foundations. They had a tremendous morale as well as destructive effect, and after a few days of steady bombardment the occupants of the fort had been reduced to a state of collapse.

Russian action

After deployment in Belgium the battery moved to the Russian front, where it repeated its successes. The howitzers were soon joined

by more examples from the Krupp works, and yet more were used on the Western Front. However, it was soon learned that the type's accuracy fell off as the barrel became worn after even a limited period of firing and that, consequently, destructive impact was reduced. Although the 'Big Berthas' had a maximum range of 9300 m (10,170 yards), their best accuracy was obtained at around 8680 m (9,490 yards). Another problem came painfully to light when it was discovered that the projectiles were very prone to detonating while still inside the barrel the instant after firing, and many barrels were destroyed in

this fashion.

The 'Big Berthas' had their maximum impact against the Belgian forts. Thereafter their importance fell away, and a measure of this can be seen in the fact that although they were used extensively during the Verdun battles, French reports make virtually no mention of their effects, a sign that their day was already past. None remained after 1918, though the Gamma howitzers, used in the development of the towed 'Big Berthas', did survive. At least one saw action in 1942, when it was used during the siege of Sevastopol.

Once the war had settled down to a face-to-face confrontation between deeply entrenched forces, the howitzer came to the fore as the main offensive weapon of the various artillery arms. The monstrous 42-cm M-Gerät was used by the Germans at Liège and Namur.

SPECIFICATION

M-Gerät
Calibre: 420 mm (16.54 in)
Length of barrel: 6.72 m (22 ft ⅔ in)
Weight: in action 42600 kg (93,915 lb)
Elevation: 0° to +65°

Traverse: 20°
Muzzle velocity: about 426 m (1,400 ft) per second
Maximum range: 9300 m (10,170 yards)
Shell weight: 810 kg (1,786 lb)

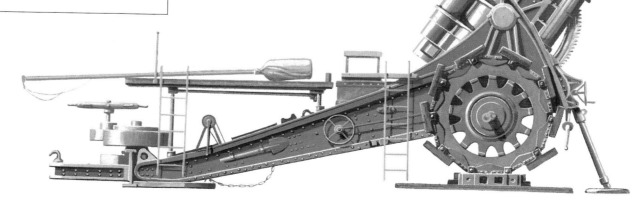

The mighty 420-mm (16.54-in) howitzer known as 'Big Bertha' was used by the German army to nullify the threat of the Belgian forts at Liège and Namur. It was a fearsome weapon, powerful and accurate (at least while the barrel was new).

lange 21-cm Kanone in Schiessgerüst The 'Paris gun'

In the morning of 23 March 1918 there were four explosions in the streets of Paris, the second killing eight people and wounding 13 more. The discovery of metal fragments allowed investigators to work out that the explosions were those of artillery shells. More shells landed as the investigators worked and a general alarm was sounded, sending the people of Paris to their shelters. By the eighth explosion the investigators had decided that the shells were from a 208-mm (8.19-in) gun and even hinted at a possible location for the gun. Their prediction was that the gun was somewhere in the Crépy region, 120 km (75 miles) distant. The bombardment continued and casualties increased.

Ballistic trials

In long-range ballistic trials the Germans had found that projectiles travelled much further than anticipated. The cause was found in the fact that the projectiles had left the thicker strata of the Earth's atmosphere, the reduction in air friction over much of the trajectory significantly boosting range. To take advantage of this effect a special gun was designed. A 380-mm (14.96-in) naval gun barrel was relined with a new 210-mm (8.27-in) barrel about 40 m (131 ft 2½ in) long, for which special charges and projectiles were developed. The new gun weighed 142 tonnes, but had a range of 132 km (82 miles) and could be made to work consistently, if only at a price. Each time the gun was fired the shell passing along the barrel produced so much wear that the internal calibre increased, and each successive shell had to be of larger diameter than that preceding it. The long barrel tended to droop, so external bracing had to be provided.

The project absorbed a great deal of Krupp's facilities, but there was a reason behind it all. Early in 1918 the Germans planned a series of war-winning offensives, and the new **lange 21-cm Kanone in Schiess gerüst** (long 21-cm gun on firing platform) was to play its part in harassing the Paris area. Later versions of the gun used a basic calibre of 232 mm (9.13 in) when the original barrel was bored out, but it must be stressed that each fired shell enlarged the barrel calibre, so carefully manufactured shells had to be fired in the correct sequence.

The firing platform for the Paris gun was of naval origin, with a turntable under the forward end and racers running on tracks at the other. The gun and its carriage were carefully bedded on a solid timber base.

French reaction

As the drizzle of shells continued to fall on Paris, the French reacted. They moved heavy railway guns into the area closest to Crépy and began to fire into the area where they suspected the gun, whose barrel had a life of only 60 rounds before needing replacement, might be located. Away to the north of the gun the advancing German armies were pushing forward with great success. They had virtually eliminated one British army, and by 30 March had advanced to Montdidier. It had already been decided that the Paris gun should then be moved to the Bois de Corbie, which is closer to the French capital than Crépy. The gun then started a second bombardment of Paris that was far more accurate than the first as the gunners were not firing at extreme range. More and more barrels were changed, but once again the Paris gun attracted the attention of French army railway guns and airborne spotters. Casualties were inflicted on the gun crew by near misses and even by one shell exploding in the gun.

By this time Parisians had begun to get used to the idea of being constantly shelled. Paris was a big place and shells could not fall everywhere so a form of normal life was resumed. The German advance on the Marne by the end of May caused much more concern.

Towering over other products of the Krupp works, a Paris gun nears completion. The gun was such a challenge to the technology of the time that a fair proportion of even such a large firm's resources was taken up by the project.

Superior position

The Paris gun was eventually moved to a new position at Beaumont in order to escape the attentions of French railway guns, and from there the third bombardment was started. This was a very carefully prepared position with a steel bed for the carriage turntable and rail access for the ammunition on a more lavish scale. By this time a 232-mm (9.13-in) barrel was in use and was shooting very well, but already the gun was having less effect as the tide of battle turned against Germany.

The ebb and flow of the battle led to a new gun location at a site in the Bois de Bruyères, and by 5 July it had bardment of Paris. But it was all to no avail. By August the Allies were once more on the move. The German attacks had finally come to an end and in the process the German army had exhausted its last reserves of men and energy. All along the line they fell back toward Germany, abandoning all the gains they had made in the early months of the year. As they retreated they moved well out of range of Paris, and the guns were dismantled and withdrawn. By that stage there was more than one gun (perhaps as many as three) though only one was used in action at any one time.

Post-war mystery

Exactly what happened to the Paris guns in the aftermath of World War I is still a mystery. None ever fell into Allied hands, although some firing platforms were found and carefully recorded for history. It seems safe to say that they were cut up to prevent the Allies from learning their secrets.

Above: A fully assembled Paris gun fires at 45° elevation. Each firing widened the bore of the barrel, and during the barrel life of some 60 rounds, a series of shells of successively increasing calibre had to be used.

Right: With a barrel length of some 40 m (131 ft 3 in), the Paris gun presented problems of construction never encountered before. The 21-cm barrel was housed inside an old naval 38-cm barrel but, being longer, a good deal protruded from the end. The external bracing was essential to prevent barrel sags.

SPECIFICATION	
Lange 21-cm Kanone in Schiessgerüst	**Muzzle velocity:** 1604 m (5,263 ft) per minute
Calibre: 210 mm (8.27 in)	**Maximum range:** 132 km (82 miles)
Length of barrel: about 40 m (131 ft 3 in)	**Shell weight:** 94-119 kg (207.25-262.3 lb)
Weight: gun 260 tonnes	
Elevation: 0° to +45°	

Ordnance, QF, 4.5-in Howitzer Heavy field howitzer

The **Ordnance, QF, 4.5-in Howitzer** used by the British Army throughout World War I was one of several weapons developed in the aftermath of the Boer War. During that colonial conflict the Royal Artillery learned in the hardest way possible that its field howitzers were too heavy, too slow in action and generally too cumbersome, so it asked for something better. For some reason the usual state arsenals were asked to submit new designs at the same time as private manufacturers, but in the end it was a private manufacturer, the Coventry Ordnance Works, that was awarded the contract.

Superior performance

This welcome change from what had up till then been a virtual state monopoly meant that when the BEF went to France in 1914 it took what was thought to be the best field howitzer in the world. This was able to outperform all its contemporaries, and yet was versatile enough to operate alongside the 18-pdr guns in a normal field

artillery regiment. This was achieved mainly by making the basic design simple and robust, and the weapon was so sound it required only one modification throughout its long service life: the rounding off of some of the sharper corners of the breech mechanism to prevent cracking after prolonged firing.

As with the 18-pdr, the 4.5-in (114-mm) howitzer was also issued to many dominion armies, including those of Australia, Canada and New Zealand. During the war the 4.5-in howitzer was also passed on to Russia, as by 1916 the Tsarist armies were in a rather poor state. These weapons were to have an eventful life as they took part in the Russian defeats of 1917, and also played their part in the events surrounding the revolutions of 1917 and the subsequent civil war. Many were still on hand when the Germans invaded in 1941, captured examples being placed in limited German service with the designation **11.4-cm leichte Feldhaubitze 363(r)**.

The 4.5-in (114-mm) howitzer was one of the best pieces of artillery used by the British Army in World War I as it was very versatile and fired a useful shell. Its design remained essentially unchanged from its first use in 1914 until World War II, when it was again shipped to France.

During World War I the 4.5-in howitzer was towed into action by a team of six horses. The full gun team was 10 men, though fewer actually served the weapon in action with the rest acting as ammunition and horse handlers. In common with most other weapons of the period, the 4.5-in howitzer was supposed to make great use of shrapnel, but the HE shell was soon found to be much more useful, though it was in short supply in 1914 and 1915, a shortage that led to a political storm

known as the 'shell scandal'. The ammunition also featured in another political uproar, this time after World War I, for the fuses used on the shells were a clockwork type first produced by Krupp in Germany. After the war Krupp took the British government to an international court to extract royalties due on every fuse fired – and won the judgement!

By the time of World War I's end in 1918, 3,177 4.5-in howitzers had been produced in addition to the 182 completed before 1914.

After 1918 these howitzers were retained in British Army service to be used again during the early campaigns of World War II. By then their original wooden spoked wheels had been replaced by new items with pneumatic tyres for powered traction. The Germans used 96 captured equipments in the Atlantic Wall with the designation **11.4-cm leFH 361(e)**. The last 4.5-in howitzers in service were those of the Irish army, whose last examples were retired only in the late 1970s.

An Australian battery of 4.5-in (114-mm) howitzers in the open warfare that finally erupted along the Western Front in August 1918. The high elevation of the short barrel produced deeply plunging fire.

SPECIFICATION	
Ordnance, QF, 4.5-in Howitzer	**Traverse:** 6°
Calibre: 114 mm (4.5 in)	**Muzzle velocity:** 308 m (1,010 ft) per second
Length of barrel: 1.778 m (70 in)	
Weight: complete 1365 kg (3,010 lb)	**Maximum range:** 6675 m (7,300 yards)
Elevation: +5° to +45°	**Shell weight:** 15.88 kg (35 lb)

BL, 60-pdr Gun Long-range 5-in heavy gun

During the Boer War some 4.7-in (119-mm) naval guns were converted to the field role, providing the Royal Artillery with an idea of what they would need in the future. From this example the gunners asked for a long-range gun, firing a 60-lb (27.2-kg) shell, for use by divisional heavy batteries, and the Elswick Ordnance Company was asked to produce the design of what became the **BL, 60-pdr Gun Mk I**. This was a large and handsome gun with a long barrel, two prominent recoil cylinders over the barrel and a heavy trail. In order to make the gun more manageable, the barrel could be drawn back over the carriage for towing, and the large wheels were based on those

of traction engines to help spread the loads over soft ground. The heavy trail was made of large slabs of steel and had a large towing bracket at its end.

Soon after World War I's start in 1914, it was found that the 60-pdr was a most useful weapon. More were demanded, but it was not an easy gun to manufacture quickly. Some short cuts had to be made to speed matters, so the facility to draw

The 60-pdr gun had a calibre of 127 mm (5 in) and fired its 27.2-kg (60-lb) shell to 11245 m (12,300 yards). The carriage used traction engine wheels, and the heavy trail produced stability when firing.

60-pdr guns fire on Turkish positions in 1918. These guns have Mk III carriages, which were much lighter than the previous marks with traction engine wheels.

back the barrel for towing was removed, and some other expedients were introduced. The result was the Mk II carriage that was heavier, but at least more equipments could be sent to France. There it was soon discovered that movement of these large guns with horse teams was an almost impossible task, so Holt tractors were introduced, making the 60-pdr one of the first British weapons to be towed by powered traction. But even with the Holt tractor the Mk II carriage was a cumbersome load, leading to the Mk III carriage in which the barrel could once more be withdrawn by the simple expedient of disconnecting the barrel from the recoil mechanism and pulling it back.

The 60-pdr initially fired mainly shrapnel shells, but these changed to HE from a time late in 1914. Thereafter, wherever the British Army went the 60-pdr went too. The 60-pdr gave sterling service, though it was always a brute to move, but in action

it was steady, reliable and accurate. New, better streamlined shells were provided to increase range, but the only real long-term answer to producing even more range was the development of a new gun, which appeared in the last months of World War I in the shape of the **BL, 60-pdr Gun Mk II**, which introduced a new type of carriage and recoil system, a longer barrel and many other detail changes. None of these Mk IIs was in service before World War I's end.

Front lines

Along the Western Front the 60-pdr was used mainly for counter-battery work, demolishing strongpoints and for what is now known as harassing fire, i.e. firing off odd rounds deep into the enemy rear to land around road junctions, railway stations etc. and so disturb the enemy's movements. To do this effectively the guns had to be moved up to close behind the front lines, no easy task in view of the bulk of the 60-pdr.

The 60-pdr remained in British service after World War I, on carriages up to several Mk IV variants, but was withdrawn from first-line service in 1941. The Germans used guns captured in France with the designation **12.7-cm Kanone 382(e)**. The US Army used the type in World War I, later giving the designation **5-in Gun M1918**, and in 1940 sold 12 to Brazil for service into the late 1960s.

A 60-pdr gun fires near La Boiselle in March 1918. The gun had a range allowing it to be sited well back from the trench lines, and thus had to be dug in only during long spells in one position.

SPECIFICATION	
BL, 60-pdr Gun Mk I	**Elevation:** -5° to +21.5°
on Carriage Mk III	**Traverse:** 8°
Calibre: 127 mm (5 in)	**Muzzle velocity:** 634 m (2,080 ft)
Length of barrel: 4.268 m	per second
(168.05 in)	**Maximum range:** 11245 m
Weight: complete 4470 kg	(12,300 yards)
(9,856 lb)	**Shell weight:** 27.2 kg (60 lb)

BL, 6-in 26-cwt Howitzer Heavy field howitzer

The **BL, 6-in 26-cwt Howitzer Mk I** is a weapon that just scrapes into the heavy artillery category, though its 6-in (152-mm) calibre would seem to categorise it more as a field artillery piece. However, the type was frequently used as heavy artillery by the British in World War I simply because there was nothing else to hand on many occasions. Thus the 6-in 26-cwt had to fill a gap, and indeed filled it very well.

When the British Army went to war in 1914 its Royal Artillery siege batteries were equipped with an elderly piece known as the BL, 6-in 30-cwt Siege Howitzer. This was very much a relic of earlier times, having a very limited range and lacking refinements such as an effective recoil mechanism. It was also too heavy for the conditions encountered in France, so a new piece was demanded. This was produced in a remarkably short

time, design beginning in early 1915 and the first examples being ready soon after the middle of that year. By the end of 1915 nearly 700 had been delivered.

The new howitzer was named the BL, 6-in 26-cwt Howitzer to differentiate it from its predecessor. It proved to be a remarkably efficient weapon, and its employment was confined almost completely to the front lines for the demolition of earthworks, trenches and bunkers. It had a short stubby barrel that could be elevated to provide the plunging fire that was required in such tasks, such elevation being made possible by the use of a heavy box trail. The recoil mechanism was so effective that it was used many years later for the 5.5-in (140-mm) gun/howitzer of World War II. A further measure of the success of the design can be seen in the fact that the 6-in 26-cwt remained virtually unchanged

The 6-in 26-cwt howitzer was a very effective piece, light enough to serve at the front as a piece of field artillery, but firing a shell heavy enough to qualify it for heavy artillery status when necessary.

apart from minor modifications, no designation higher than Mk I being required.

Widespread use

By 1916 the 6-in 26-cwt was one of the most important and numerous British heavy guns, and its use spread to many other Allied and Commonwealth armies. Two

types of projectile were fired, one weighing 45.36 kg (100 lb) and the other 39 kg (86 lb). The maximum range with the lighter shell was 10425 m (11,400 yards). Many of the howitzers were in active use when the war ended, and were retained in service until World War II. Some saw action during the

early North African battles. Exports were made to Belgium, Italy and the Netherlands, where the weapon was designated **Obusier de 6"**, **Obice da 152/13** and **Houwitzer 6"** respectively. Weapons taken over by the Germans from these sources in World War II were thus the **15.2-cm sFH 410(b)**, **sFH 412(i)** and **sFH 407(h)**, while pieces captured from the British were **sFH 412(e)**.

The 6-in 26-cwt was the subject of one of the first attempts to produce self-propelled artillery. Late in 1916 some Mk I tanks were converted to carry 6-in 26-cwt howitzers on two forward 'horns', but despite this concept's potential these were little used.

Above: A 6-in 26-cwt howitzer in action on the first day of the Battle of the Somme in July 1916 with cleated wheels for reduced ground pressure.

Left: 6-in 26-cwt howitzers of the 5th Brigade, Royal Garrison Artillery, near Peronne in March 1918.

SPECIFICATION	
BL, 6-in 26-cwt Howitzer Mk I	**Muzzle velocity:** 429 m (1,407 ft)
Calibre: 152.4 mm (6 in)	per second
Length of barrel: 2.22 m	**Maximum range:** 10425 m
(7 ft 3.55 in)	(11,400 yards) with light shell and
Weight: in action 3693.5 kg	8685 m (9,500 yards) with heavy
(8,142 lb)	shell
Elevation: 0° to +45°	**Shell weights:** 39 and 45.36 kg
Traverse: 8°	(86 and 100 lb)

8-in BL Howitzer

When the BEF went to France in 1914 it was, like most combatants: ill equipped with heavy artillery. It did not take long for the British to realise that they would need heavy artillery in great quantities and in a very short time, but there were few sources for such weapons. Unlike their German and French counterparts, the military planners were unwilling to strip the coastal defences, and there were few forts from which to remove the armament, so an alternative had to be produced quickly. The answer was the 6-in (152-mm) naval gun, already in production for Royal Navy and coast-defence purposes, but a 6-in projectile was not thought to be heavy enough for the task.

The answer was to obtain a quantity of barrels from old 6-in guns from stockpiles all over the country. These barrels were generally well worn, but this did not matter for they were considerably shortened by cutting off a length from the muzzle and boring out the barrel and chamber to a new calibre of 8-in (203-mm). The resultant barrel was then mounted on a hastily devised carriage produced at numerous railway workshops throughout the

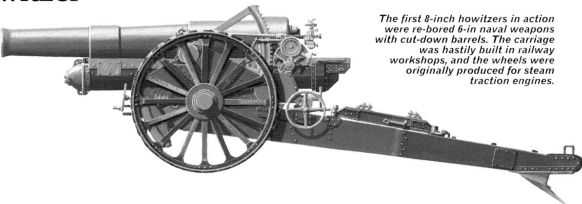

The first 8-inch howitzers in action were re-bored 6-in naval weapons with cut-down barrels. The carriage was hastily built in railway workshops, and the wheels were originally produced for steam traction engines.

UK, and to complete the makeshift nature of these guns they were mounted on traction engine wheels for ease of movement.

The **8-in BL Howitzer** was a ponderous load and a bulky weapon, but it was at least something to issue to the troops in France. Initially 100 were ordered, but these were soon followed by more, the first entering service in February 1915. These initial howitzers ran to no fewer than five marks with as many marks of carriage, all of them differing in some way or another from the rest. These were soon followed by an **8-in BL Howitzer Mk VI**, which was a purpose-built weapon with

a longer barrel than the earlier five marks for improved range. In its turn this was replaced in late 1916 by the **8-in BL Howitzer Mk VII**, which had an even longer barrel. A later **8-in BL Howitzer Mk VIII** differed only in details.

Sophisticated carriage

The Mk VII and VIII howitzers were excellent weapons that formed the basis for a family of 8-in (203-mm) guns that are in service to this day. The later marks had a much more sophisticated carriage than the early marks, and were thus easier to handle and to move to the extent that they can be considered as

different guns. Some of these late howitzer marks were handed over to the US Army when it arrived in France in 1918, and it is via them that the modern 203-mm (8-in) guns have been derived.

After 1918 the early Mks I-V were withdrawn (if they had not been retired already) but the Mks VII and

VIII were retained by the British Army and the US Army. In 1939 they were on hand for the early part of the war and were converted to a new calibre of 7.2-in (183-mm). Examples of the weapons captured in France by the Germans during 1940 were redesignated **20.3-cm sFH 501(e)** but saw little use.

SPECIFICATION	
8-in BL Howitzer Mk VII	**Traverse:** 8°
Calibre: 8-in (203-mm)	**Muzzle velocity:** 457 m (1,500 ft)
Length of barrel: 3.77 m (12 ft 4½ in)	per second
Weight: in action 9017 kg	**Maximum range:** 11245 m (12,300 yards)
(19,880 lb)	**Shell weight:** 90.7 kg (200 lb)
Elevation: 0° to +45°	

9.2-in BL Siege Howitzers

In 1914 the British Army was not entirely devoid of heavy artillery, for the Royal Artillery had in service a heavy weapon known as the **9.2-in BL Siege Howitzer Mk I**. This had its origins in a staff requirement dated 1910, but it was not until 1913 that the first examples were produced. The type was cleared for service in 1914. As its designation implies, the 9.2-in (234-mm) howitzer was intended as a siege weapon for the demolition of fortifications, and was accordingly constructed as a purely static weapon mounted on a large and heavy firing platform. On the road the howitzer was carried in three loads. Emplaced, the Mk I appeared to be a rather complex weapon, but closer examination soon showed that it was essentially a very simple gun.

The short howitzer barrel

was mounted in a cradle that contained the hydro-pneumatic recoil system. This cradle was carried on two large sideframes that in their turn sat on a segment-shaped firing platform supplied with platforms on which the crew could work. The entire unit was in turn mounted on an emplaced firing base.

Recoil mechanism

The recoil mechanism was of fairly limited efficiency, and thus there was provision in front of the carriage for what must have been the 9.2's most unpopular feature. This was a large steel box, open at the top to allow it to be filled with earth. The weight of the filled box provided more stability when the weapon was fired at low angles of elevation, for without it the entire howitzer and carriage could rear upwards on firing. Filling this box with

earth took time and labour, and before the howitzer could be moved it all had to be emptied out again.

The Mk I had only a limited range of 9200 m (10,060 yards). It was not long, therefore, before the Royal Artillery started to request a similar weapon with an increased range, and this duly appeared during late 1916.

Howitzer Mk II

This new weapon was the **9.2-in BL Siege Howitzer Mk II**, and differed mainly in that it had a longer barrel providing a range of 12740 m (13,935 yards), but for the gunners the main importance was that the recoil system was enlarged to absorb the recoil forces to such an

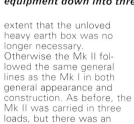

The major heavy artillery piece in British service in 1914 was the 9.2-in Siege Howitzer. As its name suggests, it was designed to be used from a fixed position, and movement involved breaking the equipment down into three sections.

extent that the unloved heavy earth box was no longer necessary. Otherwise the Mk II followed the same general lines as the Mk I in both general appearance and construction. As before, the Mk II was carried in three loads, but there was an overall increase in weight of each load by about a tonne.

Production of both marks of 9.2-in howitzer ran to 812 by the time the war ended in 1918, and many of these were either stockpiled or passed on to other nations. The US Army had been provided with some

equipments when it arrived in France during 1918, but others went to Commonwealth armies and after 1918 others ended up in such nations as Belgium, the newly-formed Baltic States and even the Soviet Union (via the White Russian forces).

In 1939 the weapon was still in Royal Artillery service, but many were lost during May and June 1940, which was highly fortuitous as ammunition for these howitzers was becoming in increasingly short supply and there were no facilities to manufacture more.

SPECIFICATION	
9.2-in BL Siege Howitzer Mk II	**Traverse:** 60°
Calibre: 9.2-in (234mm)	**Muzzle velocity:** 488 m (1,600 ft)
Length of barrel: 4.33 m (14 ft 2½ in)	per second
Weight: in action 16460 kg	**Maximum range:** 12470 m (13,935 yards)
(36,288 lb)	**Shell weight:** 131.5 kg (290 lb)
Elevation: +15° to +50°	

12-in BL Siege Howitzers

By 1915 World War I was well under way, and the pattern of the battles that were to rage for the next three years had already been set. Also established was the need for yet more and heavier artillery, and the Elswick Ordnance Company was requested to produce a heavy weapon for delivery into the line as soon as possible. Elswick simply took the existing 9.2-in (234-mm) howitzer design and scaled it up to a new 12-in (305-mm) calibre. In general the new howitzer resembled the earlier weapon, but the recoil mechanism was much revised and by early 1916 the first types were ready.

The **12-in BL Siege Howitzer Mk I** was intended for a railway mounting, but a version for road use was also required. Here Vickers became involved, and it too took the 9.2-in weapon as a starting base and enlarged it accordingly. This resulted in the **12-in BL Siege Howitzer Mk II**, which in appearance closely resembled the 9.2-in equivalent right down to the retention of the massive earth box. On the 12-in version this required no less than 20 tons of earth to prevent the recoil overcoming the stability of the carriage at low angles of elevation. Being larger than the 9.2-in weapon, the 12-in howitzer had to be transported in six loads (barrel, cradle, bedplate, carriage, earth box and accessories). Assembly was carefully thought out and accomplished by a system of girder ramps, winches and jacks, but it was a lengthy process and all for a maximum range of only 10370 m (11,340 yards).

The **12-in BL Siege Howitzer Mk III** was another railway mounting, so it was not until the appearance of the **12-in BL Siege Howitzer Mk IV** in 1917 that the field gunners got their required range increase which had been requested almost as soon as the Mk I reached the batteries.

Power rammer

The Mk IV was a lengthened Mk II which provided a range of 13120 m (14,350 yards), but other changes were incorporated at the same time. A new Asbury breech mechanism was introduced and the carriage was beefed up all round, but to the dismay of the gunner the earthbox in front of the carriage was carried over, so the spade work had to continue. A power rammer was provided, which no doubt took away a considerable workload from the gun crews, and extra ammunition handling jibs were provided at the rear. The overall effect of all these additions was to provide an increase in the rate of fire.

On the move the Mk IV was originally towed by steam traction engines in six loads, as had been the case with the Mk II. After 1918 heavy trucks were introduced for towing, and this arrangement was still in service in 1939 when the BEF took some Mk IVs over to France. There the weapons took up so much room on the road system that they were known as '12-in Road Hogs'. They did not last long, for when the Germans invaded France in 1940 their tactical initiative rendered the 12-in howitzer's lack of mobility a major disadvantage. Events simply swept around them, and all were either destroyed or captured, leaving a tiny handful in the UK for training purposes only.

May 1918, and a 12-in howitzer is in action. Note that the blast has kicked up dust from an area several yards around the equipment. The longer barrel gives the howitzer greater range than earlier models.

SPECIFICATION	
12-in BL Siege Howitzer Mk IV	**Traverse:** 60°
Calibre: 12-in (305 mm)	**Muzzle velocity:** 447 ft (1,468 ft) per second
Length of barrel: 5.65 m (18 ft 6½ in)	**Maximum range:** 13120 m (14,350 yards)
Weight: in action 57915 kg (127,680 lb) with earth box loaded	**Shell weight:** 340 kg (750 lb)
Elevation: +20° to +65°	

The **12-in BL Siege Howitzer Mk V** was another railway mounting.

15-in BL Siege Howitzers

The British Army at no time requested a 15-in (380-mm) howitzer, but was presented with such a weapon. Exactly how this came about is an odd story, but it had its origins in the Coventry Ordnance Works, which as a private venture took the 9.2-in (234-mm) howitzer as a starting point and enlarged it. One of the directors of the Coventry Ordnance Works was a recently retired senior naval officer, who contacted the Admiralty in order for them to pass on the news of the existence of the enlarged weapon to the War Office, rather along the lines of the 'Old Pals Act'. Instead the news fell upon the ears of the then First Lord of the Admiralty, Winston Churchill. His ever-active mind soon thought up a role for the big howitzer as part of a Royal Navy presence on the battlefields of the Western Front, and a single example of the Coventry gun was obtained.

Thus arrived on the military scene the **15-in BL Siege Howitzer**. In a very short time the howitzer was in France in the hands of a Royal Marine Artillery crew and in action. A further 11 were then ordered and delivered into Royal Marine hands. The Royal Navy made much of the howitzers' capabilities, but experience soon showed that it had fathered something of a problem.

Ponderous brute

The main difficulty was that the 15-in howitzer was a large and ponderous brute that lacked the range that would be expected from such a large-calibre weapon. It was true that it could fire a projectile weighing no less than 635 kg (1,400 lb) with dreadful effects on the receiving end, but the maximum range was a mere 9870 m (10,795 yards). The howitzer required a crew of no less than 12 men on the gun, and even more were involved in the weighty task of ammunition supply.

In 1916 the Royal Navy apparently tired of the whole scheme and withdrew, presenting the 12 howitzers to an unwanting Royal Artillery, which had to accept them with good grace for inter-service political reasons. But once the Royal Artillery had time to examine its new charges it lost no time in announcing that it was none too pleased about performance. The Royal Artillery considered the howitzers to be too large and too heavy for the results and range that could be obtained. And at the ranges involved they were obvious targets for counter-battery work, so disproportionate care and consideration was required for their siting in locations close to the front lines. But the weapons had to be put to some form of use, so they saw the war out at odd times and locations whenever targets could be found in situations where the howitzers' dire lack of range was of little account. As soon as the war ended they were quickly withdrawn from use and disposed of; apparently they were sent to the White Russian forces during the Russian Civil War in the early 1920s.

Arising from a private venture, the 15-in BL Siege Howitzer first saw action in the hands of the Royal Navy contingent on the Western Front. Maximum range was limited to less than 10000 m (10,936 yards), but the projectile weighed around 635 kg (1,400 lb).

SPECIFICATION	
15-in BL Siege Howitzer	**Traverse:** 25°
Calibre: 15-in (380 mm)	**Muzzle velocity:** 340 m (1,117 ft) per second
Length of barrel: 4.19 m (13 ft 9 in)	**Maximum range:** 9870 m (10,795 yards)
Weight: in action not known	**Shell weight:** 635 kg (1,400 lb)
Elevation: +25° to +45°	

Canon de 75 mle 1897 75-mm field gun

During World War I the French '75' or, more formally, the **Canon de 75 modèle 1897**, passed into French national legend as the gun that enabled the French to win the war. It was famous even before 1914 as what may now be regarded as the first of all modern field artillery designs: it coupled a highly efficient recoil mechanism with a rapid-action breech design and a carriage that enabled hitherto unheard-of rates of fire to be maintained. Before 1914 the 75 was a virtual state secret but once in action it more than proved its worth, to the extent that the French army depended on its high rate of fire to make up for deficiencies in the availability of heavier artillery weapons.

Overseas service

By 1939 the 75 was rather past its best, and was outranged by more modern field gun designs, but the French still had well over 4,500 of them in front-line use. Other nations also used the 75. The list of these nations was long for it included the US (which was producing its own **75-mm M1897A2** and **75-mm M1897A4** versions), Poland (**armata polowa wz 97/17**), Portugal, many of the French colonies, some Baltic states, Greece, Romania, Ireland and many other nations. The 75 of 1918 was also very different from the 75 of 1939 in many cases. The Americans and Poles had introduced split trail carriages to the 75 in place of the original pole trail, and many nations (including the French) had introduced rubber-tyred wheels for motor traction in place of the original spoked wheels.

The 75 also underwent some other changes in role. Before 1918 many 75 barrels had been placed on rudimentary anti-aircraft carriages, both static and mobile, and despite their limited value many were still around in 1939. The 75 also underwent some adaptation as a form of tank weapon, but it was to be left to the Americans to make the full development of this possibility when they later adapted the type as the main gun for their M3 and M4 tank series. In France the 75 was updated to **Canon de 75 modèle 1897/33** standard with a new split trail carriage, but by 1939 there were few of these weapons still in front-line service.

In the shambles of May and June 1940 huge numbers of 75s fell into the hands of the Germans, who were only too happy to use many of them for their own purposes as the **7.5-cm FK 231(f)** or, more commonly, as the **7.5-cm FK 97(f)**. At first many were issued to occupation garrisons and second-line formations, while others were later incorporated into the beach defences of the Atlantic Wall. Many more were stockpiled ready to be on hand when some use could be found for them. That came during 1941 when it was discovered the hard way that the armour of the T-34/76 Soviet tank was invulnerable to nearly all German anti-tank weapons. As a hasty stopgap improvisation the stockpiled 75s were taken from the storerooms, fitted with strengthening bands around the barrel and placed on 5-cm Pak 38 anti-tank gun carriages. A muzzle brake was fitted and special armour-piercing (AP) ammunition was hastily produced. The results were rushed to the Eastern Front and there

they proved just capable of tackling the Soviet tank armour. This rushed improvisation was known to the Germans as the **7.5-cm Pak 97/38** and was really too powerful for the light anti-tank gun carriage, but it worked for the period until proper anti-tank guns arrived on the scene.

Anti-ship weapon

The 7.5 cm Pak 97/38 was not the only wartime development of the 75, for later the Americans developed the 75 to the stage where it could be carried in B-25 Mitchell bombers as an anti-ship weapon.

After 1945 the 75 lingered on with many armies, and remained in service for many years. In its day it was an excellent artillery piece that well deserved its famous reputation.

The Canon de 75 mle 1897 was still in widespread service in 1939; this example has been fitted with large pneumatic tyres for mechanised traction. Not all World War II examples were so fitted, but in any form the old 75 was still a viable field gun in 1939 and went on to serve with the Germans after 1940.

Above: Not all the mle 1897 field guns were fitted with tyres for pneumatic traction, as demonstrated by this example on tow behind a Citroen-Kegresse halftrack.

Below: French gunners after a range training session. These 75s have all been fitted with the large pneumatic tyres, but still retain the original 1897 carriage and shield. Note the lug under the muzzle that engaged with the recoil cylinder at full recoil.

SPECIFICATION	
Canon de 75 modèle 1897	**Elevation:** -11° to +18°
Calibre: 75 mm (2.95 in)	**Traverse:** 6°
Length of piece: 2.72 m	**Muzzle velocity:** 575 m (1,886 ft)
(107.08 in)	per second
Weight: travelling 1970 kg	**Range:** 11110 m (12,140 yards)
(4,343 lb) and in action 1140 kg	**Shell weight:** 6.195 kg (13.66 lb)
(2,514 lb)	

Canon de 105 mle 1913 Schneider 105-mm field gun

In the first decade of the 20th century the French Schneider concern took over the Russian Putilov armaments factory as part of a deliberate plan of commercial expansion. Putilov had for long been the main Russian armament concern, but during the early 1900s

had been restricted in its expansionist ideas by the backwardness of the Russian commercial scene, so the infusion of French capital was a decided advantage.

Among the designs found on the Putilov drawing boards was an

advanced design of 107-mm (4.21-in) field gun that appeared to offer considerable increase in range and efficiency over comparable models. Schneider eagerly developed the model and offered it to the French army, which was at first not interested as the 75 was all

it required and there was no need for heavier weapons. But eventually the Schneider sales approach triumphed and in 1913 the Russian design was adopted by the French army as the **Canon de 105 modèle 1913 Schneider**, more usually known as the

L 13 S. The events of 1914 rammed home to the French the fact that the 75 was not capable of supplying all the artillery fire support required, and that heavier guns would be necessary. Thus the L 13 S was placed in a higher priority bracket and large

The Canon de 105 mle 1913 had its origins in a Russian design, but it was a thoroughly modern weapon that was still good for service in 1939-45. Despite its age (the gun was first accepted for service in 1913) it was a good-looking gun with a good performance, and after 1940 it was pressed into service by the occupying German army.

numbers began to roll off the Schneider production lines.

Good performance

Between 1914 and 1918 the L 13 S provided sterling service. It was a handsome gun with a long barrel and a conventional box trail that provided enough elevation for the 15.74-kg (34.7-lb) shell to reach a range of 12000 m (13,130 yards). After 1918 the L 13 S became a French export as it was either sold or handed on to numerous armies under French influence. These nations included Belgium, Poland and Yugoslavia but it was in Italy that the L 13 S achieved its main market penetration. There the L 13 S became the **Cannone da 105/28**, and it remained one of the main field guns of the Italian forces until 1943. The Poles modified their L 13 S guns to take a new split trail design, and this **armata wz 29** was in service when the Germans attacked in 1939.

After 1940 the Germans found that the L 13 S was a viable weapon and out of the 854 still in French service in May 1940 they captured many that were still intact. Large numbers were handed over to various occupation units but it was not until 1941 that a real use was found for the bulk of the booty. When the Atlantic Wall was ready to be armed the L 13 S was decided upon as one of the primary weapons to be used. There were enough on hand to become a standard weapon, and there were stockpiles of ammunition ready for use. Thus the L 13 S became the German **10.5-cm K 331(f)** and was ready to play its most important part in

World War II. Ex-Belgian guns were designated **10.5-cm K 333(b)**.

Turntable mounting

The Germans took the guns off their carriages and mounted them on special turntables protected by curved or angled armour shields. These were placed in bunkers all along the French and other coasts, and many of the bunkers can still be seen among the Atlantic sand dunes to this day. As a beach defence gun the L 13 S was more than suitable, and the bunkers were hard targets for any attacking force to destroy. Fortunately the Normandy landings of June 1944

bypassed most of these bunkers. Not all the guns in these bunkers were directly ex-French; some found their way into the defences from as far away as Yugoslavia and Poland. Captured guns used by the Germans were the **10.5-cm K 338(i)** and **10.5-cm K 338(j)** Italian and Yugoslavian weapons, while unmodified and

modified Polish weapons were the **10.5-cm K 13(p)** and **10.5-cm K 29(p)** respectively.

SPECIFICATION	
L 13 S	**Traverse:** 6°
Calibre: 105 mm (4.13 in)	**Muzzle velocity:** 550 m (1,805 ft)
Length of piece: 2.987 m (117.6 in)	per second
Weight: travelling 2650 kg	**Range:** 12000 m (13,130 yards)
(5,843 lb) and in action 2300 kg	**Shell weight:** 15.74 kg (34.7 lb) for
(5,070 lb)	French guns and 16.24 kg (35.8 lb)
Elevation: 0° to +37°	for Italian guns

Canon de 105 court mle 1935 B 105-mm howitzer

By the mid-1930s the French artillery park was beginning to appear very dated. The vast bulk of the weapons in service were items retained from World War I, and if not already obsolete were at best obsolescent. Most of the weapons involved were 75s, which despite their one-time excellence had their limitations by the 1930s and were also unable to produce the plunging fire that was so often required when attacking fixed defences. Thus the need was forecast for a new field piece capable of easy transport for the support of mechanised forces, and two weapons were produced as the result of this forecast.

Orthodox design

The first was a weapon known as the **Canon de 105 court modèle 1934 S**. It was a Schneider design which was entirely orthodox in design and appearance yet possessing a relatively short barrel. Although the mle 1934 was designated a gun, it had more in common with a howitzer. The mle 1934 was ordered into production, but only at a low priority as more was expected of a slightly better design.

The better design was a product of the state-run

Atelier Bourges and appeared during 1935, hence the designation **Canon de 105 court Modèle 1935 B** (*court*, for short, and B for Bourges). The mle 1935 was a very advanced design for its day, and it too had a relatively short barrel, shorter in fact even than that of its Schneider equivalent. The carriage had a split trail which, when opened, also splayed the wheels outwards to improve crew protection. Once spread the trails were held in place with large spades that were pushed down into the ground through the trail extremities. The wheels could be either large steel items with solid rims or more modern designs with pneumatic tyres for towing by Laffly tractors. The rate of fire was about 15 rounds per minute, which was quite high for a weapon of its calibre.

Into production

The mle 1935 was ordered into production, but this was slow to the extent that although 610 were initially ordered this total was never reached. Instead production was terminated in 1940 in order to permit the production of more anti-tank guns, which were by then realised as having a higher opera-

This photograph of a Canon de 105 mle 1935 B howitzer provides a good indication of how the steel carriage wheels were 'toed in' to provide extra protection for the carriage and the gun crew.

tional priority. Thus there were only 232 mle 1935s in service when the Germans attacked in May 1940 (and only 144 of the Schneider mle 1934s). In action they proved to be excellent small field pieces, so much so that the Germans took over as many as they could. The Germans recognised the mle 1935 for what it was and gave it a howitzer designation as the **10.5-cm leFH 325(f)**. The weapons were used for training purposes and by various second-line occupation

units. Some have been recorded as being incorporated into various coastal

and beach defences. The mle 1934 became the **10.5-cm leFH 324(f)**.

SPECIFICATION	
Canon de 105 court mle 1935 B	**Elevation:** -6° to +50°
Calibre: 105 mm (4.13 in)	**Traverse:** 58°
Length of piece: 1.76 m (69.3 in)	**Muzzle velocity:** 442 m (1450 ft)
Weight: travelling 1700 kg	per second
(3,748 lb) and in action 1627 kg	**Range:** 10300 m (11,270 yards)
(3,587 lb)	**Shell weight:** 15.7 kg (34.62 lb)

Skoda 76.5-mm kanon vz 30/100-mm howitzer vz 30

Field gun and howitzer

When the Austro-Hungarian Empire vanished in the aftermath of World War I, the new state of Czechoslovakia was left with the huge Skoda arms manufacturing complex at Pilsen. The newly independent state was thus poised to become a major supplier of all manner of arms to Central European nations. But in the years after 1919 the arms market was sated with the residue of World War I, and the only way to break into the market was to offer something that was not already on the market. By 1928 the Skoda felt it had found the breakthrough.

Weapon proposal

What the Skoda designers discovered was that there was a definite market for a gun that could be 'all things to all men'. Their suggestion was for a field gun with a high angle of barrel elevation, which would enable the weapon to be used as an anti-aircraft gun or alternatively as a useful mountain gun. At that time the limitations imposed by the requirements of the anti-aircraft weapon were still not fully appreciated, so the Skoda proposal met with significant interest. The new weapon was produced in two forms, namely a 75-mm (2.95-in) anti-aircraft and field gun, and a 100-mm (3.9-in) howitzer that could be used in a mountain role.

The first two weapons of this type were known as the **75-mm kanon vz 28** and **100-mm houfnice vz 28** as they were produced during 1928. Both types found

ready markets in Yugoslavia and in Romania, and were each based on a carriage that was conventional in appearance. What was not immediately obvious was that the barrel could be elevated to +80°. A firing table could be placed under the spoked-wheel carriage, enabling the barrel to be traversed rapidly enough to track aerial targets. Needless to say, the performance of the guns against aircraft was less than satisfactory, and by the late 1920s it was finally being recognised that there was more to an anti-aircraft capability than merely pointing a muzzle skyward. But as a field and mountain gun the vz 28 weapons were more than adequate, and the anti-aircraft role was dropped. Instead the weapons' multi-role capability was enhanced by making the carriage easy to dismantle into three loads that could be carried on three horse-drawn carts for the mountain warfare role.

Modification

In 1930 the Czechoslovak army decided to adopt the two Skoda equipments as their vz 30 weapons. The main change from the export models was the alteration of the gun's calibre to 76.5 mm (3.01 in) to suit Czechoslovak standard calibre requirements, resulting in the **76.5-mm kanon vz 30**. The **100-mm houfnice vz 30** was fitted with a new pattern of rubber-tyred wheels. The result was a more than adequate pairing of field gun and howitzer to arm the field batteries of the

Czechoslovak army.

These weapons never got a chance to prove their worth in Czechoslovak hands. Their two-part seizure of Czechoslovakia in 1938 and 1939 meant that the Germans were able to take over the large Czechoslovak army gun parks and the assets of the Skoda complex at Pilsen without a shot being fired. All the Czechoslovak guns and the bulk of the various export models eventually found their way into German army service, and Skoda was forced to supply ammunition, spares and even more guns for the

The Skoda 76.5-mm kanon vz 30 was an attempt to produce a field gun with enough barrel elevation for it to be used as an anti-aircraft gun. While it was a sound enough field gun, it proved to be of little use as an anti-aircraft weapon, but the type was used by the Czechoslovak and other armies.

SPECIFICATION	
76.5-mm kanon vz 30	**Elevation:** -8° to +80°
Calibre: 76.5 mm (3.01 in)	**Traverse:** 0°
Length of piece: 3.61 m (120.5 in)	**Muzzle velocity:** 600 m (1,968 ft)
Weights: travelling 2977 kg	per second
(6,564 lb) and in action 1816 kg	**Range:** 13505 m (14,770 yards)
(4,004 lb)	**Shell weight:** 8 kg (17.64 lb)

German army. In German service the **7.65-cm FK 30(t)** gun and **10-cm leFH 30(t)** howitzer were used by all manner of units from front-line batteries to beach defence positions along the Atlantic Wall.

Skoda 100-mm howitzer vz 14 and howitzer vz 14/19

Field howitzers

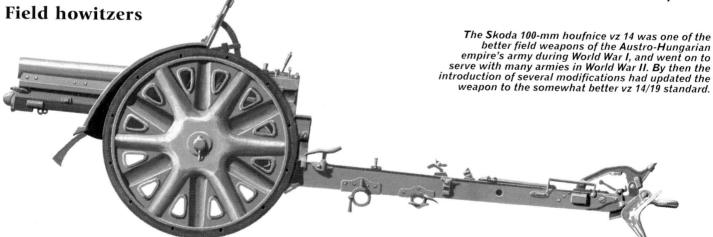

The Skoda 100-mm houfnice vz 14 was one of the better field weapons of the Austro-Hungarian empire's army during World War I, and went on to serve with many armies in World War II. By then the introduction of several modifications had updated the weapon to the somewhat better vz 14/19 standard.

In the days of the Austro-Hungarian empire the name Skoda ranked second only to that of Krupp in European armaments manufacture,

and the armies of many European nations armed themselves almost entirely with weapons produced at the massive Skoda works at

Pilsen. By 1914 Skoda's designs were as good as any produced anywhere, and the range of weapon products was greater than

that of most as Skoda also specialised in mountain guns. One of its products was a 100-mm (3.9-in) mountain howitzer mounted

on a special carriage that could be broken down into loads for carrying over difficult terrain, and this weapon attracted the attention of many armies. Unfortunately they did not like the idea of the special carriage which was heavier than many would want for field artillery use, so the adoption of a new field carriage produced the **100-mm houfnice vz 14**.

Major Italian service

The vz 14 was destined to be used mainly by the Italian army, which received large numbers in the upheavals of the break-up of the empire in 1918-19. The type became a standard Italian weapon as the **Obice da 100/17 modello 14**, which was still in large-scale service in 1940. The numbers involved were so large that the Italians produced their own spare parts and ammunition, and the type saw action in North Africa and served with Italian units on the Eastern Front alongside the Germans. But in 1943 the

Italians withdrew from the conflict and their modello 14 howitzers were taken over by the German forces and remained in use until 1945 under the designation **10-cm leFH 315(i)**, supplementing similar weapons taken over from the Austrians as the **10-cm leFH 14(ö)**. The type was also in service with the Polish and Romanian armies.

When Skoda resumed production in newly independent Czechoslovakia, the vz 14 was one of the first weapons placed back into production. However, the opportunity was taken to modernise the design, the main change being to the barrel length which was increased from L/19 to L/24, i.e. the length of the barrel was increased to 24 times the calibre (100 mm x 24 for 2.4 m/7 ft 10½ in). This improved the range, and new ammunition was also

introduced to provide the new design, soon known as the **100-mm houfnice vz 14/19**, with improved all-round capability.

The vz 14/19 was soon in demand and numbers were exported to Greece, Hungary, Poland (**Haubica wz 1914/1919**) and Yugoslavia (**M.1914/19**). Italy also acquired the parts to modernise a proportion of its modello 14s and the Czechoslovak army also adopted the vz 14/19 as one of its standard field pieces. All in all, the vz 14/19 became one of the most important Central European field pieces, and by 1939 the howitzer was in service in numbers that ran into the thousands. It was a stout weapon with few design frills, and it was capable of prolonged hard use. Many Italian examples were fitted with rubber-tyred wheels for motor traction (**Obice da 100/24**), but even after

1939 many examples retained their original spoked wheels and were pulled into action by horse teams.

In German hands

After 1940 many vz 14/19 weapons passed into service with the German army. By this date the stocks of Czechoslovak army weapons had already passed into German hands and indeed full service as a result of Germany's two-part takeover of Czechoslovakia in 1938 and 1939. Thus the vz 14/19 howitzer was widely used during the French campaign

of May and June 1940 as the **10-cm leFH 14/19(t)**. Many more of these useful howitzers were used during the initial stages of the German invasion of the USSR during 1941, but thereafter the vz 14/19 weapons were gradually relegated to second-line use. Many were incorporated into the Atlantic Wall defences of France, where they remained until 1945. Examples taken over from Greece received the designation **10-cm leFH 318(g)**, those from Poland **10-cm leFH 14/19(p)** and those from Yugoslavia **10-cm leFH 316(j)**.

SPECIFICATION	
100-mm houfnice vz 14/19	**Elevation:** -7.5° to +48°
Calibre: 100 mm (3.9 in)	**Traverse:** 5.5°
Length of piece: 2.4 m (94.5 in)	**Muzzle velocity:** 415 m (1,362 ft)
Weight: travelling 2025 kg	per second
(4,465 lb) and in action 1505 kg	**Range:** 9970 m (10, 905 yards)
(3,318 lb)	**Shell weight:** 14 kg (30.86 lb)

7.5-cm Feldkanone 16 nA and leichte Feldkanone 18

Field guns

Almost as soon as the German army began to introduce new field guns in the late 19th century it adopted 77 mm (3.03 in) as its standard field gun calibre. In 1896 the Germans produced the **C/96** in this calibre, and in 1916 updated and revised the weapon to produce the **7.7-cm FK 16** (*Feldkanone*, or field gun, with 16 standing for 1916).

After 1918 there was a drastic rethink of German weapon practices, and among the changes that emerged from this study was the adoption of 75 mm (2.95 in) as the field gun calibre. This was (and to a limited extent has been until recently) a standard field gun calibre, so the Germans were following a well trodden path. The Treaty of Versailles had left the rump of the German army with a stockpile of the old FK 16 guns, and in a modernisation effort these were rebarrelled with new 75-mm barrels to create the **7.5-cm FK 16 nA** (*neuer Art*, or new pattern).

New issue

The rebarrelled guns were issued during 1934, initially to horse-drawn batteries supporting cavalry units. The Germans continued to use horse cavalry units until 1945, but by then the FK 16

nA had fallen out of use, for it was really a relic of a past era and was as such too heavy and lacking in mobility for the cavalry role. Instead many were relegated to the training role or were issued to second-line units. Large numbers were still in service when the war ended, though, and one fired its way into history when it held up an Allied armoured formation for some time during the fighting near the Normandy beach-heads in June 1944: the gun was not destroyed until it had knocked out at least 10 Allied tanks.

Modern field gun

Even while the rebarrelling of the old FK 16 carriages was under way, a call for a new design of cavalry gun was put out. During 1930 and 1931 both Krupp and Rheinmetall produced designs, and although the Krupp design was finally chosen it was not until 1938 that the first examples were issued for service. The new design became the **7.5-cm leFK 18** (*leichte Feldkanone*, or light field gun), and this had modern features such as a split-trail carriage to increase the on-carriage traverse (so useful in the anti-armour role) and a range of ammunition that included a hollow-charge warhead for

use against tanks. The leFK 18 was judged to to be a great success, though its range was less than that of the weapon it was intended to replace, and the complex carriage made it an expensive and difficult item to produce. Consequently not many were produced and the emphasis for field artillery calibres changed to 105 mm (4.13 in). However,

This 7.5-cm FK 16 nA field gun is being used to train members of the Indian Legion, one of the units raised by the Germans from disaffected prisoners of war to fight against their former comrades.

The 7.5-cm leFK 18 offered many advantages over the FK16 nA, but was expensive to produce and also provided a notably shorter range with the same shell.

the leFK 18 was kept in production for export sales to gain influence and foreign currency. Some sales were made to South American countries, and in Brazil the leFK 18 remained in limited use into the 1980s.

SPECIFICATION	
FK 16 nA	**Elevation:** -9° to +44°
Calibre: 75 mm (2.95 in)	**Traverse:** 4°
Length of piece: 2.7 m (106.3 in)	**Muzzle velocity:** 662 m (2,172 ft)
Weight: travelling 2415 kg	per second
(5,324 lb) and in action 1524 kg	**Range:** 12875 m (14,080 yards)
(3,360 lb)	**Shell weight:** 5.83 kg (12.85 lb)

15-cm schwere Infantriegeschütz 33 Infantry howitzer

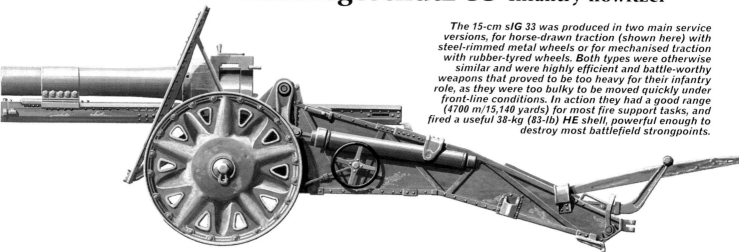

The 15-cm sIG 33 was produced in two main service versions, for horse-drawn traction (shown here) with steel-rimmed metal wheels or for mechanised traction with rubber-tyred wheels. Both types were otherwise similar and were highly efficient and battle-worthy weapons that proved to be too heavy for their infantry role, as they were too bulky to be moved quickly under front-line conditions. In action they had a good range (4700 m/15,140 yards) for most fire support tasks, and fired a useful 38-kg (83-lb) HE shell, powerful enough to destroy most battlefield strongpoints.

When the German army issued its infantry gun requirements during the early 1920s, two types of weapon were requested. One was to be a 75-mm (2.95-in) gun and the other a 15-cm (5.9-in) howitzer to act as a heavier counterpart to the light gun. Development of this heavy weapon commenced in 1927 at a leisurely pace, so that it was not finally approved for service until 1933. Even then it was 1936 before the first examples came off the production lines and they were then issued at the rate of two to each infantry battalion.

To confuse matters somewhat this 15-cm howitzer was actually designated as a gun, i.e. **15-cm schwere Infantriegeschütz 33** or **15-cm sIG 33** (15-cm heavy infantry gun model 1933). It was definitely a howitzer, however, with a short barrel set on a heavy box-trailed carriage. Early examples had pressed steel wheels with metal rims for horse traction, but later examples intended for use with the motorised formations had wheels with rubber rims.

Heavyweight weapon

Once again Rheinmetall-Börsig was responsible for the basic design (although production was carried out by several other manufacturers), and for once no unnecessarily complex features were introduced, the design of the sIG 33 being straightforward and orthodox. If anything it was too orthodox for the infantry gunners, for the adherence to standard design meant that the sIG 33 was really too heavy for the infantry role. It required a large horse team to drag the weapon, and once the sIG 33 was emplaced it was a slow and hard task to move it out. Some attempts were made before 1939 to lighten the heavy carriage by the use of light alloys, but these were in overall short supply and earmarked for the Luftwaffe so the heavy design had to be tolerated.

Throughout the war most sIG 33s were towed by horse teams, although trucks or halftracks were used whenever possible. Even with a tractor it was still a job to handle the weapon in action, and it was not until the sIG 33 was placed upon a tracked self-propelled chassis that the weapon could give its full potential. It was then much more appreciated as a powerful support weapon firing a wide array of projectiles. Most of the tracked chassis used for the self-propelled role were old tank chassis that were no longer large or powerful enough for armoured warfare; in fact the very first attempt to mount a sIG 33 on a PzKpfw I hull resulted in the very first German self-propelled artillery weapon, and this was used during the 1940 campaign in France.

As with all other weapons of its era, the sIG 33 was supposed to have an anti-tank capability and was accordingly issued with hollow-charge projectiles. In use these proved to be less than fully effective, for even a normal 150-mm HE shell striking a tank could be effective and a lot less trouble to manufacture and issue. But for really strong targets the sIG 33 could fire a muzzle-loaded stick bomb known as a Stielgranate 42. This had only a short range and was guided by fins towards its target, which was usually a blockhouse, bunker or some other strongpoint.

Left: Red Army soldiers examine a pair of 15-cm sIG 33 infantry howitzers, with the soldier in the background wielding a rammer for some destructive purpose. Note the heavy carriage and large breech of the weapon in the foreground. Many of these weapons were lost to the enemy, as they were too difficult to move.

Above: 15-cm sIG 33s of a motorised infantry unit are seen in action on the Eastern Front. The wheels of these weapons have rubber tyres, denoting that they were towed by some form of mechanised tractor.

SPECIFICATION	
sIG 33	**Muzzle velocity:** 240 m (787 ft) per second
Calibre: 150 mm (5.9 in)	
Length: barrel 1.65 m (65 in)	**Maximum range:** 4700 m (5,140 yards)
Weight: in action 1750 kg (3,858 lb)	
Elevation: 0° +73°	**Projectile weight:** HE 38 kg (83.8 lb)
Traverse: 11.5°	

The crew of a 15-cm sIG 33 undergoes training in 1938. The layer is adjusting the dial sight, while two members of the crew prepare to traverse the heavy carriage using a lever over the trail spade.

10.5-cm howitzers German field artillery family

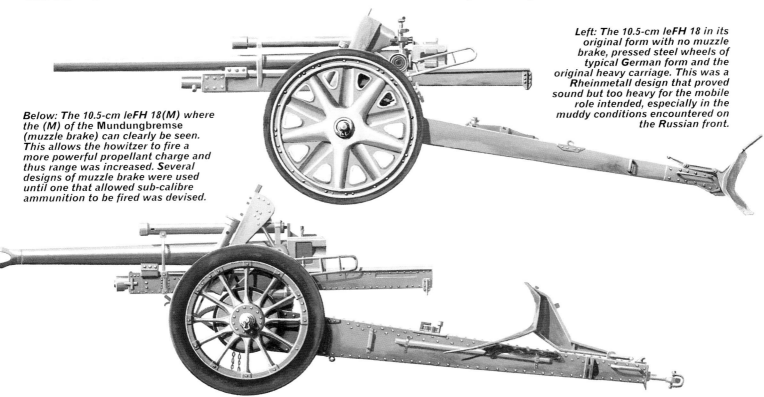

Below: The 10.5-cm leFH 18(M) where the (M) of the Mundungbremse (muzzle brake) can clearly be seen. This allows the howitzer to fire a more powerful propellant charge and thus range was increased. Several designs of muzzle brake were used until one that allowed sub-calibre ammunition to be fired was devised.

Left: The 10.5-cm leFH 18 in its original form with no muzzle brake, pressed steel wheels of typical German form and the original heavy carriage. This was a Rheinmetall design that proved sound but too heavy for the mobile role intended, especially in the muddy conditions encountered on the Russian front.

The German army had chosen the calibre of 105 mm (4.13 in) for its standard field howitzers well before World War I, and then stuck with it. During World War I the standard field howitzer had been the 10.5-cm leFH 16 (*leichte FeldHaubitze*, or light field howitzer) which used the same carriage as the then-standard 7.7-cm FK 16. After 1918 numbers of these howitzers remained with the rump of the German army and were used to train the generation of gunners who were to be the battery commanders and NCOs of World War II.

The operational analysis carried out by German war planners during the 1920s indicated that in future conflicts a 105-mm projectile would be far more effective than the 75-mm (2.95-in) equivalent for no great cost in delivery system weight, that is the artillery piece involved. Thus they plumped for a new 105-mm howitzer, and design work started as early as 1928-29. Rheinmetall was the project leader, and the result of its efforts was ready for service in 1935.

The new weapon was the **10.5-cm leFH 18**, a conventional and sound howitzer with a useful projectile weight and adequate range. If there was a fault with the leFH 18 it was that it was so soundly constructed that it was rather heavy, but as motor traction was expected to provide the bulk of the pulling power that was no great disadvantage, at least in theory. The leFH 18 became a valuable export item, and numbers were sold to Spain, Hungary, Portugal and some South American nations; large numbers also came off the production lines to equip the expanding German forces.

Muzzle brake

As ever the gunners were soon asking for more range, and as a result an increased propellant charge was introduced for the leFH 18. This dictated the introduction of a muzzle brake which meant a change of designation to **10.5-cm leFH 18(M)**, the suffix for *Mundungbremse*, or muzzle brake. The introduction of this muzzle attachment meant that a

Abandoned 10.5-cm leFH 18(M) howitzers in Normandy in June 1944. Note the obvious bulk and weight of the trail legs and spades that combined to make this howitzer much too heavy for the mobile field role.

special sabot sub-calibre 88-mm (3.46-in) projectile could not be fired until a new revised design was introduced slightly later.

Thus the leFH 18 series went to war and proved itself efficient enough until the winter campaign in the Soviet Union took its toll in 1941-42. During the thaws involved in that campaign large numbers of 105-mm howitzers were lost because the weights involved were too great for the available towing vehicles to drag weapons clear of the all-prevailing mud. Thus the overweight how-

itzers showed their disadvantage, and a hurried search for some form of alternative carriage then began.

The result was an unsatisfactory improvisation. The carriage of the 7.5-cm Pak 40 anti-tank gun was simply taken as the new mount for the leFH 18(M) gun, its associated cradle and the large shield. The result was slightly lighter than the origi-

nal (but not by very much), and the improvised arrangement gave constant problems that were never properly eradicated. It was intended that the new howitzer/carriage combination, designated **10.5-cm leFH 18/40**, would become the standard field howitzer for all the German army, but this never happened and in 1945 even the old FH 16 was still in the line.

10.5-cm leFH 18s in action in France during May 1940 when these howitzers, towed into action by halftracks, consistently outfought the more numerous French artillery units as they swept across France.

SPECIFICATION	
10.5-cm leFH 18/40	**Traverse:** 60°
Calibre: 105 mm (4.13 in)	**Muzzle velocity:** 540 m (1,770 ft)
Length of piece: 3.31 m (130¼ in)	per second
Weight: travelling and in action	**Range:** 12325 m (13,478 yards)
1955 kg (4,310 lb)	**Shell weight:** 14.81 kg (32.65 lb)
Elevation: -5° to +42°	

Cannone da 75/27 75-mm modello 06 and modello 11 field guns

One of the most elderly of all field artillery pieces still in service during World War II was the Italian army's **Cannone da 75/27 modello 06** (model 1906 75-mm L/27 gun) in the Italian standard system of artillery nomenclature. This was originally a German Krupp export model adopted by the Italian army in 1906 for licensed manufacture, and then retained until Italy's 1943 armistice with the Allies.

The original Krupp designation was **M.06**, and the weapon was an entirely orthodox design with little of note other than a sound and sturdy construction. The carriage used a form of one-piece pole trail which restricted elevation and thus range, but for all that the 75/27 still had a useful reach for a field gun. Not surprisingly, the original models had wooden-spoked wheels for horse traction, but by 1940 some had been modified to take rubber-tyred steel wheels for powered traction. It was this latter pattern that was most usually encountered outside the Italian mainland.

Gun deployment

The steel-wheeled gun was widely used throughout the North African and other Italian colonial campaigns, and was at one point issued to German field batteries in North Africa when their own equipment was not available. The Germans even supplied the 75/27 with their own designation, **7.5-cm FK 237(i)**. So widespread was the use of the 75/27 modello 06 in Italian service that special versions were even produced for use in fixed fortifications.

Model variations

The modello 06 was not the only 75/27 in Italian service. To confuse matters somewhat there was also a **Cannone da 75/27 modello 11**. This was another licence-built gun, this time from a French source, namely the Deport design centre. The 75/27 modello 11 had one unique feature, namely the original design of recoil and recuperator mechanism. On nearly all artillery pieces the recoil/recuperator mechanism is situated alongside the barrel, either above or below it and in some cases both. On the modello 11 the mechanism stayed in the horizontal position and the barrel elevated independently. The operation of the system was in no way impaired, but the feature did not catch on with other designers and soon fell into abeyance.

Nevertheless the modello 11 was still in widespread Italian service in 1940 and was used mainly in support of cavalry units, although some were issued to field batteries. As with the modello 06, some were modified to take rubber-tyred steel wheels for powered traction, and some were also used by the Germans at one time or another with the designation **7.5-cm FK 244(i)**.

An American soldier examines a captured Cannone da 75/27 modello 11. This had a barrel that elevated independently of its recoil mechanism.

SPECIFICATION	
Cannone da 75/27 modello 06	
Calibre: 75 mm (2.95 in)	**Elevation:** -10° to +16°
Length of piece: 2.25 m (88.6 in)	**Traverse:** 7°
Weight: travelling 1080 kg	**Muzzle velocity:** 502 m (1,647 ft)
(2,381 lb) and in action 1015 kg	per second
(2,238 lb)	**Range:** 10240 m (11,200 yards)
	Shell weight: 6.35 kg (14 lb)

Obice da 75/18 modello 35 75-mm light field howitzer

In contrast with many other Italian artillery pieces of World War II, the Obice da 75/18 modello 35 was a very modern and useful light field piece. Designed by Ansaldo, it was the field howitzer version of a mountain howitzer design and thus lost the facility to be broken down into several pack loads.

Ever since the establishment of Italy as a nation, a certain sector of its armed forces has associated itself with the specialised art of mountain warfare. This has required the provision of special types of artillery adapted for the mountain role. Many of these mountain artillery pieces came from the Austrian firm of Skoda, and during World War I the Italians were happily firing Austrian mountain guns at their former suppliers.

Weapon redesign

By the 1930s much of this mountain artillery was obsolescent and thoroughly overdue for replacement. The Italian firm Ansaldo thus undertook to produce a new mountain howitzer design.

By 1934 this had emerged as the **Obice da 75/18 modello 34**, a sound and thoroughly useful little mountain-warfare howitzer that could be broken down into eight loads for pack transport. In the interests of standardisation and logistics, it was decided that the 75/18 was just what was required as the light howitzer component of the normal field batteries, moreover, and thus the weapon was ordered for these as well, but this time with a more orthodox carriage without any provision for being

SPECIFICATION	
Obice da 75/18 modello 35	
Calibre: 75 mm (2.95 in)	**Traverse:** 50°
Length of piece: 1.557 m (61.3 in)	**Muzzle velocity:** 425 m (1,395 ft)
Weight: travelling 1850 kg (4,080 lb)	per second
and in action 1050 kg (2,315 lb)	**Range:** 9565 m (10,460 yards)
Elevation: -10° to +45°	**Shell weight:** 6.4 kg (14.1 lb)

Italian gunners undergo training on an Obice da 75/18 modello 35. The box by the wheel contained the sights, not ammunition. That no firing was intended can be deduced by the fact that a dust cover is still in place over the muzzle. The small size of this howitzer can be clearly seen.

broken down into loads. This field version was designated as the **Obice da 75/18 modello 35**.

Production difficulties

The modello 35 was ordered into full-scale production but, like its virtual contemporary, the modello 37 gun, could not be produced in the numbers required. This was the case despite the fact that the carriage used by the modello 35 howitzer had many features in common with that of the later modello 37 gun, as well as exactly the same barrel and recoil mechanism as used in the mountain howitzer.

The supply situation was not eased by the need for the Italians to make part of the modello 35's production available for the export market in an effort to raise much-needed foreign currency. In 1940 a sizeable

batch of the weapons was sold to Portugal, and more went to a number of South American states to pay for Italian imports of raw materials. More production capacity was diverted to the production of versions for use on various forms of Italian *semovente* (self-propelled) carriages, but very few of these self-propelled equipments ever reached the hands of the front-line forces. Those that did proved to be as efficient as any of the comparable German *Sturmgeschütze* (assault guns).

After Italy's 1943 armistice with the Allies, the Germans took modello 35 equipments under their control as swiftly as they took over the rest of the available Italian gun parks, and the diminutive howitzers took on a new guise as **7.5-cm leFH 255(i)** weapons.

Cannone da 75/32 modello 37 75-mm field gun

The Cannone da 75/32 modello 37 was another Ansaldo design, and was a good modern weapon that could stand comparison with any of its contemporaries. Its main fault for the Italian army was that there were never enough to go round. After 1943 the Germans took over, for their own use, as many as they could find.

When Italy emerged from World War I its economy, never particularly sound, was in no state to support any form of rearmament programme, and thus the weapons of World War I were bulked out by reparations from the defeated Austro-Hungarian empire, and the army was otherwise left to cope with what it already had. By the 1930s it had been realised that even the large numbers of weapons at hand constituted no real answer to more modern designs of the types fielded by a number of possible opponents, so a programme of new weapon design and manufacture was undertaken. The first weapons to be considered

were those of the field artillery, and thus the first wholly new artillery design to be introduced since the end of World War I in 1918 was a light field gun known as the **Cannone da 75/32 modello 37**.

This new gun was an Ansaldo design. It was of good, sound and modern concept and was intended from the outset for powered traction. It had a long barrel fitted with a muzzle brake, and had a muzzle velocity high enough that the weapon could be usefully employed on occasion in the anti-tank role.

When the split trail was deployed it provided a traverse of 50°, which was no doubt useful in armoured

warfare, but this was rather negated by the use of large trail spades that were hammered down into the ground through the trail legs, and thus a rapid change of traverse through a large angle was not easy. Even with this slight disadvantage, the modello 37 was a very useful field gun, and the Italian gunners clamoured for as many as they could get.

Pressure on resources

Unfortunately they clamoured in vain, for Italian industry was in no position to provide the numbers of such weapons that were required. There was quite simply no industrial potential to spare to produce the guns, and the raw materials,

or at least the bulk of them, had to be imported. Thus gun production got under way at a time when all other arms of the Italian forces were rearming: the air force was given far higher priority than the artillery, and the Italian navy was also absorbing a large proportion of the few available manufacturing and raw material resources. So demand for the modello 37 constantly exceeded sup-

ply, and by 1943 most of the Italian artillery park was still made up of weapons that dated from World War I or even earlier.

In 1943 Italy signed an armistice with the Allies. The Germans had already noted the finer points of the modello 37, and as Italy withdrew from the Axis the Germans moved swiftly to take over the Italian armoury – or at least as much of it as they could lay their hands on. In this grab for possession, large numbers of modello 37s on the Italian mainland changed their designation to **7.5-cm FK 248(i)**. The Germans used their booty until the war ended, not only in Italy but also in the confused Balkan campaigns against the Greek and Yugoslavian partisans.

SPECIFICATION	
Cannone da 75/32 modello 37	**Elevation:** -10° to +45°
Calibre: 75 mm (2.95 in)	**Traverse:** 50°
Length of piece: 2.574 m (101.3 in)	**Muzzle velocity:** 624 m (2,050 ft)
Weight: travelling 1250 kg	per second
(2,756 lb) and in action 1200 kg	**Range:** 12500 m (13,675 yards)
(2,646 lb)	**Shell weight:** 6.3 kg (13.9 lb)

70-mm Battalion Gun Type 92 Field howitzer

The little **70-mm Battalion Gun Type 92** was one of the most successful infantry support weapons of World War II, despite its rather odd appearance. It was issued to every Japanese infantry battalion and could be used in several ways, as a battery weapon or, more frequently, as an individual weapon to produce harassing fire.

Modern design

Despite its unusual look, the Type 92 was a thoroughly modern design. Much of the unusual appearance came from the use of a short barrel on a carriage travelling on large steel disc wheels. Normally the gun was towed by horses or mules, but in typical Japanese fashion there were various holes and brackets on the carriage through which long poles could be inserted to act as man-carrying handles for short moves. The shield could be removed to save weight when required, and the wheels were supported on cranked axles that could be turned through 180° to lower the silhouette of the gun when occasion demanded. Although it was

a small weapon, the Type 92 required a crew of 10 men, most of these being used for manhandling or carrying the gun and acting as ammunition suppliers. In action the maximum number required was only five.

The Type 92 fired the usual HE projectiles along with smoke and shrapnel for close-range use against personnel in the open. There was also a rather ineffective armour-piercing projectile. The maximum range was rather short, being only some 2745 m (3,000 yards), and the effective range was only about half that, but as the Type 92 had only very simple sights and was rarely used against targets other than those clearly visible. This mattered little in action, and the Type 92 was certainly used well forward. Its direct or plunging fire could be very effective, in both defence and attack, and some Allied reports speak of the Type 92 being used in the same manner as a mortar. One operational method that was developed to a fine art by the Japanese for the Type 92 was harassing fire in jungle warfare. A small

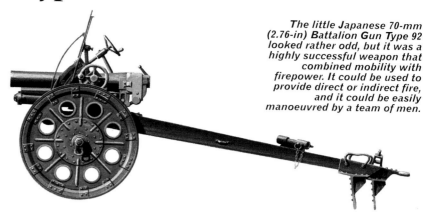

The little Japanese 70-mm (2.76-in) Battalion Gun Type 92 looked rather odd, but it was a highly successful weapon that combined mobility with firepower. It could be used to provide direct or indirect fire, and it could be easily manoeuvred by a team of men.

team would drag or carry the Type 92 forward, fire off a few rounds at a known target and then move hastily to a new fire position or out of the area altogether. A single gun could keep large bodies of Allied soldiers awake and alert by the employment of tactics as simple as this.

Short range

Although labelled as a gun, the Type 92 used a variable propellant charge system and could be fired in the upper register (i.e. above an elevation angle of 45°) to drop projectiles onto targets as close as 100 m

(110 yards) away. On target the HE projectiles were very destructive, and the shrapnel shell often proved to be very effective in breaking up massed infantry attacks such as those sometimes used by the Chinese army. There was even a version of the Type 92 developed for use in some experimental

tanks, but only a few of these (known as the Type 94) were actually produced.

The Type 92 was a small artillery piece but it often had an effect on its enemies that was quite out of proportion to its size, range and projectile weight. Many are still highly prized as museum pieces.

A team of Japanese army gunners tows a Type 92 Battalion Gun over rough terrain in the Aleutian Islands. The men are all equipped with special towing harnesses.

SPECIFICATION	
Battalion Gun Type 92	**Muzzle velocity:** 198 m (650 ft) per second
Calibre: 70 mm (2.76 in)	**Maximum range:** about 2745 m (3,000 yards)
Length of barrel: 0.622 m (24.5 in)	
Weight: in action 212.47 kg (468.4 lb)	**Projectile weight:** HE 3.795 kg (8.37 lb)
Elevation: -10° to +50°	
Traverse: 90°	

75-mm Field Gun Type 38 (Improved) Field artillery

75-mm Field Gun Type 38 (Improved) was a title given by Western intelligence agencies to a field gun that was in widespread use with the Japanese field batteries between 1935 and 1945. The gun had its origins in a Krupp design that was obtained for licence production as far back as 1905. This was the original Type 38, and during World War I the Japanese had observed enough of artillery developments elsewhere to be able to make improvements to the original design.

Box trail

Perhaps the most obvious of these Japanese innovations was the introduction of a form of box trail in place of the original Krupp pole trail. This innovation made

possible extra elevation, and the range was increased accordingly. Other alterations were made to alter the balance of the barrel on its cradle, and yet more minor changes were made to the recoil mechanism. Although the updated gun was given the full title Field Gun Type 38 (Improved) by the Allies, by 1941 few, if any, of the Type 38 guns had been left unmodified, so the extra terminology was superfluous.

Mule teams

Despite the changes introduced to the Type 38 by the Japanese, the overall design was unremarkable, and the overall performance was also unimpressive. Throughout its service life the gun was never adapted for vehi-

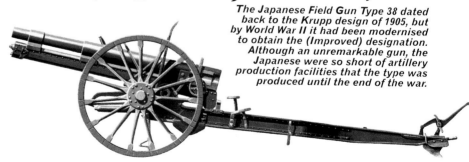

The Japanese Field Gun Type 38 dated back to the Krupp design of 1905, but by World War II it had been modernised to obtain the (Improved) designation. Although an unremarkable gun, the Japanese were so short of artillery production facilities that the type was produced until the end of the war.

cle traction, so horse or mule teams were used right up to 1945. In appearance the gun was archaic, and it was indeed a design relic of a former era, maintained in service as the Japanese were never able to develop the industrial potential to produce artillery in the amounts required. Although much more modern and powerful field guns (with calibres of 75 mm/2.95 in and upwards) were produced right up to the beginning of World War II, they were never produced in numbers sufficient to permit the replacement of the

Type 38. Thus, in the absence of anything else, Japanese gunners were saddled with obsolete equipment.

During the initial stages of the Japanese war against the Chinese during the 1930s the Type 38 proved more than adequate for all the operational tasks demanded of it, but once the Allies joined in the conflict after 1941 things were very different. Following initial easy successes, the Japanese gunners constantly found themselves outgunned by even small forces of Allied artillery, and

in these circumstances the Type 38 did not shine. In fact the Type 38 became something of a liability for, being horse-drawn, it was easily rendered immobile by enemy action or terrain conditions, and many precious Japanese guns were lost or knocked out simply because they could not be moved rapidly enough. After 1945 quantities of Type 38 guns passed into the hands of various forces in South-East Asia, some official and others unofficial, and the weapon was reported in use against French forces in Indo-China in the late 1940s.

SPECIFICATION	
Field Gun Type 38 (Improved)	**Elevation:** -8° to +43°
Calibre: 75 mm (2.95 in)	**Traverse:** 7°
Length of piece: 2.286 m (90 in)	**Muzzle velocity:** 603 m (1,978 ft) per second
Weights: travelling 1910 kg (4,211 lb) and in action 1136 kg (2,504 lb)	**Range:** 11970 m (13,080 yards)
	Shell weight: 6.025 kg (13.3 lb)

Bofors 75-mm Model 1934 Mountain howitzer

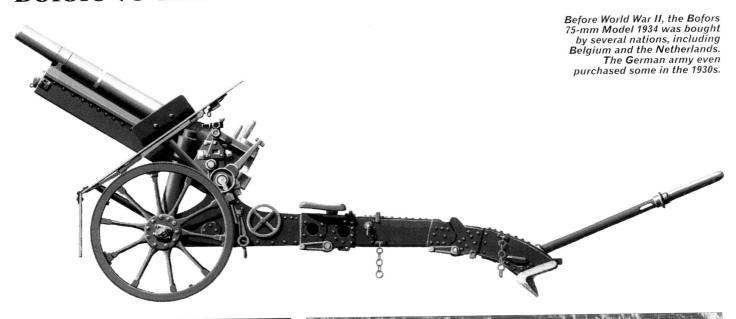

Before World War II, the Bofors 75-mm Model 1934 was bought by several nations, including Belgium and the Netherlands. The German army even purchased some in the 1930s.

SPECIFICATION	
Model 34 Mountain Howitzer	**Muzzle velocity:** 455 m (1,493 ft) per second
Calibre: 75 mm (2.95 in)	**Maximum range:** 9300 m (10,170 yards)
Lengths: piece overall 1.8 m (70.87 in); barrel 1.583 m (62.32 in)	**Projectile weight:** 6.59 kg (14.53 lb)
Weight: in action 928 kg (2,046 lb)	
Elevation: -10° to +50°	
Traverse: 8°	

The **Bofors 75-mm Model 1934** was originally designed as a mountain howitzer and was placed on the market in the 1920s. At that time the artillery markets around the world were awash with the surplus of World War I, but there was a small demand for specialised weapons and the Bofors 75-mm howitzer fell into this category. As with all products from the Bofors plant at Karlskroga, the 75-mm howitzer was well made from the finest materials, and was based on a sound and well considered design. And it was just what was required by the Dutch armed forces.

One would have thought that the last thing wanted by a nation as well endowed with flat terrain as the Netherlands was a mountain howitzer, but the Dutch needed the gun not for service at home but away on the other side of the world in the Dutch East Indies. At that time the Netherlands maintained a sizeable force of troops in the islands that now make up much of Indonesia, and as the terrain is either very overgrown or mountainous, some form of pack artillery was required.

Four-horse team

The Bofors gun was apparently just what was needed and a batch of the howitzers was duly acquired. The Bofors weapon could be broken down into eight loads, carried in special harnesses by mules, but for normal towing a four-horse team was used, with a further six mules carrying

Above: A Dutch army Bofors 75-mm (2.95-in) Model 1934 howitzer is readied for action against the Japanese in the Dutch East Indies early in 1942.

ammunition and other bits and pieces; the gunners themselves had to walk. These guns were still in use when World War II reached the Pacific, and with the Japanese invasion the guns had a brief period of action before falling into Japanese hands. Their new masters used the guns for their own purposes until the ammunition stocks ran out, and by 1945 few were left.

Some of these Bofors 75-mm howitzers were sold to Turkey in the years leading up to World War II, but the main customer was yet another unlikely client for a mountain gun. This time the recipient was Belgium, for which a special version was produced as the **Canon de 75 modèle 1934**.

This time the gun was for use by the Belgian troops based along the borders in the Ardennes region, but as this area was reasonably well provided with roads and tracks, there was no need for the full pack transport facility. Instead the modèle 1934s were produced as 'one-piece' weapons, the only feature designed to save towing length being a section of the box trail that could be folded upward while the gun was on tow. The Belgian models were intended for towing by light tracked tractors and were delivered with rubber-tyred steel disc wheels.

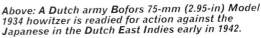

Left: The Netherlands army used its Bofors 75-mm Model 1934 howitzers in the Dutch East Indies, where they were carried into action by pack mules.

76.2-mm Field Gun Model 1936 Light artillery piece

By the early 1930s the Red Army artillery staff was becoming aware that its field gun park was falling behind those of the rest of Europe in terms of power and efficiency. So the USSR began a programme to create new weapons. One early effort, made in 1933, was the placing of a new 76.2-mm (3-in) barrel on the carriage of a 122-mm (4.8-in) field gun, but this was only a stopgap pending the introduction of what was intended to be one of the best all-round field guns in the world.

Impressive gun

The new gun was introduced in 1936, and was thus known as the **76.2-mm Field Gun Model 1936**, usually known as the **76-36**. It was an excellent design that made quite an impression on artillery designers elsewhere when the details became known. The 76-36 had a very long and slender barrel mounted on a deceptively simple split-trail carriage that provided a large traverse angle. This had been deliberately designed into the weapon as the Red Army's anti-tank philosophy had reached the point at which every Soviet gun and howitzer had to have an anti-tank capability. Even the standard HE shell

of the 76-36 had a powerful anti-armour effect.

The 76-36 first saw active service against Finland in the 'Winter War' of 1939-40. It performed effectively in this campaign, but did not fare so well in its second campaign, the German invasion of the USSR. It was not so much that the 76-36 did not perform well, but rather that it had little chance to do anything. The advancing Germans moved so fast that whole Soviet armies were cut off and destroyed. Huge numbers of 76-36s fell into German hands and, more disastrously for the Soviets, the Germans also captured a great deal of the plant that produced the guns. Thus almost their whole stock of 76-36 artillery was lost to the Soviets within a very short time.

Firing trials

German artillery experts swarmed over the captured guns, taking measurements and carrying out their own firing trials before they came up with two suggestions. One was that the 76-36 should become a standard German field gun, the **7.62-cm Feldkanone 296(r)**, as there was enough ammunition to hand to make these weapons useful for some time as longer-term plans were laid to produce the

ammunition in Germany.

The second suggestion, also implemented, was that the 76-36 should be converted into a specialised anti-tank gun for use against even the most powerfully armoured Soviet tanks. Large numbers of 76-36 guns were therefore taken to Germany, where they were modified to take new ammunition and thus emerge with the revised designation **7.62-cm Panzerabwehrkanone 36(r)**, which proved itself one of the best all-round anti-tank guns of World War II. The changes for the anti-tank role also involved some on-carriage changes (such as all the fire-control wheels being used by the layer instead of the original

A long way from home, this 76.2-mm Field Gun Model 1936 was captured on the Eastern Front by the Germans in 1941 and then converted for use as a very effective anti-tank gun before arrival in North Africa.

SPECIFICATION	
76.2-mm Field Gun Model 1936	**Elevation:** -5° to + 75°
Calibre: 76.2 mm (3 in)	**Traverse:** total 60°
Length of piece: 3.895 m (153.3 in)	**Muzzle velocity:** 706 m (2,316 ft) per second
Weight: travelling 2400 kg (5,292 lb); in action 1350 kg (2,977 lb)	**Range:** 13850 m (15,145 yards)
	Shell weight: 6.4 kg (14.1 lb)

two men) and a few other modifications.

Thus a Soviet field gun was used as much by the Germans as by the Soviets. With the disruption in production imposed by the German advances the 76-36 was never put back into full

production, although spare parts were made in a few places for use on the few 76-36s remaining in Soviet hands. By 1944 the 76-36 was no longer a Red Army weapon, for by then the Soviets had a new gun in service.

76.2-mm Field Gun Model 1942 Light artillery piece

With much of their production facilities lost to the advancing German forces during the second half of 1941, Soviet staff planners had some difficult decisions to make. Vast stockpiles of weapons of all kinds had been lost to the Germans, and the manufacture of new weapons demanded that production capacity had to be improvised hurriedly in outlying areas where factories currently did not even exist. In the Soviets' favour was the fact that their gun design bureaux were inherently conservative, preferring not large-scale innovation but a process of gradual evolution and the

combination of a new gun or carriage with an existing carriage or gun.

Smaller design

This served the Soviets well after 1941, for in 1939 they had introduced a new gun known as the **76.2-mm Field Gun Model 1939**, or **76-39**. This reflected the realisation that, good as it was, the 76-36 was too bulky in tactical terms, and thus a smaller design was desirable. The 76-39 used a shorter barrel on the carriage derived from that of the 76-36.

When the Germans struck in 1941 they did not capture the main plant for

Above: 76-42 guns with boxed ammunition and rounds ready for loading. Each artillery division had a light brigade of three (later two) 24-gun regiments.

Right: The 76.2-mm Field Gun Model 1942 was produced in greater numbers than any other artillery weapon of World War II. Also known as the 76-42 or ZIS-3, the Model 1942 was a very sound design with no frills and a good performance, firing a 6.21-kg (13.7-lb) shell to a maximum range of 13215 m (14,450 yards).

Above: Soviet troops are instructed on the use of the 76-42. This excellent weapon was allocated to the field artillery batteries of rifle (infantry) and tank units as well as to artillery formations.

Right: A 76.2-mm Field Gun Model 1942 in action in the ruins of the Tractor Works in Stalingrad during the ferocious fighting in the winter of 1942-43. Both sides exploited this weapon's anti-tank capability.

Left: A 76.2-mm Model 1939 field gun in action on the Kalinin sector of the Eastern Front in the course of 1942's fighting. Whatever their primary task, all pieces of Soviet artillery had an anti-tank capability.

76-39 barrels, though they did take the carriage plant for the 76-36. Thus it was possible to use the barrel and recoil mechanism of the 76-39 on a new carriage to allow production to get under way once more. The result was the **76.2-mm Field Gun Model 1942**, later known as the **76-42** or **ZIS-3**.

The 76-42 was to achieve fame through production in numbers greater than that of any other gun of World War II. It was produced in its thousands, and if this had not been enough it turned out to be an excellent all-round weapon capable of being used not only as a field gun but an anti-tank gun, a form of tank gun and a self-propelled gun. The new carriage was a very simple but sturdy affair using split pole trails and a simple flat shield. The gun assembly was modified to take a muzzle brake to reduce firing stresses and so allow the carriage to be lightened, and throughout the design process emphasis was given to ease of mass production. In action the 76-42 proved light and easy to handle, and also had excellent range. To simplify the Red Army's logistic load the ammunition was ruthlessly standardised to the point at which the 76-42 fired the same ammunition types as the 76.2-mm gun of the T-34 medium tank and many other similar guns. Only two types of projectile were generally used in World War II, namely HE and AP, though smoke was fired on occasion.

Still in service

The Germans used captured examples of the 76-42 as the **7.62-cm FK 288(r)**. The 76-42 was produced in numbers so great that it remains in service with some nations to the present. Examples were encountered in Korea and Indo-China, and the gun is still fielded in Africa and the Far East. The 76-42 was widely delivered to guerrilla groups such as the PLO in the Middle East and SWAPO in South-West Africa, and there seems to be no time limit on its active life.

Numerous attempts were made to mount the 76-42 on self-propelled carriages but only one was ever produced in any quantity. This was the SU-76, another Soviet weapon in widespread service until recent times.

October 1944, and men of the US Army fire a Soviet Model 1942 gun against the Germans. Thus the gun, a product of one Allied nation, was used by another against the Axis power which had first captured it.

SPECIFICATION	
76.2-mm Field Gun Model 1942	**Elevation:** -5° to +37°
Calibre: 76.2 mm (3 in)	**Traverse:** total 54°
Length of piece: 3.246 m (127.8 in)	**Muzzle velocity:** 680 m (2,230 ft) per second
Weight: travelling and in action 1120 kg (2,470 lb)	**Range:** 13215 m (14,450 yards)
	Shell weight: 6.21 kg (13.7 lb)

Ordnance, Q.F., 25-pdr Mk 2

The finest all-round piece of British field artillery in World War II, the 25-pdr Field Gun was a gun/howitzer providing first-class capabilities in the direct-fire gun and indirect-fire howitzer roles. The first such weapon was the 25-pdr Mk 1, which was the 18-pdr gun bored out to take the 25-pdr separate-loading ammunition and mounted on a box or split-trail carriage. The definitive 1940 model was the classic 25-pdr Mk 2 with a new and higher-elevating ordnance mounted on a box-trail carriage whose wheels could be located on a turntable for rapid changes in bearing.

The 25-pdr Field Gun Mk 2 in action. The weapon's one major limitation was its weight, which precluded the development of a version for the use of airborne forces, but in overall terms the weapon served the British and their allies well in World War II and for a long period after the end of that conflict.

Above: It is thought that the last occasion in which the 25-pdr Field Gun saw extensive action was during the 1971 war between India and Pakistan, in which both sides used the weapon. This weapon however, is seen in the hands of the South African Defence Force as late as the 1980s.

Right: A 25-pdr Field Gun Mk 2, in a camouflaged position and identifiable by its lack of a muzzle brake, is seen in the recoiled position with propellant gases still streaming from the muzzle.

Below: The muzzle flash of a 25-pdr Field Gun firing at night reveals the gap between the two sides of the box trail, which allowed the ordnance to be elevated to +40°.

SPECIFICATION

Ordnance, QF, 25-pdr Mk 3 (otherwise 25-pdr Field Gun Mk 3 on Carriage 25-pdr Mk 1)

Gun

Calibre: 87.6 mm (3.45 in)
Barrel length: 2.35 m (7 ft 8.5 in)
Muzzle brake: double-baffle type

Weight

Travelling and in action (complete with turntable): 1801 kg (3,970 lb)

Dimensions

Length travelling: 7.924 m (26 ft)
Width travelling: 2.12 m (6 ft 11.5 in)
Height travelling: 1.65 m (5 ft 3 in)
Height of bore axis (firing with barrel horizontal): 1.168 m (3 ft 10 in)
Ground clearance: 0.342 m

(1 ft 1.5 in)
Wheel track: 1.778 m (5 ft 10 in)

Tyres

9.00x16

Elevation/traverse

Elevation: -5° to +40°
Traverse: 8° on carriage and 360° on turntable

Ammunition types

HE, AP (solid shot), Canister, Smoke, Coloured Smoke, and Illuminating

Range

12250 m (13,400 yards)

Rate of fire

Nominal: 5 rounds per minute

Detachment

6 men

Above: The rate of fire of a 25-pdr Field Gun served by a willing and well-trained crew could be very high, and this imposed a great strain on the logistical organisation charged with keeping the guns fed.

Below: Artillery batteries were a favoured target for bombers and fighter-bombers, so it was only sensible for the crews of weapons such as this 25-pdr gun to conceal their charges under outline-breaking camouflage netting.

Above: The crew of a 25-pdr Field Gun ready their weapon for action. It was important that the turntable on which the gun sat was firmly bedded into the ground to absorb the recoil forces without moving and to allow rapid training.

Below: The 25-pdr gun was not best suited to jungle operations as a result of its weight and width. The Australians therefore developed a 'baby' version for pack transport.

Ordnance, Q.F., 25-pdr Mk 2

Limber and ammunition

The 25-pdr Field Gun's ready-use ammunition was carried in a two-wheel limber normally interposed between the gun carriage and the towing vehicle. The five most important types of separate-loading projectile were HE, AP, Canister, Smoke and Illuminating. The HE projectile weighed 11.34 kg (25 lb) and left the muzzle at 518 m (1,700 ft) per second for a maximum range of 12230 m (13,400 yards), while the solid shot AP projectile weighed 9.2 kg (20.3 lb) and left the muzzle at 609 m (2,000 ft) per second to penetrate 70 mm (2.75 in) of armour at 0° at a range of 365 m (400 yards). A HEAT projectile was later added to the inventory.

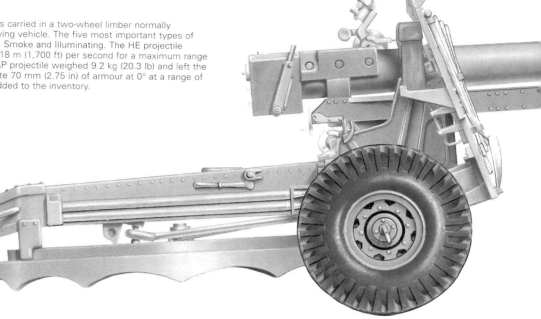

Detachment

The 25-pdr Field Gun was served by a detachment of six men, including the layer who was seated to the left of the breech. The layer used a sight of the rocking bar type incorporating a calibrating range drum. The official rate of fire was five rounds per minute, but a well-trained crew was generally capable of producing a rate well in excess of this nominal figure. Three basic charges were provided, each represented by a coloured bag in the brass cartridge case, and there was also a 'Charge Super' special sealed cartridge. An increment to the charge super was used with the AP projectile for greater muzzle velocity.

Two-wheel carriage

The 25-pdr Mk 2 was a very successful compromise between the demand of firepower and tactical mobility. The latter resulted from the installation of the ordnance on the Carriage Mk 1 with a shield, two wheels and a humped box trail fitted with a towing eye that could be hooked easily and quickly to the fitment at the rear of any towing vehicle or the two-wheel limber. The use of a box trail meant that the ordnance had a good elevation arc (-5° to +40°) without any need to open the legs, as would have been the case with a split-trail carriage, and the ordnance could also be traversed 8° on the mounting.

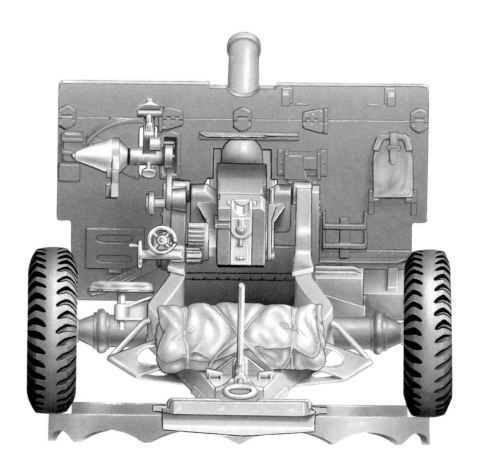

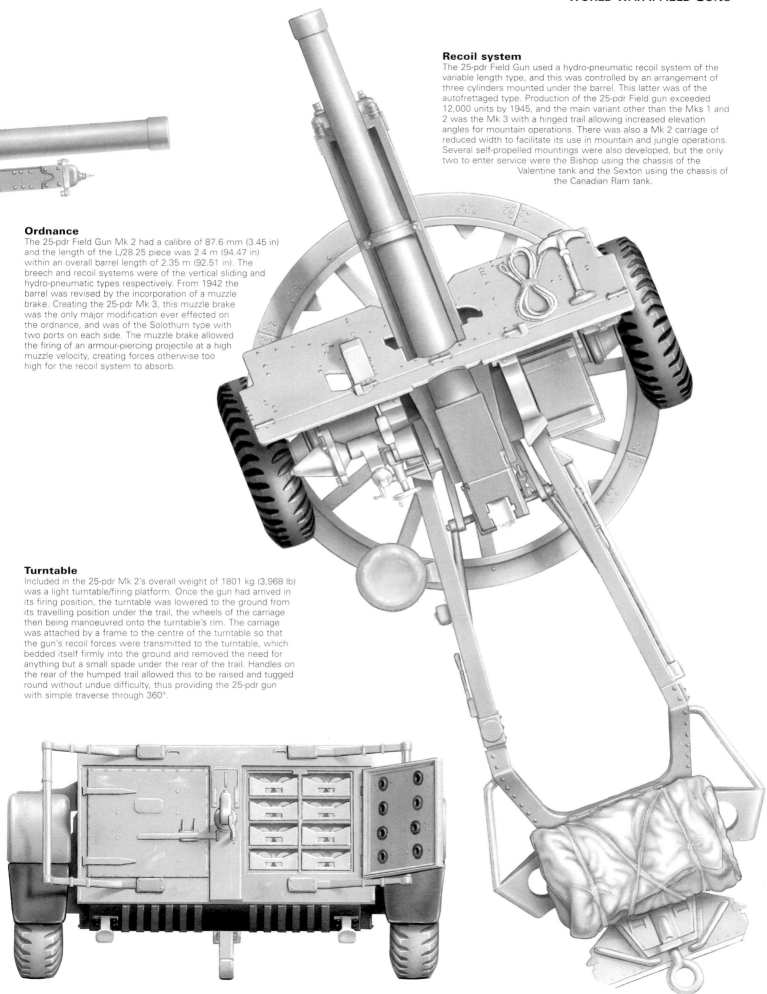

Recoil system

The 25-pdr Field Gun used a hydro-pneumatic recoil system of the variable length type, and this was controlled by an arrangement of three cylinders mounted under the barrel. This latter was of the autofrettaged type. Production of the 25-pdr Field gun exceeded 12,000 units by 1945, and the main variant other than the Mks 1 and 2 was the Mk 3 with a hinged trail allowing increased elevation angles for mountain operations. There was also a Mk 2 carriage of reduced width to facilitate its use in mountain and jungle operations. Several self-propelled mountings were also developed, but the only two to enter service were the Bishop using the chassis of the Valentine tank and the Sexton using the chassis of the Canadian Ram tank.

Ordnance

The 25-pdr Field Gun Mk 2 had a calibre of 87.6 mm (3.45 in) and the length of the L/28.25 piece was 2.4 m (94.47 in) within an overall barrel length of 2.35 m (92.51 in). The breech and recoil systems were of the vertical sliding and hydro-pneumatic types respectively. From 1942 the barrel was revised by the incorporation of a muzzle brake. Creating the 25-pdr Mk 3, this muzzle brake was the only major modification ever effected on the ordnance, and was of the Solothurn type with two ports on each side. The muzzle brake allowed the firing of an armour-piercing projectile at a high muzzle velocity, creating forces otherwise too high for the recoil system to absorb.

Turntable

Included in the 25-pdr Mk 2's overall weight of 1801 kg (3,968 lb) was a light turntable/firing platform. Once the gun had arrived in its firing position, the turntable was lowered to the ground from its travelling position under the trail, the wheels of the carriage then being manoeuvred onto the turntable's rim. The carriage was attached by a frame to the centre of the turntable so that the gun's recoil forces were transmitted to the turntable, which bedded itself firmly into the ground and removed the need for anything but a small spade under the rear of the trail. Handles on the rear of the humped trail allowed this to be raised and tugged round without undue difficulty, thus providing the 25-pdr gun with simple traverse through 360°.

The six-man detachment of a 25-pdr Field Gun Mk 1 fire their weapon during an operation by the British 8th Army in North Africa. On the right is the two-wheel Artillery Trailer No. 27, a limber that carried the gun's ready-use ammunition and also helped to support the trail when the equipment was being towed, allowing the use of a vehicle, such as the Humber Quad 4x4 truck, lighter than would otherwise have been the case.

British Artillery at El Alamein

A revitalised Royal Artillery, well equipped with 25-pdr guns and using its own command system, was one of the major keys to General Montgomery's victory in the 2nd Battle of El Alamein.

One of the least known facts regarding the battle now known familiarly as El Alamein is that there were two battles, of which the first was once known as the Battle of Ruweisat (7/8 July 1942) but now as the 1st Battle of El Alamein.

The battle took the form of a holding operation to keep the advancing Axis columns away from the vitally important stores and communications centres located along the Suez Canal and around Cairo. By mid-1942 the Desert War had swayed to and fro across the North African deserts several times. The Axis forces were again on a winning streak, having trounced a large Allied foray and forced the Allies back to an area where there was no room to the south for the usual Afrika Korps flanking move, which was barred by the impassable Qattara Depression. Just to the north of this was the Ruweisat Ridge, with El Alamein railway station to the north.

The Axis forces were operating at the end of a very long logistic chain and almost at the end of their operational tank strength. When they finally attacked the Ruweisat Ridge area, the Allies were emplaced and were ready for them.

Using whatever artillery fire support could be scraped together, the Allies stopped the German columns in their tracks. The action was notable for several factors. One was that it was the last time that British 25-pdr field guns had to be used in an anti-tank role, for after 1st El Alamein there were enough

25-pdr gun/howitzer crews in action in the Western Desert. Here the weapon proved itself one of the decisive features of the Allied arsenal for both static and mobile warfare.

25-pdr in action British Army field gun

The 25-pdr Field Gun was capable of undertaking the tasks of both the flat-trajectory gun and high-trajectory howitzer. The gun was heavy, but strong, thoroughly reliable, and provided with just the right types of projectile, fired with the aid of a multi-charge propellant system, for a host of tactical applications. Produced in large numbers, the 25-pdr gun was a key element of the success of the British and imperial forces in the later stages of World War II, and remained in service long after World War II.

One of the features of nocturnal artillery operations that cannot effectively be hidden or disguised is the huge muzzle flash as the emergence of the shell from the muzzle allows an expanding torrent of incandescent gas to follow in its wake, for the briefest of moments turning night into day.

6-pdr anti-tank guns for the 25-pdr guns to revert to their proper field roles. These 25-pdr actions had always been desperate affairs. The 25-pdr gun had not been created for the direct anti-tank role, and made a large target for Axis tank gunners to engage with tank or machine-gun fire well before they came within the anti-tank range of the 25-pdr guns, whose crews had little cover other than the thin gun shield.

Revitalised Royal Artillery
Another reason why the 1st Battle of El Alamein should be remembered was that it marked the end of a period of relative disorganisation within the Royal Artillery. Starting some time in 1941 the internal structure of the Royal Artillery had been considerably disrupted by a series of internal reorganisations that seriously affected its combat efficiency. By the time of 1st El Alamein things were changing back. Once again the Royal Artillery was

provided with its own form of centralised control. Batteries moved back to a tidier internal organisation, and the chain of communication between units was being re-formed.

Some time after his repulse at 1st El Alamein, Rommel made another almost half-hearted attempt to break through at Alam el Halfa, but that too was repulsed. Things then settled down for more than two months, a period in which the Axis forces re-supplied themselves and brought up as much equipment as they could muster. It was not easy for them in the face of Allied air and sea power, but gradually the Axis forces grew in number and strength.

On the Allied side a new commander had come upon the scene. Bernard Montgomery took over a motley and not particularly happy bunch, and immediately started to rebuild morale and strength before tackling the Axis forces in

the 2nd Battle of El Alamein. In true World War I style the battle was to open with a barrage involving, among others, 834 25-pdr guns and a grouping of 48 assorted heavier guns. A careful fire plan was to open the Axis positions, by that time protected by belts of land mines and barbed wire, and to cover the activities of sapper parties who were to clear a way through the obstacles.

The fire plan started at 21.30 on the night of 23 October 1942. At the time it was the largest of its kind since 1918. Not all the guns were involved at any one time. The usual number involved was rarely more than 480 guns, for the gun crews had to stand ready to switch fire to new targets and prepare ammunition for the next part of the fire plan. It was later estimated that well over one and a half' million shells were fired, and the ammunition supply problem was enormous. Trucks constantly

trundled to and from the ammunition dumps in the Canal Zone area and from the forward supply locations placed farther forward.

Effective fire-control
One of the principal reasons for the success of the barrage was that it was carried out under the central control of the Royal Artillery itself. For the first time in a long period the gunners were able to carry out their own plans and fire missions using their own centralised chain of command. An artillery adviser was on hand at all command levels from division to corps as the fighting swung to and fro during the nine days that marked the progress of 2nd El Alamein. Montgomery constantly switched the point of attack from one location to another, forever keeping the enemy on guard until the final thrust to allow XXX Corps to make the final breakthrough.

Once the breakthrough was made the Allied pursuit moved forward, but not at a

breakneck pace. The 8th Army staff was only too aware that a headlong rush by its eager but still ill-trained forces would probably be met with a fierce countermove by Rommel's seasoned forces, and that any such knock would probably stop the whole operation in its tracks. Instead, Montgomery allowed his forces to move forward in strict limits, with each move covered by plenty of artillery fire support. The 'pursuit' began in earnest on 3 November 1942 and did not cease until the approaches to Tunisia, by which time the Allies were well in command, with their

25-pdr guns still a decisive element in the fighting as the gunners were able to advance at the same rate as their 'customer' formations: using Quad and other tractors, the 25-pdr guns moved forward remorselessly to carry out their operational task under proper control.

Ordnance, Q.F., 25-pdr

Gun/howitzer

The British 25-pdr was one of the 'classic' field artillery weapons of World War II. It served in all theatres after 1940 and made its initial mark during the famous barrage at El Alamein. As well as being used as a field gun, it was at one time pressed into action as an anti-tank gun in the Western Desert.

The gun that was to become one of the most famous of all British artillery pieces had its origins in operational analysis after World War I indicating that it would be desirable to give the Royal Artillery a light field piece that could combine the attributes of a gun and a howitzer. In the mid-1930s the go-ahead was given to develop the new weapon to replace the British Army's ageing stock of 18-pdr field guns and 114-mm (4.5-in) howitzers.

Dunkirk

There were large stocks of the old 18-pdr guns still around in the 1930s and the Treasury insisted that a way be found to use them. From this came the **Ordnance, Q.F., 25-pdr Mk 1**, which was a new barrel placed on an 18-pdr carriage. It was with this gun that the BEF went to war in 1939. The old carriages had been updated with new pneumatic wheels and other changes, but the 25-pdr Mk 1 had little chance to shine before most of them were lost at Dunkirk.

By then the **25-pdr Mk 2 on Carriage 25-pdr Mk 1** was on the scene. This was a purpose-built weapon which would replace the old pieces and can be described as a gun-howitzer. It used an ammunition system with

variable charges as in a howitzer but could also be used for lower register firing with no loss in efficiency. The barrel itself was orthodox and used a heavy vertical sliding breech mechanism, but the carriage had some unusual features. It was a humped box trail carried on a circular firing table that enabled one man to make large changes of traverse easily and quickly. The gun was intended from the start for powered traction, the usual tractor being one of the large 'Quad' family.

Muzzle brake

Almost as soon as the first 25-pdr guns saw action in North Africa they were pressed into use as anti-tank guns. It was then that the circular firing table came into its own, for the guns could be rapidly moved from target to target, but the 25-pdr had to rely on shell power alone for its effects as there was no armour-piercing ammunition. Such a round was developed, but it entailed the use of an extra charge which in turn dictated the use of a muzzle brake, and in this form the 25-pdr was used throughout the rest of World War II.

Some changes were made to the carriage design

to suit local requirements. A narrower version was developed for jungle and airborne warfare (**25-pdr Mk 2 on Carriage 25-pdr Mk 2**) and a version with a hinged trail (**25-pdr Mk 2 on Carriage 25-pdr Mk 3**) was produced to increase elevation for hill warfare. The Australians produced a drastic revision for pack transport, and there was even a naval version mooted at one time. The 25-pdr went self-propelled in the Canadian Sexton carriage and there were numerous trial and experimental versions, one classic expedient being the stopgap mounting of 17-pdr anti-tank barrels on 25-pdr carriages. Captured examples were designated **8.76-cm FK 280(e)** by the Germans.

The 25-pdr provided sterling service. It had a useful range and the gun and carriage proved capable of absorbing all manner of punishment. It remained in service with a number of

armies for many years after 1945. The 25-pdr was a 'classic' gun, and many former gunners remember operating the weapon with much affection.

25-pdrs on a training range are manned by Canadian gunners, the 25-pdr being the standard field gun for many Commonwealth armies. This photograph probably dates from mid-1943.

SPECIFICATION	
Q.F., 25-pdr Mk 2	
Calibre: 87.6 mm (3.45 in)	**Traverse:** on carriage 8°; on firing table 360°
Length of piece: 2.4 m (94.5 in)	
Weight: travelling and in action 1800 kg (3,968 lb)	**Muzzle velocity:** 532 m (1,745 ft) per second
Elevation: -5°to +40°	**Range:** 12253 m (13,400 yards)
	Shell weight: 11.34 kg (25 lb)

95-mm Infantry Howitzer Mk II Light howitzer

At some point during 1942 a decision was made to produce a light howitzer for use by British infantry battalions but at that time the infantry themselves had not been consulted: perhaps the planners were influenced by the use of infantry artillery in nations such as Germany and the US. In order to conserve production facilities it was decided that the new weapon would incorporate features from a number of existing weapons. The barrel was to be machined from a 94-mm (3.7-in) anti-aircraft gun liner, the breech mechanism would come from the 25-pdr field gun and the recoil system and cradle came from 6-pdr anti-tank gun components. To simplify matters the new weapon would fire the

same ammunition as the old 32-inch Pack Howitzer and the close-support howitzers fitted in some tanks. The term **95-mm Infantry Howitzer Mk II** was applied to the project, the 95-mm being chosen to differentiate between this and other 94-mm weapons.

Not a success

The Mk II Howitzer was not one of the success stories of World War II. The amalgamation of components from a variety of weapons allied to a new welded steel box carriage looked rather odd, and performed poorly. The 6-pdr recoil system was simply not up to the task of absorbing the recoil loads and frequently broke. The wheel track was too narrow, leading to tow instability.

The experimental 95-mm (actually 3.7-in/94-mm) Infantry Howitzer was created using various parts of existing weapons. This howitzer was not a great success, especially since the infantry did not particularly want it, so the weapon was never accepted for full-scale military service.

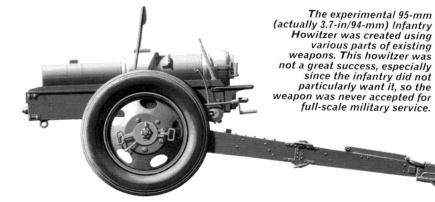

The poor overall construction, designed for pack transport in 10 loads, was such that components could be shaken loose in prolonged firing. More development could have eliminated many of these defects, but by the time they emerged the weapon was already in production.

Not wanted

It was at this point that the infantry were drawn into the programme. They quickly announced that they did not

want the new weapon. They had not been consulted in its development, and they already had quite enough weapon types within their battalions.

This finally killed off the 95-mm Infantry Howitzer project altogether, and the majority of the equipments produced were never issued. They were scrapped after the war.

Only two projectiles were produced for use with this weapon, High Explosive and smoke. There were plans

for an antitank HEAT projectile, but that was an offshoot of the 95-mm tank howitzer programme. Mention also can be found of a proposed flare shell. These projectiles were to be fired using a three-charge system.

The entire 95-mm Infantry Howitzer project now seems like a textbook example of how not to go about the design, development and production of a new military weapon system.

SPECIFICATION	
95-mm Infantry Howitzer	
Calibre: 94 mm (3.7 in)	**Traverse:** 8°
Lengths: barrel 1.88 m (74.05 in); bore 1.75 m (69 in)	**Muzzle velocity:** 330 m (1,083 ft) per second
Weight: in action 954.8 kg (2,105 lb)	**Maximum range:** 5486 m (6,000 yards)
Elevation: -5° to +30°	**Projectile weight:** 11.34 kg (25 lb)

75-mm Pack Howitzer M1A1 Light howitzer

In the aftermath of World War I the 1920 Westervelt Board recommended the design of a new 75-mm (2.95-in) light howitzer for mountain warfare and as a general-issue pack howitzer. This was one of the few proposals that was actually pursued at the time, and by 1927 the **75-mm Pack Howitzer Mk 1** had been standardised; some later production changes altered the designation to **M1A1**.

Carriage

The howitzer was mounted on a carriage of ingenious design that could be easily broken down into six loads. The howitzer itself could be broken down for transport, and was so arranged that the barrel was held in a trough and kept in place by a cover along the top: this gave the weapon a distinctive appearance. A screw mechanism aided the traverse and the cradle carried the elevation mechanism.

The first M1A1s were mounted on the Carriage M1, which was intended for animal traction and so had wooden spoked wheels. The introduction of mechanised traction led to the adoption of the Carriage M8, which used rubber-

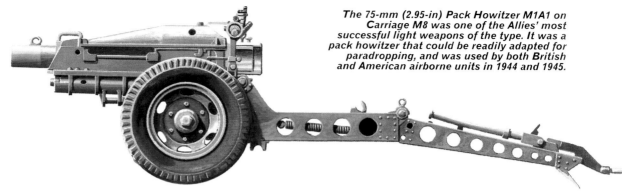

The 75-mm (2.95-in) Pack Howitzer M1A1 on Carriage M8 was one of the Allies' most successful light weapons of the type. It was a pack howitzer that could be readily adapted for paradropping, and was used by both British and American airborne units in 1944 and 1945.

tyred metal wheels. This little howitzer became one of the first Allied airborne artillery weapons, for it was issued to nearly every Allied airborne formation, including the British airborne divisions. But it should not be thought that the M1 carriage went out of fashion: many were produced during World War II for issue to Allied armies such as the Chinese, who also used the howitzer.

On either carriage the M1A1 was a very useful weapon. It was easy to serve in action, and it could be used to provide fire support at ranges up to 8925 m (9,760 yards).

Despite its light weight, conversions to the self-propelled role were made with some being mounted on halftracks, and it was just as successful in that guise.

Partisan use

One role for which the M1A1 was not much used, ironically, was in mountain warfare. There were few campaigns where mountain weapons were needed by the Allies. One exception was Yugoslavia. There, partisan troops were trained on the M1A1 by British officers, and the partisans made good use of the guns during the later stages of their war of self-liberation.

It was as one of the first Allied airborne artillery pieces that the M1A1 will probably be best remembered. It was used at Arnhem when some were landed from General Aircraft Hamilcar gliders, but the howitzer could also be broken down into nine loads for paradropping.

Not all M1A1s had such an adventurous life. Many were used simply as infantry support weapons or as pack artillery in the dense jungles of the Far East. However, the M1A1 was light enough to take part in the initial stages of amphibious assaults such as that on Walcheren in 1944.

SPECIFICATION	
M1A1	
Calibre: 75-mm (2.95-in)	**Traverse:** 6°
Lengths: piece 1.321 m (52 in); barrel 1.194 m (47 in)	**Muzzle velocity:** maximum 381 m (1,250 ft) per second
Weight: complete 587.9 kg (1,296 lb)	**Maximum range:** 8925 m (9,760 yards)
Elevation: -5° to +45°	**Projectile weight:** 6.241 kg (13.76 lb)

105-mm Howitzer M2A1 Field howitzer

When the US entered World War I in 1917 the US Army was poorly equipped. The Americans decided to equip themselves with the French 75 and began production in the USA for their own use. Production was just getting under way when the war ended, leaving the US Army with a huge stockpile of 75s that was to last until 1942.

Early origins

The Westerveldt Board of 1919 recommended a 105-mm (4.13-in) howitzer. At the time little was done to put the suggestions into practice, so it was not until 1939 that the design was completed. The weapon was placed into production the following year and thereafter the **105-mm Howitzer M2A1** poured off the American production lines by the thousand.

The M2A1 was destined to become one of the most

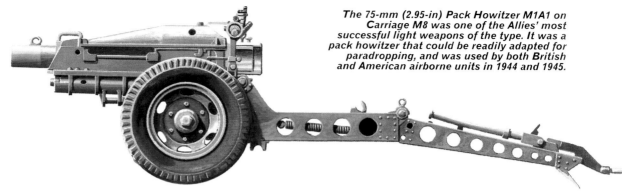

Although proposed as far back as 1919, the first examples of the M2A1 were not ready until 1939. Thereafter it was produced by the thousand, and it became the standard USA army field artillery howitzer. Rugged and basically simple, it was able to withstand all manner of hard use.

widely used of all American weapons in World War II.

The M2A1 was an orthodox piece of artillery, with little of note in its overall design. The associated **Carriage M2A2** was a split-trail design with the gun assembly mounted in such a way that the centre of balance was just forward of the

breech. The weapon was never intended for animal traction and so was fitted with rubber-tyred wheels from the outset. The M2A1 was heavy for its calibre, but the over-engineering meant that strength was so 'built-in' that the howitzer never seemed to wear out. The barrel and carriage could

take enormously hard use and still keep firing. The M2A1 was used in all theatres, from Europe to the Pacific.

Wartime development

Through the war years the basic design was the subject of numerous trials and improvements, and the ammunition underwent the same development process. By the time the war ended the range of ammunition

fired by the M2A1 ranged from the usual HE through propaganda-leaflet shells and various smoke marker shells to non-lethal tear gas shells.

Not all of the 105-mm (4.13-in) howitzers were towed. Some were fitted to self-propelled carriages, one of the most widely used being the M7, known to the British gunners who used it for a while in their formations as the 'Priest'.

Left : A 105-mm M2A1 in action during the Korean War. Taken in 1950, this photo is typical of many of the actions in which it was used. Eventually re-designated M101, at the beginning of the 21st century the gun is still in service with the US Marine Corps and with more than 50 other countries worldwide.

SPECIFICATION	
Howitzer M2A1	
Calibre: 105-mm (4.134-in)	**Elevation:** -5° to +65°
Length of piece: 2.574 m (101.35 in)	**Traverse:** 45°
Weight: travelling and in action 1934 kg (4,260 lb)	**Muzzle velocity:** 472 m (1,550 ft) per second
	Range: 11430 m (12,500 yards)
	Shell weight: 14.97 kg (33 lb)

Skoda 149-mm vz 37 howitzer (K4) Heavy field howitzer

By the early 1930s the Skoda company at Pilsen in Czechoslovakia was in a position to design, develop and produce entirely new artillery pieces that owed nothing to the obsolescent World War I weapons that had hitherto been the company's main output. By 1933 Skoda had produced, among other things, an entirely new 149-mm (5.87-in) range of howitzers known as the K series. The first of these, the **K1**, was produced in 1933 and the entire output of these **vz 33** (*vzor*, or model) weapons went for export to Turkey, Romania and Yugoslavia. The K1 was a thoroughly modern piece with a heavy split trail, and was designed for either horse or motorised traction. For the latter the piece could be towed as one load, but for the former the barrel could be removed to be towed as a separate load.

Further development

Despite the success of the K1, the Czechoslovak army decided that the weapon did not meet its exact requirements and therefore funded further development. This led to the **K4** model, which fully met the specification. The K4 had much in common with the K1, but had a shorter barrel and, as the Czechoslovak army was making considerable strides towards full mechanisation, no provision for separate

movement of the barrel. The K4 also had pneumatically tyred wheels in place of the K1's steel wheels with solid rubber tyres, and a number of other modifications were introduced to suit the equipment for towing by an artillery tractor.

Replacement

The Czechoslovak army decided to adopt the K4, with these changes, as its standard heavy field howitzer to replace the large range of elderly weapons remaining from World War I. The K4 was given the army designation **15-cm hrubá houfnice vz 37**, vz 37 denoting the equipment's acceptance for service in 1937. Skoda drew up production plans, but this lengthy process was overtaken by the Germans' 1938 occupation of the Sudetenland border region of Czechoslovakia. Production planning then became even more frantic but, with the Sudetenland line of defences occupied, Czechoslovakia was wide open to further aggression and in 1939 the Germans marched in to take over the rest of the country.

The Germans also secured the Skoda works, finding on the production lines the first full-production vz 37 weapons. Only a few examples had been produced by this time, and these the German army tested on its ranges back in

Germany, discovering that the vz 37 was a sound and serviceable howitzer with a good range of 15100 m (16,515 yards) and the ability to fire a very useful 42-kg (92.6-lb) projectile. Thus the Germans decided to keep the vz 37 in production at Pilsen for their own requirements, the vz 37 thereupon becoming the German army's **15-cm schwere Feldhaubitze 37(t)**, or 15-cm heavy field howitzer model 1937 (Czechoslovak), the (t) denoting *tschechisch*. In the German army the **sFH 37(t)** became a standard weapon of many formations, forming part of the divisional artillery equipment and being used even by some corps batteries. The howitzer was used during the French cam-

The high water mark of German success on the Eastern Front came in the late summer of 1942 as elements of Army Group 'A' penetrated more than 300 km (185 miles) to the south-east of Stalingrad. Here an sFH 37(t) 15-cm howitzer pounds Soviet positions in the foothills of the Caucasus mountain range.

SPECIFICATION	
sFH 37(t)	
Calibre: 149.1 mm (5.87 in)	**Elevation:** -5° to +70°
Length of piece: 3.6 m (11 ft 9.¾ in)	**Traverse:** 45°
Weight: travelling 5730 kg (12,632 lb) and in action 5200 kg (11,464 lb)	**Muzzle velocity:** 580 m (1,903 ft) per second
	Maximum range: 15100 m (16,515 yards)
	Shell weight: 42 kg (92.6 lb)

paign of May and June 1940, and later in the invasion of the USSR during 1941. Some equipments were still in service on the Eastern Front as late as 1944, but by then many had been passed

to the various Balkan forces under German control and operating within what was later Yugoslavia; the Slovak army was another one of the recipients of this weapon.

Skoda 220-mm howitzer Heavy howitzer

Whereas the Skoda vz 37 howitzer was a completely new design, the slightly earlier **Skoda 220-mm howitzer** was a product that could trace its origins back to somewhat earlier days and an older pattern of warfare. In the period up to 1918, when Skoda had been the largest armament producer for the army of the Austro-Hungarian empire in World War I, the Pilsen works had been only slightly behind the German Krupp concern in the manufacture of really heavy artillery, and the heavy Skoda howitzers were second to none in overall capability. Thus, when the Skoda works started production again in what was then an independent Czechoslovakia, the 'classic' howitzer became one of the company's primary products.

However, the accent in heavy artillery was no longer just on a very large calibre.

Despite their dreadful efficiency in demolishing fortifications, as proved in World War I on both the Western and Eastern Fronts, such equipments were ponderous beasts to move and their rate of fire was also extremely slow. Moreover, they were fearfully expensive to buy and to use. So when some of the new nations formed after World War I's end started to arm themselves against a difficult future they still wanted heavy artillery, but not too heavy. An interim calibre of about 220 mm (8.66 in) was still adequate for the task of destroying fixed fortifications and other heavy structures, but it was necessary that the howitzer itself should not be too ponderous. Skoda sensed the needs of this new market and produced the required 220-mm design incorporating much of its considerable experience in such matters,

Skoda produced some of the best heavy artillery pieces of World War I, and continued the tradition with the 220-mm howitzer, which was exported to both Poland and Yugoslavia. After the Germans had invaded and seized much of eastern and southern Europe, they used the captured weapons against the Soviet fortress city of Sevastopol in the Crimea.

and it was not long before customers arrived.

The first was Yugoslavia, formed from several of the pre-World War I Balkan states. The new nation decided it had much to fear from its neighbours, and thus became involved in numerous purchases of weapons of all kinds throughout Europe. Yugoslavia was a good customer of Skoda, and in 1928 took delivery of a batch of 12 220-mm Skoda howitzers under the designation **M.28**. Another customer was Poland, which ordered no fewer than 27. These latter

featured prominently in many pre-war propaganda photographs of the Polish army. All of these photographs had one feature in common: the breech mechanism was always obscured in some way, usually by a soldier, as part of the normal Polish security procedure in any artillery illustration intended for publication.

Useful weapon

It did the Poles no good, for in 1939 the Germans invaded Poland, and in a one-month campaign destroyed or captured the entire Polish gun

park. The unfortunate Yugoslavs suffered the same fate just over 18 months later. Thus the Germans found themselves with a useful quantity of 220-mm howitzers, which promptly became part of their army's inventory. There was not much of a role for such a relatively heavy piece in the German *Blitzkrieg* concept, so the captured howitzers were distributed mainly to garrison and static units in the occupied territories. Some of these were as distant as Norway, but late in 1941 a number of the how-

itzers were gathered for addition to the siege train that was sent to invest the Soviet fortress of Sevastopol in the Crimea. This was the last classic investment of a fortress by the age-old method of assembling and

using a siege train, and the fortress fell after the howitzers had played a useful part. They were then scattered to several parts of Germany's European empire, and saw little use during the rest of World War II.

SPECIFICATION	
Skoda 220-mm howitzer	**Elevation:** +40° to +70°
Calibre: 220 mm (8.66 in)	**Traverse:** 350°
Length of piece: 4.34 m (14 ft 3 in)	**Muzzle velocity:** 500 m (1,640 ft) per second
Weight: travelling 22700 kg (50,045 lb) and in action 14700 kg (32,408 lb)	**Maximum range:** 14200 m (15,530 yards)
	Shell weight: 128 kg (282.2 lb)

10.5-cm Kanone 18 and 18/40 Field guns

Among the requirements for a new German artillery park to replace the weapons lost in World War I was that for a new long-range gun to be used by corps rather than field artillery batteries. This project was one of the very first put out to the underground German armaments industry, for by 1926 both Krupp and Rheinmetall had produced specimen designs, and by 1930 were ready with prototype hardware.

Standard weapon

As it turned out, the German army could not decide which design to approve, resulting in the compromise adoption of the Rheinmetall barrel on the Krupp carriage. This latter was destined to become one of the most widely used of all the German artillery carriages, for it was the same as that used on the larger 15-cm sFH 18 howitzer series. It was 1934 before the first guns actually reached the troops and for a while the new gun, known as the **10.5-cm K 18** (*Kanone*, or gun), was the standard weapon of the medium artillery batteries.

This state of affairs did not last long, for the choice of 105-mm (4.13-in) calibre for a medium gun proved to be an unhappy one. In a nutshell the gun was too heavy for the weight of projectile

fired. The larger 150-mm (actually 149-mm/5.87-in) howitzers fired a much more efficient projectile over almost the same range and at no great increase in weapon weight. There was also another snag: when the K 18 entered service it was at a time when the German army had yet to become even partially mechanised, so the guns had to be pulled by horse teams: the gun was too heavy for one horse team to tackle, so the barrel and carriage had to be towed as separate loads, which was a bit much for a 105-mm gun. Later, the introduction of half-tracked tractors enabled the piece to be towed in one load, but by then the K 18 was on a very low production priority.

Upgraded version

In order to make the K 18 a more powerful weapon, the German staff planners called for an increase in range. There was no way to produce this increase without increasing the length of the barrel from the original L/52 to L/60. The first of these improved models was ready in 1941 and was known as the **10.5-cm K 18/40**, but it was not put into production until much later when the designation had been changed yet again to **10.5-cm sK 42** (*schwere Kanone*, or heavy gun). Very few were produced.

By 1941 the disadvantages of the 105-mm gun in its K 18 and later versions had been recognised, but there remained a role for them for any task in which their considerable weight and bulk would be only a relatively minor disadvantage. This task was coast defence. Weapons for Germany's Atlantic Wall defences in France, at that time still under construction, were in both great demand and short supply, so the K 18 was assigned to that relatively static role. As a coast defence weapon, the piece had a considerable advantage in its long range, even though the projectile weight was still rather low for the anti-ship role. To enable it to be used to greater advantage when firing at long

Above: A 10.5-cm K 18 stands in splendid isolation in the middle of an abandoned German field position in the Western Desert. In the background is one of the famous '88' Flak guns, giving an indication that the position was intended to be some form of strongpoint.

ranges against maritime targets, a new range of ammunition was introduced, among which was a special sea marker shell for ranging purposes.

SPECIFICATION	
10.5-cm K 18	**Elevation:** 0° to +48°
Calibre: 105 mm (4.13 in)	**Traverse:** 64°
Length of piece: 5.46 m (17 ft 11 in)	**Muzzle velocity:** 835 m (2,740 ft) per second
Weight: travelling 6434 kg (14,187 lb) and in action 5624 kg (12,400 lb)	**Range:** 19075 m (20,860 yards)
	Shell weight: 15.14 kg (33.38 lb)

Below: British infantry examine a 10.5-cm K 18, which is notable for its sheer size. In the foreground is a handspike, used to move the trail legs either for a rapid change of traverse or to join them together in preparation for a move to a new position.

15-cm schwere Feldhaubitze 18 Heavy field howitzer

Within Germany the two major artillery manufacturing concerns had been Krupp and Rheinmetall since the turn of the century. Both firms survived World War I intact, but with their usual markets shattered both decided to start again with new products. Thus for both the 1920s was a period of retrenchment and research so that by the time the Nazi party came to power in 1933 both were ready to supply their new customer. The new customer was shrewd enough to invite both parties to submit designs for every new artillery requirement made by the expanding German forces, and thus when a call was made for a new heavy field howitzer each company was ready with a suitable design.

The trouble for the army selectors was that the sub-

missions were as good as each other. Therefore, the eventual equipment was a compromise, the Rheinmetall ordnance being placed on the Krupp carriage. This selection was made in 1933 and given the designation of **15-cm schwere Feldhaubitze 18 (15-cm sFH 18)**, although the actual calibre was 149 mm (5.87 in). The howitzer quickly became the standard German heavy

Shown here in an Eastern Front camouflage scheme, the 15-cm sFH 18 was a compromise between Krupp and Rheinmetall design and became the standard German heavy field ordnance of World War II.

field howitzer and it was churned out from numerous production lines all over Germany.

sFH 18 variants

The first version of the sFH 18 was intended for horse traction and was towed in two loads, namely barrel and carriage. However, before long a version intended to be towed by a halftrack tractor was produced, and this soon became the more common version. It proved to be a sound and sturdy howitzer and served well throughout all of Germany's World War II campaigns. Once the invasion of the Soviet Union was under way in 1941, however, it soon became apparent to the Germans that the piece was

outranged by its Soviet 152-mm (6-in) equivalents. Various attempts were made to increase range, including two more powerful propellant charges to be added to the six already in use. These extra charges worked to a limited extent but caused excessive barrel wear in the process and also overstrained the carriage recoil mechanism. To overcome the latter problem some howitzers were fitted with a muzzle brake to reduce recoil forces, but this modification was no great success and the idea was dropped; weapons so modified received the designation **15-cm sFH 18(M)**.

As the war went on the sFH 18 was placed on a self-propelled carriage known

as the Hummel (bumblebee), and thus formed part of the artillery component of a few Panzer divisions. This variant is discussed separately. Not all sFH 18 weapons were used in the field role. Divisions that found themselves installed along the Atlantic Wall defences used their sFH 18s to bolster coastal defences, usually under German navy control. Some sFH 18s were handed out to some of Germany's allies, notably Italy (where the type recived the local designation **obice da 149/28**) and, for a while, Finland (as the **m/40**).

The sFH 18 was still in use in very large numbers when the war ended in 1945 and for a period the howitzers were used by many armies. Remarkably, Czechoslovakia used an updated version of the sFH 18 until relatively recently, and the type was also used by the Portuguese army for a considerable period. Some examples survived in parts of Central and South America into the 1980s, and the sFH 18 has proved to be one of the soundest and sturdiest of all German artillery pieces.

This sFH 18 is being towed into an Me 323 transport by an SdKfz 7 halftrack. The majority of German artillery was horse-drawn, but the 15-cm howitzer was modified early in the war to be towed by vehicles.

SPECIFICATION	
15-cm sFH 18	
Calibre: 149 mm (5.87 in)	**Elevation:** -3° to +45°
Length of piece: 4.44 m (14 ft 6¼ in)	**Traverse:** 60°
Weight: travelling 6304 kg (13,898 lb) and in action 5512 kg (12,152 lb)	**Muzzle velocity:** 520 m (1,706 ft) per second
	Maximum range: 13325 m (14,570 yards)
	Shell weight: 43.5 kg (95.9 lb)

15-cm Kanone 18 Heavy field gun/coastal defence gun

When a German army requirement for a heavy gun to arm the new divisional artillery batteries was made in 1933, Rheinmetall was able to land the contract. Using the same carriage as that submitted for the 15-cm sFH 18 competition, Rheinmetall designed a long and well proportioned gun with a range of no less than 24500 m (26,800 yards), which was well in excess of anything else available at the time. Production did not begin immediately for at the time priority was given to the sFH 18. It was not until 1938 that the army received its first examples as the **15-cm Kanone 18 (15-cm K 18)**.

When the German army

A 15-cm K 18 forms the centrepiece of a German artillery park captured by the British in Libya. This Rheinmetall design had an impressive range, but was dangerously time-consuming to deploy or withdraw.

began to receive the 15-cm K 18 weapon it was very impressed with the range and the projectiles, but was less than enchanted with some of the features of the carriage. One of these was the fact that as the gun was so long the gun and carriage could not be towed together except over very short distances. For any long move the barrel had to be withdrawn from the carriage and towed on its own special transporter carriage. The carriage itself was towed on its own wheels and a small limber axle carrying another two wheels. All this preparation for travel took a good deal of time, an undesirable feature when the troops needed to get the gun into and out of action rapidly, and this time was

increased by another carriage feature, the use of a two-part turntable onto which the gun was lifted to provide 360° traverse. This too had to be got into and out of action, and the carriage was equipped with ramps and winches so that even when sectionalised for towing it made up into two heavy loads.

Poor rate of fire

As if the time-consuming installation and removal drawbacks were not enough, the rate of fire of the K 18 was at best two rounds per minute. Not surprisingly, the gunners requested something better but in the interim the gun was in production and the gunners had to put up with things as they were. As things turned out, many of

the K 18s were allocated to static coastal defence batteries or garrison divisions where their relative lack of mobility was of small account. Not surprisingly, the coastal batteries soon found that the K 18 made an excellent coastal gun: its long range and the easily traversed carriage made it ideal for the role, and it was not long before special marker projectiles using red dyes were produced specially for the marking and ranging of the guns.

Production of the 15-cm K 18 ended well before the end of the war in favour of heavier weapons. However, for the guns already in the field a range of ammunition in addition to the marker shells was made available. There was a special concrete-piercing shell with a

much reduced explosive payload, and another was tailored to produce just the opposite effect, being a thin-walled shell with an increased explosive content for enhanced blast effect.

Assessment

On paper the K 18 should have been one of Rheinmetall's better designs, as it had an excellent range and fired a heavy (43-kg/94.8-lb) projectile.

However, for the gunners who had to serve this weapon it must have provided the source of a great deal of hard work. Gunners are always trained to get in and out of action as rapidly as possible, whatever weapon they are using, but the K 18 seems to have provided them with something that only hard work could turn into an acceptable battlefield weapon.

SPECIFICATION	
15-cm K 18	**Traverse:** on platform 360° and on
Calibre: 149.1 mm (5.87 in)	carriage 11°
Length of piece: 8.2 m (26 ft 10¾ in)	**Muzzle velocity:** 865 m (2,838 ft) per second
Weight: travelling 18700 kg (41,226 lb) and in action 12460 kg (27,470 lb)	**Maximum range:** 24500 m (26,800 yards)
Elevation: -2° to +43°	**Shell weight:** 43 kg (94.8 lb)

15-cm Kanone 39 Coastal defence gun/heavy field gun

The gun that became known to the Germans as the **15-cm Kanone 39** (**15-cm K 39**) came to them via a circuitous route. The gun was originally designed and produced by Krupp of Essen for one of its traditional customers, Turkey, during the late 1930s. The gun was intended to be a dual field/ coastal defence gun and so used a combination of split-trail carriage allied with what was then an innovation, namely a portable turntable onto which the gun and carriage would be hoisted to provide 360° traverse, a feature very useful in a coastal defence weapon. Two of the ordered batch had been delivered in 1939 when World War II broke out, and there was then no easy way of delivering any more to Turkey. With a war on its hands the German army decided it needed as many new field guns as possible and the design was taken into German service without modification as the 15-cm Kanone 39, and the type remained on the production lines at Essen for the German

army alone.

Thus the German army found itself with a large and useful gun that had to be transported in three loads: barrel, carriage and turntable. For most purposes the turntable was not really necessary and was only used when the gun was emplaced for coastal defence; the unit consisted of a central turntable onto which the carriage was placed, a series of outrigger struts and an outer traversing circle. The whole turntable was made of steel, and in use was anchored in place. The spread trails were secured to the outer traverse circle, and the whole gun and carriage could then be moved by using a hand crank arrangement. This platform attracted a great deal of attention from many other design teams, including the Americans who used it as the basis for the 'Kelly Mount' used with 155-mm (6.1-in) M1 guns.

The K 39 could fire conventional German ammunition, but when first introduced into service it

The 15-cm Kanone 39 was a Krupp design commissioned by Turkey. Only two examples had been supplied when war broke out and the German army adopted it instead, along with large stocks of ammunition built to Turkish specifications.

A 15-cm K 39 lies abandoned on the frozen steppes, providing a subject of interest for the columns of Soviet troops marching westwards. The K 39 was eventually withdrawn to a training role for logistic reasons. Some were emplaced in the Atlantic Wall as a coastal defence gun – the weapon's original role.

came with sizable stocks of ammunition produced for Turkish use and to Turkish specifications. This involved a three-charge system and included a high explosive shell and a semi-armour-

piercing projectile originally intended by the Turks to be used against warships. All this non-standard ammunition was gradually used up before the Germans switched to their normal ammunition types.

By that time the K 39 was no longer in use as one of the standard weapons of the German army. The full production run for the army amounted to only about 40

units, and this was understandably thought to be too awkward a number for logistical comfort. Thus the K 39s were diverted to the training role and then to the Atlantic Wall defences, where they reverted to their intended purpose. On the static Atlantic Wall sites the turntables could be carefully emplaced to best effect and the guns could use their long range to good purpose.

SPECIFICATION	
15-cm K 39	**Traverse:** on turntable 360° and on
Calibre: 149.1 mm (5.87 in)	carriage 60°
Length of piece: 8.25 m (27 ft ¾ in)	**Muzzle velocity:** 865 m (2,838 ft) per second
Weight: travelling 18282 kg (40,305 lb) and in action 12200 kg (26,896 lb)	**Maximum range:** 24700 m (27,010 yards)
Elevation: -4° to +45°	**Shell weight:** 43 kg (94.8 lb)

17-cm Kanone 18 and 21-cm Mörser 18 Heavy howitzers

When it came to artillery design in the years during both world wars, Krupp of Essen can be regarded as the virtual leaders. The company's sound approach, coupled with the thorough development of innovations, led to some of the most remarkable artillery pieces in use anywhere in their day, and one of these innovations featured on what were two of the most remarkable artillery pieces in service during World War II. This innovation was the 'double recoil' carriage on which the normal recoil forces were first taken up by the ortho-

dox recoil mechanism close to the barrel and then by the carriage sliding inside rails set on the bulk of the travelling carriage. In this way all the recoil forces were absorbed with virtually no movement relative to the ground, and firing accuracy was thus enhanced. Further improvements also ensured that the entire barrel and carriage could rest on a light firing platform that formed a pivot for easy and rapid traverse.

Krupp weapons

This double-action carriage was used mainly with two

Krupp weapons. The smaller was the **17-cm Kanone 18** (the actual calibre of which was 172.5 mm/ 6.79 in) and the larger the **21-cm Mörser 18** (the Germans often followed the continental practice of calling heavy howitzers a mortar). These two weapons were first introduced in 17-cm (6.8-in) form in 1941 and in 21-cm (8.3-in) form in 1939. Both proved to be excellent weapons and demand was such that Krupp had to delegate extra production to Hanomag at Hannover. Of the two weapons priority was at first given to the **21-cm Mrs 18**, and a wide range of special projectiles was developed for this weapon, including concrete-piercing shells. But with the advent of the **17-cm K 18** it soon became apparent that the 17-cm shells were only marginally less effective than their 21-cm equivalents, and that the 17-cm gun had a much greater range (29600 m/ 32,370 yards as opposed to 16700 m/18,270 yards). Thus in 1942 priority was given to the 17-cm K 18, production of the 21-cm Mrs 18 ceasing.

As the 8th Army advanced deeper into Tunisia, this 17-cm K 18 was captured intact and used against its Afrika Korps former owners. Longer ranged than the 21-cm Mrs 18, production facilities were devoted exclusively to the K 18 after 1942.

However, the 21-cm Mrs 18 remained in use until the end of the war, as did the 17-cm K 18 which continued to impress all who encountered it, either as recipients of the 68-kg (149.9-lb) shell or as gunners. In fact the Allies sometimes acted as gunners, for in 1944 some Allied batteries used captured 17-cm K 18s when ammunition supplies for their normal charges were disrupted by the long logistical train from Normandy to the German border. For all

their weight and bulk, both the 17-cm (6.8-in) and 21-cm pieces were fairly easy to handle. A full 360° traverse could be made by only one man, and although both pieces had to be carried in two loads the carriage was well equipped with winches and ramps to make the process of removing the barrel from the carriage a fairly light and rapid task. For short distances both weapons could be towed in one load by a heavy half-track tractor.

SPECIFICATION

17-cm K 18
Calibre: 172.5 mm (6.79 in)
Length of piece: 8.529 m (27 ft 11¾ in)
Weight: travelling 23375 kg (51,533 lb) and in action 17520 kg (38,625 lb)
Elevation: 0° to +50°
Traverse: on platform 360° and on carriage 16°
Muzzle velocity: 925 m (3,035 ft) per second
Maximum range: 29600 m (32,370 yards)
Shell weight: HE 68 kg (149.9 lb)

21-cm Mrs 18
Calibre: 210.9 mm (8.3 in)
Length of piece: 6.51 m (21 ft 4⅘ in)
Weight: travelling 22700 kg (50,045 lb) and in action 16700 kg (36,817 lb)
Elevation: 0° to +50°
Traverse: on platform 360° and on carriage 16°
Muzzle velocity: 565 m (1,854 ft) per second
Maximum range: 16700 m (18,270 yards)
Shell weight: HE 121 kg (266.8 lb)

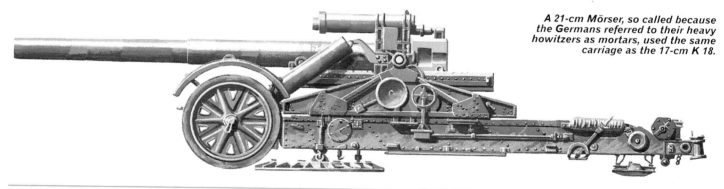

A 21-cm Mörser, so called because the Germans referred to their heavy howitzers as mortars, used the same carriage as the 17-cm K 18.

24-cm Kanone 3 and 35.5-cm Haubitze M.1

German ultra-heavy guns

During 1935 Rheinmetall began design work on a new heavy gun to meet a German army requirement for a long-range counterbattery gun firing a heavy projectile. The first example was produced during 1938, and a small batch was ordered soon after as the **24-cm Kanone 3** **(24-cm K 3)**. The K 3 was a fairly massive piece of artillery that used the 'double recoil' carriage coupled to a firing table that could be easily traversed through 360°. The barrel could be elevated to 56° and thus fired in the upper register to ensure that plunging fire against fortifications and field works would make the shells as effective as possible.

The K 3 carriage was well endowed with all manner of

technical novelties. In order to make the gun as mobile as possible the whole gun and carriage were broken down into six loads, and assembly on site was made as easy and rapid as possible by a number of built-in devices such as ramps and winches. Various safety measures were incorporated in case assembly was in some way incorrect; for instance, incorrect breech assembly left the gun unable to fire. Other safety measures ensured that if a winch cable broke the component involved could not move far enough to cause any damage. For all these measures it took some 25 men 90 minutes to get the gun into action. Once the gun was in action a generator, an integral part of the

carriage, was kept running to provide power for the gun's services. Not many K 3s were produced; most references mention eight or 10. They were all used operationally by one unit, schwere Artillerie Abteilung (mot) 83. This motorised artillery battalion had three batteries (each with two guns), and it was in action all over Europe from the USSR to Normandy.

Sabot projectiles

The K 3 was the subject of much experimentation by German designers. Special barrels were produced in order to fire experimental projectiles with body splines that aligned with the barrel rifling as the projectile was rammed into the chamber. Other barrels fired projectiles fitted

with sabots to increase range, and there was even a device fitted over the muzzle that 'squeezed' back skirts around special sub-calibre projectiles, again in an attempt to increase range. Some smooth-bore barrels were produced to fire the long-range *Peenemünder Pfeilgeschosse* (arrow shells).

By a quirk of production schedules the Rheinmetall-designed K 3 weapons were actually manufactured by Krupp of Essen. The Krupp engineers were not highly impressed by the engineering of the K 3 and decided they could do better, so producing their own version, the **24-cm K 4**. This was a very advanced design with the mounting carried on the move between two turretless

Tiger tanks. There was even supposed to be a self-propelled version, but in 1943 the prototype was destroyed during an air raid on Essen and the whole project was terminated. The K 3 was still in action when the war ended and at least one example fell into US Army hands. This was taken to the United States and underwent a great deal of investigation. Once the trials were over it went to Aberdeen Proving Grounds in Maryland, where it can still be seen.

In 1935 the German army asked Rheinmetall to produce an enlarged version of its 24-cm K 3, and although the design of that gun was still at an early stage, the Rheinmetall company went ahead and produced a new design with an actual calibre of 355.6 mm (14 in). The first example was produced ready to enter service in 1939, and emerged as a scaled-up version of the 24-cm (9.37-in) design. The new weapon was designated the **35.5-cm Haubitze M.1 (35.5-cm H M.1)** and incorporated many of the features of the 24-cm design including the double-recoil carriage. The weapon was even carried in six loads, but an extra load had to be involved for the special gantry needed to assemble and disassemble the massive weapon. This gantry used electrical power from a generator carried on the same 18-tonne halftrack tractor that towed the disassembled gantry. Other 18-tonne halftracked tractors were used to tow the other components; these were the cradle, top carriage, barrel, lower carriage, turntable and rear platform.

There appears to be no record of how long it took to get the H M.1 into action, but the time involved must have been considerable. It is known that the weapon was used by only one unit, namely 1 Batterie der Artillerie Abteilung (mot) 641. This motorised artillery battery was certainly involved in

the siege of and assault on Sevastopol, but its exact whereabouts at other times are not certain.

Manufacture

There are still a number of unknown facts regarding the service career of the H M.1. Even the exact number produced is uncertain. It is known that the weapon was manufactured by Rheinmetall at Dusseldorf, but the number completed varies from three to seven depending on the reference consulted. The projectiles fired included a 575-kg (1,267.6-lb) HE shell, and there was also a 926-kg (2,041.5-lb) concrete-piercing shell. Four charges propelled these shells. It was possible to effect 360° traverse on the carriage platform by using power jacks.

For all its weight and bulk, the range of the H M.1 was limited, so the efficiency of the weapon must have been questionable. It now seems doubtful that the considerable investment of money, manpower and equipment in a howitzer with such a range was worth the efforts involved. But the H M.1 fired a shell that must have been devastating in effect when it landed on target. Even the strongest fortification would

The career of the monstrous 35.5-cm H M.1, seen here in action on the Eastern Front, is still shrouded in mystery. Several of them were used to pulverise the Soviet fortifications at Sevastapol.

be hard put to remain operational after a few hits from such a shell, and this no doubt made the howitzer a viable weapon. But there were few such targets for the H M.1 to pulverise, and the only time that the howitzers were put to any great use was at Sevastopol. There are records of these howitzers firing 280 rounds, though they must have taken

some time to accomplish this, for the rate of fire of the

H M.1 was at best one round every four minutes.

SPECIFICATION	
24-cm K 3	**35.5-cm H M.1**
Calibre: 238 mm (9.37 in)	**Calibre:** 356.6 mm (14 in)
Length of piece: 13.104 m (42 ft 11¾ in)	**Length of piece:** 10.265 m (33 ft 8 in)
Weight: travelling (six loads) 84636 kg (186,590 lb) and in action 54000 kg (119,050 lb)	**Weight:** travelling 123500 kg (272,271 lb) and in action 78000 kg (171,960 lb)
Elevation: -1° to +56°	**Elevation:** +45° to +75°
Traverse: on turntable 360° and on carriage 6°	**Traverse:** on platform 360° and on carriage 6°
Muzzle velocity: 870 m (2,854 ft) per second	**Muzzle velocity:** 570 m (1,870 ft) per second
Maximum range: 37500 m (41,010 yards)	**Maximum range:** 20850 m (22,800 yards)
Shell weight: 152.3 kg (335.78 lb)	**Shell weight:** HE 575 kg (1,267.6 lb) and anti-concrete 926 kg (2,041.5 lb)

Obice da 210/22 modello 35 Italian heavy howitzer

During the late 1930s the Italian army decided to attempt to replace the bulk of its heavy artillery park, which by that time resembled an oversize artillery museum. It selected two good and thoroughly modern designs, one a gun with a calibre of 149 mm (5.87 in) and the other a howitzer with a calibre of 210 mm (8.26 in). The howitzer was designed by an army organisation known as the Servizio Tecnici Armi e Munizioni (STAM), but production was carried out by Ansaldo at Pozzuoli.

The howitzer was known as the **Obice da 210/22 modello 35**. Although shown in prototype form in 1935, it was not accepted for service until 1938 when a production order for no less than 346 was placed. The modello 35 was a very sound and modern design. It used a split-trail carriage with two road wheels on each side. When

the howitzer went into action these wheels were raised off the ground and the weight was assumed by a firing platform under the main axle. The entire weapon could then be traversed easily through 360° once the stakes that anchored the trail spades to the ground had been raised.

The main problem for the Italians was that having designed a first-rate howitzer they could not produce it quickly enough. Despite the good intentions of the Italian army, it had to enter the war with its antique gun park still largely undisturbed by modern equipments, and by the autumn of 1942 the grand total of modello 35s was still only 20, five of them in Italy and the rest in action in the Soviet Union. Part of this state of affairs was due to the fact that despite the requirements of the Italian army, modello 35s were sold

to Hungary as they came off the production line, no doubt in exchange for raw materials and food products. The Hungarians found it necessary to make their own carriage modifications to suit this **21-cm 39.M** to the rigours of their service and eventually set up their own **21-cm 40.M** and finally **21-cm 40a.M** production line in 1943.

Service history

In service the modello 35 was successful enough. It could be transported in two loads, but for prolonged moves it could be further broken down into four loads with an extra load for assembly equipment and accessories. The modello 35 attracted the attentions of the Germans, and when the Italians surrendered in September 1943, the Ansaldo concern was forced to continue production for German units based in

Italy made extensive use of heavy artillery in World War I, but by the 1930s these big guns were obsolete and new weapons were ordered. The 210-mm howitzer was an excellent design, but Italian industry could not produce the guns with sufficient speed.

Italy. Thus the modello 35 became the **21-cm Haubitze 520(i)** and was still in action with the Germans when the war ended.

After 1945 attempts were made by Ansaldo to sell the modello 35 on the home and

export markets. There were no takers as the home market was sated with American equipment that was freely supplied to the Italian army and war surplus equipment was widely available elsewhere.

SPECIFICATION	
Obice da 210/22	
Calibre: 210 mm (8.26 in)	**Traverse:** 75°
Length of piece: 5 m (16 ft 4¾ in)	**Muzzle velocity:** 560 m (1,837 ft) per second
Weight: travelling (two loads) 24030 kg (52,977 lb) and in action 15885 kg (35,020 lb)	**Maximum range:** 15407 m (16,850 yards)
Elevation: 0° to +70°	**Shell weight:** 101 or 133 kg (222.7 or 293.2 lb)

Most of Italy's 210-mm howitzers found their way into Hungarian hands for service on the Eastern Front. Those still in Italy at the time of the surrender were promptly manned by Germans, and made their contribution to the tenacious defence of the peninsula until 1945.

Soviet 152-mm guns Models 1910/30, 1937 and 1910/34

The 152-mm gun-howitzer M 1937 had a box-section split trail carriage, and its double tyres were filled with sponge rubber. On the move, a two-wheeled limber was secured under the trails.

When considering Soviet artillery development it is as well to remember that the Soviet artillery design teams rarely produced anything innovative. Instead they placed great emphasis upon a steady programme of development in which a new piece of ordnance was placed on an existing carriage, or in which a new carriage was allied to an existing gun or howitzer. Their continual aim was to produce an artillery piece that was as light as possible but firing as heavy a projectile as possible to as great a range as possible.

Principal types

This was particularly true of the Soviet 152-mm (6-in) heavy guns. There were three main types of these, although others existed and the earliest of them could trace its origins back to 1910. Despite its age this weapon, designated the **152-mm Pushka obr. 1910g**, was updated in 1930 to become the **152-mm Field Gun Model 1910/30**. In this form it was still in service when the Germans invaded in 1941. The Model 1910/30 was an unremarkable piece of artillery, so heavy that it had to be carried in two loads. This was considered to be too much of a disadvantage for modern use, and by 1941 the Model 1910/30 was being phased out of use. The Germans designated captured equipments **15.2-cm K 438(r)**.

In 1937 the Soviet design teams came up with a replacement. This was the **152-mm Gaubitsa-Pushka obr. 1937g (182-mm Gun-Howitzer Model 1937)** which emerged as a new and rather long gun barrel mounted on the carriage of an existing piece, the 122-mm (4.8-in) Field Gun Model 1931/37. This combination was a gun-howitzer rather than a gun, and turned out to be a very versatile and powerful weapon, known to the Germans as the **15.2-cm K 433/1(r)** in captured service.

Carriage combination

The Soviets wanted vast numbers, but the Artillery Plant Number 172 at Perm could not produce enough so another source of these gun-howitzers was sought. This turned out to be the same barrel as the Model 1937 but mounted on the carriage of an earlier 122-mm field gun, the Model 1931. This combination was known for some reason as the **152-mm Gun-Howitzer Model 1910/34** to the Soviets and as the **15.2-cm K 433/2(r)** to the Germans.

There was also one other Soviet 152-mm field gun about which little is now known. This was apparently a long 152-mm naval barrel placed on the carriage of the 203-mm (8-in) howitzers produced as a form of emergency design in 1941-42. Few details of this weapon now exist.

These two major field gun designs, the Model 1937 and the Model 1910/34, formed the mainstay of the heavy field gun batteries of the Red Army throughout the war. Later development tended to concentrate on howitzers, but the field guns proved to be very useful weapons. They were often able to outrange their German counterparts and so impressed the German gunners that they used as many captured Soviet 152-mm guns as they could lay their hands on. Many of these captured weapons were used against their former owners and as many again were diverted to the Atlantic Wall defences.

Perhaps the best indication of how good the Model

Seen here in German hands as a coastal defence piece, the Soviet 152-mm gun was a tough and reliable weapon and was produced in vast numbers. Massed batteries of heavy artillery played a vital role in driving the Germans back from Moscow to Berlin.

1937 gun-howitzer was at the time it was introduced can be seen by the fact that it was still in widespread use throughout the Cold War.

Known as the **ML-20**, it remained in service with many Soviet-influenced armies throughout the world until relatively recently.

SPECIFICATION		
Model 1937		
Calibre: 152.4 mm (6 in)	**Traverse:** 58°	
Length of piece: 4.925 m (16 ft 2 in)	**Muzzle velocity:** 655 m (2,149 ft) per second	
Weight: travelling 7930 kg (17,483 lb) and in action 7128 kg (15,715 lb)	**Maximum range:** 17265 m (18,880 yards)	
Elevation: -2° to +65°	**Shell weight:** 43.5 kg (95.9 lb)	

Soviet 152-mm howitzers Models 1909/30, 1910/30 1938 and 1943

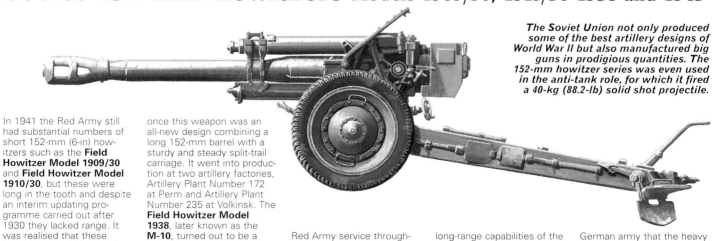

The Soviet Union not only produced some of the best artillery designs of World War II but also manufactured big guns in prodigious quantities. The 152-mm howitzer series was even used in the anti-tank role, for which it fired a 40-kg (88.2-lb) solid shot projectile.

In 1941 the Red Army still had substantial numbers of short 152-mm (6-in) howitzers such as the **Field Howitzer Model 1909/30** and **Field Howitzer Model 1910/30**, but these were long in the tooth and despite an interim updating programme carried out after 1930 they lacked range. It was realised that these howitzers would have to be replaced and in 1938 the replacement appeared. For

once this weapon was an all-new design combining a long 152-mm barrel with a sturdy and steady split-trail carriage. It went into production at two artillery factories, Artillery Plant Number 172 at Perm and Artillery Plant Number 235 at Volkinsk. The **Field Howitzer Model 1938**, later known as the **M-10**, turned out to be a great success and was widely used, later becoming one of the main types in

Red Army service throughout the war. The Red Army came to value the flexibility of the howitzer over the

long-range capabilities of the gun to a great extent, and found during the early days of the war with the invading

German army that the heavy 51.1-kg (112.6-lb) high explosive shell was also a powerful anti-tank weapon.

Anti-tank service

The use of the 152-mm howitzer in the anti-tank role derived from the Red Army practice of using every available field piece as an anti-tank weapon, and was so successful that a special solid-shot projectile was introduced for use by the Model 1938. This weighed 40 kg (88.2 lb) and could knock out any known tank. The Germans also prized the Model 1938 highly, using as many as they could capture under the designation **15.2-cm sFH 443(r)**, either in the Soviet Union or as part of the Atlantic Wall defences. More turned up in Italy and France.

In their constant striving to make their progeny as light and efficient as possible, the Soviet artillery designers later converted the Model 1938 to be mounted on the carriage of the 122-mm (4.8-in) Model 1938 howitzer. A larger muzzle brake was fitted to reduce, at least in part, the recoil forces of the heavier barrel, and the new combination became the **152-mm Field Howitzer Model 1943**. As its designation implies this new howitzer/carriage combination was first produced in 1943 and soon replaced the earlier Model 1938 in production. It continued to fire the same range of ammunition as the Model 1938 and the range capabilities remained the same. By 1945 it was in service with the Red Army in huge numbers and was later designated the **D-1**.

Post-war service

Post-war the Model 1938 and Model 1943 went on to serve in many more conflicts. Gradually the Model 1938 faded from use and it was last used in a front-line capacity by Romania, but the Model 1943 remained very much in evidence. It was still in Red Army service into the early 1980s, although only with reserve units. The weapon was bestowed the accord of being thought fit to be copied by the Chinese army, which produced its own version, known as the **Type 64**. The Model 43 was used by nearly every nation that came under Soviet influence, ranging from Czechoslovakia to Iraq and from Cuba to Vietnam. It even appeared in Ethiopia and Mozambique.

SPECIFICATION	
Model 1943	**Traverse:** 35°
Calibre: 152.5 mm (6 in)	**Muzzle velocity:** 508 m (1,667 ft) per second
Length of piece: 4.207 m (13 ft 9⅔ in)	**Maximum range:** 12400 m (13,560 yards)
Weight: travelling 3640 kg (8,025 lb) and in action 3600 kg (7,937 lb)	**Shell weight:** HE 51.1 kg (112.6 lb)
Elevation: -3° to +63.5°	

203-mm Howitzer Model 1931 Heavy howitzer

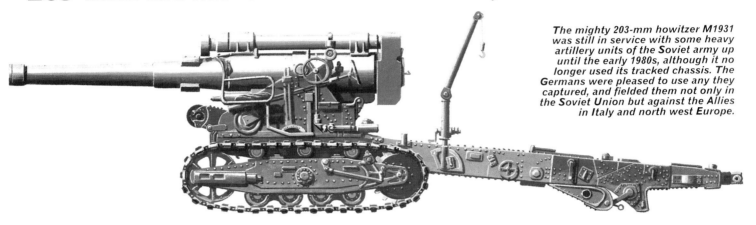

The mighty 203-mm howitzer M1931 was still in service with some heavy artillery units of the Soviet army up until the early 1980s, although it no longer used its tracked chassis. The Germans were pleased to use any they captured, and fielded them not only in the Soviet Union but against the Allies in Italy and north west Europe.

The heaviest of the field-type weapons used by the Soviets between 1941 and 1945 was the **203-mm Howitzer Model 1931**, also known as the **B-4**. This was a powerful but heavy weapon that is now generally remembered as being one of the few artillery weapons to use a carriage that ran on caterpillar tracks. This was an outcome of the huge Soviet investment in tractor factories during the 1920s and 1930s, and the use of these tractor tracks was thus an obvious and economic measure for the Soviet carriage designers to take. The use of these tracks meant that the Model 1931 could traverse very bad or soft terrain where other weapons of similar weight could not venture.

This was an important point for the Model 1931, which was a heavy piece. It was so heavy that although most versions could be towed for short distances in two loads, long moves involved the breaking down of the weapon into as many as six separate loads. Some versions could move in five loads but there were about six different variants of the Model 1931. All of them used the tracked carriage but varied in the way they were towed. Movement of the Model 1931 involved the use of a limber onto which

the split trails were lifted to be towed, usually by some form of heavy tracked tractor with (again) agricultural origins. Some of these limbers used tracks again and some had large single road wheels. Others had twin road wheels of smaller diameter.

In action

To the soldier at the front all these variations made little difference as the howitzer itself remained much the same throughout its service life. It was rather a ponderous weapon to use in action, and the rate of fire was usually limited to one round every four minutes, although higher rates could be attained. It made a powerful barrage weapon but was also used for the demolition of heavy strongpoints, a heavy 100-kg (220-lb) high explosive shell being provided for the role. But essentially it was a weapon for static use, being limited on the move to a maximum speed of no more than 15 km/h (9.3 mph). Not surprisingly, whenever mobile warfare was possible, the Model 1931 was at a disadvantage and consequently many fell into German hands as they could not be moved quickly enough. The Germans were so short of heavy artillery that they used as many as they could,

mainly in the Soviet Union but also in Italy and in north west Europe after 1944, under the designation **20.3-cm H 503(r)**.

Later service

After 1945 the Model 1931 appeared to fade from service but in later years it once again emerged. It remained part of the equipment of the Red Army heavy artillery brigades into the early 1980s, and would have been used for the destruction of strongpoints and any fortresses that it might have encountered. By this stage it had lost the tracked travelling arrangements and in their place had a new wheeled road-wheel suspen-

The heaviest Soviet gun in field use during the war, the 203-mm Howitzer Model 1931 was mounted on converted agricultural tractor tracks widely available in the Soviet Union as a result of Stalin's lopsided industrialisation programme. It fired a 100-kg (220-lb) shell to a maximum range of 18 km (11 miles).

sion with two wheels in tandem on each side. This form of carriage allowed the Model 1931 to be towed in one load. The arrival of the 203-mm 2S7 (M-1975) self-propelled gun from the mid-1970s finally rendered the Model 1931 redundant.

SPECIFICATION	
Model 1931	**Traverse:** 8°
Calibre: 203 mm (8 in)	**Muzzle velocity:** 607 m (1,991 ft) per second
Length of piece: 5.087 m (16 ft 8¼ in)	**Maximum range:** 18025 m (19,712 yards)
Weight: in action 17700 kg (39,022 lb)	**Shell weight:** 100 kg (220.46 lb)
Elevation: 0° to +60°	

4.5-in Medium Gun Mk 2 Medium artillery

By the late 1930s, British gunnery staff officers were aware that something better than existing equipments would soon be required for their medium gun regiments. It was proposed that a new 4.5-in (114-mm) gun sharing the same carriage as a proposed 5.5-in (139-mm) howitzer would be suitable, and this proposal was adopted, the required range being 20,000 yards (18290 m).

Service entry

The design phase of the gun itself was straightforward and gun production commenced during late 1940. Thanks mainly to a period of difficulty with carriage production, it was mid-1941 before the first examples were given to gunners. This was just in time for the latter phases of the North African campaigns. It was not long before the old 4.5-in Mk 1 guns were relegated to the training role back in the United Kingdom.

Apart from the ordnance, the **4.5-in Mk 2** gun (the Mark 2 differentiating it from the Mark 1, a converted 60-pdr gun with limited range performance) and 5.5-in howitzer were visually almost identical, the gun barrel of the 4.5-in gun being only marginally longer than that of the howitzer. The 4.5-in ordnance fired a 24.97-kg (55.04-lb) high-explosive projectile to 18758 m (20,513 yards), compared to the 14823 m (16,210 yards) achieved by the 5.5-in howitzer.

Limited firepower

However, there was one significant drawback to the 4.5-in projectile as far as the gunners were concerned. For various reasons its high-explosive payload was small in comparison with the projectile weight so the destructive effects on the target proved to be less than might have been wished. For this reason the 5.5-in howitzer became the preferred weapon, especially as it fired a useful 36.32-kg (80.07-lb) projectile with an excellent on-target performance. Production priorities therefore switched to the howitzer, although in-service guns continued to be employed in the important counter-battery role. The 4.5-in Mk 2 gun was not used by any other army other than the British, and

no other projectile apart from high explosive was developed for it.

The carriage of the 4.5-in Mk 2 gun had a few minor modifications from that of the howitzer to accommodate the different weight and length of the gun barrel, but it remained of the split-trail type with the barrel's muzzle preponderance balanced by two prominent equilibriator pillars. Barrel traverse was 30° right and left.

Gun handling

The equipment proved to be sturdy and largely trouble-free once a few early carriage problems had been eliminated. Handling the relatively heavy carriage by the crew of up to eight or so was greatly assisted by the balance of the equipment over its two prominent pneumatic-tyred wheels, although opening and closing the split-trail legs could be a heavy task. The gun was fired 'off its wheels', all recoil forces being absorbed by the hydro-pneumatic recoil system and two large recoil spades at the extreme ends of the trail legs.

Although the 4.5-in Mk 2 gun was withdrawn from service soon after the war ended in 1945, small numbers were retained as training weapons until at least the late 1950s, largely to consume the remaining stockpiles of 4.5-in ammunition.

A British 4.5-in gun fires on the Anzio beachhead, 17 March 1944. The shell from this mission reportedly scored a direct hit on a house that was being used by the Germans as a command post.

Right: The 4.5-in Medium Gun Mk 2 first saw combat during the closing stages of the campaign in North Africa.

Below: Normandy 1944, and the Allies advance on Tilly-sur-Seulles. Here a 4.5-in gun is seen firing in support of British infantry. A crew of up to eight was required to manhandle the 4.5-in gun carriage in action.

SPECIFICATION	
4.5-in Gun Mk 2	**Traverse:** 30°
Calibre: 114 mm (4.5 in)	**Muzzle velocity:** up to 686 m
Length of piece: 4.764 m (15.62 ft)	(2,250 ft) per second
Weight: in action 5842 kg	**Maximum range:** 18758 m
(12,879.4 lb)	(20,513.9 yards)
Elevation: -5° to +45°	**Shell weight:** 24.97 kg (55 lb)

7.2-in Howitzers Mks I-V and 6 Heavy artillery

Between the wars the British Army tended to neglect artillery, so when heavy artillery was required in 1940 all that there was to hand was a quantity of World War I 8-in (203-mm) howitzers with ranges too short for the conditions. As a stopgap it was decided to reline existing 8-in barrels to a calibre of 7.2 in (183 mm) and to develop a new range of ammunition. The original 8-in carriages were retained, with new pneumatic balloon-tyred wheels added to what became known as the **7.2-in Howitzer**.

Fearsome recoil

The new ammunition provided a useful increase in range, but when the weapon fired the full charge the recoil forces were too much for the carriage to absorb. Firing the 7.2-in howitzer on full charge was risky, for the whole equipment tended to rear up and jump backwards. Some of this unwanted motion could be partly overcome by placing behind each wheel wedge-shaped ramps, but sometimes even these were insufficient and the howitzer would jump over them. But the conversion proved to be an excellent projectile-delivery system capable of good range and accuracy, to the extent that the gunners in the field called for more.

In order to provide more, the number of 8-in howitzer conversions eventually ran to

The story of British heavy artillery after 1918 is the familiar one of inaction and neglect. When war broke out again, heavy guns had to be improvised by re-lining old 8-in howitzers to a calibre of 7.2-in to give them a respectable range.

six marks depending on the original barrel and type of conversion; some of the 8-in barrels came from the US. The first 7.2-in howitzers were used in action during the latter period of the war in North Africa and were later used following the Normandy landings.

But by 1944 numbers of 7.2-in barrels were being placed on imported

American M1 carriages. These excellent carriages proved to be just as suitable for the 7.2-in howitzer as they were for the American 155-mm (6.1-in) gun and 203-mm howitzers, and the first combination of a 7.2-in barrel with the M1 carriage was the **7.2-in Howitzer Mk V**. Few, if any such combinations were made as it was obvious that the M1

carriage was capable of carrying more than the original conversion. Thus a much longer 7.2-in barrel was placed on the M1 carriage and this was the **7.2-in Howitzer Mk 6**. The longer barrel produced a considerable range increase to 17985 m (19,667 yards) and the carriage was much more stable than the old 8-in carriage. As more M1 carriages

became available they were used to mount the new Mk 6 barrels, and by the end of 1944 there were few of the original 8-in carriages left. With the increased stability came increased accuracy, and the Mk 6 howitzer gained an enviable reputation for good shooting, to the extent that they were retained for many years after the end of the war in 1945.

SPECIFICATION	
7.2-in Howitzer Mks I-V	**Traverse:** 0
Calibre: 183 mm (7.2 in)	**Muzzle velocity:** 518 m (1,700 ft)
Length of piece: 4.343 m	per second
(14 ft 3 in)	**Maximum range:** 15453 m
Weight: in action 10387 kg	(16,900 yards)
(22,900 lb)	**Shell weight:** 91.6 kg (202 lb)
Elevation: 0° to +45°	

The 7.2-in howitzer could be as terrifying to its crew as to the target. Seen here in action at Routot, France, in September 1944, the 10-ton gun leaps into the air after firing at full charge. Surprisingly for such a makeshift design, the 7.2-in proved fairly efficient.

240-mm Howitzer M1 Heavy artillery

In 1939 the US Army resurrected a joint project for a 203-mm gun/240-mm howitzer on a common carriage that had been first suggested in 1919. The first 203-mm (8-in) guns were not issued until 1944, but the 240-mm (9.4-in) howitzer was less problematic and was ready by May 1943. This **240-mm Howitzer M1** was a fairly massive piece of artillery using what was virtually an enlarged M1 carriage as used on the 155-mm (6.1-in) Gun M1. But the 240-mm howitzer carriage did not travel with barrel fitted, instead it travelled on a six-wheeled carriage and once on site its wheels were removed. The barrel was towed on a form of semi-trailer. At the chosen site the carriage was emplaced and a pit was dug to permit barrel recoil at full elevation. The barrel was then lifted into position, usually by a mobile crane that was also used to place the carriage into position and spread the trails.

Once in place the howitzer proved to be a powerful weapon and was used whenever the fighting settled down behind static lines for

Weighing over 30 tons, the US 240-mm howitzer originated from a project begun after World War I, but little progress had been made before 1940, and America had been at war 18 months before the 240-mm weapon was ready. However, once in action it proved very useful against German emplacements in Italy and north-west Europe

any time. There was little call for the type to be employed whenever fighting was fluid as it took too long to emplace the weapons or get them out of action, but when they were used the heavy 163.3-kg (360-lb) high-explosive shells were devastating weapons. The howitzers

were used by both the US and British armies, and served into the 1950s.

A 240-mm howitzer prepared for action: it travelled on a six-wheel carriage, which was emplaced over a pit dug to absorb the recoil.

SPECIFICATION	
240-mm Howitzer M1	**Traverse:** 45°
Calibre: 240 mm (9.4 in)	**Muzzle velocity:** 701 m (2,300 ft)
Length of piece: 8.407 m (27 ft	per second
7 in)	**Maximum range:** 23093 m
Weight: complete 29268 kg	(25,255 yards)
(64,525 lb)	**Shell weight:** 163.3 kg (360 lb)
Elevation: +15° to +65°	

155-mm Gun M1 Heavy gun

When the US entered World War I in April 1917 its army was ill-equipped with heavy artillery, and as a result received various types of Allied artillery, including the French 155-mm (6.1-in) GPF (Grand Puissance Filloux). This was one of the best guns of its type at that time, but in the years after 1918 American artillery designers sought to improve the overall efficiency of the gun and carriage by introducing a series of prototypes throughout the 1920s. Sometimes this programme stood in abeyance for years, but by the late 1930s the new design (very basically the original GPF barrel equipped to accommodate an Asbury breech mechanism) was accepted for standardisation as the **155-mm Gun M1 on Carriage M1**, and production of this 6.1-in weapon started at a steady pace at several American arsenals.

The M1 gun and carriage combination was very much an overall improvement on the French GPF design, but introduced some new features. The barrel was an L/45 unit, and the carriage was of a heavy split-trail type carried on four double-tyred road wheels forward. This carriage arrangement meant that in action the wheels were lifted to allow the carriage to rest on a forward-firing platform: in use this proved to be an excellent arrangement offering great stability. This made the gun very accurate, and eventually the carriage was adopted by the British for use with their 7.2-in (183-mm) howitzer. For towing, the trail legs were hitched up onto a limber

device. There were two of these, the M2 and the M5, the latter having a rapid up-and-over lift arrangement that permitted quick use in action but which could also be dangerous to an untrained crew. For this reason the M2 limber was often preferred.

Improved models

The M1 was gradually developed into an **M1A1** form and then, late in 1944, into the **M2**. The changes were limited mainly to production expedients and did not affect the gun's performance, which proved to be excellent: a 43.1-kg (95-lb) shell could be fired to a range of 23220 m (25,395 yards).

The M1 soon became one of the standard heavy guns of the US Army, and its combination of accuracy and range meant that it was often used for counter-battery work. Numbers of the guns were issued to Allied nations, and the M1 was soon part of the British Army gun park, seeing

active service in Europe from the time of the June 1944 Normandy landings onward.

The M1 also went self-propelled. This was carried out using a much-modified M4A3E8 Sherman tank chassis with the gun mounted in an open super-structure, and in this form the vehicle/gun combination was known as the **M40**. It was 1945 before the M40 entered production, so its main career was post-war but it was widely used by many nations, again including the UK.

Revised designation

After 1945 the US Army underwent a period of internal reorganisation and in the process the M1 and M2 guns became the **M59**. The post-war period also saw the end of the limber devices after it was discovered that, with most of the heavy tractors then in service, all that was needed was to join the trails and connect them direct to the tractor towing eye, usually with chains. In this form the 155-mm (6.1-in) M59 served on into the 1990s with many armies around the world, and is still in limited service as it is considered to be a good gun, albeit a piece of ordnance rather lacking in range and range flexibility as a result of its use of fixed charges.

The gunner covers his ears as his 155-mm (6.1-in) 'Long Tom' gun blasts off a round against Japanese artillery positions in the hills beyond Dulag on the Filipino island of Leyte during 1944. Its long range made the M1 an excellent counter-battery weapon.

A 155-mm (6.1-in) 'Long Tom' gun fires in the Nettune area of the Allied 5th Army's Anzio beach head in Italy during the first part of 1944. Longer-range weapons such as the M1 gun were vital in such campaigns to keep the Germans from swamping the beach head.

SPECIFICATION	
155-mm Gun M1A1	**Elevation:** -2° to +65°
Calibre: 155 mm (6.1 in)	**Traverse:** 60°
Length of piece: 7.366 m (24 ft 2 in)	**Muzzle velocity:** 853 m (2,800 ft) per second
Weight: travelling 13880 kg (30,600 lb) and in action 12600 kg (27,778 lb)	**Maximum range:** 23221 m (25.395 yards)
	Shell weight: 42 kg (92.6 lb)

The 155-mm (6.1-in) M1 gun in travelling mode, trails together and connected to the limber. Still used by more than a dozen countries into the 1980s, it was served by a 14-man crew and could maintain a rate of fire of two rounds per minute.

8-in Howitzer M1 Heavy howitzer

In addition to receiving the French 155-mm (6.1-in) gun, the US Army in France received during 1918 the British 8-in (203-in) howitzer, which was subsequently used as the basis for post-war US heavy howitzer design. The M1 howitzer resulted from years of intermittent, underfunded research and was not standardised until 1940. Once in action, however, it was an impressive piece. Accurate and hard-hitting, it is still in extensive service, and was developed into the M110 self-propelled equipment.

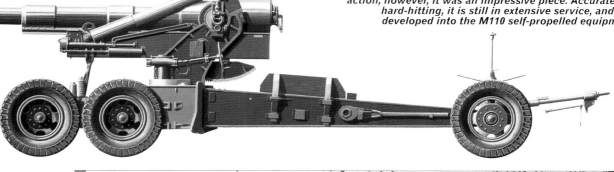

After the US entry into World War I, among the various types of heavy artillery its army received in France were the British 8-in Howitzer Mks VII and VIII, which were incidentally being produced in the US to a British order. The US Army took to this howitzer with a will, for it soon discovered that it was a very accurate weapon. In the years after 1918 the army set about producing its own version. This was under the aegis of an advisory body known as the Westervelt Board, which also recommended the introduction of the 155-mm Gun M1. The board also recommended that the 155-mm (6.1-in) gun and the 203-mm (8-in) howitzer should share the same carriage, and thus the new howitzer used the same M1 carriage as the 155-mm Gun M1.

Slow development

Despite the recommendations of the Westervelt Board, however, the development of the new howitzer was slow and erratic, and at times ceased altogether for years on end. So it was 1940 before the howitzer was standardised as the **8-in Howitzer M1**. This owed much to its British origins, but was longer, and as it used the M1 carriage it was still more accurate than its predecessor. It should not be thought, however, that because the 8-in Howitzer M1 and the 155-mm Gun M1 shared the same carriage that the two barrels were readily interchangeable: an exchange of the two barrels involved a

great deal of workshop time and a great deal of trouble.

Once the powerful Howitzer M1 had been introduced to service, it quickly became a very popular weapon. Its accuracy allowed it to be used to bring down heavy fire on spot targets quite close to friendly troops, and it was frequently used thus to destroy strongpoints and bunkers. The shell fired by the M1 was initially a 90.7-kg (200-lb) high explosive shell also used by 203-mm (8-in) coast guns, but this was later replaced by a special HE shell known as the M106, which had the same weight as the earlier shell but could be fired to a range of 16596 m (18,150 yards). The M106 is still in service with the Howitzer M1 which, in a

post-war designation reshuffle, became the **M115**.

Like the 155-mm Gun M1, the Howitzer M1 also went self-propelled, although the first version did not appear until 1946. This was the **M43** which used a much-modified M4A3E8 tank chassis as the carrier. Subsequent development along these lines led to the M110 series which originally used the 8-in howitzer in a form virtually unchanged from its towed version but which was then developed to the M110A2 using a much lengthened howitzer.

The M115 towed howitzer is still in widespread service with eight armies. Thus the 8-in howitzer can lay claim to being one of the longest-lived of all modern heavy artillery pieces: tracing its origins back to World War I, it is still in service.

Left: The blast effect of an 8-in (203-mm) howitzer firing hits not just the ears but the whole body as the shock wave passes outward. This is the first 8-in howitzer in action in Normandy during 1944, firing during the barrage the Americans organised for Independence Day on 4 July.

Above: Driving through the bitter December 1944 weather of western Europe, these 8-in (203-mm) howitzers are travelling through Belgium to join the US 1st Army. Artillery was particularly effective in areas like the Ardennes, where roads were few and chokepoints obvious.

Above: A view of the interrupted-screw breech mechanism of an 8-in (203-mm) howitzer in action. Four crew members prepare to lift the 90.7-kg (200-lb) shell, whose size gives some clue as to why the maximum rate of fire was just one round per minute.

SPECIFICATION	
8-in Howitzer M 1	**Elevation:** -2° to +65°
Calibre: 203 mm (8 in)	**Traverse:** 60°
Length of piece: 5.324 m	**Muzzle velocity:** 594 m (1,950 ft)
(17 ft 5.6 in)	per second
Weights: travelling 14515 kg	**Maximum range:** 16595 m
(32,000 lb) and in action 13471 kg	(18,150 yards)
(29,698 lb)	**Shell weight:** 90.7 kg (200 lb)

Canon de 240 sur affut-truc Modèle 93/96 Railway gun

When the French army decided to adopt railway guns during World War I it used a large number of 240-mm (9.45-in) barrels culled from all manner of places, but when it decided to use the Modèle 93/96 coastal defence gun for the role it soon found that such a relatively modern and powerful gun had to have a more complex type of carriage than the more hasty improvisations produced to suit the less powerful weapons of the same calibre. Consequently the Modèle 93/96 guns were placed on well platforms mounted fore and aft on six-axle bogies with an arrangement that allowed the gun platform to be lowered onto the track for the firing proper. On the move the **Canon de 240 sur affut-truc Modèle 93/96** gun and carriage was dismantled into three main sections.

Up to 1918 the Modèle 93/96 was used for a variety of purposes, ranging from long-range counter-bombardment close to the trench lines to acting as a mobile reserve for coast defence. After 1918 most of the remaining equipments were diverted almost entirely to the coast-defence roles, in which they generally remained at various central depots for long periods at a time with little practice firing and often very little maintenance. In 1939 that changed and the surviving guns were quickly renovated and new crews were trained so that by the time the Germans invaded France several guns in good condition were ready for the Germans to take over after the fall of France.

German service

With the Germans the Modèle 93/96 started a new career, this time as the **24-cm Kanone (E) 558(f)** or **24-cm Kanone (E) Modell 93/96(f)**. For a while they were retained as railway guns to equip a few training units, but by 1943 most of these had been scrapped or diverted for use as coastal defence guns. In this role the guns were completely removed from their railway mountings altogether. They were emplaced on fixed turntables that were securely based in concrete foundations, and once in place there they stayed. By late 1943 only eight of these guns were still in full-time use although some others were kept in reserve at various points. Of these eight, four were emplaced near the important U-boat port of St Nazaire, two at La Bats and the other two at Prefailles.

Narvik defence

The remaining four guns were sent off on a long foray to Norway, where all four were emplaced at Ofoten near the important naval base at Narvik. So far as is known none of these guns ever had to fire a shot in anger, and as soon as the war was over they were scrapped. However, it now seems that the Norwegians, not wanting to see good guns go to waste in 1945, kept the four at Ofoten in service for some years and it is far from certain that they were ever removed. It may well be that the old French guns remained there, though Norwegian security sensitivities make any confirmation of this very difficult to determine.

A characteristic of many French railway guns dating from World War I is that the gun and carriage were separated while travelling. Here a Canon de 240 Modèle 1903 is shown.

Incidentally, Schneider produced a 240-mm (9.45-in) railway gun with an L/51 barrel in 1928 and sold it to Japan. It was still around in 1941 but what subsequent use was made of it is now not known and no records survive of it being used in any action.

SPECIFICATION	
Canon de 240 sur affut-truc Modèle 93/96	(308,640 lb)
Precise calibre: 240 mm (9.45 in)	**Weight of shell:** 162 kg (357 lb) high explosive
Length of barrel: 9.6 m (31 ft 6 in)	**Range:** 22700 m (24,825 yards)
Weight complete: 140000 kg	

The Canon de 240 sur affut-truc Modèle 93/96 in travelling configuration. These guns, formerly coast defence weapons, needed a more complex mount than less powerful weapons of the same calibre.

French 320-mm railway guns

When the French army started to produce large numbers of railway guns during World War I it used a large number of what had been considered obsolete naval guns or odd items from the manufacturers' stockpiles. Among these were guns with calibres of 274 mm and 285 mm (10.79 in and 11.22 in), some of which were still in use during the early days of World War II. A number passed into German service for a while, but generally speaking they were mainly 'one-offs' of limited military value so they were often used for training or else scrapped – their limited stocks of ammunition were used as land mines and roll-bombs to bolster beach and coastal defences.

However, the next calibre up the French scale was 320 mm (12.6 in), and here there were several models of guns pressed into action, nearly all of naval origins. All of them dated originally from 1870 but to complicate matters nearly every barrel had been provided with an updating programme in different years thereafter and consequently no two barrels were exactly alike. For instance there were the **Modèle 70/80**, the **Modèle 70/84** and the **Modèle 70/93**. To make things even more complicated, the last model had an elongated chamber to accommodate a larger charge introduced to boost performance, so it was non-standard to the others. In addition, the same carriage, which had a sliding platform to absorb the considerable degree of recoil produced on firing, was also used to mount a

A 320-m 70/93 being taken into action in 1939 by French army troops, who are apparently not expecting air attack. After the fall of France these weapons were used by the Germans for coastal defence.

much more modern gun, based on the Modèle 1870 series but manufactured in 1917 especially for the railway role. This was the **Canon de 320 T 17**, which transformed the elderly Modèle 1870 into a good modern weapon with a useful range. Nearly all these guns, being naval in origin, used an interrupted screw thread, opened and closed by a worm-gear cranking system, and, being originally intended for use in turrets, guns were not uncommonly found with their breech blocks opening to either the right or the left. With the fall of France in 1940 the

various 320-mm (12.6-in) railway guns fell into German hands.

In enemy hands

In fact so many were captured intact and in good working order that the Germans took them into their own service. The old Modèle 1870 series of guns became the **32-cm Kanone (E) 651(f)**, with a special **32-cm Kanone (E) 651/1(f)** designation to denote the guns with the enlarged chambers and thus a special ammunition supply arrangement. The more modern 1917 guns became the **32-cm Kanone (E) 652(f)**.

These railway guns spent the remaining years of the war being trundled around the French coastlines and were used on occasion as propaganda weapons when they were towed through some of the major French cities in dramatic shows of force.

At least one was based in the south of France. The weapons appear to have made little impression during the invasions of the Normandy coast or the south of France (both in 1944) and many of them were later captured in a wrecked condition.

The Canon de 320 T 17 showing its overhead gantry for ammunition handling. Sharing the same carriages as much older designs dating from the previous century, the Modèle 1917 was derived from naval designs.

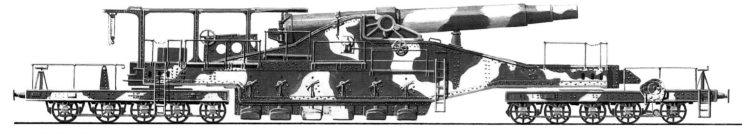

French 340-mm railway guns

As with the French 320-mm (12.6-in) railway guns, there was more than one type of 340-mm (13.4-in) gun converted to the railway gun role, usually from barrels that were either naval in origin or design. To complicate matters further, there were two types of carriage in use for a single barrel type, the **Modèle 1912**.

The first type of mounting that should be considered is the sliding mount. This was a simple concept in which the central section of the gun carriage was either lowered onto the railway tracks or chocked into place on them in such a way that the recoil forces were absorbed by the carriage sliding along the track, which was usually not very far in view of the large weights and masses involved. While being simple to design, produce and use, this type of carriage had the disadvantage that there was no form of traverse control, the gun being trained by its accurate positioning on the curve of a railway track. As the gun had to be winched or pushed back into a carefully surveyed point on the track after every shot, the rate of fire was very slow and the whole system was most laborious. However, the gun and carriage combination was produced in a very short time by Schneider et Cie of Le Creusot and the type was still used in 1939.

The 340-mm (13.4-in) barrels used originally had a form of rifling that limited the potential power of the guns and the rifling was subsequently altered to capitalise on this potential. However,

this considerably increased the stresses produced on firing, to the extent that a new type of carriage had to be evolved. This new carriage had a cradle type of gun barrel support that enabled recoil cylinders and recuperators to be used to absorb the increased firing stresses. This new carriage was produced by the St Chamond concern, but even as it was entering service Schneider was still producing the original sliding mounts for the unaltered barrels. Thus there emerged a quartermaster's nightmare in the form of variable guns, carriages and their ammunition, all in service at the same time. At one point there were four different types of gun variation in use at one time on the sliding mounts alone.

Wartime service

With the coming of peace in 1918 many of these supply difficulties were resolved by a rationalisation of types in service. None of the 340-mm (13.4-in) guns remaining saw much use between the wars, but in 1940 many were still available to fall into German hands. Nearly all of them entered German army service either as fully operational guns based in France or kept to provide spare parts for others. Four had a special destination. These were known to the Germans as the **34-cm Kanone-W-(E) 674(f)**, with

This Schneider Modèle 1912 railway gun was captured by the German Army in 1940 and used for coastal defence.

the W (*Wiege*, or cradle) denoting that the guns were of the cradle-carriage pattern. These four were removed from their railway carriages and transported by road to a coastal defence site at Plouharnel in Brittany. Once emplaced they stayed here until they were removed for scrap after the war.

Seen in 1918, this Schneider Modèle 1912 railway gun has been dismounted from its carriage onto a turntable and extensively camouflaged.

15-cm and 17-cm Kanonen (Eisenbahn) Railway guns

The **15-cm Kanone (Eisenbahn)** and **17-cm Kanone (Eisenbahn)** railway guns were direct results of the 1936 *Sofort-Program* (emergency programme) to produce new railway gun equipments in a very short time. As with the other results of this programme, the guns were produced by placing old, stockpiled Krupp barrels onto new carriages. The 15-cm (5.9-in) and 17-cm (6.7-in) barrels were elderly ex-naval U40 weapons. The carriage, however, was a modern piece of engineering that enabled the relatively light barrels and their mountings to traverse through 360°. When the equipments were emplaced,

much of the recoil stresses produced when the gun was fired were taken up by outriggers with jacks on each side of the railway mounting. These outriggers hinged upwards when not in use.

Railway carriages

The carriages for these guns were the same – long and flat railway cars with multiple bogies at each end. The gun itself was mounted on a large platform, mounted in turn on a heavy turntable. Some of the 15-cm guns had most of the firing platform and gun in an armoured turret.

The first 15-cm equipments were delivered in 1937 and they immediately went into full-scale service,

even though only four were eventually produced. The main reason for this short production run was that the design was too expensive for the calibre involved. The 15-cm calibre was used by the bulk of the German army's corps artillery, while the railway guns were intended for use at a higher level and thus had to be heavier to justify the effort involved. In the short term the problem was partially resolved by using 17-cm ex-naval barrels, but even then the calibre was too light for the expense of a railway carriage mounting. Eventually, only six 17-cm railway guns were produced between 1937 and 1938, and the production run then came to an end.

Operational service

The 15-cm and 17-cm railway guns produced were all initially issued to army batteries but the 15-cm equipments later passed to the navy when they became **'Batterie Gneisenad'**, a title that was kept when the guns once more came under army control; the original battery title was **Eisenbahn-batterie 655**. The 17-cm guns were used by two batteries, Eisenbahnbatterien 717 and 718. In service, these guns had very varied careers. When they were first introduced they spent a lot of time being pulled around the Reich on propaganda tours, the guns being openly deployed in marshalling yards and sidings on public show; by this measure the 10 guns appeared to be available in greater numbers than they were.

However, with the com-

This battery of 17-cm Kanonen (Eisenbahn) was captured in Holland in 1945. An outrigger leg can be seen in its folded position in the foreground.

ing of war the guns settled down to a more mundane routine. They had little to do before 1940, when they were used to bolster coastal defences along the captured French coast, and later some of them were incorporated into the formal coastal defences north of the Pas de Calais and along the Belgian and Dutch coasts. The batteries were frequently moved. In 1945 some of the guns were still in service, but their light calibre and vulnerability to air attack and counter-battery fire rendered them of little practical use.

SPECIFICATION	
15-cm K (E)	
Nominal calibre: 15 cm (5.9 in)	**Weight complete:** 74000 kg (163,140 lb)
Precise calibre: 149 mm (5.87 in)	**Weight of shell:** 43 or 52.5 kg (95 or 116 lb)
Length of barrel: 5.57 m (18 ft 3⅓ in)	**Range:** 22500 m (24,605 yards)

SPECIFICATION	
17-cm K (E)	
Nominal calibre: 17 cm (6.7 in)	**Weight complete:** 80000 kg (176,365 lb)
Precise calibre: 172.6 mm (6.8 in)	**Weight of shell:** 62.8 kg (138 lb)
Length of barrel: 6.90 m (22 ft 7⅓ in)	**Range:** 26100 m (28,545 yards)

In service, it soon became clear that the time and effort taken to place a 15-cm barrel onto a large and heavy carriage was not worth the ballistic results actually achieved. These are shown in France in 1941.

21-cm Kanone 12 (Eisenbahn) Experimental railway gun

In many ways the **21-cm Kanone 12 (Eisenbahn)** was not so much an operational gun but a full-scale exercise in internal and external ballistics. The weapon had its origins in the infamous 'Paris Gun' of 1918, used to bombard Paris at ranges of up to 116 km (72 miles), but at a very slow rate of fire. What really caused the introduction of the **21-cm K 12 (E)**, however, was the fact that the Paris Gun had been a German navy project. This severely irritated the German artillery arm, to the extent that it felt that it should have a comparable weapon to match the performance of the Paris Gun, or even better it. The end of the war in November 1918 stopped that idea temporarily, but the inter-war years were spent in working out all the many and varied

mathematical problems involved in long-range gun design, to the extent that by 1935, some laboratory tests could be undertaken.

Early tests

The first tests were carried out with a 105-mm (4.13-in) test barrel, demonstrating that one way to avoid the excessive wear attendant on using large propellant charges and long barrels to produce long ranges was to fit the projectile with machined splines that fitted into the rifling of the barrel. Following on from these tests, a 21-cm (8.3-in) barrel was produced in 1937, but this barrel introduced its own problems. One was that it was so long that special bracing struts had to be

built around much of its length to prevent it from bending under its own weight. The full length was L/158 (the barrel was 158 times as long as its calibre, resulting in a length of 33.34 m/109 ft 4½ in). The carriage designed to mount so long a barrel had its own problems, one of which was that to balance the barrel the pivots had to be placed so that when the gun recoiled it would strike the ground unless a pit had been made.

'Secret weapon'

The K 12 (E) provided its designers with a great deal of practical experience in long-range gunnery and ballistics, but the German army was not so certain of the value of the weapon.

The 21-cm K 12 (E) was designed to fire over distances of about 115 km (71.5 miles). Its only major use was to shell the coast of Kent, with little real effect.

SPECIFICATION	
21-cm K 12 (E)	**Weight complete:** 309000 kg
Precise calibre: 21 cm (8¼ in)	(681,215 lb)
Length of barrel: 33.34 m (109 ft 4¼ in)	**Weight of shell:** 107.5 kg (237 lb)
	Range: about 115 km (71.5 miles)

As the Allies won the upper hand, large weapons like the 21-cm K 12 (E) became increasingly vulnerable. The 21-cm K 12 (E) was of limited operational value.

However, in 1938 it entered service and was kept under wraps as a form of 'secret weapon'. Tests showed that its maximum range was of the order of 120 km (75 miles), but that the wear problem the splined ammunition was supposed to alleviate only attenuated the problem, to the extent that barrel life was about 90 rounds.

In 1940 the K 12 (E) went into action from the Pas de Calais area, when it fired a few projectiles at Kent across the English Channel. The farthest-reaching of

these projectiles is recorded as having been fired at Rainham, a distance of about 88 km (55 miles) from the gun, but others probably went unnoticed for the 21-cm shell carried only a small payload of explosive. In fact the payload was too small for all the cost and effort involved, and the gun was an operational failure.

Ballistic data

Nevertheless, a new design to overcome many of the original carriage shortcomings was developed. The new carriage had an elevating device that raised the barrel level on firing so that the breech would not strike the ground. Only one of these guns was in use at any one time, in the charge

of Eisenbahnbatterie 701. This unit trundled its huge charge up and down the coast of occupied Europe between the Pas de Calais and Holland. Now and again it fired a round, mainly for experimental purposes, but there were few opportunities to make any use of its extreme range and the second gun was captured in the

Netherlands during the Allied advances of 1945. The cost and manpower investment in the 21-cm K 12 (E) were enormous, and the weapons achieved little other than providing a mass of ballistic data that was soon to be rendered academic by the advent of the guided missile and high-speed aircraft.

28-cm Kanone 5 (Eisenbahn) Railway gun

Whereas the *Sofort-Program* weapons were based on existing barrels and carriage drawings, the **28-cm Kanone 5 (Eisenbahn)** was designed from scratch from 1934. Drawing extensively from the earlier decade of theoretical research, the Krupp designers drew up plans for a well-balanced design with a good operational range and firing a large projectile with a useful payload. After a period of test firing with 15-cm sub-calibre models, production went ahead for a series of railway guns that became known as the **28-cm K 5 (E)**, a design that was to emerge as one of the finest railway guns ever, the **schlanke Bertha** (slim Bertha).

K 5 (E) into service

The first K 5 (E)s entered service in 1936, and the type remained in production until 1945. The final number produced is now uncertain, but it is believed that between 25 and 28 were built. In almost every way the K 5 (E) was a sound, thorough design with a 'clean' carriage, extensive ammunition handling equipment, and a long slender barrel that provided the gun with its nickname. By February 1940 eight were in service. But soon thereafter came a

series of unexplained barrel failures. A series of trials and experiments then began, and during the course of these a barrel with shallower grooves was produced. This barrel proved to be entirely satisfactory, so it was adopted for subsequent production and the troubles disappeared. Production went ahead at full speed, for the K 5 (E) proved to be so good that demands came from all fronts for more.

Along with the demands came various modifications to the detail design. For the German artillery design staffs no design was ever considered perfect, and a variety of minor changes were introduced to try out new ideas and to improve performance. One of these ideas involved a muzzle brake, and in another experiment the traditional German horizontal-action breech mechanism was replaced by a screw-type breech block.

The ammunition was prone to all manner of experimentation but one trial that later led to service adoption was the introduction of a rocket-boosted projectile that allowed the rocket motor to fire just when the normal momentum was dropping away. This enabled very long ranges to be achieved, but

only at the cost of very poor accuracy as a result of the inherent unreliability of the rocket motor 'burn'; moreover, only a small explosive payload could be carried. Once again, German technical ingenuity was unmatched by operational success.

K 5 Glatt

One complete K 5 (E) was produced with a smooth barrel to become the **K 5 Glatt** (smooth). This conversion was intended to fire the long-range Peenemünde Pfiel Geschoss (Peenemünde arrow shell) and a series of seven of the variant was ordered. Apparently only two were made by the time the war ended but both were used operationally to fire at Maastricht from a base near Bonn during 1945. Another idea mooted for the K 5 (E) was the ability for the gun and the main carriage section to be carried between two turretless Tiger tanks across country. This project was intended to provide the gun with mobility without railways, but the idea got no further than the model stage even though full development was planned.

In service, the 28-cm (11-in) K 5 (E) proved to be a formidable weapon and it was widely used on all

One of the finest artillery pieces ever built, the K 5 (E) saw a great deal of combat action. A K 5 shot was typically accompanied by a giant muzzle flash.

fronts. On the Atlantic Wall the type was used by the German navy for coastal defence duties, including some cross-Channel shelling against Dover, and in some locations, special protected hangars were constructed to protect the guns and their carriages. Two guns from a special railway artillery regiment were in action during the siege of Leningrad and more were used during the early stages of the massive battles around Stalingrad. There were plans to take at

least one to Tunisia during the last stages of the campaign there but that came to nothing; the guns intended for North Africa remained in Italy instead, subsequently taking part in the Anzio battles. Wherever the German army fought, there was usually a K 5 (E) involved, and the special railway trains pulling one or two guns along with all their special ammunition wagons and accommodation carriages were seen all over occupied Europe.

SPECIFICATION	
28-cm Kanone 5 (E)	**Weight complete:** 218000 kg
Precise calibre: 28.3 cm (11 in)	(480,600 lb)
Length of barrel: 21.54 m (70 ft 8 in)	**Weight of shell:** 255 kg (562 lb)
	Range: 62400 m (68,240 yards)

Here, a K 5 (E) is shown in a possible firing position, although much greater elevations were obtainable. A pair of these weapons caused considerable damage to the Anzio beachhead over a period of some four months.

80-cm Kanone (Eisenbahn) 'Schwere Gustav' Railway gun

The largest gun ever built had an operational career of just 13 days, during which it fired a total of 48 shells. It took 25 trainloads of equipment and 2,000 men up to six weeks to assemble and fire. It seems highly unlikely that such a weapon will ever be seen again.

Above: 'Gustav' fired its last five operational shells on 17 June 1942. The target was Sevastopol's Fort Maxim Gorky and its attendant coastal battery.

Right: The 80-cm Kanone (Eisenbahn) (K (E)) (railway cannon) moves ponderously around the corner of its firing traverse at Bakhchisaray, the village from which it bombarded Sevastopol.

King of all Hitler's railway guns, the leviathan christened **'schwere Gustav'** (heavy Gustav) was inspired by the Führer. It was one of Hitler's greatest follies and was a monumental waste of precious resources.

Krupp's engineers set to work in 1937, but it took three years before the first barrel was ready to be test fired, and another two before a complete weapon could be assembled. By the time it was ready in 1942, the gun's original target – the Maginot Line – was rusting far behind German lines. But there were other targets. The British fortress at Gibraltar was one, but the Spanish dictator Franco refused to join Hitler in an attack.

Target Sevastopol

Sevastopol, the Russian naval base on the Black Sea was another. This town was under siege and the commander of the German 11th Army, Generaloberst von Manstein, was in a hurry. Already supported by a formidable concentration of bombers, Manstein had amassed a siege train including the 60-cm self-propelled mortar 'Thor'. Now, in 25 train-loads, 'Gustav' was shipped to join him.

'Gustav' was assembled with the aid of two 110-ton cranes. It took six weeks to lay the track and assemble the weapon. At last, on 5 June 1942, 'Gustav' fired its first shots in anger. The targets were coastal batteries that protected the Russian fortress. The fall of shot was reported by an artillery spotter aircraft. Eight rounds later, the fort was silent.

Two types of shell were used: a 7-ton armour-piercing round designed to smash through concrete, and a 5-ton high explosive round.

Plunging fire

The next day 'Gustav' turned its attention on Fort Molotov. That took seven rounds to destroy, and left time to attack an especially challenging target: the underground (and underwater) magazine dug beneath Sevastopol and out under Severnaya Bay. Nine rounds were fired, travelling some 25 km (15.50 miles) before plunging

Left: A round is rammed into the barrel of the 'Gustav'. The size of a destroyer, it took a battleship's crew of 1,500 men to assemble the gun and, in operation, required a crew of 500.

Gun mount
There was little design innovation in the 80-cm K (E). The gun tube was mounted in a huge cradle, which was slung between the two main carriage sections.

Bogies
The 80-cm gun was mounted on four huge rail bogies. These ran on parallel tracks in pairs, with each pair locked together to form a double unit.

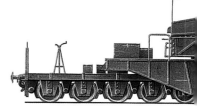

*Above: Assembling the 80-cm **K (E)** was a huge task. More than a kilometre of double track had to be built in a specially-dug railway cutting. Then two massive gantry cranes, used to assemble the gun, were constructed. The whole process took up to six weeks. For the amount of resources that it required, the gun gave little return.*

Above: Two powerful ammunition hoists were used on the 80-cm gun. The one on the left lifted the projectile; the one on the right moved the propellant. Two light anti-aircraft defence battalions always accompanied the 'schwere Gustav' in the field, to ward off enemy air attacks and reconnaissance aircraft.

SPECIFICATION	
80-cm Kanone (Eisenbahn)	**Muzzle velocity:** 820 m (2,690 ft)
Calibre: 80-cm (31.52-in)	per second (HE) or 710 m (2,329 ft)
Length: 42.98 m (141 ft); barrel	per second (concrete-piercing)
32.48 m (106 ft 6 ¾ in)	**Max range:** 47000 m (154,199 ft)
Weight: 1350 tonnes (1329 tons)	with 4800-kg (10,582-lb) round;
Maximum elevation: 65°	38000 m (124,672 ft) with 7100-kg
Ammunition: 4800-kg (10,582-lb)	(15,653-lb) round
high-explosive or 7100-kg (15,653-lb)	**Crew:** 1,500 men to assemble and
concrete-piercing explosive	500 to service weapon in action

Right: The massive artillery piece fires a round at Sevastopol. In its immensely expensive career, the 'schwere Gustav' had fired about 300 rounds, fewer than 50 of which were in combat.

through 30 m (98 ft) of sea floor and the concrete roof to explode inside. 'Gustav' continued in action all week as von Manstein's siege guns systematically pulverised every Russian position. However, the defenders still held out and had to be killed inside the labyrinth of tunnels that connected the forts. On 1 July 1942 the few survivors surrendered.

'Gustav' was dismantled and returned to Germany. The siege train was supposed to be re-united in summer 1943 for an all-out attack on Leningrad, but this was intended as the sequel to a successful attack at Kursk. However,

Operation Zitadelle failed, and it was the Russians' turn to attack. 'Gustav' does not appear to have been re-assembled. Parts of the 80-cm guns were discovered on trains in 1945, but nothing remains now but a few inert projectiles.

Structure
The gun was housed on a fairly standard box-girder structure, although the size of this structure made it impossible to be housed on a single rail mount. Thus it was designed to be fired from a double rail mount.

Ammunition handling
A long working platform, mounting the ammunition-loading hoists, extended backwards from the gun breech. The preparation and firing process was so complex that a maximum of only 14 rounds could be fired per day.

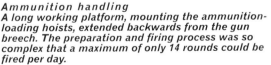

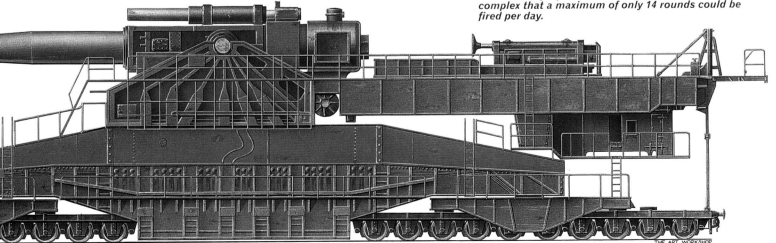

German armoured trains Eisenbahn Panzerzug

Almost as soon as the 'new' German army began to rearm during the early 1930s, high on the list of priorities were armoured trains. Their numbers and importance grew over the next decade until by 1943 there were 80 in service. Known as **Eisenbahn Panzerzug** (armoured railway train), the type was used mainly on the Eastern Front after 1941, and only a few were ever deployed in the West.

Prime capacity

The main function of many of the German armoured trains was anti-partisan activity on the vast expanses of the Soviet steppes. For this purpose the trams were equipped with varying types of armament and other equipment. The main component of each train was usually a number of twin-axle wagons each with large slab-sided superstructures mounting turrets that might be anything from converted tank turrets to specialised turrets mounting converted artillery pieces. Added to these armoured wagons would be more flatbed trucks carrying anything from more converted tank turrets to field artillery pieces lashed to the flatbed. A variation on the flatbed wagon theme was an open-sided wagon carrying a small tank, usually of a type too ancient or light for any-

thing other than anti-partisan operations. In action these light tanks could be rolled off their wagons and taken directly into action. Each train also had its own anti-aircraft armament, usually in the form of quadruple 20-mm cannon mountings. On the simplest versions these were simply mounted or, bolted onto flatbeds, but other variations were protected by armoured turrets or simpler concrete walls.

Armament array

All manner of armament was used on these trains, ranging from the latest type of anti-tank gun to captured artillery and AFV turrets of all types and sizes. Every train had its own staff, which included self-defence infantry, signallers, railway repair and maintenance staff and specialist artillerymen.

By 1943 there was a total of 80 armoured trains in German service. These Eisenbahn Panzerzuge were almost exclusively employed on the Eastern Front.

To supplement its total of 80 armoured trains, the German army also impressed into service ex-Czech and Polish armoured trains, and ex-Soviet trains were later added to the numbers. In Italy locally-produced trains often ended up in German use, including one famous example that had once been presented to Mussolini by Hitler himself. Numerous examples of a type of small self-contained armoured units known as the **Panzerdraisine** (armoured trolley) were later produced for general patrol duties and these were of two main types. One was armed with a single PzKw IV tank turret with a short-barrel 7.5-cm (2.95-in) gun and the other mounted two PzKw IV tank turrets each with a long-barrel 7.5-cm anti-tank gun. These light self-propelled units were mainly employed on internal patrol duties.

Flak trains

In a slightly different category and not always armoured were the special German anti-aircraft (Flak) trains that were used inside the Reich to bolster local defences during some of the more prolonged Allied air offensives against major German cities such as Berlin and Hamburg. These Flak trains generally mounted 8.8-cm (3.46-in) guns but also had lighter weapons for close defence purposes.

A posed photograph showing crew manning an open truck, mounting what appears to be a short 7.5-cm (2.95-in) gun – note the rangefinder in the background.

British armoured trains Train A to Train M

The British army operated armoured trains as far back as 1894 in the UK. However, for several reasons the army was not well versed in the subject in 1940, despite the operation of some examples in France and Belgium during World War I. When active consideration was given to using armoured trains as mobile defensive weapons in coastal areas in 1940, a certain amount of improvisation took place. The type of armoured train was formally established, the improvisation coming from the actual arming and armouring of the rolling stock, which was often carried out on an ad hoc basis, the work being completed in railway company workshops and military establishments alike.

2-4-2 types

The locomotives to be used were all 2-4-2 types with integral coal stowage and side water tanks. Only limited armour was at first added to these locomotives (though this was later increased) but some form of camouflage paint finish was applied in all cases. Fore and aft of the locomotive at first were open flatbeds, but

these were later changed to tiltcovered or closed cargos. At both the back and front of the train were the fighting or armoured trucks. These were converted steel coal-carrying waggons divided into two open compartments. One of these compartments was for riflemen or machine-gunners firing through embrasures in the sides. The other compartment, at the front and rear of the train, mounted a rather unusual weapon in the form of a 6-pdr (57-mm) gun of the type used during World War I to arm the original tanks. When the old tanks were declared obsolete their guns and mountings were placed into store pending some likely employment, and the armoured trains eventually formed that employment. On the trains the 6-pdr guns were mounted, together with their original tank armour shields, on pivots designed to allow fire to each side of the track. Anti-aircraft defence was usually provided by some form of machine-gun on a central high-angle pivot mounting. At first these machine-guns were Lewis guns, but these were later replaced by Bren Guns.

Designations

The trains were allotted designations from **Train A** to **Train M**, and were assigned to the various army commands, initial priority being given to the East Coast and Kent areas. Each train was given a length of track to patrol, the train returning to its own central location where the crews were housed and headquartered. As time went on the early armour thicknesses were increased and more rolling stock, usually in the

One of the British armoured trains manned by Polish troops on the east coast of Scotland during winter 1940-41, providing defence against German landings.

form of accommodation, was added to each train. An extra tender carrying more coal and water was another addition, and in some cases extra anti-aircraft flatcars carrying 40-mm Bofors guns were introduced. Some trains even had the luxury of their own armoured reconnaissance vehicles on that strength. These were usu-

ally light armoured vehicles or Universal Carriers mounting machine-guns, but special anti-aircraft light tanks were at one time considered. At one point, some armoured trains even had their own small tank component, which could convert a basically defensive train into a useful fighting unit with offensive potential.

Soviet armoured trains

Armoured trains had been a feature of the Russian method of warfare since the 1918-22 Civil War, for only the railway train had any chance of being able to encompass the vast distances that travel inside Russia involves. For the Russians armoured trains provided a method of transporting troops and weapons over long distances to bolster a front, or provide a mobile reserve or to protect internal communications and lines against the attentions of raiding forces and internal dissidents.

Important weapon

Following the Bolshevik Revolution of 1917, the armoured train remained as important a weapon as ever for the Red Army and was extensively used by both sides during the Civil War of 1918-22. Thereafter, the trains that remained in service were kept in service but no more were built as the internal reorganisation of the USSR had other priorities. Thus in 1941 the armoured trains still in existence were the same as those in use in 1918.

As such the trains were serviceable enough, but all had an aura of age about them. This was the result mainly of the large circular turrets mounted on many of the armoured trains and the high smokestacks of the locomotives. The armament of these old trains was usually made up of a mix of 76.2-mm (3-in) guns and a number of Maxim machine-guns, with armoured carriages carrying both the living and office accommodation for the large numbers of men involved with each aromoured train.

Red Army service

When the Germans invaded the Soviet Union in 1941, they captured several of these Tsarist-era trains and used them for their own purposes. But these were soon replaced in Red Army service by a number of improvised armoured trains of several different patterns. Some of these were little more than armoured boxes with a held piece firing from its own carriage. Others were more complicated with carefully armoured and curved superstructures

involving modern guns in turrets with quite involved fire-control systems. To these large trains were added substantial numbers of what became virtually a Soviet railway warfare trademark, namely the mounting of armoured cars on railway wheels to be driven up and down tracks either in concert with or quite independent from full armoured train units. These railway armoured car units had several military tasks, ranging from the patrol of the tracks to keep them free of mines and obstacles, to the countering of raiding parties that often broke through the wide-open lines of the Eastern Front. One feature that the newer Red Army armoured trains always had

Left: Armoured trains were widely used in Russia during the Civil War, and the survivors remained in service at the time of the Barabarossa.

Below: A Soviet armoured train captured by the Germans with 76.2-mm (3-in) guns and a quadruple Maxim gun anti-aircraft mounting.

Railway armoured car units were used for various tasks, including patrolling the tracks to ensure they were free of mines and other obstacles.

that the earlier models lacked was anti-aircraft defence weapons. On most Red Army trains these were quadruple Maxim machine-gun mountings, with almost every waggon having at least one further machine-gun mounting somewhere. Another Soviet practice followed German example by using tank turrets with anti-tank weapons on many trains.

Every Red Army formation

at army level had at least one armoured train under its control, and sometimes more. They were used to follow up the Red Army as it advanced and were often used by some formations as mobile headquarters during the preparation for major operations, and as staff headquarters during an advance. At least one armoured train was employed during the brief war against Japan in 1945.

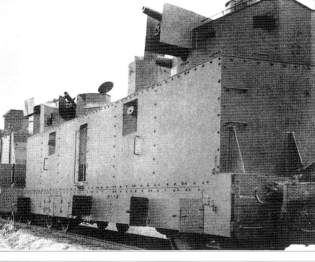

Above: It was common practice for each Red Army formation to be equipped at army level with one or more armoured train. These followed the Soviet advances and were also used as mobile command centres during the planning phases of major offensives. At least one example was active during the USSR's brief war against Japan in 1945.

British 9.2-in railway guns Mk 10 and Mk 13 guns

When the British Army started to demand railway guns in 1915, the well-established 9.2-in (234-mm) coastal defence gun was an obvious candidate for consideration. Not only did production facilities exist for the gun, but there were also existing ammunition supply lines on tap and, probably more important at the time, there were trained gunners already in service who both knew the gun well and were aware of all its attributes and drawbacks. Unfortunately the urgency of the times produced a large number of odd extemporised gun and carriage combinations to the extent that by the time the war ended the whole 9.2-in railway gun scene had to be drastically curtailed to impose some measure of order into what had become a chaotic situation.

In the end only one type of gun and carriage was retained for possible future use. This was the **9.2-in Gun Mk 13 on Mounting Railway Truck Mk 4**, which by that time was a very different beast from the original coastal guns placed on simple flat-bed trucks. The Mk 13 gun was purpose-built for the railway gun task and was a very good specimen of its type. The carriage had three axles fore and aft supporting a flat steel-bedded platform, at the centre of which was a large turntable. On this turntable were mounted the gun mounting proper and the firing platform. As with other designs the firing platform for the gun crew extended well to the

rear of the breech and mounted an ammunition-handling crane to raise the heavy shells from ground level to the breech level. The firing platform could traverse through 360° along with the gun, but to provide some measure of stability when firing four outriggers (two on each side) could be lowered to the ground from outrigger arms. Some mountings retained the **Mk 10** gun, which was kept in service long after 1918 to the extent that it was still in service in 1939, but the Mk 13 gun was the preferred type.

Firing demonstrations
Between the wars the 9.2-in railway guns were little used apart from the odd demonstration shoot on special occasions. Most were wrapped and coated in grease, and then placed in strange corners around the UK, to the extent that when war broke out in 1939 no-one appeared to know where they all were. The equipments had to be searched out by special parties, who found them in some very odd places indeed, but by early 1940 enough had been found to equip the British Army's reformed School of Railway Artillery at Catterick, an establishment mainly staffed by old railway gunners from World War I. They provided the crews and the equipment for two 9.2-in railway guns that were sent to France to back up the British Expeditionary Force, but there was no ammunition to send with them. The outcome of this sorry state of

affairs was that both guns were unable to contribute anything to the conflict, and were captured near Dunkirk during May 1940.

After Dunkirk the remaining 9.2-in railway guns were moved south to the Dover area, where they spent the next few years as part of the mobile anti-invasion defence. From time to time they were fired to impress visiting dignitaries, but they could do little else and by 1944 they had been withdrawn, their crews sent to other tasks, and eventually all were scrapped.

Above: A 9.2-in gun and its full detachment 'somewhere in the Dover area' during 1941. Not all of these men would actually be on the gun in action.

Right: A 9.2-in howitzer is brought into action on its field carriage in 1917, clearly showing the advantages of mounting such heavy pieces on railway mountings.

Below: A 9.2-in railway gun fires during a practice at the School of Railway Artillery, Catterick. The mounting is a Mk 5: note the chains to restrain recoil.

British 12-in railway howitzers Mks 1, 3 and 5 mountings

While the tale of the 12-in (305-mm) railway howitzers followed the same general lines as that of the 9.2-in (234-mm) railway guns the overall story was much simpler, at least as far as the World War I period was concerned. The first model was the **12-in Howitzer on Mounting Railway Truck Mk 1**, produced by the Vickers Elswick company, but this design had some in-service limitations and it was soon replaced in use by the **Mk 3**. This in turn was supplemented by the later **Mk 5**. The Mk 3 and Mk 5 both mounted the same type of howitzer but varied mainly in their types of mounting. The Mk 3 was theoretically capable of firing through 360° of traverse,

but in practice this had to be limited to within 20° of the centreline on each side. The Mk 5 could fire through 360° of traverse, but again it was often deemed sensible to place extra supports or ties to add stability when firing directly to the flanks.

Howitzer carriages
The carriages for the 12-in howitzers consisted of two two-axle bogies, one at the front and one at the rear. These bogies supported a well-decked platform in the centre of which was the turntable surmounted by the firing platform. The firing platform had ample room for the loading and laying members of the crew and the usual ammunition-hoisting jib was provided at the rear.

An impressive array of three 12-in railway howitzers at the School of Railway Artillery in 1940. These howitzers were moved to the Dover area, where they remained until 1943.

The long loading platform also acted as a counter-weight to balance the forward weight of the barrel.

By 1918 only the Mk 3 and the Mk 5 were still in use and these were almost immediately placed into store, where they were forgotten about until 1939. They once more came to light after the usual search and became part of the equipment of the Army's School of Railway Artillery at Catterick Camp. From there four complete equipments were sent to France to support the British Expeditionary Force, but

they proved to be of no avail against the rapid tank attacks of the German army and all four of them fell into German hands. At least two of them appear to have been 'spiked' to prevent any further use and in this the gunners' efforts appear to have been successful for the type, although appearing in a list of captured equipment, does not appear to have been used by the German forces.

Back in the UK,

the remaining 12-in railway howitzers moved south to the English Channel coast to become part of the mobile defences but like the 9.2-in (234-mm) guns alongside which they served, they had little to do other than be rolled out to impress visiting VIPs. By 1944 there were no such equipments left in the Channel area for the threat of invasion had long since diminished. Most were put back into their protective wraps and their crews were dispersed to other duties. When the war ended they were scrapped.

SPECIFICATION	
Mk 3	
Precise calibre: 12 in (304.8 mm)	**Weight complete:** 61976 kg (136,630 lb)
Length of barrel: 5.72 m (18 ft 9 in)	**Weight of shell:** 340 kg (750 lb)
	Range: 13715 m (15,000 yards)

SPECIFICATION	
Mk 5	
Precise calibre: 12 in (304.8 mm)	**Weight complete:** 77220 kg (170,240 lb)
Length of barrel: 5.72 m (18 ft 9 in)	**Weight of shell:** 340 kg (750 lb)
	Range: 13715 m (15, 000 yards)

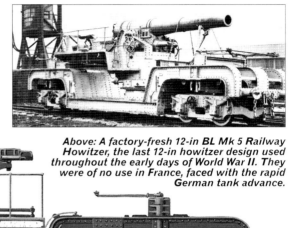

*The 12-in **BL** (breech-loading) Railway Howitzer Mk 3, with the barrel at its maximum 65° degree elevation to give maximum plunging fire.*

*Above: A factory-fresh 12-in **BL Mk 5** Railway Howitzer, the last 12-in howitzer design used throughout the early days of World War II. They were of no use in France, faced with the rapid German tank advance.*

British 13.5-in railway guns Long-range siege weapons

The story of the British 13.5-in (343-mm) railway guns began in 1916, when it was decided to mount 14-in (356-mm) naval gun barrels onto a new type of railway mounting to provide the British Army in France with a really powerful long-range gun of the type the French army was just beginning to bring into service. The 14-in naval gun barrels came from a batch originally intended for export to Japan, and the first of these was mounted onto its carriage at the Elswick Works at Newcastle during late 1917. It was early 1918 before the first two equipments were sent to France, one named **'Boche-Buster'**, the other **'Scene-Shifter'**. Once in France both did sterling work until the war ended.

Back in the UK during

1919 the two guns were sent off to store, 'Scene-Shifter' being hidden away at an ordnance depot at Chilworth minus its barrel. The same fate awaited the other two carriages that had been ordered, both of which were stored away without their intended barrels as soon as they were finished. There they remained until 1940 when the need for some form of counter-bombardment gun was urgently needed in the Dover region to deal with the long-range batteries being constructed in the Pas de Calais area. The Prime Minister, Winston Churchill, took a personal hand in the measures that provided a new role for the World War I gun carriages and he personally kept in touch with all stages of the guns' return to service.

The 14-in guns that were

originally intended for the carriages had been declared obsolete in 1926 and had subsequently been scrapped. Replacement barrels were sought and found, tucked away in Royal Navy stores, in the form of a number of 13.5-in (343-mm) guns taken from the old 'Iron Duke'-class battleships. These barrels were in reasonable condition and their dimensions were such that they could be fitted into the 14-in railway carriages without too much trouble. Thus, the conversions were made and the old carriages were provided with a thorough renovation and update.

Royal Marine crews

The 13.5-in guns were manned by men from the Royal Marines Siege Regiment and the first of them, **HMG** (His Majesty's

Gun) **'Scene-Shifter'** was ready in November 1940. Soon after it was joined by **HMG 'Piece-Maker'** and **HMG 'Gladiator'**. Distributed along various railway lines in the hinterland of Dover, these three guns then went into action at times, firing the odd shell in the general area of the Pas de Calais. Unfortunately the fall of these shells could only rarely be observed so their effectiveness was often uncertain. The three guns also had an anti-invasion role as their considerable ranges enabled them to cover a considerable length of coast-

line, but thankfully they were never called upon to undertake that task.

In November 1943 the guns once more came under Army control and went into training for some possible task involved with the invasion of Europe. It was intended that they would follow up the invasion forces to knock out the Pas de Calais defences from the rear, but in the event they were not required. The war ended with the three guns still in the UK, and in 1947 they were finally declared obsolete and scrapped. Today, nothing of them remains.

SPECIFICATION	
British 13.5-in railway gun	
Precise calibre: 13.5 in (342.9 mm)	**Weight complete:** 244590 kg (539,920 lb)
Length of barrel: 15. 9 m (52 ft 2 in)	**Weight of shell:** 567 kg (1,250 lb)
	Range: 36,575 m (40,000 yards)

A side view of the 13.5-in Railway Gun ready for loading. The carriage design was the last ever produced for a British railway gun and was considered to be among the best ever produced, but only a few were built in 1918, and none after this time.

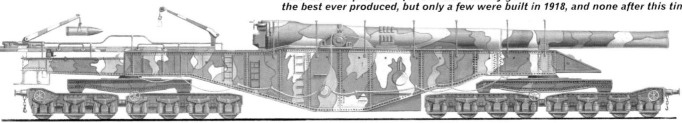

Semovente da 149/40 Self-propelled gun

The Italian army was not far behind the Germans in realising the need for assault guns, and developed a string of vehicles that outwardly resembled the German StuG III. These Italian assault guns were produced in appreciable numbers, for they were better armoured and in relative terms quicker to produce than contemporary Italian tanks. But by the time significant numbers had been issued Italy was effectively out of the war, and most of these Italian assault guns fell into German hands.

High demand

The majority of Italian self-propelled weapons, known as *semovente*, mounted 75-mm (2.95-in) or 105-mm (4.13-in) guns and howitzers of varying lengths, but since these were direct-fire mounts, the Italian artillery arm still required self-propelled artillery weapons to support the armoured formations. Accordingly Ansaldo diverted some of its precious development facilities to design a powerful artillery weapon that

could be carried on a trucked chassis. In the end Ansaldo plumped for an existing weapon, the long Canone da 149/40 modello 35, and decided to place it on a much modified Carro Armato M.15/42 tank chassis. The selection of these two items of equipment was made in order to produce as good a carriage/weapon combination as possible, but the snag was that the Italian army was already crying out for large numbers of both the gun and tank. Italian industry quite simply could not keep up with the existing demands and so the new self-propelled weapon, known as the **Semovente da 149/40** got off to a shaky start.

Unprotected weapon

The Semovente da 149/40 was a completely unprotected weapon as the long gun barrel was placed on an open mounting carried on the turretless tank chassis. The gun crew stood in the open to serve the gun, which had its trunnions mounted right to the rear to

The long, lean lines of the Italian Semovente da 149/40 can be seen at the Aberdeen Proving Grounds in Maryland. It still looks very serviceable as a modern artillery weapon despite the lack of crew protection and stowage on the vehicle for ammunition and other items.

absorb some of the recoil forces produced on firing. It was late 1942 before the first prototype was ready for prolonged firing trials, but even before these were over, unsuccessful attempts were being made to start production. Before the lines could start rolling the Italians surrendered to the Allies, and the Germans took over what was left of the Italian economy. Thus the Semovente da 149/40 prototype remained the sole example of what seemed to

be a promising design. The gun of the Semovente da 149/40 was certainly a useful weapon: it could fire a 46-kg (101.4-lb) projectile to a range of 23700 m (25,919 yards), at which distance the lack of protection for the gun crew would have been of relatively little

importance.

The prototype survived the war, and can now be seen at the Aberdeen Proving Grounds in the US. It still looks a thoroughly modern piece of equipment that would not be too out of place in many modern gun parks.

SPECIFICATION

Semovente da 149/40	in); width 3 m (9 ft 10 in); height 2
Crew: (on gun) 2	m (6 ft 6⅔ in)
Weight: 24000 kg (52,911 lb)	**Performance:** maximum road
Powerplant: one SPA petrol engine	speed 35 km/h (21.75 mph)
developing 186.4 kW (250 hp)	**Armament:** one 149-mm (5.87-in)
Dimensions: length 6.6 m (21 ft 7¾	gun

Type 4 HO-RO Self-propelled howitzer

The Japanese were behind in armoured warfare development throughout all their World War II campaigns. Their early military excursions into China and Manchuria misled them into disregarding the need for heavy armoured vehicles, and instead they concentrated on what were regarded elsewhere as light tanks and tankettes. This approach was supported by the state of Japanese industry, which was still in a relatively early state of industrial development and lacked large-scale production capability. Thus it was that the Japanese army fell way behind in the development of self-propelled artillery, and ultimately only a small number of equipments were produced.

Howitzer conversion

One of these was the **Type 4 HO-RO**, a self-propelled howitzer that allied the Type 38 150-mm (5.9-in) howitzer with the Type 97 medium tank. The conversion to the self-propelled role was a straightforward design task in which the howitzer was mounted in a

The Type 97 mounted a short Type 38 howitzer with limited range, but the Japanese were never able to produce the numbers required and they were mainly used in ones and twos as local fire-support weapons.

shield which provided forward and side armour protection while leaving the top and rear open; the side armour, it is worth noting, did not extend even to the rear of the fighting compartment. The howitzer dated from 1905 and was derived from a Krupp design. It fired a 35.9-kg

(79.15-lb) projectile to a range of 5900 m (6,452 yards), but most of these weapons were so old and worn that they had been withdrawn from general use after about 1942. They had a slow rate of fire as a result of the type of breech mechanism employed, but they were

apparently thought good enough for the self-propelled role.

The chassis used for the Type 4 was the Type 97 CHI-HA, a medium tank by Japanese standards and dating from 1937. It was a mobile enough vehicle, but showed a relative lack of development in its thin

armour, which was only about 25 mm (1 in) thick on the gun shield frontal armour, and in its overall riveted construction. The use of rivets in tank construction had elsewhere long disappeared, but the Japanese had no option but to retain the method as they lacked any

The Type 97 had its 150-mm howitzer mounted in place of the turret normally carried. The howitzer was meant to be used as a form of mobile field artillery but was normally used as close support artillery.

other form of construction capability.

Limited production

They also lacked the ability to produce the Type 4 HO-RO in anything but small numbers. Even those were virtually hand-built, with few pretensions to mass production. Even then the Japanese did not concentrate on the Type 4 HO-RO alone, for they also produced a version known as the Type 2 mounting a 75-mm (2.95-in) gun and designed to double as a

self-propelled artillery platform and a tank-killer. The Type 4 HO-RO vehicles appear not to have been organised into anything larger than four-howitzer batteries. No records survive of larger formations and most accounts refer to these vehicles being captured or knocked out in ones or twos. Very often they were assigned for island defence in the amphibious campaign leading to the Japanese mainland, and only a few were captured intact.

SPECIFICATION	
Type 4 HO-RO	(18 ft 2 in); width 2.286 m (7 ft
Crew: 4 or 5	6 in); height to top of shield
Weight: not recorded, but about	1.549 m (5 ft 1 in)
13600 kg (29,982 lb)	**Performance:** maximum road
Powerplant: one V-12 diesel	speed 38 km/h (23.6 mph)
developing 126.8 kW (170 hp)	**Armament:** one 150-mm (5.9-in)
Dimensions: length 5. 537 m	howitzer

sIG 33 auf Geschützwagen Self-propelled infantry support howitzer

The German infantry battalions each had a small artillery complement of four 7.5-cm (2.95-in) light howitzers and two 15-cm (5.9-in) infantry howitzers for their own local fire support. The 15-cm howitzer was known as the schwere Infantrie Geschütz 33 (sIG 33, or heavy infantry gun) and was a very useful and versatile weapon, but it was heavy and the only 'equipment' allocated to most infantry formations for the movement of the weapons were horse teams. Thus when an increasing degree of mechanisation began to filter through the German army the sIG 33 was high on the list for consideration.

Mobile weapon

The first form of mobile sIG 33 was used during the French campaign of May 1940. It was one of the simplest and most basic of all the German self-propelled equipments, for it consisted of nothing more than a sIG 33 mounted complete with carriage and wheels on to a turretless PzKpfw I light tank as the **15-cm sIG 33 auf Geschützwagen I Ausf B**. Armoured shields were provided for the crew of four, and that was that. It was not a very satisfactory conver-

One of the first German self-propelled artillery conversions was the mounting of the 15-cm sIG 33 infantry howitzer onto the hull of a PzKpfw I light tank in order to create the 15-cm sIG 33 auf Geschützwagen I Ausf B.

sion as the centre of gravity was rather high and the chassis was overloaded. Moreover, the armour protection was not good, and so in 1942 the PzKpfw II was the subject for conversion. This **15-cm sIG 33 auf Geschützwagen II ausf C SdKfz 121** conversion had the howitzer mounted low in the chassis, and was so suc-

cessful that during 1943 a version with a lengthened hull was produced as the **15-cm sIG 33 auf Fgst PzKpfw II (Sf) Verlänget**.

The ex-Czech PzKpfw 38(t) was also converted to act as a sIG 33 carrier. In 1942 the first of a series of vehicles known collectively as the **15-cm sIG 33 (Sf) auf PzKpfw 38(t) Bison SdKfz 138** were produced. The first series had the sIG 33 mounted forward on the hull top behind an open armoured superstructure, and this weapon/vehicle arrangement proved to be so successful that it was formalised in 1943 by the production of a new version. This was a factory-produced model rather than a conversion of existing tanks and had the vehicle engine mounted forward (instead of at the rear as originally located), this entailing the movement of the fighting compartment to the hull rear. This was the **SdKfz 138/1** (SdKfz for *Sonder Kraftfahrzeug*, or special vehicle) and it was this vehi-

cle that was retained as the German army's standard sIG 33 carrier until the end of the war. The SdKfz 138/1 had a crew of four men including the driver, and 15 shells were carried on the vehicle. There was no room for more because the fighting compartment was rather restricted for space.

Different version

There was one other sIG 33 self-propelled version, this time on a PzKpfw III chassis. This **15-cm sIG 33 auf PzKpfw III** appeared in 1941 and used a large box superstructure on a PzKpfw III to house the sIG 33. This proved to be rather too much of a good thing, for

the chassis was really too large for the weapon which could be easily carried by lighter vehicles. Thus production never got properly under way, being terminated after only 12 conversions had been made. These vehicles were used in action on the Eastern Front.

All the sIG 33 self-propelled equipments were used for their original role, i.e. the direct fire-support of infantry units in the field. Perhaps the most successful of these self-propelled carriages were the Bison and the later SdKfz 138/1. Over 370 of the vehicles were produced, and they were still in production in late 1944.

Taken from a German newsreel, this shot clearly shows how high and awkward the mounting of the 15-cm howitzer really was on the PzKpfw I chassis. The crew had only limited protection and stowage was minimal, but it provided the Germans with an indication of what would be required in future.

SPECIFICATION	
SdKfz 138/1	height 2.4 m (7 ft 10½ in)
Crew: 4	**Performance:** maximum road
Weight: 11500 kg (25,353 lb)	speed 35 km/h (21.75 mph);
Powerplant: one Praga 6-cylinder	maximum road range 185 km
petrol engine developing 111.9 kW	(115 miles)
(150 hp)	**Fording:** 0.914 m (3 ft)
Dimensions: length 4.835 m (15 ft	**Armament:** one 15-cm (5.9-in)
10⅓ in); width 2.15 m (7 ft ⅞ in);	howitzer

Wespe Self-propelled field howitzer

Even as early as 1939 it was obvious that the days of the little PzKpfw II tank were numbered, for it lacked both armament and armour. However, it was in production and quite reliable, so when the need arose for self-propelled artillery the PzKpfw II was selected to be the carrier for the 10.5-cm (4.13-in) leFH 18 field howitzer. The conversion of the tank hull to carry the howitzer was quite straightforward, as the howitzer was mounted behind an open topped armoured shield towards the rear of the hull and the area where the turret had been was armoured over and the space used for ammunition stowage. The maximum armour thickness was 18 mm (0.7 in).

Cumbersome

The result was the self-propelled howitzer known as the **Wespe** (wasp), although its full official designation was the rather more cumbersome **leFH18/2 auf Fgst PzKpfw II (Sf) SdKfz 124 Wespe**, but to everyone it was just the Wespe. It was a very popular self-propelled weapon that soon gained a reputation for reliability and mobility. The first of them were based on the PzKpfw II Ausf F chassis and went into action on the Eastern Front during 1943. On this front they were used by the divisional artillery batteries of the Panzer and Panzergrenadier divisions. They were usually organised into batteries of six howitzers with up to five batteries to each separate Abteilung (battalion). The rationale behind their deployment was to provide all mobile formations with proper and effective indirect fire support.

Wasp's nest

The Wespe was so successful in its artillery support role that Hitler himself made an order that all available PzKpfw II chassis production should be allocated to the Wespe alone, and the many other improvised weapons on the PzKpfw II chassis were dropped or their armament diverted to other chassis. The main Wespe construction centre was the Fame plant in Poland, and there production was so rapid that by mid-1944 682 examples had been built. Some time around that date manufacture of the Wespe ceased, but not before 158 had been completed without howitzers; these vehicles had the gap in the armour plate for the howitzer sealed off, the space behind the armour being used for resupply ammunition needed by batteries in the front line.

A typical Wespe went into action carrying its crew of five, including the driver, and 32 rounds of ammunition. A Wespe battery was completely mobile, although

The SdKfz 124 Wespe was a purpose-built carrier for a light 105-mm howitzer, based on the chassis of the PzKpfw II light tank. It was first used during 1942 and had a crew of five.

This shot of a Wespe on the move shows that the top of the fighting compartment was open, but protection was provided at the rear. Note how small the vehicle actually was by comparing it to the stature of the gun crew in the compartment.

SPECIFICATION

Wespe
Crew: 5
Weight: 11000 kg (24,251 lb)
Powerplant: one Maybach 6-cylinder petrol engine developing 104.4 kW (140 hp)
Dimensions: length 4.81 m (15 ft 9.¼ in); width 2.28 m (7 ft 5¾ in); height 2.3 m (7 ft 6.⅜ in)

Performance: maximum road speed 40 km/h (24.85 mph); road range 220 km (137 miles)
Fording: 0.8 m (2 ft 7½ in)
Armament: one 105-mm (4.13-in) howitzer with 32 ready-use rounds and one 7.92-mm (0.31-in) MG34 machine-gun

some of the vehicles were soft-skinned trucks for carrying ammunition and other supplies. The forward observers were usually carried in light armoured vehicles although some batteries used ex-Czech or captured French tanks for this purpose. Fire orders were relayed back to the battery by radio, and from

the battery fire command post the orders were relayed to the gun positions by land lines. The standard 10.5-cm leFH 18 as used by towed batteries was carried by the Wespe, although most were fitted with muzzle brakes, and they used the same ammunition. They also had the same range of 10675 m (11,675 yards).

Hummel Self-propelled field howitzer

The self-propelled artillery vehicle that became known as the **Hummel** (bumble bee) was a hybrid combining components of the PzKpfw III and PzKpfw IV tanks into a new vehicle known as the **Geschützwagen III/IV**. The first of these hybrids was produced during 1941 and used a lengthened PzKpfw IV suspension and running gear combined with the final drive assemblies, track and transmission of the PzKpfw III. Onto this new hull was built an open superstructure formed with light armour plates, and two types of weapon were mounted. Vehicles intended for use as tank destroyers mounted a version of the 88-mm (3.46-in) anti-tank gun, but vehicles intended for use as self-propelled artillery mounted a special version of the 15-cm (5.9-in) FH 18

The Hummel (bumble bee) was a purpose-built self-propelled artillery piece that used chassis components from both the PzKpfw III and IV. Used on all fronts, it was a successful weapon that remained in production until the war ended. It had a crew of five.

field howitzer.

The FH 18 vehicle was the **15-cm Panzerfeldhaubitze 18M auf GW III/IV SdKfz 165 Hummel**, and it formed the heavy field artillery element

of the Panzer and Panzergrenadier divisions from 1942 onwards. The ordnance was known as the Panzerfeldhaubitz 18/1, and could fire a 43.5-kg (95.9-lb) projectile to a range of

13325 m (14,572 yards). The first howitzers produced for the self-propelled role were fitted with large muzzle brakes, but experience demonstrated that these were not really necessary

and were accordingly left off later production versions. The armour was 50 mm (1.97 in) thick.

Driver luxury

The Hummel had a crew of

SPECIFICATION	
Hummel	**Performance:** maximum road speed 42 km/h (26.1 mph); road range 215 km (134 miles)
Crew: 5	
Weight: 24000 kg (52,911 lb)	
Powerplant: one Maybach V-12 petrol engine developing 197.6 kW (265 hp)	**Fording:** 0.99 m (3 ft 3 in)
	Armament: one 15-cm (5.9-in) howitzer with 18 rounds of ready use ammunition and one 7.92-mm (0.31-in) machine-gun
Dimensions: length 7.17 m (23 ft 6¼ in); width 2.87 m (9 ft 5 in); height 2.81 m (9 ft 2½ in)	

five, including the driver who sat in an armoured position forward. The provision of an armoured compartment for the driver alone was considered a luxury in war-production terms, but instead of eliminating this feature the designers made the whole thing cheaper by enlarging the armoured position and employing more flat steel plates. Thus more internal space was provided for one of the crew members.

The Hummel could carry only 18 rounds of ammunition so more had to be kept nearby and brought up when necessary. Trucks were often of little value for this task, so by late 1944 no less than 150 Hummels were produced without the howitzer and the divided front armour plates replaced by a single plate. These vehicles were used as ammunition carriers for the Hummel batteries.

Ostkette

By late 1944 no less than 666 Hummels had been produced and the type remained in production until the end of the war. They proved to be useful and popular weapons, and were used on all fronts. Special versions with wider tracks known as Ostkette were produced for use during the winter months on the Eastern Front, and the open superstructures were often covered with canvas tarpaulins to keep out the worst of the weather. The gun crew generally lived with the vehicle, so many Hummels were festooned not only with camouflage of all kinds but also with bed rolls, cooking pots and items of personal kit.

The Hummel was one of the Germans' best examples of purpose-built self-propelled artillery. It had plenty of room for the crews to serve the gun, and the carriage gave the howitzer the desired mobility to keep up with the Panzer divisions.

Waffentrager Self-propelled howitzer carrier

The **Waffentrager** (literally 'weapons carrier') was a novel concept for the Germans when it was first mooted during 1942. The idea was that the Waffentrager was to be not so much a form of self-propelled artillery but a means of carrying an artillery piece in a turret into action, where it would be removed from the tank, emplaced, used in action, and picked up again when no longer required. The exact tactical requirement for this arrangement is still uncertain, for in 1942 the Panzer divisions were still dictating mobile warfare to all opponents and the need for a static artillery piece seems remote.

Conversions

Be that as it may, a series of eight vehicles known generally as **Heuschrecke IVB** (locust) were produced during 1942. These vehicles were converted PzKpfw IV tanks with a gantry at the rear to lift off the turret mounting a 10.5-cm (4.13-in) light field howitzer. The turret could be emplaced on the ground for action or it could be towed behind the vehicle on wheels carried on the rear specifically for this purpose; this arrangement allowed the vehicle to be used as an ammunition carrier for the turret.

The eight vehicles pro-

duced were no doubt used in action, for one of them was captured and is now in the Imperial War Museum in London, but at the time no more were requested.

German defensive

By 1944 things had changed somewhat. The German army was everywhere on the defensive and anything that could hold up the advancing Allies was investigated. The Waffentrager concept came within this category, and more designs were initiated. One was an interim design in which a normal field howitzer, a 10.5-cm leFH 18/40, was carried in an armoured superstructure on top of a modified Geschützwagen III/IV (normally used for the Hummel). The howitzer could be fired from the vehicle, but it was also designed to be removed from the carrier using a block and tackle and mounted on the ground as a normal field piece once the wheels and carriage trails had been fitted. This design did not get far for it was overtaken by a series of design projects that were in turn overtaken by the end of the war.

These late-1944 and early-1945 Waffentrager all adopted the removable turret concept used in the 1942 Heuschrecke IVB. They had a variety of chassis, including both the modified PzKpfw IV

This Heuschrecke prototype was one in which a 105-mm field howitzer was carried on a chassis produced from PzKpfw III and IV components. The design called for the howitzer to be lowered to the ground when in a selected firing position.

and Geschützwagen III/IV. The artillery pieces involved ranged from 10.5-cm to 15-cm (5.9-in) howitzers. One that got as far as model form was to have carried either the 10.5-cm or 15-cm howitzer on a cruciform carriage that would have been used with the '43' series of weapons had they ever advanced further than the prototype stage. These howitzers were mounted in an

The Heuschrecke was one of a number of experimental German vehicles that were meant to carry an artillery piece to a firing site and then lower the piece to the ground for firing. The Heuschrecke was the only one of many similar designs to be produced.

open-backed turret, and could be fired from the carrier or from a ground mounting. They could also be towed behind the carrier on their field carriages. It was all rather complicated and over-engineered as it involved the use of ramps

and winches, and the concept was typical of many that never got to the hardware stage. But a few such equipments were built only to be overtaken by the end of the war, being broken up or scrapped in the immediate post-war years.

SPECIFICATION	
Heuschrecke NB	(19 ft 4¼ in); width 2.87 m (9 ft 5 in); height 2.25 m (7 ft 4½ in)
Crew: 5	
Weight: 17000 kg (37,479 lb)	
Powerplant: one Maybach petrol engine developing 140.2 kW (188 hp)	**Performance:** maximum road speed 45 km/h (28 mph); road range 250 km (155 miles)
	Armament: one 10.5-cm (4.13-in) howitzer
Dimensions: length 5.9 m	

Karl series Self-propelled siege howitzers

The weapons known as **Karl** were originally devised as anti-concrete weapons for the demolition of the Maginot Line forts and other such fortified locations. They were produced during the 1930s following a great deal of mathematical and other theoretical studies carried out during the 1920s. Work on the actual hardware began during 1937, and the first equipment was ready by 1939.

The Karl series must be regarded as being the largest self-propelled artillery weapons ever produced. There were two versions. One was the **60-cm Mörser Gerät 040** which mounted a 60-cm (23.62-in) barrel and the other the **54-cm Mörser Gerät 041** which mounted a 54-cm (21.26-in) barrel. Both weapons were also known as the **Thor** in service with the German army.

'Bunker-busters'

Both weapons fired special concrete-piercing projectiles. The range of the Gerät 040 was 4500 m (4,921 yards) and that of the Gerät 041 6240 m (6,824 yards). Both could penetrate between 2.5 and 3.5 m (8 ft 2½ in and 11 ft 6 in) of concrete before detonating to produce maximum effect. These projectiles were massive items. The 60-cm shell weighed no less than 2170 kg (4,784 lb), although a lighter version was also used. The 54-cm shell weighed 1250 kg (2,756 lb).

Both Karl weapons were huge, ponderous equipments. Although technically self-propelled, their mobility was limited by their sheer weight and bulk and the tracked carriages were meant for only the most local of moves. It is reported that the Karl was capable of creeping along at only 4.8 km/h (3 mph) on the 432.5 kW (580 hp) provided by their tracked carrier's diesel engines. For long-distance travel they were carried slung between special railway trucks. Shorter moves were made by removing the barrel from the carriage and placing both the barrel and the carriage on separate special trailers towed by heavy tractors.

Assembly and breakdown was carried out using special mobile gantries. The whole process was difficult to an extreme, but the Karl weapons were not intended for mobile warfare. They were produced to reduce fortresses and that meant a long, planned approach to the firing site, a slow rate of fire (the best was one round every 10 minutes) and a steady withdrawal once the fortress had been reduced. A ground crew of 109 was needed to support the Karl howitzer in action, of which about 30 were needed for the support of the carriage.

Siege of Sevastopol

The Karls were too late for the Maginot Line, which fell along with the rest of France in 1940. Their first real

The Karl howitzers had to be carried to the firing positions by special trailers and assembled on site. For this purpose, they were aided by the ammunition carrier version of the PzKpfw IV.

engagement was the siege of Sevastopol in exactly their designed role. Following the successful end of that siege more Karls were used during the Warsaw uprising when they were used to demolish the centre of Warsaw and crush the Polish underground fighters.

By then it was 1944. Most of the early 60-cm barrels had then been replaced by 54-cm barrels, but Warsaw was their last period in action. The increasing mobile warfare of the last year of the war gave the Karls no chance to demonstrate their destructive powers, and most were destroyed by their crews in the last stages of the war. Only a few of the special PzKpfw IV ammunition carriers produced to carry projectiles for the Karls survived for Allied intelligence staffs to examine. It is possible that one example of the Karl may survive as a museum piece in Russia.

The massive 60-cm and 54-cm Karl howitzers were really fortification-smashing equipments, and had only limited tactical mobility.

SPECIFICATION	
Gerät 041	6.24 m (20 ft 6 in); length of
Crew: around 30	carriage 11.15 m (36 ft 7 in); track
Weight: 124000 kg (273,373 lb)	2.65 m (8 ft 8½ in)
Powerplant: one V-12 petrol	**Performance:** maximum speed
engine developing 894.8 kW	around 4.8 km/h (3 mph)
(1,200 hp)	**Armament:** one 54-cm (21.26-in)
Dimensions: length of barrel	howitzer/mortar

Brummbär Self-propelled heavy assault howitzer

Despite their overall success, the StuG III assault guns were considered by 1943 as being too lightly armoured for the assault role, and a new heavy assault vehicle was required. The existing 15-cm (5.9-in) sIG 33 self-propelled equipments lacked the armour protection required for the close-support role and so, with the PzKpfw IV tank gradually being replaced by the Panther and Tiger tanks, there was the chance to produce a purpose-built vehicle using the later versions of the PzKpfw IV as a basis.

The first examples of this new vehicle appeared during 1943 under the designation **Sturmpanzer IV Brummbär** (grizzly bear). The Brummbär used a box structure formed from sloping armour plates set over the front of a turretless PzKpfw IV, and mounted a specially developed howitzer

in a ball mounting on the front plate. This howitzer was known as the Sturmhaubitze 43 and was a shortened version, only 12 calibres long, of the 15-cm sIG 33. Armour was provided all round (the frontal armour being 100 mm/2.54 in thick), so the crew of five men were well protected. Later standoff side armour was added, and most vehicles acquired a coating of Zimmerit plaster paste to prevent magnetic charges being stuck on to the hull by close-in tank killer squads. A machine-gun was mounted on the hull front plate on late production models, earlier versions

Most German self-propelled equipments carried only light armour, so when a call was made for a special close-support assault gun the result was the heavily armoured Brummbär.

having lacked this self-defence weapon.

The roomy fighting compartment of the Brummbär could accommodate up to 38 rounds of 15-cm ammunition. The commander sat to the rear of the howitzer using a roof-mounted periscope to select targets. Two men served the gun and handled the ammunition, while another acted as the gun layer. The driver normally remained in his seat at the left front. Most targets were engaged with direct fire, but provision was made for indirect fire.

Production

About 313 Brummbär vehicles were produced before the war ended, and most appear to have been used in direct support of Panzergrenadier and infantry units. The vehicles moved forward with the first waves of attacking troops and provided fire to reduce strongpoints and smash bunkers. Infantry had to remain close to prevent enemy tank-killer squads from coming too close to the Brummbär vehicles,

which were always vulnerable to close-range anti-tank weapons, especially as some of their side armour was as thin as 30 mm (1.18 in). Brummbär vehicles were generally used in ones and twos split up along an area of attack. As defensive weapons they were of less use, for the short howitzer had only a limited performance against armour as its prime mission was the delivery of blast effect HE projectiles. One factor that restricted the Brummbär's overall mobility was its weight, which gave the vehicle a rather poor ground-pressure 'footprint': it was fast enough on roads, but across country it could get bogged down in soft ground.

The Brummbär was a well-liked vehicle that often provided exactly the degree of fire support required by infantry formations. On the debit side it was heavy, rather ponderous and the early examples lacked close-in protection. But they were well protected against most weapons and they carried a powerful howitzer.

The Brummbär was normally used when close-in infantry tank-killer squads were likely to be encountered, and often in street fighting. It was therefore liberally covered with a plaster-like substance known as Zimmerit that prevented magnetic charges from sticking to the hull.

SPECIFICATION	
Brummbär	**Performance:** maximum road
Crew: 5	speed 40 km/h (24.85 km/h);
Weight: 28200 kg (62,170 lb)	maximum road range 210 km
Powerplant: one Maybach V-12	(130 miles)
petrol engine developing 197.6 kW	**Fording:** 0.99 m (3 ft 3 in)
(265 hp)	**Armament:** one 15-cm (5.9-in)
Dimensions: length 5.93 m (19 ft	howitzer and one or two 7.92-mm
5½ in); width 2.88 m (9 ft 5 in);	(0.3-in) machine-guns
height 2.52 m (8 ft 3 in)	

Sturmtiger Assault gun

Stalingrad taught the German army many lessons, not least of which was that the Germans were ill-equipped for the art of close-quarter street fighting. In typical fashion they decided to meet any future urban warfare requirements by a form of overkill by using a super-heavy weapon that would do away with the need for house-to-house fighting by simply blowing away any defended houses or structures. This they decided to do with a land version of a naval weapon, the depth charge.

In 1943 the Germans produced a version of the Tiger tank known by several names including **38-cm Sturmmörser**, **Sturmpanzer VI** and **Sturmtiger**. Whatever the designation, the weapon was a Tiger tank with the turret replaced by a large box-shaped superstructure with a short barrel poking through the front sloped plate. This barrel was not a gun but a 38-cm (15-in) Raketenwerfer 61 rocket projector of an unusual type, for it fired a rocket-propelled depth charge that weighed no less than 345 kg (761 lb). As this projectile was based upon the design of a naval depth charge nearly all the weight was high explosive; the effect of this upon even the stoutest structure can well be imagined. The rockets had a maximum range of 5650 m (6,180 yards), and the projector barrel was so arranged that the rocket efflux gases were diverted

Largest of all the German close-support weapons was the Sturmtiger, carrying a 38-cm rocket projector that fired a form of naval depth charge to demolish buildings. They were designed for urban warfare. This example has been captured by American troops.

forward to vent from venturi around the muzzle ring. The Sturmtiger was exceptionally well armoured, with 150 mm (5.9 in) at its front and between 80 and 85 mm (3.15 and 3.35 in) at the side.

Crew

The Sturmtiger had a crew of seven including the commander, a fire observer and the driver carried within the large armoured superstructure. The other four men served the rocket projector. Because of their massive size, only 12 projectiles could be carried inside the superstructure, with the possibility of one more inside the projector. Loading the rockets into the vehicle was helped by a small crane jib mounted on the superstructure rear, and a small hatch nearby allowed access to the interior. Once inside overhead rails assisted in the movement of the rockets to and from their racks along each side, and loading into the projector was carried out using a loading tray.

Although the Sturmtiger prototype was ready by late 1943, it was not until August 1944 that production

of this massive vehicle got under way. Only about 10 were ever produced, and these were used in ones and twos on most fronts but in situations where their powerful armament was of little advantage. Consequently most were soon either knocked out in action or simply abandoned by their crews once their fuel allocation had been used.

In action

Used as they were in isolation and in such areas as the North Italian campaign, the hulks fascinated the Allies who encountered

them and many detailed intelligence reports were written on them. Most realised that the Sturmtiger was a highly specialised weapon that was simply pushed into the field during the latter stages of the war in the German effort to get

any weapon into action. If the Sturmtigers had been used as intended for street fighting, they would have been formidable weapons. Instead, by the time they were ready the time of concentrated urban warfare had passed.

SPECIFICATION	
Sturmtiger	height 2.85 m (9 ft 4 in)
Crew: 7	**Performance:** maximum road
Weight: 65000 kg (143,300 lb)	speed 40 km/h (24.86 mph); road
Powerplant: one Maybach V-12	range 120 km (75 miles)
petrol engine developing 484.7 kW	**Fording:** 1.22 m (4 ft)
(650 hp)	**Armament:** one 38-cm (15-in)
Dimensions: length 6.28 m (20 ft	rocket projector and one 7.92-mm
7 in); width 3.57 m (11 ft 8 in);	(0.3-in) machine-gun

Sturmgeschütz III Assault gun

Following from its experiences in World War I, the German army saw the need for an armoured mobile gun that could follow infantry attacks and provide fire support and the firepower to knock out strongpoints and bunkers. During the late 1930s such a gun was developed using the chassis, suspension and running gear of the PzKpfw III tank. This armoured gun was known as the **Sturmgeschütz III** though its formal designation was **Gepanzerte Selbstfahrlafette für Sturmgeschütz 7.5-cm Kanone SdKfz 142**, and it had the usual upper hull and turret of the tank replaced by a thick carapace of armour with a short 75-mm (2.95-in) gun mounted in the front. This weapon was first issued for service in 1940 (**StuG III Ausf A**) and was soon followed by a whole series of vehicles that gradually incorporated overall and detail improvements, to the extent that when the war ended in 1945 many were still in service on all fronts. The 1941 models were the **StuG III Ausf B**, **C** and **D**, while the slightly improved **StuG III Ausf E** appeared in 1942.

Upgunned models

The main change to the StuG III series was a gradual programme of upgunning. The original short 75-mm gun was an L/24 weapon (i.e. the length of the barrel was 24 times the calibre) and had limitations against many targets except at short ranges. Thus it was replaced by longer guns with improved performance, first an L/43 (**StuG III Ausf F**) and then an L/48 gun (**StuG**

Two StuG IIIs move forward in the Soviet Union in 1944. They are armed with long 75-mm (10.5-in) anti-tank guns and are carrying extra lengths of track links for added protection. More protection comes from the stand-off side plates known as 'Schützen' carried to defeat close-range hollow-charge anti-tank warheads.

III Ausf G). The latter gun also provided the StuG III series with an anti-tank capability, and this was in a way to the detriment of the original assault support concept, for it was far easier to produce a StuG than it was a tank, so many StuG IIIs with L/48 guns were diverted to the Panzer divisions in place of battle tanks. Used as a tank-killer the StuG III had its moments, but it lacked traverse and adequate protection for the task. It had to be retained as such, however, for German industry simply could not supply enough tanks for the Panzer divisions.

As an assault gun the StuG III series was far more successful. Eventually the type was upgunned to the

Right: A StuG is seen on the Eastern Front against a distant target. In order to better observe the fire, one of the gun crew is using the hull roof for observation. The vehicle is equipped with 'Ostkette' tracks for use on snow and soft ground.

stage late in the war when many StuG IIIs were armed with the powerful 10.5-cm (4.13-in) Sturmhaubitze, a special assault howitzer produced for the **StuG III für 10.5-cm StuH 42**. The first of these was completed in 1943, but manufacture of this variant was initially slow. Instead the version with the 75-mm L/48 gun was rushed off the production lines for the Panzer divisions.

The StuG III had a crew of four and extra machine-guns were often carried behind a shield on the roof. The protective mantlet for the main

gun underwent many changes before it ended up as a *Saukopf* ('pig's head') mantlet which proved very good protection. More pro-

75-mm gun
Initially fitted with a short 75-mm (2.95-in) gun, the F model shown here was introduced in 1942 and carried a long 75-mm weapon, significantly improving anti-tank capability.

Tank destroyer
The G model with its 75-mm L/48, heavier armour and smoke dischargers, was designed more as a tank destroyer than a self-propelled gun. By contrast, as early as 1941 variants were in production mounting a 105-mm (4.1-in) howitzer.

The Sturmgeschütz Sdkfz 142 was based on the chassis of the PzKpfw III with the gun mounted in the hull. The drivers's station was unaltered from the tank, but behind was now a large but cramped fighting compartment. Absent from this vehicle, armoured skirts were fitted as standard from 1943.

PETER SARSON & TONY BRYAN.

Above: Designed to a 1936 Wehrmacht requirement for an armoured close support vehicle, the StuG III was introduced in 1940 and fought in all theatres until 1945, both in an artillery and tank destroyer role.

Right: A StuG III Ausf F, with a PzKfw I mounting a 4.7-cm (1.85-in) gun approaching (centre background). The divisional emblem identifies the StuG as belonging to the elite SS Adolf Hitler Division.

Below: StuG crews were considered the elite of the artillery units and were issued special field grey uniforms. StuG IIIs had accounted for an impressive 20,000 enemy tanks by spring 1944.

tection against short-range hollow-charge warheads was provided with the addition of Schützen ('skirts') along both sides. These were simply sheets of stand-off armour to detonate the warheads before they hit the vehicle armour, and were used on many German tanks after 1943.

As a close-range assault support weapon the StuG III series was an excellent vehicle/weapon combination. It was also relatively cheap and easy to produce, and in wartime Germany that mattered a lot. Therefore the

series was built in some numbers and numerically it was one of the most important German armoured vehicles.

StuG III in combat

Moving into action in a StuG III cannot have been a very pleasant experience. Like those of most armoured vehicles, the interior of the StuG III was cramped and uncomfortable. Much of the interior of the main fighting compartment was taken up by the breech of the 7.5-cm gun. Ammunition racks lined the lower portion of the

white-painted walls, while radios and other black boxes occupied what was left of the bulkhead space. The driver sat in his own position to the left front, most of the time peering through his armoured vision slits and trying to make out where he was going. Generally the driver was guided by orders from the commander, who sat under his cupola behind the driver. When possible the commander kept his hatch open and raised his head for better vision, but in action and closed down he could often see little more than the driver. The loader sometimes aimed and fired the 7.92-mm (0.31-in) machine-gun by controls from within the vehicle. When occasion allowed this was usually used from behind a shield on the roof. To the right of the commander sat the loader, who had his own overhead hatch that was seldom used in action; he also had a small hatch in the rear wall through which spent cases were despatched. Just in front of the commander and almost in his lap sat the gun layer with his gun controls. His outlook was limited to what he could see through his sighting devices: a small panoramic telescope was set in the roof for laying indirect fire and a telescope was placed in front for direct aiming. Given the noise of the engine, the constant jolting from the suspension, and the fumes and smells of the gun and fuel, life for the StuG crews must have been very unpleasant. But they could take heart from the fact that they at least had more armour around them than most of their tankborne colleagues, and that many tank interiors were even more unpleasant and cramped than that of the StuG III.

SPECIFICATION	
StuG III Ausf E	height 2.16 m (7 ft 1 in)
Crew: 4	**Performance:** maximum speed
Weight: 23900 kg (52,690 lb)	40 km/h (24.9 mph); road range
Powerplant: one Maybach V-12	165 km (102 miles)
petrol engine developing 197.6 kW	**Fording:** 0.8 m (2 ft 7½ in)
(265 hp)	**Armament:** one 75-mm (2.95-in)
Dimensions: length 6.77 m (22 ft	gun and two 7.92-mm (0.3-in)
2½ in); width 2.95 m (9 ft 8 in);	MG34 or MG42 machine-guns

SU-76 76.2-mm self-propelled gun

During the desperate days of 1941 the Red Army lost so much materiel that Soviet planners were forced to list mass production as their top priority, and in order to cut down the numbers of different equipments being produced only a few types were selected for future use. One of these types was the superlative ZIS-3 76.2-mm (3-in) gun, which was not only an excellent field piece but for that period also a good anti-tank gun. Thus when it was decided to adopt the ZIS-3 in quantity the Red Army had a very good weapon for the future, especially when the chance arose to make the weapon a self-propelled one.

The events of 1941 had shown the Red Army that its light tanks were virtually useless and the type was scheduled for withdrawal from production and service. A production line was available for the T-70 light tank, however, and it was decided to convert the T-70 to take the ZIS-76 gun as a highly mobile anti-tank weapon. Thus was born the **SU-76** (SU for *Samokhodnaya Ustanovka*, or self-propelled mounting). The conversion to take the 76.2-mm gun and 62 rounds of ammunition was a simple one, but the T-70 chassis had to be widened somewhat and an extra road wheel was added to take the additional weight. The first examples had the gun mounted centrally, but later models had the gun offset to the left. Maximum armour thickness was 25 mm (0.98 in).

Fire-support role

It was late 1942 before the first SU-76s were produced, and it was mid-1943 before they had entered Red Army service in any appreciable numbers. By that time the ZIS-3 gun had lost much of

Above: The Soviet SU-76 was a wartime and rather rushed conversion of the T-70 light tank to carry a 76.2-mm field gun, and although it was produced in large numbers it was little liked by its crews, who called it the 'Bitch'.

Right: Red Army soldiers attack under the close supporting fire of SU-76 76.2-mm guns, providing a graphic example of what close-range artillery support really means. By 1945 the SU-76 was used almost exclusively in this role after being used at one point as a mobile field artillery piece.

its edge against the ever-thickening German tank armour, and thus the SU-76 was gradually phased over to the direct fire-support of Red Army infantry formations. Some anti-tank capability was retained when new anti-armour ammunition was introduced, but by the end of the war the SU-76 was being phased out in favour of vehicles with larger-calibre guns. By June 1945, over 14,000 SU-76s had been

constructed, at Factory 30 in Kirov; Factory 40 in Mytischchi and the GAZ Factory in Gorkii. Once the guns had entered service in the summer of 1943, they were initially sent to mixed self-propelled artillery regiments, with each unit having 21 vehicles, which included four batteries of five vehicles and a commander's vehicle, although after a while it was realised that the gun was better suited to the close support of the infantry. To this end, by 1944 many guns were allotted to light self-propelled artillery batteries of 16 vehicles each which would operate with the regular infantry divisions.

Many SU-76s were pressed into other roles by 1945. The usual process was to remove the gun and use the vehicle as a supply and ammunition carrier, as an

artillery tractor and as a light armoured recovery vehicle. Some were fitted with anti-aircraft cannon.

The 'Bitch'

After 1945 there were still many SU-76s to hand, and the Soviets handed them on to many friendly nations including China and North Korea with whom the type saw another bout of action during the Korean War that started in 1950. More went to some of the Warsaw Pact armed forces. It is doubtful that the new recipients welcomed the SU-76 for it was very much a wartime expedient vehicle with no crew

comforts whatsoever. Apart from a few examples that had an armoured roof, the crew compartment of the SU-76 was open to the elements and the driver had to sit next to the twin engines with no intervening bulkhead. The Red Army referred to the SU-76 as the *Sukarni* (Bitch).

Thus the SU-76 started life as a mobile anti-tank weapon and ended up as an artillery support weapon. It was no doubt a very useful weapon in the latter role, but essentially it was a hasty expedient rushed into production at a time of desperate need.

SU-76s wait to take part in one of the massive artillery actions that usually took place before any major Red Army offensive. The open structure of the SU-76 must have made life very uncomfortable for their crews under such conditions, as only tarpaulin covers were normally carried.

SPECIFICATION	
SU-76	height 2.17 m (7 ft 1.4 in)
Crew: 4	**Performance:** maximum road
Weight: 10800 kg (23,810 kg)	speed 45 km/h (28 mph); road
Powerplant: two GAZ 6-cylinder	range 450 km (280 miles)
petrol engines each developing	**Fording:** 0.89 m (2 ft 11 in)
52.2 kW (70 hp)	**Armament:** one 76.2-mm (3-in) gun
Dimensions: length 4.88 m	and one 7.62-mm (0.3-in)
(16 ft ⅛in); width 2 ½m (8 ft 11½ in);	machine-gun

ISU-122 and ISU-152 122-mm and 152-mm self-propelled guns

The first of the heavy Soviet self-propelled artillery carriages was the SU-152, which first appeared in 1943, just in time to take part in the tank battles at Kursk. It was built onto a KV-2 heavy tank chassis and was typical of later World War II designs in that the tank chassis was taken virtually unchanged and a large armoured box was built on to the front of the hull. The weapon was a 152-mm (6-in) M-1937 howitzer mounted in a large and heavy mantlet on the front superstructure plate and there were roof hatches, one of which had provision for mounting an anti-aircraft machine-gun.

This first vehicle was intended for use as much as an anti-armour weapon as a heavy assault weapon, for the Red Army made no differentiation between anti-tank and other weapons when it came to tactics. The SU-152 relied upon sheer projectile weight and kinetic power to defeat enemy armour.

When the KV tank series was replaced in production

The ISU-152 was a straight-forward conversion of an IS series heavy tank to carry a 152-mm howitzer as a powerful close-support artillery weapon; it was also a powerful tank killer. The howitzer was housed in a thick superstructure with dense frontal armour.

by the IS series, these too were used for the SU self-propelled role. The conversion closely followed that of the original SU-152, and the IS-based conversion was known as the **ISU-152**. To the average observer the SU-152 and ISU-152 were visually identical but the ISU-152 mounted a more modern howitzer, known as the ML-20S (with 20 rounds), technically a gun/howitzer and a very powerful weapon, especially at the assault ranges favoured by Red Army tactics. The weapon was protected by an armoured box made up from sloping plates of thick armour, with hand rails around the edge of the roof for use by 'tank

descent' infantry who used the vehicles to carry them into action. Maximum armour thickness was 75 mm (2.95 in).

The ISU-152 was joined by the **ISU-122**, a virtually identical vehicle carrying a powerful 122-mm (4.8-in) gun known as the M-1931/4 or A-19S (with 30 rounds), the ordnance being a modification of the then-standard 122-mm M-1931/37, though there was also another gun known as the D-25S which was ballistically identical to the A-19S but differed in the way it was constructed. Numerically the ISU-122 was less important than the ISU-152, but the 122-mm version was potentially the more powerful weapon as it fired a higher-velocity projectile than the heavier 152-mm

weapon, which relied more upon shell weight for its destructive effects.

Battle for Berlin

During 1944 and 1945 the ISU-152 and ISU-122 were in the vanguard of the Red Army advances through Germany towards Berlin. Some of the first Red Army units entering Berlin were ISU-152 units, which used their howitzers to blast away strongpoints at close ranges and clear the way to the remains of the city centre.

If the ISU weapons had a fault it was that they lacked internal ammunition stowage space. Thus they had to have a virtual constant supply of ammunition brought forward by armoured carriers, which was often a hazardous undertaking. But

the massive weapons carried by the ISU vehicles were considered to be of great value in the direct support of Red Army tank and motorised infantry divisions.

Mass production of the ISU-152 continued until 1955 by which time 2,450 vehicles had been built, in addition to the 4,075 vehicles produced during the war. Production of the ISU-122 had been terminated at the end of the war, although it was restarted in 1947.

The IS chassis was later utilised for carriage of the R-11 (SS-1b 'Scud-A') ballistic missile, although these launchers were later replaced by the more familiar MAZ wheeled launchers in Soviet army service. The type was also used as a prime mover.

Above: ISU-152s cross a river during the latter stages of World War II. These locally-camouflaged vehicles appear to be carrying their crewmembers on the roof, but in action they would be carrying squads of 'tank descent' assault infantry instead. Note the size of the howitzer's muzzle brake.

Right: The ISU-122 was a conversion of the IS tank to accommodate a front-mounted 122-mm howitzer in a well-armoured and well-sloped superstructure. It was produced in large numbers for the close-support role, but could also be used for stand-off artillery fire.

Left: ISU-152s were still in front-line service in 1956 when the Red Army ruthlessly crushed the Hungarian uprising. In the streets of Budapest the lack of traverse proved a serious disadvantage. The gun mechanism was never modernised; elevation and loading was done by hand.

SPECIFICATION	
ISU-122	height 2.52 m (8 ft 3 ½ in)
Crew: 5	**Performance:** maximum road
Weight: 46430 kg (102,361 lb)	speed 37 km/h (23 mph); road
Powerplant: one V-12 diesel	range 180 km (112 miles)
developing 387.8 kW (520 hp)	**Fording:** 1.3 m (4 ft 3.2 in)
Dimensions: length overall 9.8 m	**Armament:** one 122-mm (4.8-in)
(32 ft 1 ¾ in) and hull 6.805 m (22 ft	gun and one 12.7-mm (0.5-in)
3 ¾ in); width 3.56 m (11 ft 8.2 in);	anti-aircraft machine-gun

Sexton Self-propelled gun-howitzer

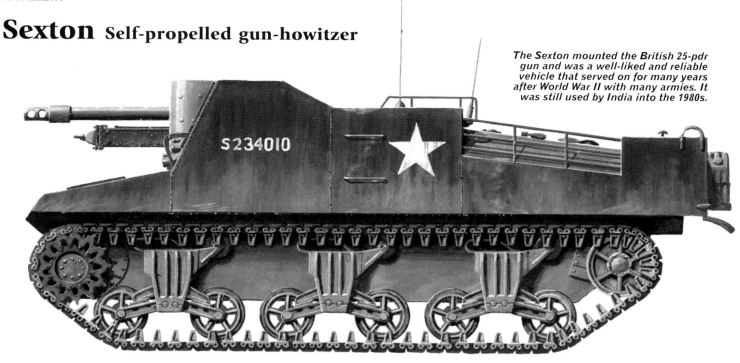

The Sexton mounted the British 25-pdr gun and was a well-liked and reliable vehicle that served on for many years after World War II with many armies. It was still used by India into the 1980s.

During early 1941 the British Purchasing Commission in Washington asked the Americans if the M7 Priest could be altered to allow it to carry the British 25-pdr (87.6-mm/3.45-in) gun-howitzer. While the British appreciated the amenities of the M7 Priest, it had the major disadvantage of mounting a 105-mm (4.13-in) howitzer that was not a standard British weapon calibre at that time. The Americans accordingly produced the M7 with the 25-pdr and named it the T51, but at the same time announced that there was no way that they could produce it in quantity as they had their production hands full already. The British accordingly looked around and noted that the Canadians had set up a production line for the Ram tank, a type that was soon to be replaced by the American M3 and M4. The Ram was accordingly altered to accommodate the 25-pdr, and thus was born the **Sexton**.

The Sexton used the over-all layout of the M7 Priest, but many changes were introduced to suit British requirements. These included the movement of the driver's position to the right-hand side. The Sexton lacked the pronounced 'pulpit' of the M7, but the fighting compartment was left open with only a canvas cover to provide weather protection for the crew. The Sexton had a crew of six and much of the interior was taken up with lockers for ammunition and some of the crew's personal kit; more stowage was provided in boxes at the rear. Maximum armour thickness was 32 mm (1.25 in).

Anti-tank capability

The 25-pdr gun-howitzer was carried in a special cradle produced by the Canadians specifically for the Sexton. This allowed a traverse of 25° left and 40° right, which was very useful for the anti-tank role (18 AP rounds) but in the event the Sexton had little need of this facility.

Instead it was used almost exclusively as a field artillery weapon (87 HE and smoke rounds) supporting the armoured divisions in north-west Europe from 1944 onwards. There were several variations, all of them incorporating the production changes progressively introduced on the lines of the Montreal Locomotive Works at Sorel. Production continued there until late 1945, by which time 2,150 Sextons had been manufactured.

The Sexton was a well-liked and reliable gun and weapon combination that proved so successful that many remained in use in odd corners of the world for many years after the war. One example is preserved as a museum piece at the Royal School of Artillery at Larkhill, Wiltshire.

There were a few in-service variants of the Sexton, some being converted to 'swim' for possible use on D-Day, but none appear to have been used in this role on the day. A more common con-version was the replacement of the gun-howitzer by extra map tables and radios in the **Sexton Gun Position Officer** command vehicle; there was usually one of these to a battery. In post-war years some Sextons were handed over to nations such as Italy who preferred the 105-mm howitzer; in this instance the 25-pounders were replaced with German 105-mm howitzers.

Above: The British Army used the Sexton until the late 1950s, an example seen here taking part in early combined operations with a Hoverfly Mk II helicopter.

Left: Operated by a crew of six (commander, driver, gunner, gun layer, loader and radio operator), the Sexton self-propelled gun-howitzer was used almost exclusively for artillery support of armoured divisions.

SPECIFICATION	
Sexton	speed 40.2 km/h (25 mph); road
Crew: 6	range 290 km (180 miles)
Weight: 25855 kg (57,000 lb)	**Fording:** 1.01 m (3 ft 4 in)
Powerplant: one Continental 9-cylinder radial piston engine developing 298.3 kW (400 hp)	**Armament:** one 25-pdr gun-howitzer, two unmounted 0.303-in (7.7-mm) Bren Guns and
Dimensions: length 6.12 m (20 ft 1 in); width 2.72 m (8 ft 11 in); height 2.44 m (8 ft)	(on some vehicles) one pintle-mounted 0.5-in (12.7-mm) Browning machine-gun
Performance: maximum road	

Bishop Self-propelled gun-howitzer

The Bishop was an early British attempt to produce self-propelled artillery by placing a 25-pdr gun onto a Valentine tank chassis. The gun was mounted in a fixed turret with only limited elevation and the result was not a success, being replaced in service by the Priest as soon as possible.

The vehicle that became known as the **Bishop** was conceived at a time when 25-pdr batteries in the North African desert were perforce used as anti-tank weapons and were taking a terrible pounding as a result. It was decided to place the 25-pdr on a mobile carriage to increase protection for the gun crews, and it was soon clear that the Valentine infantry tank would make a good basis for such a conversion. Unfortunately the exact role of this gun/tank combination was uncertain from the start. The tank exponents saw it as a variant of the heavy-gun tank theme, while the gunners wanted a self-propelled carriage. These arguments were never really solved, and the result was something of a compromise even though the gunners won in the end.

Valentine conversion

The Valentine 25-pdr emerged as a straightforward conversion (officially the **Mounting, Valentine, 25-pdr Gun Mk I on Carrier, Valentine, 25-pdr Gun, Mk I**), the usual turret being replaced by a much larger turret mounting the 25-pdr. This new turret was fixed, and was a large slab-sided design too large for battlefield concealment and too small to allow much room inside for the gun crew. The turret design also had one major disadvantage for the gunners in that it restricted the elevation of the barrel and thus curtailed range to only 5852 m (6,400 yards) which was a considerable reduction from the normal 12253 m (13,400 yards). The only way to increase this performance was the tedious and tactically-hampering construction of earth ramps up which the vehicle could be driven to increase the elevation angle. Traverse was also severely restricted, to a maximum of 4° to each side. Internal ammunition stowage was 32 rounds but more could be carried in a limber towed behind the vehicle. Armour varied in thickness from 8 mm (0.315

in) to 60 mm (2.36 in).

The 25-pdr Valentine went into action in North Africa during the latter stages of the campaign in that theatre, by which time the 25-pdr was no longer in use as an anti-tank gun, so the vehicles were used as self-propelled artillery with no distraction and the Royal Artillery learned a lot from their use. The type was eventually named Bishop, and it went on to be used in Sicily and the Italian mainland during the opening stages of these campaigns. Throughout these campaigns the Bishop demonstrated all its several drawbacks, but also provided an indication of the potential of self-propelled artillery for it was the first British self-propelled weapon to see active service. The need for supporting logistics was more than emphasised, as was the need for improved radio links with forward observers.

The Bishop also demonstrated things to avoid in future designs. The most obvious one was for the gun to have its full range of movement if it was to be of any use; additionally, more

room was needed to serve the gun, for the turret of the Bishop was cramped and ill-ventilated. More internal ammunition stowage was needed and the carrier had to be fast enough to keep up with tanks. Being an infantry tank, the Valentine chassis was too slow to keep up with the armoured formations.

All these things were put right when the gunners were issued numbers of M7

A Bishop in action near Naples during the later stages of its operational career. The gun number is passing ammunition to the gun turret after taking it from the ammunition limbers, one of which can be seen in the foreground and was normally towed behind the vehicle.

Priests. The gunners took to the Priest with a will, and before long the Bishops had been discarded. They may have been less than perfect,

but they taught the gunners a lot and the Bishop has the distinction of being the British Army's first self-propelled artillery piece.

SPECIFICATION

Bishop
Crew: 4
Weight: 7911 kg (17,440 lb)
Powerplant: one AEC 6-cylinder diesel developing 97.7 kW (131 hp)
Dimensions: length 5.64 m (18 ft 6 in); width 2.77 m (9 ft 1 in);

height 3.05 m (10 ft)
Performance: maximum road speed 24 km/h (15 mph); road range 177 km (110 miles)
Fording: 0.91 m (3 ft)
Armament: one 25-pdr (87.6-mm/3.45-in) gun-howitzer

*Left: Ammunition stocktaking takes place on a Bishop with the projectiles laid out on the engine covers for counting. The Bishop could carry only 32 rounds internally, as space inside the fixed turret was cramped. The projectiles are 25-pdr **HE** shells, the normal round fired, although smoke could also be carried.*

Far left: A Bishop on the ranges with the gun detachment commander outside the fixed turret, as there was room for only two gunners inside. The fixed turret restricted the barrel elevation and thus range.

M7 Priest 105-mm self-propelled howitzer

The British gunners nicknamed the American M7 the 'Priest' after seeing the pulpit that housed the 0.5-in (12.7-mm) machine-gun for anti-aircraft and local defence.

Experience gained with 105-mm (4.13-in) howitzers mounted on halftracks enabled the US Army to decide that it would be better if the howitzer was mounted in a fully tracked carriage, and accordingly an M3 medium tank chassis was modified to take such a weapon. The M3 chassis was considerably reworked to provide an open-topped superstructure with the howitzer mounted in its front. The development vehicle was known as the **T32**, and following trials which added a machine-gun mounting to the right-hand side of the fighting compartment, the vehicle was adopted for service as the **Carriage, Motor, 105-mm Howitzer, M7**. The maximum armour thickness was 25.4 mm (1 in).

Priest in action

The first production examples were for the US Army, but many were soon diverted to the Lend-Lease programme for the Allies, among them the British Army. The British soon named the M7 the **Priest**, a popular myth being that the prominent machine-gun mounting gave the impression of a pulpit. The British gunners adopted the M7 with enthusiasm, and the type first went into action with them at the Second

Battle of El Alamein in October 1942. The British asked for 5,500 M7s to be produced for their use alone by the end of 1943, but this order was never completed in full. The figure nonetheless provides an indication of the success of the M7 with the British gunners. They appreciated the space and mobility of the carriage and also the extra space for personal stowage. The one

snag was that the howitzer was not a standard British Army type: thus ammunition (stowage was provided for 69 rounds on each vehicle) had to be supplied separately for the M7 batteries, which made for a considerable logistic complication. This was not resolved until the first Sextons with 25-pdr weapons were issued in 1944. The British M7s were used all through the Italian

campaign, and some were landed in Normandy in June 1944, though they were soon replaced by Sexton equipments.

The M7 then began a new service career in a revised form: the howitzer was removed and the hull was used as an armoured personnel carrier nicknamed the **Kangaroo**. This soon became a normal fate for unwanted M7s, and the idea soon spread to Italy.

American service

The US Army also made wide use of the M7, although production for the US Army was not a constant process. After 1942 M7 pro-

duction proceeded in fits and starts. At one stage the original M3 chassis was replaced by the later M4A3 Sherman chassis, and such M7s were known by the designation **M7B1**.

After 1945 large numbers of M7s were handed over to other countries such as Brazil and Turkey. The M7 was also used during the Korean War. The 105-mm howitzer is still a standard weapon all over the world. Throughout their service life the M7s gave outstanding reliability, and demonstrated their ability to cross all types of rough terrain, although performance in mountainous areas was disappointing.

Right: The M7's weight of 22967 kg (50,634 lb) caused some difficulties for the mobility of the vehicle, and hampered wartime operations in mountainous areas.

Below: An M7 tank destroyer is seen here with US Army markings, although many of the vehicles were supplied to the UK under the Lend-Lease agreement.

SPECIFICATION	
M7	(375 hp)
Crew: 5	**Performance:** maximum road
Weight: 22967 kg (50,634 lb)	speed 41.8 km/h (26 mph);
Dimensions: length 6.02 m (19 ft 9 in); width 2.88 m (9 ft 5¼ in); height 2.54 m (8 ft 4 in)	maximum range 201 km (125 miles)
	Fording: 1.22 m (4 ft)
Powerplant: one Continental R-975 air-cooled 9-cylinder radial engine developing 279.6 kW	**Armament:** one 105-mm (4.13-in) M2 howitzer and one 0.5-in (12.7-mm) M2 machine-gun

Left: An M7 in action in the Ardennes in 1945, with the open fighting compartment covered by a tarpaulin to keep out the worst of the bitter weather. The tank obstacles behind the M7 were taken with ease.

Carriage, Motor, 155-mm Gun, M40 Self-propelled gun

Although the M40 arrived on the scene late in World War II, it was one of the best of all wartime self-propelled guns and went on to enjoy a long post-war career. It used the chassis of the M4 tank as its basis.

The first 155-mm (6.1-in) self-propelled gun produced in quantity by the Americans during World War II was the **M12**, a design originally known as the **T6** and built on a converted M3 medium tank chassis. Starting in December 1943 a new weapon/carriage combination was initiated. The gun was the 155-mm M1A1 known as the 'Long Tom' (with 20 rounds) and the carriage was based on the chassis of the M4A3 medium tank, though much widened and fitted with new suspension springing. The engine was moved from the rear to a new forward position, and a spade which could be lifted for travel was added to absorb some of the recoil. A working platform under the breech was also provided. The gun had a range of 23514 m (25,715 yards) and fired a projectile weighing 43.1 kg (95 lb), which made it a useful counter-battery and long-range bombardment weapon. Armour thickness was 12.7 mm (0.5 in).

The development of this **Carriage, Motor, 155-mm Gun, M40** took rather longer than expected, so it was not until January 1945 that the

first production examples rolled off the lines. They were rushed across the Atlantic in time to see the end of the war in Germany.

M40s took part in the bombardment of Cologne and the short campaigning after this. Between January and May 1945 no less than 311 M40s were built, and production continued after the war. The M40 then saw service during the Korean conflict, where the design

proved to be excellent.

On the M40 there was no protection for the crew as the equipment was intended for use so far behind the front line that none would be necessary. The M40 had a crew of eight and there was provision on the carriage for their weapons and kit. The same carriage was also used to mount an 8-in (203-mm) howitzer, but this version (the **Carriage, Motor, 8-in Howitzer, M43**)

was not used in great numbers; only 48 were built. After 1945 M40s were distributed to other armies. The British Army used the type for some years. More were used by nations such as France, where the type saw extensive service in Indo-China. There was one variant of the M40, the **Cargo Carrier T30**, which could be used as a general supply carrier though its normal deployment was for the

delivery of ammunition to M40 batteries.

The M40 was significant in that it paved the way for the generation of self-propelled weapons that saw service into the 1990s. The type was used extensively for trials to provide protection for the crew. The M40 proved that the only proper protection comes from an armoured turret, and modern self-propelled weapons now use this design feature.

Above: The M40's driver sat at the front of the vehicle with the engine behind him. Two roof hatches were fitted for access to the front of the vehicle.

Above: the M40 was unusual by today's standards in having an open fighting compartment. This was rendered useless by the advent of nuclear weapons.

Left: When the M40's 155-mm gun was being fired, the members of the gun's crew stood on a hinged platform over the spades at the rear of the vehicle.

SPECIFICATION	
M40	air-cooled radial engine developing
Crew: 8	294.6 kW (395 hp)
Weight: 37195 kg (82,000 lb)	**Performance:** maximum road speed
Dimensions: length overall 9.04 m	38.6 km/h (24 mph); maximum range
(29 ft 8 in); width 3.15 m (10 ft 4 in);	161 km (100 miles)
height 2.84 m (9 ft 4 in)	**Fording:** 1.07 m (3 ft 6 in)
Powerplant: one Continental R-975	**Armament:** one 155-mm (6.1-in) gun

Ordnance, Q.F., 2 pdr

40-mm static anti-tank gun

Right: 2-pdr gun crews undergo training during a chemical warfare exercise. The gun in the foreground shows the ammunition box carried on each weapon.

The **2-pdr** anti-tank gun (or more formally the **Ordnance, Q.F., 2 pdr**) is one of those unfortunate weapons that has been given a bad reputation for no real reason other than it had to be used at a time when it was no longer a viable weapon. In its day it was as good as, if not better than any contemporary design, but the rapid increases in tank armour thicknesses during the late 1930s rendered it obsolete just at a time when it was being placed into widespread service.

The 2-pdr had its origins in a British staff requirement dated 1934. Much of the original development was carried out by Vickers-Armstrongs, and the first guns and carriages were produced for commercial sales. Some went to Spain, but the main recipient was the British Army which received its first examples during 1938. Further development was required until the full Army specification could be met and it was not until 1939 that the most commonly encountered carriage (the **Carriage, 2 pdr, Mk III**) was issued.

Compared with many other designs then in existence, the 2-pdr was a complex piece of ordnance and it was almost twice as heavy as any other gun in its

class. The main reason for this weight was the carriage which, in action, rested on a low tripod carriage that provided the gun with 360° traverse. A high shield was provided for the gun crew and there was provision for an ammunition chest to be carried on the back of the gun shield. The philosophy behind the design differed from contemporary thought as well. Many European armies intended the anti-tank gun to be used in a mobile attacking role, but the 2-pdr was intended for use in static defensive positions. The type was also manned by specialist anti-tank personnel from the Royal Artillery.

Shortcomings

The events of 1940 showed the 2-pdr to be at best obsolescent, and the BEF had to leave the bulk of its 2-pdr guns behind at Dunkirk. The gun lacked the power to punch through the thick armour of most of the German tanks, and the effective range was too short for tactical comfort; the projectiles were too light to cause damage at ranges outside the machine-gun range of the target tanks, and many gun crews were thus decimated before they could fire a useful shot. In the United Kingdom, however, the production facilities

A drill-book photograph of a 2-pdr gun and crew in action with the gun about to be loaded. Note that the ammunition is being passed from a box to the rear as the box on the gun shield was for emergencies only.

to produce any modern form of anti-tank gun for the Army that was almost devoid of any form of defence against tanks was quite simply not available. Industry had therefore to carry on producing the 2-pdr at a time when it was realised that it was no longer an effective weapon. The results of this had to be

borne during the North African campaigns of 1941-42, when the 2-pdr proved to be almost useless against the Afrika Korps, to the extent that the 25-pdr field piece had to be used for anti-tank work in its place.

All manner of remedies to make the 2-pdr more successful were tried, one measure being the placement of the gun on the back of an open truck to provide a mobile platform, and another the development of the Littlejohn Adaptor, a squeeze-bore device

attached to the muzzle and firing special skirted projectiles to improve projectile performance.

Neither of these measures saw much use, however, and after 1942 the 2-pdr was withdrawn from use and passed to infantry units for their anti-tank defences. The type did not remain in use for long in that role, but in the Far East the 2-pdr remained in service until 1945, for there the target tanks were generally lighter and the gun could still cope with them.

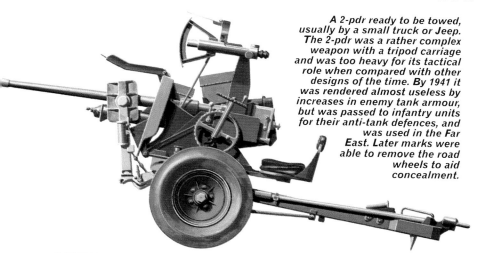

A 2-pdr ready to be towed, usually by a small truck or Jeep. The 2-pdr was a rather complex weapon with a tripod carriage and was too heavy for its tactical role when compared with other designs of the time. By 1941 it was rendered almost useless by increases in enemy tank armour, but was passed to infantry units for their anti-tank defences, and was used in the Far East. Later marks were able to remove the road wheels to aid concealment.

SPECIFICATION	
Ordnance, Q.F., 2 pdr	**Elevation:** -13° to +15°
Calibre: 40 mm (1.575 in)	**Muzzle velocity:** AP 792 m
Length of piece: 2.082 m (6 ft 10 in)	(2,626 ft) per second
Length of rifling: 1.672 m (5 ft 5.84 in)	**Maximum effective range:** 548 m (600 yards)
Weight: complete 831.6 kg (1,848 lb)	**Projectile weight:** 1.08 kg (2.375 lb)
Traverse: 360°	**Armour penetration:** 53 mm (2.08 in) at 455 m (500 yards)

Ordnance, Q.F., 6 pdr 57-mm anti-tank gun

British weapon planners had foreseen the need for an anti-tank gun more powerful than the 2-pdr as early as April 1938, but it took time to develop and then to produce the new gun. During late 1940 production was delayed

as 2-pdr guns occupied the production lines, so that it was not until late 1941 that the new gun reached the troops. This new weapon had a calibre of 57 mm (2.244 in) and fired a projectile weighing about 6 lb

31 May 1942, and a truck-mounted 6-pdr goes into action near Tobruk. Within a month Rommel would have taken the town, and at the same time forced the 8th Army back towards Mersa Matruh and El Alamein.

(2.72 kg) so the new gun was known as the **6-pdr**.

By the time the 6-pdr reached the troops it was sorely needed, and once in action it proved to be effective against the enemy tanks then in use. Compared with the 2-pdr, the 6-pdr was much more conventional and used a split-trail carriage that gave a useful 90° traverse. There were two main variants, the **Ordnance, Q.F., 6 pdr Mk II** and **Ordnance, Q.F., 6 pdr Mk IV**; the **Ordnance, Q.F., 6 pdr Mk I** was used for training only, and the Mks III and V were tank guns. The main difference between the Mks II

and IV was barrel length, that of the Mk IV being slightly longer. Some slight carriage variations were produced but the most drastic was the **Carriage, Q.F., 6 pdr, Mk III**, which was developed for use by airborne units. This was narrower than the norm and the trail legs could be shortened for stowage in gliders; a number of these special conversions were used at Arnhem.

The 6-pdr provided some sterling service in North Africa, but once the Tiger tank appeared on the scene it was realised that the day of the 6-pdr was almost over, for the 2.85-kg (6.28-lb) pro-

jectile was unable to penetrate the thick frontal armour of the Tiger and only a lucky shot to the side could be effective. As a result, the 6-pdr was gradually withdrawn from Royal Artillery use from 1943 onwards. They were issued instead to infantry anti-tank companies and with the infantry the 6-pdr saw out the war. Many were supplied to the Red Army.

The Soviets were not the only recipients of the 6-pdr, for the type was adopted by the Americans also. When the Americans realised that they too would need a heavier anti-tank gun than their

37-mm (1.46-in) M1 they saw that the easiest way to produce something was to copy the 6-pdr, and in early 1941 they obtained a set of drawings from the British and adapted them to suit their own production methods. The result was the **57-mm Antitank Gun M1**. At first the American carriage had a handwheel traverse in place of the shoulder pad of the British original, but in time the Americans adopted the shoulder pad also and in this form the **M1A2** was used until the war ended in 1945. However, it was as a weapon mounted on a

self-propelled carriage that the American gun was most important. Large numbers of M1 guns were produced for mounting on halftracks and in this form the American guns were widely used by the British Army and many other Allied forces as well as by the US Army. The 6-pdr may have been outclassed by heavy tanks such as the Tiger, but against nearly all other German tanks it proved to be effective enough. It was also a relatively light and handy weapon and served on with many armies for long after the end of World War II.

SPECIFICATION	
Ordnance, Q.F., 6 pdr, Mk IV	**Traverse:** 90°
Calibre: 57 mm (2.244 in)	**Elevation:** -5° to +15°
Length of piece: 2.565 m (6 ft 8.95 in)	**Muzzle velocity:** 900 m (2,700 ft) per second
Length of rifling: 2.392 m (7 ft 10.18 in)	**Projectile weight:** 2.85 kg (6.28 lb)
Weight: complete 1112 kg (2,471 lb)	**Armour penetration:** 68.6 mm (2.7 in) at 915 m (1,000 yards)

Although its operational career as a specialist anti-tank gun was relatively short (from 1941 to 1943 at the most), the 6-pdr went on to be a useful infantry anti-tank and support weapon. It was copied by the Americans as the 57-mm Antitank Gun M1 and M1A2 and was used by nearly all the Allied armies at some time or another.

Ordnance, Q.F., 17 pdr 3-in anti-tank gun

By 1941, the rapid increase in the armour protection of tanks was being forecast to the extent where it was realised that not even the 6-pdr would be able to cope. To deal with the expected armour increases it was decided to produce the next generation of anti-tank guns with a calibre of 3-in (76.2-mm) to fire a projectile weighing no less than 17 lb (7.65 kg). It was realised that the resultant gun would be a fair-sized piece of artillery but at the time there seemed to be no other option open, and the development of the gun proceeded with haste.

The first guns, soon known as the **Ordnance, Q.F., 17 pdr** or **17-pdr**, were made as early as August 1942 but these guns were prototypes only and getting the gun into full production took more time. This was to have dramatic results for from North Africa came news that the first consignment of Tiger tanks was expected in the theatre in the very near

future. At that time some guns were ready but they had no carriages. To get some form of heavy anti-tank weapon into the hands of the troops it was decided to fly 100 guns to North Africa, where they were hastily fitted onto 25-pdr field gun carriages to produce a hybrid known as the **17/25-pdr**. The conversions were made just in time, for a few weeks later the first Tigers appeared and the 17/25-pdr was on hand to tackle them. These 17/25-pdr guns served until 'proper' 17-pdr guns were to hand during the early stages of the Italian campaign in 1943.

When the 17-pdr guns arrived the overall design was

low and not too cumbersome. The carriage had long and angled split trails and a large double-thickness armoured shield was fitted. The gun was proportionately long, and was fitted with a muzzle brake and a large and heavy vertical block breech mechanism. To handle the gun a detachment of at least seven men was required, and more were needed if any man-handling was necessary. In mitigation of this factor the gun proved capable of firing a projectile that could penetrate any enemy tank at long ranges and the rate of fire was such that 10 rounds per minute were not uncommon.

By 1945 the 17-pdr was

the standard anti-tank gun of the Royal Artillery anti-tank batteries and many had been handed on to Allied armed forces. The 17-pdr proved to be the last of the British Army's conventional anti-tank guns (a 32-pdr with a calibre

of 94-mm/3.7-in was proposed but a 120-mm/4.72-in recoilless gun was selected instead), and many served on until the 1950s with the British Army. Various types of 17-pdr tank guns were produced as well.

SPECIFICATION	
Ordnance, Q.F., 17 pdr	**Traverse:** 60°
Calibre: 3 in (76.2 mm)	**Elevation:** -6° to +16.5°
Length of piece: 4.443 m (14 ft 6.96 in)	**Muzzle velocity:** 950 m (2,900 ft) per second
Length of rifling: 3.562 m (11 ft 8.25 in)	**Projectile weight:** 7.65 kg (17 lb)
Weight: in action 2923 kg (6,444 lb)	**Armour penetration:** 130 mm (5.12 in) at 915 m (1,000 yards)

By September 1944 the 17-pdr had proved an extremely effective weapon, and in the 8th Army's assault on the Gothic line was well to the fore to deal with German heavy armour.

First introduced into service in small numbers in late 1942, the 17-pdr went on to be one of the most powerful Allied anti-tank guns. Although rather heavy and awkward to move, the 17-pdr had a calibre of 3-in (76.2-mm) and could penetrate up to 130 mm (5.12 in) of armour at about 1000 m (1094 yards). It was used on occasion as a field gun firing HE shells.

3.7-cm Pak 35/36 Anti-tank gun

The origins of the gun that was to become the **3.7-cm Pak 35/36** (Pak standing for *Panzerabwehrkanone*, or anti-tank gun) can be found in 1925. In this year Rheinmetall began the creation of a new anti-tank gun. Manufacture began in 1928, and as the German army was at that time still largely horse-oriented the gun was fitted with spoked wheels for horse traction. In its design the gun was a very modern weapon for the period, and used a well-sloped shield, tubular split-trail legs and a long slender barrel.

Expanded production

At first production was relatively limited, but once the Nazi party came to power in 1933 production was greatly accelerated. In 1934 there appeared the first version with steel wheels and pneumatic tyres suitable for vehicle traction, and the designation 3.7-cm Pak 35/36

was formally assigned to the gun in 1936.

It was in 1936 that the Pak 35/36 first saw action, during the Spanish Civil War. Here the small gun proved eminently capable against the relatively light armoured vehicles used during the conflict. It also proved successful in 1939 against the lightly armed Polish forces, but in 1940 the Pak gun crews encountered the more heavily armoured French and British tanks and had the unfortunate experience of seeing their carefully aimed armour-piercing projectiles bouncing off the hulls of attacking tanks. The truth was that by 1940 the Pak 35/36 had had its day. It was no longer powerful enough to penetrate the armour of the more modern tanks, and larger-calibre weapons had to take its place. However, these latter could not be produced quickly enough, so the 37-mm (1.46-in) guns had to

be rushed to action during the German invasion of the USSR – Operation Barbarossa – in June 1941: here the Pak 35/36 proved to by wholly incapable against the T-34/76 tank. Some attempts were made to prolong the service life of the gun by firing large stick bombs that fitted over the muzzle: these projectiles, although effective, were essentially close-range missiles of dubious combat worth. Consequently the Pak 35/36 was passed to second-line and garrison units, and to some training schools, so the type was still in limited service in 1945. Many carriages were later converted to take 75-mm (2.95-in) barrels for service in the infantry support task.

Export success

The Pak 35/36 was widely exported before 1939, and the design was widely copied in Japan as the **Type 97**. Other

The Pak 35/36 is seen here on exercises before World War II. A Rheinmetall design first produced during the 1920s, at the time of its introduction the gun had a great effect on anti-tank gun design in other nations.

recipient nations were Italy (**Cannone contracarro da 37/45**), the Netherlands (**37-mm Rheinmetall**) and the USSR. In this last the Pak 35/36 was known as the **M30**, was widely copied and formed the basis for a whole family of 37-mm and 45-mm (1.77-in) anti-tank guns that served on for many years

even after 1945. The design was also copied in the US to create the 37-mm Antitank Gun M3, although only the concept was copied as the M3 had many detail differences from the German original. At one point the Germans produced a special version of the Pak 35/36 for paradropping.

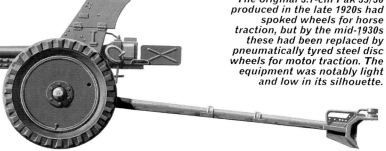

The original 3.7-cm Pak 35/36 produced in the late 1920s had spoked wheels for horse traction, but by the mid-1930s these had been replaced by pneumatically tyred steel disc wheels for motor traction. The equipment was notably light and low in its silhouette.

SPECIFICATION	
3.7-cm Pak 35/36	**Muzzle velocity:** 760 m (2,495 ft)
Calibre: 37 mm (1.46 in)	per second with AP ammunition
Length of gun: 1.665 m (5 ft 5½ in)	**Maximum range:** 7000 m
Length of rifling: 1.308 m (4 ft	(7,655 yards)
3½ in)	**Projectile weight:** AP 0.354 kg
Weights: travelling 440 kg (970 lb)	(0.78 lb) or HE 0.625 kg (1.38 lb)
and in action 328 kg (723 lb)	**Armour penetration:** 38 mm
Traverse: 59˚	(1.48 in) at 30˚ at 365 m (400 yards)
Elevation: -8˚ to +25˚	

5-cm Pak 38

Anti-tank gun

By 1940 the 3.7-cm Pak 35/36 was of very limited value against the armour of the most modern tanks. Fortunately for the German army this had been foreseen as early as 1937, and by 1938 Rheinmetall-Borsig had developed a new gun in 50-mm (1.97-in) calibre. By 1939 the gun was ready for production, but it was not until the mid summer of 1940 that the first examples reached the troops. By then the new gun, designated the **5-cm Pak 38**, was too late to take part in any western European campaign, and it was not until 1941 that the new gun saw its first combat use in a major campaign.

Soviet tank killer

That was the invasion of the USSR, and by that time the new gun had been supplied with a new type of tungsten-cored ammunition known as AP40. This ammunition had been developed from captured Czechoslovakian and Polish

ammunition, and was adopted because the dense tungsten core of the new projectiles offered a considerable increase in armour penetration. This was just as well, for when the Soviet T-34/76 appeared on the battlefield the Pak 38 firing AP40 ammunition proved to be the only gun/projectile combination capable of penetrating the Soviet tank's thick hide. However, the numbers of Pak 38s in the field were limited, the gun could not be everywhere

Above: Soviet troops examine a captured Pak 38 early in the war. With tungsten-cored shot, this 5-cm weapon was the only gun able to knock out the Soviets' T-34/76 tank in 1941 and was still in use in 1945.

The 5-cm Pak 38 was light and possessed a low silhouette, facilitating movement and concealment. A removable dolly wheel under the trail spades eased manhandling. The extensive use of light alloys in the manufacture of its carriage also meant that the gun was easily handled.

and it was some time before extemporised conversions of old French 75-mm (2.95-in) guns could be hurried up to fill the many gaps in the anti-tank defence lines. After that the 50-mm gun proved good enough to remain in use for the rest of the war, although later it was largely replaced by heavier-calibre weapons.

The Pak 38 was a well-designed gun with a curved shield, steel wheels and a tubular split-trail carriage that locked out the torsion-bar suspension when the trail legs were spread. Light alloys were used throughout the construction of the carriage, which made it easy to handle, and a small dolly wheel was mounted under the trail legs for manhandling. The barrel had a muzzle brake.

The Pak 38 was one of the German army's standard anti-tank guns and was further developed with an automatic feed device for the ammunition. The provision of this system allowed the gun to be used as a heavy aircraft weapon, and at one point a variant was fitted to a variant of the Me 262 jet fighter. This same weapon was further adapted for service as a ground-based anti-aircraft gun, but that was only late in the war and it seems that no production was undertaken. There was also a tank gun equivalent of the Pak 38 that was produced in a number of models, many of these weapons finding their way into service as beach-defence guns in Germany's so-called 'Atlantic Wall'.

The Pak 38 was mounted on a number of tracked Panzerjäger carriages. At one point the British Army had captured so many of these weapons that they were reconditioned and stockpiled as contingency weapons in the event of a crisis in the manufacture of British anti-tank guns.

SPECIFICATION	
5-cm Pak 38	**Muzzle velocity:** AP 835 m
Calibre: 50 mm (1.97 in)	(2,903 ft) per second, AP40 1180 m
Length of piece: 3.187 m (10 ft	(3,870 ft) per second, and HE 550 m
5½ in)	(1,805 ft) per second
Length of rifling: 2.381 m (7 ft	**Maximum range:** HE 2650 m
9¾ in)	(2,900 yards)
Weights: travelling 1062 kg	**Projectile weight:** AP 2.06 kg
(2,341 lb) and in action 1000 kg	(4.54 lb), AP40 0.925 kg (2.04 lb) and
(2,205 lb)	HE 1.82 kg (4 lb)
Traverse: 65°	**Armour penetration:** AP40 101 mm
Elevation: -8° to +27°	(3.98 m) at 740 m (820 yards)

7.5-cm Pak 40 Anti-tank gun

By 1939 intimations regarding the next generation of Soviet tanks were filtering back to the German war planner staffs in Berlin. Although the new 50-mm (1.97-in) Pak 38 gun had yet to reach the troops, it was felt that something heavier would be needed to counter the armour of the new Soviet tanks, and consequently Rheinmetall-Borsig was asked to produce a new design. In basic terms what Rheinmetall did was to scale up the Pak 38 to 75-mm (2.95-in) calibre with an L/46 length. The resulting weapon was adopted in 1940 as the **7.5-cm Pak 40**, but it was not until late in the following year that the first examples off the production line reached the hard-pressed troops on the Eastern Front.

Pak 38 origins

In appearance the Pak 40 resembled its predecessor, but there were many differences apart from the scale. The basic layout of the 50-mm gun was retained, but as the expected shortages of many raw materials (especially light alloys that had been earmarked for the Luftwaffe production requirements) were becoming apparent, the Pak 40 was constructed mainly of steel and was thus proportionately much heavier than the smaller gun. To simplify and speed production the shield was formed from flat instead of curved plates, and there were several other such alterations including the omission of the dolly wheel that had made it easy to manoeuvre the trail spades of the Pak 38. However, the result was an excellent gun, able to tackle virtually any Allied tank encountered on all fronts.

The Pak 40 was destined to remain in production until the end of World War II in 1945. It had a tank gun equivalent that was progressively developed, but the Pak 40 itself remained in service virtually unchanged.

A 7.5-cm Pak 40 firing on Polish underground fighters concealed in the ruins of Warsaw during the last stages of the uprising of September and October 1944. Normally the Pak 40 would not be used in such circumstances: the Germans used all the weapons they could to crush the uprising.

A version intended for use as an aircraft weapon was developed as the **Bordkanone 7.5**, and the carriage was even adapted to allow short 75-mm (2.95-in) barrels to be fitted and so create a hybrid infantry support and anti-tank gun to be used by infantry formations. The gun itself was even placed on a 105-mm (4.13-in) howitzer carriage to form a light field artillery piece, though another approach was to use the Pak 40 itself as a field gun: by 1945 there were several artillery formations using this gun as the **7.5-cm FK 40** (FK standing for *Feldkanone*, or field gun).

But it was as an anti-tank gun that the Pak 40 was most important. Many German gunners rated it their best all-round weapon, and many Allied tank crews had occasion to agree with them. The Pak 40 fired a wide range of ammunition, varying from the straightforward solid armour-piercing (AP) shot to the tungsten-cored AP40 projectile. Also available were high explosive (HE) shells that carried enough payload to make the type a useful field artillery piece, and various hollow-charge projectiles. A measure of the gun's efficiency can be seen in its range/armour penetration figures: at a range of 2000 m (2,185 yards) the AP40 projectile could penetrate no less than 98 mm (3.86 in) of armour plate, and a combat range in the order of 500 m (545 yards) this figure increased to 154 mm (6.06 in).

As the German army's 'standard' weapon in its class, the Pak 40 replaced earlier 3.7-cm and 5-cm weapons with specialist battalion and brigade anti-tank units, and was widely used until the end of the war. German anti-tank gun tactics saw Pak 40s distributed to fill the gaps between the heavier 88-mm guns that were often in short supply.

SPECIFICATION	
7.5-cm Pak 40	(2,460 ft) per second, AP40 930 m
Calibre: 75 mm (2.95 in)	(3,050 ft) per second and HE 550 m
Length of piece: 3.7 m (12 ft	(1,805 ft) per second
1¾ in)	**Maximum range:** HE 7680 m
Length of rifling: 2.461 m (8 ft)	(8,400 yards)
Weight: travelling 1500 kg (3,307 lb)	**Projectile weight:** AP 6.8 kg
and in action 1425 kg (3,141.5 lb)	(15 lb), AP40 4.1 kg (9.04 lb) and HE
Traverse: 45°	5.74 kg (12.65 lb)
Elevation: -5° to +22°	**Armour penetration:** 98 mm
Muzzle velocity: AP 750 m	(3.86 in) at 2000 m (2,185 yards)

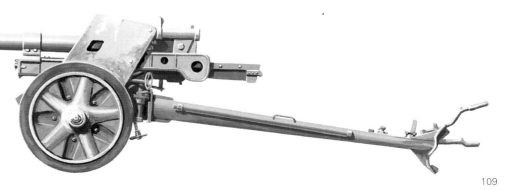

The Pak 40 was considered an excellent weapon and became the German army's 'standard' anti-tank gun. The weapon was first used in action late in 1941.

8.8-cm Pak 43 and 8.8-cm Pak 43/41 Anti-tank guns

The success of the 8.8-cm Flak 18 (Flak for *Fliegerabwehrkanone*, or anti-aircraft gun) as an anti-tank weapon led to the development of a similar weapon for use as a tank gun to arm the large Tiger tank. Further design thought ran along the lines of developing a comparable family of guns for tank, anti-tank and anti-aircraft use. From this came a series of design studies known as the *Gerät 42* (*Gerät* was the designation for equipments still in the design stage), but in the event the anti-aircraft gun specification was pitched at a level where the 88-mm (3.46-in) calibre could not cope and thus the designers concentrated on the tank and anti-tank guns.

Krupp was given the eventual production contract for the new anti-tank gun, and in 1943 produced the **8.8-cm Pak 43**. This was a truly superb gun, but it was also a fairly large one. To move it required a powerful tractor and a large gun team, and once emplaced the gun was removed from its twin-axle carriage to rest upon a large cruciform carriage. It thus lacked the mobility of the smaller anti-tank guns but could knock out virtually any tank likely to enter its sights, even at ranges of over 2500 m (2,735 yards). The Pak 43 bristled with advanced features such as a semi-automatic breech mechanism, an electrical firing circuit with safety cut-outs to prevent firing over unsafe arcs, and a low turntable carriage. It was also difficult to produce in quantity, a factor not helped by the continuous attention given to the various Krupp factories by the Allied bomber fleets, so output was constantly disrupted.

Service entry

When the Pak 43 appeared in service, commanders on all fronts called for more and more of the type and demand consistently outstripped supply. In typical German fashion an extemporised way was found out of this situation by asking Rheinmetall-Borsig to produce its own version from existing resources. The result was the **8.8-cm Pak 43/41**, a combination of various weapons cobbled together to provide the required gun. The basic ordnance of the Pak 43 was retained, but in this instance placed on a new single-axle carriage with a conventional split trail. The carriage came from one gun, the wheels from another and various other components were derived from other sources.

A new shield was produced and the result was a most cumbersome and ungainly design that had one saving grace, the fact that it worked. For despite being very difficult to handle and emplace, the gun retained the power of the original Pak 43. Thus it was tolerated but never gained the respect and praise bestowed upon the superb Pak 43.

A small number of halftrack conversions mounting the '88' on a 12-ton chassis were made, and these saw service in France in 1940.

Tank gun

By 1945 both guns were still in production. The Pak 43 was modified for use on various self-propelled carriages and as the 8.8-cm **KwK 43** tank gun was the main armament of the powerful Tiger II tank. The ammunition fired by these weapons was different from the 88-mm (3.46-in) ammunition fired by the earlier anti-aircraft guns that were the origins of the '43' family, and used a more powerful propellant system.

This ammunition was considered suitable for use in the field artillery role and despite the desperate need for anti-tank guns on all fronts by 1945 many of these guns were used by field artillery batteries.

The German 8.8-cm Pak 43 on its carriage. At the 1000-m (1094-yard) plus range favoured, it was capable of knocking out virtually any Allied tank. However, demand constantly outstripped supply – much to the relief of Allied tank crews.

Left: Advancing British infantry take cover near a concealed 8.8-cm Pak 43, while a British 17-pdr stands ready in the background, during late summer 1944.

SPECIFICATION	
8.8-cm Pak 43	**Muzzle velocity:** AP 1130 m
Calibre: 88 mm (3.46 in)	(3,707 ft) per second, and HE 950 m
Length of piece: 6.61 m (21 ft 8 in)	(3,118 ft) per second
Length of rifling: 5.13 m (16 ft 9¾ in)	**Maximum range:** HE 15150 m (16,570 yards)
Weight: travelling 4750 kg (10,472 lb) and in action 3650 kg (8,047 lb)	**Projectile weight:** AP 10.16 or 7.3 kg (22.4 or 16.1 lb), and HE 9.4 kg (20.7 lb)
Traverse: 360°	**Armour penetration:** 184 mm (7.244 in) at 2000 m (2,190 yards)
Elevation: -8° to +40°	

Below: This self-propelled anti-tank carriage was an early attempt to place the famous '88', the 8.8-cm Flak 18, onto a mobile platform, in this case a 12-ton artillery tractor halftrack.

Taper-bore anti-tank guns

The German taper-bore guns were an odd off-shoot from the main avenue of anti-tank development that, although successful, foundered for the simple fact that the German war economy could not afford the raw materials required to produce them. Three guns were produced and issued for service, and all relied on what is commonly known as the Gerlich principle. In simple terms this involved the use of a small projectile core made from tungsten, a hard and very dense metal ideal for punching a way through armour plating. In order to provide this tungsten core with the maximum punch the Gerlich system involved the use of guns with calibres that tapered downwards in size from the breech to the muzzle. The special projectiles involved used flanged or 'skirted' forms that allowed the flanges to fold back as the bore narrowed. This had the advantage of increasing the emergent velocity of the projectile, enabling it to travel farther and to hit the target harder. The principle was attractive to the German ordnance designers who adapted it for the anti-tank gun, but the principle had some disadvantages: to ensure the maximum power of the gun expensive and relatively rare tungsten had to be used for the projectile core, and the guns themselves were costly to produce.

The first of the taper-bore guns to enter service was the **2.8-cm schwere Panzerbüchse 41 (2.8-cm sPzB 41)**, which was really little more than a heavy anti-tank rifle, with a bore that tapered from 28 mm (1.1 in) at the breech to 20 mm (0.787 in) at the muzzle. It used a light carriage, but an even lighter version of the carriage was produced for the German airborne formations. Both types were still in use at the end of the war.

Light anti-tank gun

Second in this series of taper-bore guns was the **4.2-cm leichte Panzerabwehrkanone 41**

(**4.2-cm lePak 41**, or light anti-tank gun 41). This used the carriage of the 3.7-cm Pak 35/36 but the ordnance was tapered from 40.3 mm (1.586 in) at the start to 29.4 mm (1.157 in) at the muzzle. These guns were issued to airborne units, namely the Luftwaffe's Fallschirmjäger.

Largest of the trio was the **7.5-cm Pak 41**. This was a very powerful and advanced gun in which the bore decreased from 75 mm (2.95 in) to 55 mm (2.16 in). At one time this gun showed so much promise that it almost took over from the 7.5-cm Pak 40 as the standard German anti-tank gun, but despite having a better armour-piercing performance it was passed over because of the German tungsten shortage. Tungsten was normally used for the machine tools to produce more weapons, but the raw materials had to be brought into Germany by blockade runners and when these were repeatedly intercepted on the high seas the supplies dwindled. It was a choice between anti-tank guns and machine tools, and the result had to be the machine tools. Thus production of the taper-bore guns

Above: The 2.8-cm schwere Panzerbüsche 41 was the smallest of the German taper-bore guns, and was produced in two forms: one had large road wheels while a special airborne version, shown here, had small wheels and a light tubular alloy carriage.

ceased. Only 150 Pak 41s were made, and once their ammunition had been expended they passed from use. The same applied to the other two guns, though the sPzB 41 was still in use in 1945 as its small projectiles made few demands on available stocks.

SPECIFICATION	
7.5-cm Pak 41	**Elevation:** -10° to +18°
Starting calibre: 75 mm (2.95 in)	**Muzzle velocity:** AP 1230 m (4,035 ft) per second
Emergent calibre: 55 mm (2.16 in)	**Projectile weight:** AP 2.5 kg (5.51 lb)
Length of barrel: 4.32 m (14 ft 2 in)	
Weight: in action 1390 kg (3,064 lb)	**Armour penetration:** 171 mm (6.73 in) at 455 m (500 yards)
Traverse: 60°	

Below: A 2.8-cm sPzB 41 is carried on a Kfz 15 light signals vehicle in order to provide a useful boost in firepower to a normally lightly-armed unit. The gun is carried complete with its light wheeled carriage.

SPECIFICATION	
2.8-cm sPzB 41	**Elevation:** -5° to +45°
Starting calibre: 28 mm (1.1 in)	**Muzzle velocity:** AP 1400 m (4,593 ft) per second
Emergent calibre: 20 mm (0.787 in)	**Projectile weight:** AP 0.124 kg (0.27 lb)
Length of barrel: 1.7 m (5 ft 7 in)	
Weight: in action 223 kg (492 lb)	**Armour penetration:** 56 mm (2.205 in) at 365 m (400 yards)
Traverse: 90°	

SPECIFICATION	
4.2-cm lePak 41	**Traverse:** 60°
Starting calibre: 40.3 mm (1.586 in)	**Elevation:** -8° to +25°
Emergent calibre: 29.4 mm (1.157 in)	**Muzzle velocity:** 1265 m (4,150 ft) per second
Length of barrel: 2.25 m (7 ft 4.6 in)	**Projectile weight:** AP 0.336 kg (0.74 lb)
Weight: in action 560 kg (1,234.5 lb)	**Armour penetration:** 72 mm (2.835 in) at 455 m (500 yards)

The 7.5-cm Pak 41 was the largest of the German taper-bore guns, but was prevented by the general tungsten shortage then prevalent in Germany from becoming the standard German army heavy anti-tank gun.

8.8-cm Pak 43/41

The 8.8-cm Pak 43/41 was produced by Rheinmetall-Borsig in an attempt to simplify the manufacture of the 8.8-cm Pak 43. The barrel was unaltered, but the breech and breech mechanism were much simplified and the main carriage was adapted from that of the 105-cm 1eFH 18 field howitzer. The wheels came from the 15-cm sFH 18 howitzer. A brute to handle and move, its crews nicknamed it 'Scheunentor' (barn door). Nevertheless, it retained all of the power of the '88' and was deadly to almost all Allied armour. Despite appearing somewhat cobbled together, the powerful Pak 43/41 was rushed into production to augment the other '88s' in the field.

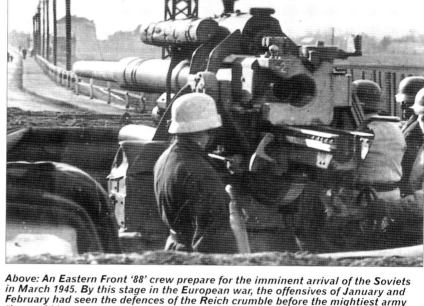

Above: An Eastern Front '88' crew prepare for the imminent arrival of the Soviets in March 1945. By this stage in the European war, the offensives of January and February had seen the defences of the Reich crumble before the mightiest army the world has ever seen, the Soviets were within 100 km (62 miles) of Berlin, and for the '88', the war was almost over.

Left: This Flak '88' is seen in the elevated firing position. When deployed as an AA weapon, the '88' was operated by a team of six plus ammunition handlers.

Below: A Flak 18 anti-aircraft gun is manhandled across a pontoon bridge during the May 1940 campaign in France. The river may be the Meuse, where around eight '88s' were used not only to make the crossing possible but also to break up isolated French attacks once a bridgehead was established.

The combination that destroyed so many British and Commonwealth tanks in the desert war comprised the 8.8-cm Flak 18 and its companion SdKfz halftrack. This 8-ton prime-mover could carry 12 personnel and their equipment plus ammunition. This example was active during the Battle of El Alamein in October 1942.

Desert '88's

Rommel had gained first-hand experience of the effectiveness of the '88' as a tank-killer when these weapons knocked out Valentine Mk II tanks at Arras in 1940, but the gun was to find further success during Rommel's desert war.

In many respects the 'Eighty-Eight', as it would be known to British and Commonwealth forces in North Africa, was similar to many other medium anti-aircraft guns developed between the wars. The difference was that the Germans brought it into the front-line to use as an anti-tank gun. At the factory it was fitted with both anti-aircraft and anti-tank sights, but the AA sights were often removed in the field.

Long-range engagements

In the wide expanses of the North African desert the '88' could reign truly supreme. Often tank targets could be spotted over considerable range, but the first intimation that an '88' was in the vicinity came when an Allied tank exploded. The speed at which the incoming projectile travelled was such that it impacted before the sound of the gun firing could be heard, and the use of delayed-action fuses meant that the shells exploded only after they had penetrated the tank armour. Under these conditions the '88' became a highly feared weapon, but its effect was often enhanced by Allied tactics. British cavalry style tank tactics as well as the poor design of the 8th Army tanks made them very vulnerable to the '88'. All too often British and Commonwealth tanks simply charged at points heavily defended by the Germans, with the result that they were

Above: A Flak '88' is pictured in the North African desert. Wheel bogies were retained near to the cruciform firing platforms for a possible rapid withdrawal. High and bulky, the '88' could be vulnerable in flat terrain.

Below: An '88' in action in the Western Desert during June 1942. A number of these guns were handed over to the Italian army in Africa, who designated them Cannone Antiaero da 88/56 modello 36.

picked off by the emplaced '88's. On more than one occasion the '88's were instrumental in breaking up tank attacks even before they began.

In North Africa when the '88' was jacked down onto its cruciform platform and dug in, the heat haze made it very hard to detect and it provided a potent anti-tank screen behind which Afrika Korps tanks could retire. As with all weapons in the desert the blast when the gun fired kicked up

dust and sand, and so to ensure that he could spot targets the commander was normally in a trench off to one side.

Crew protection

As an anti-aircraft gun the '88' was not provided with a shield, but to give the crew protection against machine-gun fire and shrapnel, a large square shield was fitted. As was common practice, Afrika Korps crews painted black and white 'kill' bands around the barrel to indicate how many British and Commonwealth tanks they had knocked out. Such was the reputation of the '88' that almost any incoming fire, whether from artillery or anti-tank guns was always attributed to '88's.

Reflecting overall German strategy, which emphasised the avoidance of conventional tank versus tank actions, the Afrika Korps frequently lured impetuous British and Commonwealth tanks into carefully prepared '88' killing grounds, where they were subsequently shot to pieces by the dug-in anti-tank guns. Note the 'kill' bands applied to the barrel of this gun.

8.8-cm Pak 43/41

8.8-cm Pak 43 anti-tank gun

Almost as soon as development of a new family of multi-role guns got under way the planners decided to increase the specifications demanded from the AA gun, and Krupp promptly withdrew from the contest (the gun was never developed by anyone else) but instead went ahead with the anti-tank and tank guns. This gun owed nothing to the earlier AA guns and fired an entirely new range of ammunition. It retained the two-wheeled bogie units and the cruciform layout for the carriage, but the gun was mounted low down on a 360° turntable and was protected by a well-sloped shield. The Pak 43 turned out to be one of the best anti-tanks produced anywhere during World War II and had a remarkable performance that surpassed even that of the Flak guns. The main problem was that Germany could not produce enough of them. Almost as soon as it got under way, production at Essen was disrupted by Allied air raids and more time was lost as the production facilities were established elsewhere. Also the gun was rather demanding of materials and facilities to the point where an alternative was sought. The alternative was found in the shape of the equally powerful 8.8-cm Pak 43/41.

A change of role

The '88' was known to the Germans as the 8.8-cm Flak 18 (Flak being the abbreviation of *Fliegerabwehrkanone*, or anti-aircraft gun) and it was issued both to the army and the emergent Luftwaffe as the defence of Germany against air attack was deemed to be a matter for the Luftwaffe. The army guns went to anti-aircraft battalions under direct army control. As such they were intended for the protection of field units against air attack, and initially they were used only in this role. But that changed at some point during the Spanish Civil War that raged from 1936 to 1939. The exact point at which the '88' made the transition from anti-aircraft gun to anti-tank gun is now shrouded in mystery but it probably took place during the fighting that went on around Madrid for much of the war. On the Republican side large numbers of tanks were supplied from various sources, while on the Nationalist side there was the direct intervention of German and Italian contingents armed with the appropriate weapons. This included '88's on the German side, and at some point a tank attack was countered by the simple expedient of lowering the barrel of one or more of the '88' guns emplaced for anti-aircraft use to fire directly at the attacking armour. The results must have been spectacular, for the tanks of the day were only lightly armoured, and the impact of an '88' projectile would have been devastating.

'88' variants

By 1941 the 8.8-cm Flak 18 had been joined in service by two further versions, the 8.8-cm Flak 36 and 8.8-cm Flak 37. These two guns differed from one another in details such as the fire-control systems and changes to the carriages, but many items were interchangeable between them and the earlier 8.8-cm Flak 18. These three guns remained in service throughout the war, the 8.8-cm Flak 36 and 8.8-cm Flak 37 remaining in production right until 1945. They had to bear the brunt of the anti-aircraft defence of the Reich, and also of the army units in the field, so there gradually grew up what was to become a constant source of squabbling between the various user arms. The Luftwaffe demanded more and more guns to defend the Reich, and the army wanted more and more for its dual purpose gun requirements. It was a squabble that was never resolved to anyone's satisfaction, despite various efforts to get new models into the field.

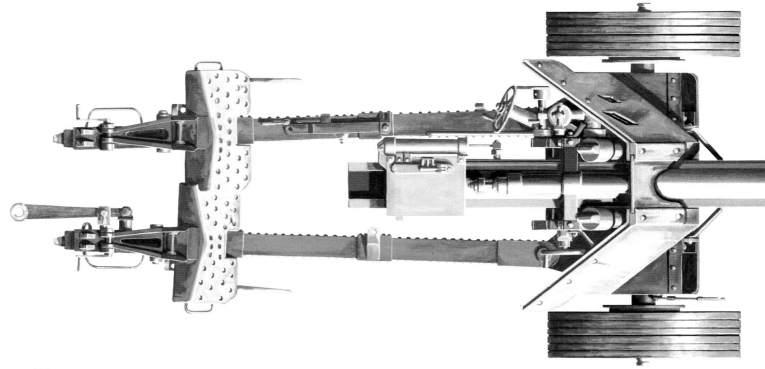

Operation Barbarossa

By the time the Germans invaded the Soviet Union in 1941, the '88' was well established as an anti-tank gun, which was just as well, for the '88' was the only gun to hand (other than the 5-cm Pak 38 firing special AP40 ammunition) that could tackle the T-34/76 tank. Special anti-armour projectiles had been developed for the '88', including an armour-piercing shot that could penetrate 100 mm (3.94 in) of armour at 1830 m (2,000 yards).

Battle of France

The short duration of the war in Poland and the overwhelming defeat of the Poles had the effect of disguising the new role of the '88', so that when the Germans advanced into France in May 1940 the effect of the '88' came again as a definite shock, this time to the French and British armies. The '88' was used as a bunker-buster during the short approach to the River Meuse through the Ardennes, and during the crossing of the Meuse more were used to cover the risky crossings. However, it was left until the British armoured counter-attack around Arras for the point to be rammed home that the Germans had a weapon that could defeat even the heavy armour of the Matilda infantry tanks. The crews of these tanks suffered terribly as the heavy projectiles smashed their way into the interiors before exploding, destroying both the tank and the crew, and this British suffering continued once the '88' was taken to North Africa with the Afrika Korps.

Panzer armament

Not all the '88's were towed. The original '88' was developed into a tank gun, the 8.8-cm KwK 36, and this was mounted in the Tiger tank. The 8.8-cm Pak 43 also had a tank counterpart, the 8.8-cm KwK 43 fitted to the massive Tiger II.

Waffen SS man an '88' in Greece during May 1941. By this time, the '88' was widely used in the anti-armour role with specialist projectiles. Frontal shields were often added for crew protection.

Range

Experience showed that tanks could be knocked out by the '88' at ranges of over 2000 m (2,190 yards). The '88' also demonstrated that is was equally useful as a device for knocking out battlefield emplacements and bunkers, the high explosive projectile intended for use against aircraft being equally effective against structures. These facts were duly noted by the German war planners, and thus the '88' became a dual-purpose weapon, and a key component of the German army's tactical repertoire. Outside Spain few other military observers took notice of the fact, so during the invasion of Poland in September 1939, the '88' took the defenders completely by surprise: the Poles learned the hard way that their tanks were vulnerable at ranges hitherto thought safe.

'88' shortcomings

Despite all its power and effectiveness, the '88' was not a perfect anti-tank weapon: it was very bulky, and it was slow to get in and out of action. It was possible to fire the gun directly from its wheeled carriage, but for full use to be made of the gun it had to be emplaced on the cruciform carriage. This meant lowering it from the two-wheeled bogie units, a time-consuming business. Moreover, to enable the '88' to be used in the anti-tank role, much of the anti-aircraft fire control instrumentation had either to be removed or rendered useless, which limited the utility of the gun and diverted it from its intended purpose. A shield could be added to provide the crew with some measure of protection but this was often not used so the crew was vulnerable to incoming fire, which was used by the Allies as a means to counter the weapon. If possible the area around the gun was saturated with artillery fire.

'88' in action From Flak to tank-killer

One of the oddest facts relating to anti-tank guns in service during World War II is that the most famous such weapon was not an anti-tank gun at all but an anti-aircraft (AA) gun. This was the famous (or infamous) '88', the gun that could knock out any tank it could see at ranges well outside those of normal anti-tank guns. The weapon gained for itself a reputation that in some ways overshadowed the disadvantages of the gun, but the fact was that the '88' was used as an anti-tank gun on the very day World War II started and it was still knocking out tanks when the war ended.

8.8-cm Flak 18
Designed by a Krupp team in Sweden (in order to circumvent the conditions of the Treaty of Versailles) the 8.8-cm Flak 18 (right) entered production in 1933, and with the National Socialist state was to become legendary. Originally made with a one-piece barrel, later models were equipped with multi-sectioned barrels to allow replacement of worn sections. Seen here on the Sonderhanger 201 carriage (the later model 202 travelled with the barrel to the rear), the Flak 18 was usually towed by the eight-tonne SdKfz 7 halftrack.

Improving the '88'
One of the earliest measures taken to improve the '88' was the introduction of a new model, the 8.8-cm Flak 41. This was an entirely new gun designed and developed by Rheinmetall-Borsig, but despite the facts that it had excellent all-round performance and fired an entirely new range of ammunition, it had too many technical faults (which proved to be inherent) and the bulk of those produced were assigned to anti-aircraft defences only. Shortly after the 8.8-cm Flak 41 entered service, Krupp was asked to develop a new design of gun that could be used as an anti-aircraft, anti-tank and tank gun. Krupp assigned the new design the cover name Gerät 42. This emerged as the 8.8-cm Pak 43 anti-tank gun.

Above and below: The key to the success of the '88' was the very high velocity of its shells. It could damage most Allied tanks even when firing high-explosive rounds, and with armour-piercing shot it was lethal. Anti-tank guns and AA guns have a number of key features in common – both are designed to fire projectiles at high velocities with flat trajectories. Give an AA gun the right kind of ammunition, and it becomes a highly effective tank killer. However, at the outbreak of the war, the only AA gun equipped to fight tanks was the Flak 18.

8.8-cm Flak 41
The 8.8-cm Flak 41 (right) was never really free from problems in its service career, as a result of its complicated construction. Seen here dismounted from its Sonderhanger carriage, the Flak 41 was usually retained for service within the Reich. In spite of operational difficulties, it was widely regarded as the finest of the German heavy AA weapons. Although capable of firing 25 rounds per minute, and with a muzzle velocity of 1000 m (3,280 ft) per second giving a maximum effective ceiling of 14700 m (48,320 ft), the complexity of manufacture allowed only 318 pieces to see operational deployment.

Eisenbahn '88'
The '88' was also adopted as a railway gun. Although in this role the '88' was used only for anti-aircraft work, large numbers were used on special trains that were pulled around the Reich to defend areas affected by Allied air attacks.

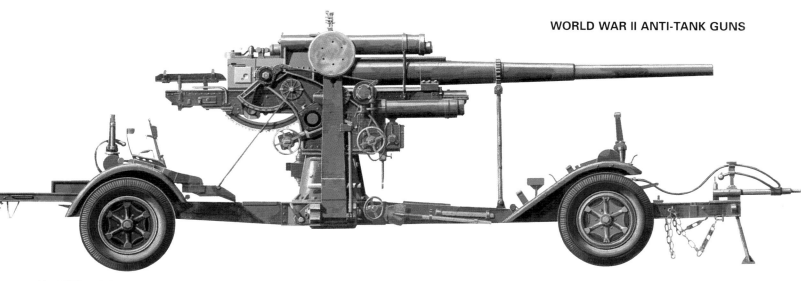

Above: An '88' is put on tow after its capture by the 7th Army in January 1945. For a brief period, these guns were used by the US Army. A rear-pointing barrel was the identifying feature of the Sonderhanger 202 wheeled carriage.

Below: An 8.8-cm Flak 36 anti-aircraft gun is seen in action during the Soviet campaign. After the tribulations of the bitter winter of 1941, the German army had by now become more familiar with sub-zero fighting.

Mobile '88's

Early on in the life of the 8.8-cm Flak 18 attempts were made to convert the guns for the self-propelled role. One of the earliest of these involved the use of a wheeled bus chassis, but by 1940 the '88' was carried into action in France mounted on halftrack chassis (heavy halftracks were also used to tow '88s'). After the introduction of the 8.8-cm Pak 43, numerous tracked chassis were converted to carry the gun in a self-propelled role. One of the earliest of these was the Elefant, which proved to be a spectacular failure during the Battle of Kursk in 1943. Later vehicles were more successful, while others never passed the project stage. One of the best of the self-propelled '88's was the Jagdpanther, which mounted a special version of the 8.8-cm Pak 43 in a well-sloped superstructure built onto the chassis of a Panther tank. This combination was by far the best all-round tank destroyer design of World War II.

Early development

The '88' was designed and developed as an anti-aircraft gun, the actual design and development of the gun being carried out not in Germany but in Sweden during the 1920s when gun designing was forbidden to Krupp by the terms of the Treaty of Versailles. Krupp got around this by setting up a design team based in Sweden but funded by the German army. By 1932 they had produced an excellent anti-aircraft gun carried between two bogie axle units and pivot-mounted on a cruciform carriage when emplaced. The barrel was long and slender and it had a high muzzle velocity between 820 and 840 m (2,690 and 2,755 ft) per second. The projectile weighed 9.6 kg (21.16 lb) and the maximum ceiling to which this projectile could be fired was 10600 m (34,775 ft). For the period, this performance was little short of excellent and when the new German army started to re-arm during 1933, numbers of '88's were already coming from the Krupp production lines at Essen.

Böher 4.7-cm Austrian anti-tank gun

The diminutive **Böhler 4.7-cm** (1.85-in) anti-tank gun was first produced in 1935, and is thus sometimes known as the **Model 35**. It was first produced in Austria but its use soon spread outside that nation and licences to produce the gun were taken up by Italy. In fact the Italian production run reached the point where the Böhler gun became regarded almost as an indigenous Italian weapon, designated as the **Cannone da 47/32 M35**.

The Böhler gun was a useful weapon that was soon diverted into other roles. It was widely issued as an infantry gun and as it could be rapidly broken down into a number of pack loads it was also employed as a mountain gun. But though, as it turned out, the Böhler was something of a multi-purpose weapon, it was not entirely successful in any of these extra roles. It did prove to be a fairly effective anti-tank gun, however, and was widely used during the early war years by a number of nations. Italy was the main user, but others were employed by the Netherlands (**Kanon van 4.7**), and Romania, and the type also turned up in the Soviet Union (in relatively small quantities) as the **M35B**. Some also found their way into German army service when Austria came under German domination after 1938, receiving the designation **4.7-cm Pak**.

There were several developments on the basic Böhler theme that issued from the company's Kapfenberg works. Although the basic gun remained unchanged, there were numerous variations on such things as types of carriage wheel, the width of the carriage axle and so on. Some models had muzzle brakes while others did not. All models had a feature whereby the wheels could be removed and the gun then rested on the trail legs and a small platform under the axle for firing. This gave the gun a lower silhouette for firing and concealment. The gun could fire both armour piercing and high explosive projectiles, the latter having a range of 7000 m (7,655 yards) to provide the gun with a useful infantry support role. As the armour thicknesses of tanks increased, the Böhler increasingly assumed this infantry support role.

There was one odd side-line to the story of the Böhler that is still little known. In 1942 the Allied armies in North Africa were still relatively short of many weapons and the large numbers of captured Italian Böhler guns were a useful windfall. About 100 were refurbished at a Captured Weapons Depot in Alexandria and issued to various units for second-line service. But perhaps the oddest item in this story was that 96 were actually

Above and left: In action the 47-mm Böhler anti-tank gun was often used with the wheels removed and with the forward part of the carriage resting on a firing platform. A periscope sight was used, even for anti-tank use, and no shield was usually fitted. The gun could be broken down into loads for pack transport on mules.

converted by the British for use by airborne forces: the fire-control system of the original gun was altered so that one man (instead of the original two) could lay the gun, and the carriage was modified to allow dropping by parachute; a rifle telescope for aiming and a shoulder pad from a 6-pdr gun were also added. These were, according to the records, issued for service where they proved 'very popular'. Unfortunately it has not yet been possible to trace the units involved, but these Böhler guns must have been among the very first guns adopted for the airborne role.

Built in great numbers in Italy, this Cannone da 47/32 M35 is seen in the infantry support role in North Africa, with the barrel elevated for increased range.

SPECIFICATION	
Cannone da 47/32 M35	**Muzzle velocity:** AP 630 m
Calibre: 47 mm (1.85 in)	(2,067 ft) per second and HE 250 m
Length of barrel: 1.68 m (5 ft 6 in)	(820 ft) per second
Length of bore: 1.525 m (5 ft)	**Maximum range:** HE 7000 m
Length of rifling: 1.33 m (4 ft 4⅓ in)	(7,655 yards)
Weight: travelling 315 kg (694.5 lb)	**Projectile weight:** AP 1.44 kg
and in action 277 kg (610.6 lb)	(3.175 lb) and HE 2.37 kg (5.225 lb)
Traverse: 62°	**Armour penetration:** 43 mm
Elevation: -15° to +56°	(1.7 in) at 500 m (550 yards)

Skoda 47-mm kanon P.U.V. vz 36 Czech anti-tank gun

The Czech firm of Skoda, based at Pilsen, was one of the first European armaments manufacturers to turn its attention to the production of specialised anti-tank guns. All through the 1920s Skoda's technicians and designers carried out a long chain of experiments and design studies to formulate a viable anti-tank gun, and in 1934 the company produced a gun with a calibre of 37 mm (1.46 in). For various reasons this weapon was not widely adopted (it was generally felt that something heavier would be needed) and in 1936 there appeared the **Skoda 47-mm kanon P.U.V. vz 36** (vz for *vzor*, or model). The vz 36 had a cali-

bre of 47 mm (1.85 in) and was immediately ordered into production by the Czech army.

In its day the vz 36 was one of the most powerful and hardest-hitting of all the contemporary European anti-tank guns. It fired a relatively heavy projectile, weighing 1.65 kg (3.6 lb), and this projectile could penetrate any tank then in service at ranges of up to 640 m (700 yards) at a time when most similar guns were confined to targets no more than 186 to 275 m (200 to 300 yards) distant. But despite this power the vz 36 appeared a rather clumsy design. It had anachronistic spoked wheels

German soldiers manhandle their 4.7-cm Pak 36(t) during training prior to the 1940 invasion of France. The soldiers are wearing drag-rope slings for towing the gun, and a full gun crew would comprise at least four men.

and a very long trail which split to form two legs when in the firing position. The crew was protected by a shield that had over the wheel flaps that were folded out in action, but an oddity was that the upper rim of the shield was finished off as an asymmetric curved line to aid concealment, the wavy line breaking up the

outline. The gun had a prominent recoil cylinder over the barrel and another recognition feature was the unusual single-baffle muzzle brake.

vz 36 in service

Production for the Czech army proceeded at a high priority, and a few guns were exported to Yugoslavia at one point. In service the vz 36 was issued to the specialist anti-tank companies of the Czech army, but was found to be a bit of a handful for the infantry anti-tank units, for whom a developed version of the earlier 37-mm gun was placed in production. This became the **kanon P.U.V. vz 37** and although this gun followed the same general lines as the larger 47-mm model it was recognisable by the use of more modern steel

wheels with rubber tyres.

The vz 36 was destined never to fire a shot for its Czech masters, for the Munich Agreement of 1938 allowed the Germans to take over the Czech Sudetenland defences without a shot being fired. This allowed the Germans to impress large numbers of a very special version of the vz 36 that had been developed for use in static fortifications, but large numbers of the wheeled vz 36 fell into German hands during the following year when Germany took over control of the rest of Czechoslovakia. The vz 36 then became the **43-cm Pak 36(t)** and was eagerly added to the German gun parks. The Czech gun became a virtual standard weapon with the German army and remained in use with some

of their second-line units until the end of the war in 1945. It was mounted on several types of tracked chassis to become the armament of several German Panzerjäger and proved itself to be a very viable anti-armour weapon. However, the vz 37s did not remain in German service long after 1941.

An illustration from a Skoda brochure that advertised their 47-mm Model 1936 anti-tank gun for export sale. The gun is here being towed using drag ropes.

SPECIFICATION	
Kanon P.U.V. vz 36	**Muzzle velocity:** AP 775 m
Calibre: 47 mm (1.85 in)	(2,543 ft) per second
Length of barrel: 2.04 m (6 ft 8 in)	**Maximum range:** 4000 m (4,375 yards)
Weight: travelling 605 kg (1,334 lb) and in action 590 kg (1,300 lb)	**Projectile weight:** AP 1.64 kg (3.6 lb) and HE 1.5 kg (3.3 lb)
Traverse: 50°	**Armour penetration:** 51 mm (2 in) at 640 m (700 yards)
Elevation: -8° to +26°	

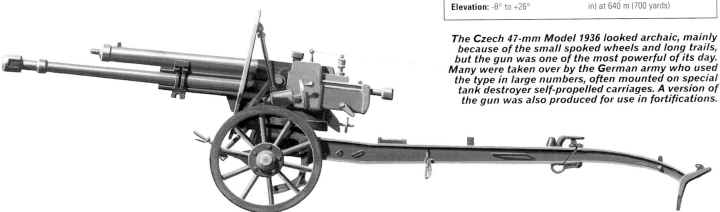

The Czech 47-mm Model 1936 looked archaic, mainly because of the small spoked wheels and long trails, but the gun was one of the most powerful of its day. Many were taken over by the German army who used the type in large numbers, often mounted on special tank destroyer self-propelled carriages. A version of the gun was also produced for use in fortifications.

47-mm Anti-tank Gun Type 1 Japanese anti-tank gun

As with so many other weapons, Japan was short of anti-tank guns and had only a limited capacity to produce the numbers required. In 1934 it had introduced the 37-mm Gun Type 94 for use by infantry units, but realised even then that this gun would have only a limited performance, and it was therefore supplemented by the licence production of the 37-mm Anti-tank Gun Type 97, the origin of which was the German 3.7-cm Pak 35/36.

It was not until 1941 that a heavier gun was introduced in the form of the **47-mm Anti-tank Gun Type 1**. In overall design terms the Type 1 was entirely orthodox and used a split-trail carriage and a well-sloped shield. Compared with designs then being produced in Europe the Type 1 was not very powerful, but the Japanese considered it adequate as it had the advantage of a semi-automatic sliding breech carried over from the 37-mm (1.46-in) German gun, giving it a relatively high rate of fire; this was a possible 15 rounds a

The Japanese Anti-tank Gun Type 1 was the only indigenous Japanese weapon produced exclusively for the anti-tank role, and although it was effective against most light Allied armour it was never produced in significant enough numbers to make any overall impression.

minute. As with many other Japanese weapons ease of handling was given high priority, and the Type 1 proved to be easy to handle in action and it was relatively light. In combat this advantage was often squandered for as the Allies advanced these guns were often statically emplaced and were manned by crews who favoured death rather than capture.

Extreme measures

Production of the Type 1 was never sufficient to meet the needs of hard-pressed Japanese army units as the Allies advanced on all fronts, and consequently the Japanese were forced to use all manner of anti-tank

methods, ranging from pressing into use naval and anti-aircraft guns to the extreme of suicide attackers armed with pole charges and explosive blocks. By 1945 the use of such measures was becoming commonplace.

Despite the fact that the Japanese learned early on in the conflict that their small tanks were likely to be of very limited use against their Allied equivalents, they still diverted a proportion of the Type 1 gun production

towards producing a tank gun for their Type 97 tank. The Type 1 was regarded as the standard Japanese anti-tank gun, and most of them were issued to regi-

mental and divisional anti-tank battalions. The 47-mm Anti-tank Gun Type 1 remained in production from 1941 until the war ended in 1945.

SPECIFICATION	
47-mm Anti-Tank Gun Type 1	**Muzzle velocity:** AP 824 m
Calibre: 47 mm (1.46 in)	(2,700 ft) per second
Length of barrel: 2.527 m (8 ft 3½ in)	**Projectile weight:** APHE 1.528 kg (3.37 lb) and APHE 1.4 kg (3.08 lb)
Weight: in action 747 kg (1,660 lb)	**Armour penetration:** 51 mm (2 in) at 915 m (1,000 yards)
Traverse: 60°	
Elevation: -11° to +19°	

Soviet 45-mm anti-tank guns Models 1932, 1937, 1938 & 1942

The Soviet Union purchased a batch of 37-mm (1.46-in) Rheinmetall anti-tank guns as early as 1930, and standardised the type as the M30 well before the German army adopted the identical model as the 3.7-cm Pak 35/36. The Soviets decided to licence-produce the 37-mm gun, but in 1932 produced their own variant with a calibre of 45 mm (1.77 in). This was the **M1932**, and this could be identified by the wire-spoked wheels that were fitted to the otherwise unchanged Rheinmetall-based carriage. By 1940 there were large numbers of these guns in service with the Red Army and some had even been used in action on the Republican side during the Spanish Civil War.

In 1937 the slightly revised **Model 1937** appeared, and in the following year a tank gun variant, the **M1938**, was produced. These two guns first saw major action during the short but intense war with Finland during 1939 and 1940, but in many ways this war gave the Red Army the wrong impression of the effectiveness of their guns. The Finns had only small numbers of light armoured vehicles and the M1932 and M1937 proved quite effective

against these. But when the Germans invaded the Soviet Union in 1941, the Red Army found out the hard way that its guns could not penetrate the armour of most German tanks. The only way the Red Army could stop the German attacks was to use massed artillery fire against the German formations, and although there was an obvious need for heavier anti-tank guns the Soviet war industry was in no position to produce any such new weapons. The huge German advances had overrun many of the Soviet military industrial centres, and it took time to set up new facilities deep in the hinterland of the Soviet Union.

Lengthened model

When a new gun did appear it was nothing more than a lengthened version of the existing gun. The original M32 had a barrel that was about 46 calibres long (L/46) while the new gun had a barrel that was 66 calibres long. This extension of barrel length increased the muzzle velocity and provided the projectile with more penetrating power. The new and longer gun was produced some time during 1942 and was thus named the **M1942**, but it took time for appreciable numbers to reach the

A Model 1942 in action in early 1945 on the final approaches to Danzig as the Red Army advanced westwards during the last winter of the war. The Model 1942 was still in large scale Red Army use at this time and remained so post-war.

front line. In the meantime the M1938 tank gun was called upon partially to fill the gaps. Numbers of these tank guns were placed on simple improvised carriages and rushed into action. These conversions were of limited value as they had only a small traverse arc, but they did work and as such were

better than nothing.

M1942 in service

When the M1942 did get into the front line it proved to be more effective than the earlier guns, but only marginally so, yet the Soviets continued to produce large numbers throughout the war. These

SPECIFICATION	
45-mm M1942	**Muzzle velocity:** 820 m (2,690 ft) per second
Calibre: 45 mm (1.77 in)	**Projectile weight:** 1.43 kg (3.151 lb)
Length of barrel: 2.967 m (9 ft 8¾ in)	**Armour penetration:** 95 mm (3.74 in) at 300 m (330 yards)
Weight: in action 570 kg (1,257 lb)	
Traverse: 60°	
Elevation: -8° to +25°	

M1942 guns had pressed steel wheels in place of the earlier wire-spoked units, and the trail legs were longer, but the Rheinmetall origins could still be seen. Although it would appear that the M1942 had only a limited performance against the later tanks the type long remained in service with some of the smaller Soviet-influenced armies following the war. Some were encountered during the Korean War and during some of the Middle East wars.

In 1941, the Soviet designers followed the increase in anti-tank calibres prevalent elsewhere. The first gun to be introduced had a calibre of 57 mm (2.24 in) and is known as the M1941 and in 1944 a massive gun with a calibre of 100 mm (3.94 in) was introduced as the M1944.

A Soviet 45-mm anti-tank gun in action. Copied and enlarged from a German design, the weapon was really too small for use against heavier German armour, but was retained in use.

Below: The 45-mm (1.77-in) Model 1942 was a scaled-up version of the earlier 37-mm (1.46-in) Model 1930. The Model 1930 was a licence-produced version of the German Pak 35/36 but the 45-mm Model 1945 had a proportionately much longer barrel and very often wire wheels in place of the original steel disc wheels.

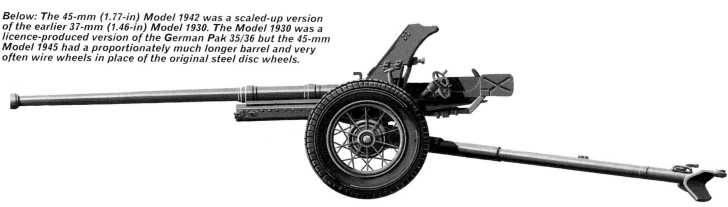

Soviet 76.2-mm guns Models 1936, 1939, & 1942

One of the most widely used of the German heavy anti-tank guns was not originally a German weapon at all but a Soviet design. This hybrid weapon was originally designed as a field gun and was known as the 76.2-mm (3-in) **M1936**. It was the latest in a line of gun designs that stretched back many years, and the first of them were issued to the Red Army during 1939. The M1936 was a rather heavy gun for the field role and it possessed a long slender barrel mounted on a heavy but strong carriage that was ideally suited to the harsh conditions of the Soviet terrain.

In 1941 the lack of a suitable anti-tank gun other than the 45-mm (1.77-in) M1932 led to the simple expedient of using field guns for defence against tanks. In this role the M1936 proved itself to be an excellent anti-armour gun and, even firing high-explosive shells, was powerful enough to inflict damage on German tanks of all kinds. This fact was duly noted by the Germans when they came to contemplate a use for the huge stockpiles of M1936 guns that they captured during 1941 and 1942. Many were simply turned around against their former owners, but large numbers were returned to Germany where they were reconditioned and altered to accommodate German ammunition. A muzzle brake was added and the fire controls altered for the

anti-tank role, the result being the **7.62-cm Pak 36(r)**, an excellent heavy anti-tank gun that was used on all fronts from North Africa to the Soviet Union.

Back in the Soviet Union, as early as 1939, a new field gun lighter than the M1936 was produced as the **M1939**. This was smaller overall than the M1936 with a shorter barrel. Again, many fell into German hands in 1941, and these were converted for German use, some as anti-tank guns. The Soviet designers produced other 76.2-mm field guns in 1941 and at one desperate point were even placing 76.2-mm tank guns on lash-up carriages in order to produce something to keep the advancing German army forces at bay, but in 1942 came the first of what can be regarded as dual-purpose guns.

Dual-role gun

This was the 76.2-mm **M1942**, or **ZiZ-2**, a versatile light field gun that could be readily used as an anti-tank gun if and when necessary. The M1942 had a light carriage that used split tubular trails, and the gun barrel was fitted with a muzzle brake. By the time it first appeared at the front, the Red Army was well versed in the art of using field artillery against attacking armoured vehicles and during many battles the Red Army relied on field guns alone for defence. They simply turned their guns, of all calibres, against the target

A Model 1936 field gun in service with the Germans in North Africa converted for anti-tank use as the 7.62-cm Pak 36(r), a role in which the gun excelled.

and started firing. The well-balanced M1942 was ideal for this type of employment. It was also very sturdy, and as it fired a shell weighing 6.21 kg (13.69 lb), it could pack a useful punch when fired against tanks. The M1942 turned out to be one of the best artillery

pieces ever produced in the Soviet Union, where the type was churned out in thousands, and the type continued to remain a front-line equipment with many

armies around the world during the Cold War. Between 1943 and 1945, the German also found any captured examples very useful indeed.

Above: The Soviet 76.2-mm gun made a superb specialist anti-tank gun and was considered by many to be one of the best all-round anti-tank guns of the war.

Left: Red Army artillerymen fire 76.2-mm anti-tank guns on the First Ukrainian front during 1944. Note the use of both rifles and sub-machine guns as personal weapons.

SPECIFICATION	
7.62-cm Pak 36(r)	**Elevation:** -6° to +25°
Calibre: 76.2 mm (3 in)	**Muzzle velocity:** AP40 990 m
Length of piece: 4.179 m (13 ft	(3,250 ft) per second
8½ in)	**Maximum range:** HE 13580 m
Length of rifling: 2.93 m (9 ft	(14,585 yards)
7⅓ in)	**Projectile weight:** AP 7.54 kg
Weight: in action 1730 kg	(16.79 lb) and AP40 4.05 kg (8.9 lb)
(3,770 lb)	**Armour penetration:** AP40 98 mm
Traverse: 60°	(3.86 in) at 500 m (545 yards)

The Soviet 76.2-mm Model 1942 ZiZ-2 field gun was not intended primarily to be an anti-tank gun, but on many occasions it was used as such and proved to be very effective. Firing mainly HE shells it was able to knock out nearly all contemporary tanks or at least inflict severe damage.

37-mm Antitank Gun M3 Anti-tank gun

When the US Army Ordnance Department decided to develop an anti-tank gun before 1939 it obtained an example of the German 3.7-cm Pak 35/36, and using this as a starting point proceeded to design a similar weapon, also in 37-mm (1.46-in) calibre. The result was outwardly different from the German original but was in fact closely influenced by it. The American gun was designated the **37-mm Antitank Gun M3**, but only a few had been made before it was decided to fit the gun with a muzzle brake, the change making the M3 the **M3A1**.

The muzzle brake was fitted in an attempt to reduce the recoil forces on the carriage, which was even lighter than the German orig-

Although it appeared to be a very different weapon, the 37-mm M3A1 was closely influenced by the German Rheinmetall 3.7-cm Pak 35/36. Soon overtaken by armour increases in Europe, many were used as infantry support weapons in the Pacific.

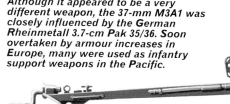

inal, but as it was soon discovered that the muzzle brake was unnecessary it was removed, though the guns were still produced with the fixtures on the muzzle for ease of production. The rest of the gun and carriage was quite unremarkable. The carriage used the usual split trails but the

main carriage axle was rather wider than on other similar designs. A small flat shield was provided for the gun crew and the breech mechanism was copied directly from the German gun and remained a vertical drop block.

Pacific service

By the time the diminutive M3A1 had been taken into service it was obsolete. By 1941 events elsewhere had demonstrated that something larger than 37 mm would be required to penetrate the armoured hides of in-service enemy tanks and although the M3A1 was used in North Africa by the US Army the type was withdrawn there and replaced by heavier guns. However, it was a different scenario in the Pacific theatre where the expected enemy tanks were light (and in any event few and far between), so a place could be found for the M3A1 as an infantry support

Although the European war had shown it to be obsolete, the M3 was still in US Army service at the Kasserine Pass in 1943, where it proved disastrously inadequate against the veteran Afrika Korps armour.

weapon. HE and canister rounds were developed for use during the various island-hopping campaigns and the armour-piercing (AP) projectiles were often called upon during 'bunker-busting' operations. The light weight of the gun proved to be highly effective during these amphibious operations, so production continued specifically for the Pacific operations. By 1945 no fewer than 18,702 M3s had been produced. A tank gun version was also produced in large numbers for use in American light tanks and armoured cars.

After 1945 many M3A1s

were handed out to nations friendly to the Americans, and many long remained in use in some Central and South American states. Numbers were also converted to become saluting guns with blank cartridges.

During World War II many attempts were made to turn the M3A1 into a self-propelled anti-tank weapon, but very few were ever used operationally for the simple reason that the gun lacked the power to tackle the tanks it was likely to encounter in the field. However, as an infantry support gun it proved to be excellent.

SPECIFICATION	
37-mm Antitank Gun M3A1	**Muzzle velocity:** AP 885 m
Calibre: 37 mm (1.45 in)	(2,900 ft) per second
Length of piece: 1.98 m (6 ft	**Maximum effective range:**
10½ in)	457 m (500 yards)
Weight: travelling 410.4 kg (912 lb)	**Projectile weight:** 0.86 kg (1.92 lb)
Traverse: 60°	**Armour penetration:** 25.4 mm
Elevation: -10° to +15°	(1 in) at 915 m (1,000 yards)

3-in Antitank Gun M5 Anti-tank gun

When the US Army Ordnance Department decided during 1942 to produce a new heavy anti-tank gun it took a course of action that had already been taken elsewhere: it decided to combine existing weapon components to produce a new gun. The gun itself was taken from the 3-in (76.2-mm) Antiaircraft Gun M3 but the chamber had to be altered slightly to take different ammunition. The new gun was modified to take the breech mechanism of the 105-mm (4.13-in) Howitzer M2A1, then in full-scale production, and the same howitzer was used to supply the carriage and the recoil system. The new carriage became the **Gun Carriage M1** and in

this form the original straight shield of the 105-mm howitzer was retained but in time the shield was modified to have sloping shield plates and this became the **Gun Carriage M6**.

Penetration power

The new gun itself became the **3-in Antitank Gun M5**, and it turned out to be a remarkably workmanlike-looking weapon. It was rather large and heavy for its role, but in this respect was no worse than many of its contemporaries and in action soon proved capable of being able to penetrate up to 84 mm (3.3 in) of sloping armour at ranges of almost 2000 m (2,190 yards). Not surpris-

ingly the M5 proved to be a popular weapon with the anti-tank batteries of the US Army, and the type was used in all theatres of the war. Numerous types of armour-piercing ammunition were developed for the M5, but one of the more widely used was the capped armour-piercing (APC) projectile known as the **M62**. However, the M5 did have a disadvantage and that was its weight. Rapid movement of the M5 proved to be a major task, and a heavy 6x6 truck had to be used to tow the weapon although lighter tractors could be used on occasions where the terrain permitted.

The first M5s were issued for service in December 1941 but it took

time for the weapon to be issued widely. The M5 was also in demand as the armament for a series of self-propelled tank destroyer projects, the most important of which turned out to be the M10A1 (discussed elsewhere), an open-topped M4 Sherman variant that mounted the M5 in a special turret. The importance of this demand can be seen as 2,500 M5s were completed for the anti-tank gun

role compared to 6,824 guns produced for the M10A1.

Withdrawal

Despite its success, once the war ended the M5 was gradually withdrawn from US Army service and passed to reserve units. It was overtaken by newer and more technologically advanced forms of anti-tank weapon and few examples remained in use after 1950.

SPECIFICATION	
3-in Antitank Gun M5	(2,600 ft) per second; APC 853 m
Calibre: 76.2 mm (3 in)	(2,800 ft) per second
Length of piece: 4.02 m (13 ft	**Maximum effective range:**
2½ in)	1830 m (2,000 yards)
Weight: travelling 2653.5 kg	**Projectile weight:** AP and APC
(5,850 lb)	6.94 kg (15.43 lb)
Traverse: 46°	**Armour penetration:** 84 mm
Elevation: -5.5° to +30°	(3.31 in) at 1830 m (2,000 yards)
Muzzle velocity: AP 793 m	

The 3-in Antitank Gun M5 was an improvised weapon using the barrel of an anti-aircraft gun and the breech and carriage of a 105-mm howitzer together with some new components. The resultant weapon worked surprisingly well and proved to be a very effective tank destroyer although it was rather cumbersome to move in a hurry.

French 25-mm anti-tank guns SA-L mle 1934/1937

The first of two French 25-mm (0.98-in) anti-tank guns (in many references the correct term should be cannon instead of guns as the calibre of 25 mm is generally considered too light to apply to a gun) was the **Canon léger de 25 antichar SA-L mle 1934**. Produced by Hotchkiss et Cie, this weapon was based on the design of a gun originally intended for use in World War I tanks but

too late for that conflict as its development was not completed until 1920. In 1932 Hotchkiss conceived the idea of placing the design on a light wheeled carriage in response to a French army requirement. The design was adopted in 1934 (hence the mle 1934 in the designation), and by 1939 there were well over 3,000 such equipments in service with the French army.

The other French 25-mm. gun was the **Canon léger de 25 antichar SA-L mle 1937**. This was a later arrival, designed and developed by the Atelier de Puteaux (APX), and first offered for service in 1937. It was not adopted for service until 1938 and the numbers produced for service never approached those of the mle 1934. In appearance the mle 1937 looked very similar to the mle 1934,

but it was much lighter and had a slightly longer barrel. In fact the two guns were intended for different service roles: the mle 1934 was issued to nearly all French army armoured units and specialised anti-tank units, while the mle 1937 was intended for use by the support companies of infantry battalions. The latter equipments were towed by horses, one horse pulling the gun towed behind a small limber vehicle, this carrying the ammunition and all the gun crew's kit and equipment. When the mle 1937 was towed in this fashion the cone-shaped muzzle brake was removed and stowed over the breech.

British Army use

The mle 1934 was a serviceable enough weapon, but its calibre was too small for the gun to be of much use against the German armour that swept across France in 1940. By that time the mle 1934 was also in use with the British Army. In a show of Allied co-operation it had been decided that the BEF would use the mle 1934 as its anti-tank gun but this did not turn out well in practice. The BEF was the only all-mechanised formation in

Europe at that time and when it tried to tow the mle 1934s behind its vehicles the guns very quickly proved to be too flimsy to withstand the hard knocks involved. Thus the BEF carried the guns on its vehicles and the mle 1934 became the first British portée gun. The mle 1937 fared even less well in service. It was even less stoutly built than the mle 1934 and ran into weakness problems even when confined to the horse-drawn role. The main problem with both guns was that the round they fired was too small to make any sort of impact on attacking armour and their combat ranges were limited to something like 300 m (330 yards). Even in 1940 this was far too low for tactical comfort, but the French army had invested heavily in the 25-mm guns, so all too often they were the only such weapons available.

In the 1940 campaign large numbers of these 25-mm guns fell into the hands of the Germans, who retained some for a while under the designations **2.5-cm Pak 112(f)** and **2.5-cm Pak 113(f)** to provide their occupation divisions with some form of anti-tank weapon. They do not appear to have been used long after 1942.

Right: Too flimsy for towing, the 25-mm Hotchkiss anti-tank gun, once issued to the BEF, was light enough to be carried on a 15-cwt truck.

Below: Seen in a retouched image, the Canon léger de 25 antichar SA-L mle 1934 proved to be virtually useless against even light tank armour in 1940.

SPECIFICATION	
Canon léger de 25 antichar SA-L mle 1937	per second
Calibre: 25 mm (0.98 in)	**Maximum range:** 1800 m (1,968 yards)
Length of barrel: 1.925 m (6 ft 4 in)	**Projectile weight:** AP 0.32 kg (0.7 lb)
Weight: in action 310 kg (683.5 lb)	**Armour penetration:** at 25° 40 mm (1.57 in) at 400 m (440 yards)
Traverse: 37°	
Elevation: -10° to +26°	
Muzzle velocity: 900 m (2,953 ft)	

Canon de 47 antichar SA mle 1937 French anti-tank gun

The best of the French anti-tank guns was the **Canon de 46 antichar SA mle 1937**, designed by the Atelier de Puteaux. It was developed rapidly and introduced into service once the French army had become aware of the armour thickness of the PZKpfw IV tank. Considering the rush with which the mle 1937 was developed it was one of the best anti-tank weapons in service anywhere in 1939.

The main trouble for the French army was that there were not enough of them to hand in May 1940.

The mle 1937 was introduced into limited service in 1938, but the main production run was in 1939. The type was issued to artillery batteries operating in support of army divisions and brigades, and was operated in batteries of six guns each. The guns were usually towed into action behind Somua

halftracks, and in action their low profile made them easy to conceal. They were capable of penetrating the armour of any tank likely to be put into action against them. In appearance the mle 1937 looked powerful and low. The gun carriage used pressed steel wheels with solid rubber rims. On top of the shield was a corrugated outline to break up the shape.

Along with production of the towed model went production of a similar gun for use in the permanent fortifications of the Maginot Line. This version lacked the carriage of the towed version and instead was swung into its firing position (through

specially constructed firing slits) suspended from overhead rails. In 1939 there appeared a slightly revised version known as the **Canon de 47 antichar SA mle 1937/39**, with detail differences. In 1940 there appeared the **Canon de 47 antichar SA mle 1939**. This used the original gun mounted on a new tripod carriage so arranged that once it was emplaced the gun could be swung through 360°. To emplace the gun a forward leg of the tripod was swung down, the trail legs were spread and the wheels were then raised to positions on

each side of the shield. This concept never saw service, for the events of May 1940 intervened before production could start.

May and June 1940 saw the bulk of the mle 1937s pass into German hands. The Germans regarded the mle 1937 highly, and after 1940 they used the mle 1937 widely as the **4.7-cm Pak 141(f)**; the gun was still in service when the Allies landed in Normandy in June 1944. The Germans also used the mle 1937 to arm many early Panzerjäger conversions produced from captured French tanks.

The Puteaux mle 1939 was a more involved development of the 47-mm mle 1937 using a complex all-round traverse carriage, although some were produced with normal wheeled carriages.

SPECIFICATION	
Canon de 47 antichar SA mle 1937	**Elevation:** -13° to +16.5°
Calibre: 47 mm (1.85 in)	**Muzzle velocity:** 855 m (2,805 ft) per second
Length of barrel: 2.49 m (8 ft 2 in)	**Maximum range:** 6500 m (7,110 yards)
Weight: travelling 1090 kg (2,403 lb) and in action 1050 kg (2,315 lb)	**Projectile weight:** 1.725 kg (3.8 lb)
Traverse: 68°	**Armour penetration:** 80 mm (3.15 in) at 200 m (220 yards)

15-cm Wurfgranate 41 HE/smoke artillery rocket

The 15-cm (5.9-in) German artillery rockets were the mainstay of the large number of German army *Nebelwerfer* (literally smoke-throwing) units, initially formed to produce smoke screens for various tactical uses but later diverted to use artillery rockets as well. The 15-cm rockets were extensively tested by the Germans at Kummersdorf West during the late 1930s and by 1941 the first were ready for issue to the troops.

The 15-cm rockets were of two main types: the **15-cm Wurfgranate 41 Spreng** (high explosive) and **15-cm Wurfgranate 41 w Kh Nebel** (smoke). In appearance both were similar and had an unusual layout, in that the rocket venturi that produced the spin stabilisation were located some two-thirds of the way along the rocket body with the main payload behind them. This ensured that when the main explosive payload detonated the remains of the rocket motor added to the overall destructive effects. In flight the rocket had a distinctive droning sound that gave rise to the Allied nickname 'Moaning Minnie'. Special versions were issued for arctic and tropical use.

Launcher types

The first launcher issued for use with these rockets was a single-rail device known as the **'Do-Gerät'** (after the leader of the German rocket teams, General Dornberger). It was appar-

ently intended for use by airborne units, but in the event was little used. Instead the main launcher for the 15-cm rockets was the **15-cm Nebelwerfer 41**. This fired six rockets from tubular launchers carried on a converted 3.7-cm Pak 35/36 anti-tank gun carriage. The tubes were arranged in a rough circle and were fired electrically one at a time in a fixed sequence that lasted around 10 seconds. It was recommended that the launcher crew withdrew to a distance of at least 15 m

(16 yards) prior to firing.

The maximum range of these rockets was variable, but usually about 6900 m (7,545 yards), and they were normally fired en masse by batteries of 12 or more launchers. When so used the effects of such a bombardment could be devastating as the rockets could cover a considerable area of target terrain and the blast of their payloads was powerful.

Halftrack carriers

On the move the Nebelwerfer 41s were usually towed by light halftracks that also carried extra ammunition and other equipment, but in 1942 a halftracked launcher was issued. This was the **15-cm Panzerwerfer 42** which continued to use the 15-cm rocket with the launcher tubes arranged in two horizontal rows of five on the top of an Opel SdKfz 4/1 Maultier armoured halftrack. These effective vehicles

Above: The 15-cm Panzerwerfer 42 was not only more mobile, but more survivable; rockets betrayed their position the moment they fired, so to avoid enemy artillery fire they needed to change position rapidly.

The 15-cm (5.9-in) rockets were among the earliest in widespread use by the German army, following an extensive pre-war test programme. Originally fired from a 6-barrel mount converted from the Pak 35/36 anti-tank gun carriage, by 1942 the 10-tube launcher had been developed.

were used to supply supporting fire for armoured operations, and their mobility ensured them greater survivability than static projectors. The Panzerwerfer 42 could carry up to 10 rockets ready for use in the launcher and a further 10 weapons inside the armoured body. Later in the war similar launchers were used on armoured schwere

Wehrmachtschlepper (SWS) halftracks that were also used to tow more Nebelwerfer 41s. The SWS could carry up to 26 rockets inside its armoured hull.

The 15-cm rockets were also used with the launchers intended for the 30-cm (11.8-in) rockets, with special rails for the smaller rockets fitted into the existing 30-cm launcher rails.

SPECIFICATION

15-cm Wurfgranate 41 Spreng
Dimensions: length 979 mm (38.55 in); diameter 158 mm (6.22 in)
Weights: overall 31.8 kg (70 lb); propellant 6.35 kg (14 lb); filling 2.5 kg (5.5 lb)
Performance: initial velocity 342 m (1,120 ft) per second; range 7055 m (7,715 yards)

15-cm Wurfgranate 41 w Kh Nebel
Dimensions: length 1.02 m (40.16 in); diameter 158 mm (6.22 in)
Weights: overall 35.9 kg (79 lb); propellant 6.35 kg (14 lb); filling 3.86 kg (8.5 lb)
Performance: initial velocity 342 m (1,120 ft) per second; range 6905 m (7,550 yards)

21-cm Wurfgranate 42 HE artillery rocket

Following on from the success of their 15-cm (5.9-in) rockets, German designers decided to produce a larger rocket which by 1941 emerged as a 210-mm (8.27-in) design. At first sight this rocket, known as the **21-cm Wurfgranate 42 Spreng**, looked exactly like a

conventional artillery projectile, but closer examination showed that the base had 22 angled venturi to impart the important spin stabilisation. The long streamlined nose was also deceptive, for it was hollow and the warhead proper was located some distance from the tip.

This rocket contained no less than 10.17 kg (22.4 lb) of high explosive which on detonation produced a powerful blast effect. The weapon

Entering service in 1943, the 21-cm Wurfgranate 42 was to have used the same carriage as the 15-cm (5.9-in) rocket, but the number of tubes had to be reduced to five to compensate for the increased charge. The Americans were so impressed by the 21-cm weapon that they copied it.

SPECIFICATION

21-cm Wurfgranate 42 Spreng
Dimensions: length 1.25 m (49.21 in); body diameter 210 mm (8.27 in)
Weights: overall 109.55 kg (241.5 lb); propellant 18.27 kg (40.25 lb); explosive 10.17 kg (22.4 lb)
Performance: initial velocity 320 m (1,050 ft) per second; range about 7850 m (8,585 yards)

was so successful in this destructive role that only high explosive versions were produced.

Rocket projector

The 21-cm rocket was used with only one type of projector, the **21-cm Nebelwerfer 42**. The first such equipment appeared in action in the Soviet Union during 1943 as it took some time to finalise the launcher design.

Originally this was to have been a simple enlargement of the existing 15-cm Nebelwerfer 41 complete with six launcher tubes, but the larger calibre gave rise to some imbalance problems when the launcher was being towed and fired, so the number of tubes was eventually reduced to five and that solved the problems. In all other respects the carriage was the same as the earlier design and was a modification of the 3.7-cm Pak 35/36 anti-tank gun carriage. As with the 15-cm rockets the firing of the 21-cm weapon was by electrical means. Once the rockets had been loaded in

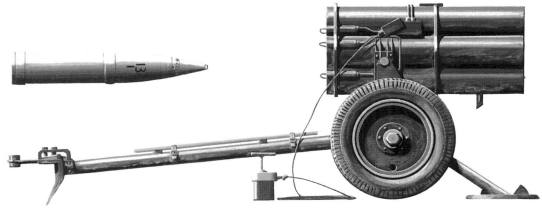

their tubes the launcher crew withdrew to a safe distance (or even took cover), and on receipt of the firing order one of the crew operated a special switch-gear box and the full load of rockets were fired one at a time in a fixed sequence.

The salvo firing of the rockets produced a considerable amount of smoke and dust that revealed the launcher and battery position to the enemy, and during their trajectory the rockets

produced their characteristic moaning noise that made them so distinctive as a weapon.

This combination of smoke, dust and noise meant that the Nebelwerfer troops had to be experts at getting in and out of action quickly, for any firing of the large salvoes necessary to cover a target quickly produced counterbattery artillery or rocket fire that could have the effect of neutralising the launcher units.

The 21-cm rocket superficially resembled a conventional artillery round, but its streamlined nose was hollow and its base had 22 angled venturi to produce spin stabilisation.

US copy

The 21-cm rockets made a considerable impression on all who had to endure their effects, and the Americans in particular considered the rocket and launcher design to be so far in advance of anything they could produce that they took some examples back to the US

and copied them. The US version was the 210-mm (8.27-in) **T36**, which was used for a series of trials and research programmes that did nothing to produce an operational weapon but which added considerably to the Americans' knowledge of artillery rocket technology.

28-cm and 32-cm Wurfkörper HE/incendiary artillery rockets

The 28-cm (11-in) and 32-cm (12.6-in) rockets preceded the 15-cm (5.9-in) rockets in service with the German army, the first of them being issued for use during 1940. The two rockets shared the same rocket motor, but differed in their payload. Both were awkward and bulky rockets with a poor ballistic shape, but both had powerful payloads.

The smaller weapon was the **28-cm Wurfkörper Spreng**, which used a heavy high explosive warhead, while the larger weapon was the **32-cm Wurfkörper M F1 50** with an incendiary warhead in heavy liquid form. Both had a range limitation of just over 2000 m (2,185 yards) and were highly inaccurate despite their spin stabilisation, and were consequently used en masse whenever possible. Counterbalancing these disadvantages was the fact that both were devastating in their effects if they hit a target, and the high explosive rocket was highly regarded for use in urban fighting where houses or other structures had to be demolished.

Launching methods

Both rockets were issued to the troops in wooden carrying crates, or **Packkiste**. These crates doubled as launching frames and were fitted with simple forward supporting legs for rudimentary aiming purposes. In this form both rockets could be used by assault pioneers to demolish bunkers or strongpoints, but more

The short-ranged but powerful 28-cm and 32-cm rockets were among the first to be fitted to vehicles, in this case the ubiquitous SdKfz 251 halftrack. This conversion was known as the 'Foot Stuka' or 'Howling Cow'.

often the rockets were used in batches of four resting on simple launcher frames known as the **schweres Wurfgerät 40** or **schweres Wurfgerät 41**, which differed from each other only in that the latter was tubular steel-framed rather than wooden-framed. Both could be used for pre-arranged barrages, as during the siege of Sevastopol in 1942. However, this launching method was static, and to provide some form of mobility the **28/32-cm Nebelwerfer 41** was developed. This was a simple trailer with frames for six rockets in two superimposed rows of three, and after the 15-cm Nebelwerfer 41, this launcher was the

most important early equipment of the Nebelwerfer units.

Halftrack launcher

Another and still more mobile launcher for these rockets was the **schwerer Wurfrahmen 40**, in which six launcher frames were mounted on the sides of an SdKfz 251/1 halftrack. The rockets were mounted on the side frames still in their carrying crates. Aiming was achieved by simply pointing the vehicle towards the target, and the rockets were then fired one at a time in a set sequence. This rocket/vehicle combination had several names but was often known as the **'Stuka-zu-Fuss'** or

'heulende Kuh' ('Foot Stuka' or 'Howling Cow') and was often used to support Panzer operations, especially in the early days of Operation Barbarossa, the invasion of the Soviet Union. Later in the war other vehicles, usually captured French or other impressed vehicles, were

used to bulk out the numbers of mobile launchers available. All manner of light armoured vehicles were used in this role, some carrying a reduced load of four launchers. Many of these improvised launcher vehicles were used during the fighting in Normandy in 1944.

SPECIFICATION	
28-cm Wurfkörper Spreng	**32-cm Wurfkörper M F1 50**
Dimensions: length 1.19 m (46.85 in); body diameter 280 mm (11 in)	**Dimensions:** length 1.289 m (50.75 in); body diameter 320 mm (12.6 in)
Weights: overall 82.2 kg (181 lb); propellant 6.6 kg (14.56 lb); filling 49.9 kg (110 lb)	**Weights:** overall 79 kg (174 lb); propellant 6.6 kg (14.56 lb); filling 39.8 kg (87.7 lb)
Performance: range about 2138 m (2,337 yards)	**Performance:** range about 2028 m (2,217 yards)

30-cm Wurfkörper 42 Artillery rocket

Compared with 28-cm (11-in) and 32-cm (12.6-in) rockets which preceded it, the **30-cm Wurfkörper 42 Spreng** (also known as the **Wurfkörper Spreng 4491**) was a considerable improvement on the earlier designs when it appeared on the artillery scene during late 1942. Not only was it in aerodynamic terms a much smoother and cleaner design, but it had a much higher propellant/payload ratio than any other German artillery rocket. However, to the troops in the fields these technicalities were far less important than the fact that the more advanced type of propellant used with the new rocket produced far less smoke and exhaust trails than the other rockets, and was thus far less likely to give away the firing position. But for all this improvement the 30-cm (11.8-in) rocket did not have any marked range advantages over the existing rockets. It had a theoretical range of some 6000 m (6,560 yards), but practical ranges were of the order of

4550 m (4,975 yards).

Rail launcher
The first launcher used with the new 30-cm rockets was the **30-cm Nebelwerfer 42**. This was a simple conversion of the 28/32-cm Nebelwerfer 41 with the simple rail launching frames altered to accommodate the new rocket shape and size. But this simple conversion did not last long, for almost as it was issued a new programme of rationalisation was drawn up and the special trailer of the Nebelwerfer 41 and 42 was eliminated. Instead, a new trailer based on the carriage of the 5-cm (1.97-in) Pak 38 anti-tank gun was placed into production and the 30-cm launcher frames were placed on this to produce the **30-cm Raketenwerfer 56**; to ensure that the new launcher could be used to the maximum each was provided with a set of launcher rail inserts to allow 15-cm (5.9-in) rockets to be fired if required. When not in use, these 15-cm rails were stacked on

A gunner places some rather optimistic camouflage over a 30-cm (11.8-in) rocket launcher. Initially fired from modified 28/32-cm launchers, the 30-cm rocket was soon provided with its own carriage, based on that of the 5-cm (1.97-in) Pak 38 anti-tank gun.

top of the 30-cm frames.
Yet another rationalisation was that the 30-cm rockets could also be fired from the schwerer Wurfrahmen launcher frames of the SdKfz 251/1 halftrack, originally intended for use by the 28-cm and 32-cm rockets. When launched from these frames, the 30-cm rockets were fired from their carrying crates or Packkiste, and no doubt the 30-cm rockets were used by assault pioneers for direct firing from their crates in the same manner as the earlier 28-cm and 32-cm weapons.

Limited action
Despite its relative improvements over the earlier artillery rockets, the 30-cm rocket was not used in very great numbers. The earlier rockets remained in service right until the end of the war despite a late attempt to replace all existing weapons, including the 30-cm type, by

an entirely new 12-cm (4.72-in) spin-stabilised design. This decision was made too late in the war for anything actually to reach the troops, and it now appears doubtful if any 12-cm rockets were ever made.
One unusual installation for the 30-cm 42 Wurfkörper Spreng was on the submarine *U-511*, which received an experimental rack for six such weapons in summer 1942. Launches were conducted from a depth of 12 m (39 ft) with the aim of creating a shore-bombardment weapon.

The Wurfkörper 42 was an improvement over its immediate predecessors, being cleaner aerodynamically and leaving less smoke in its wake. Despite these advantages it could not be produced in sufficient quantity to supplant the designs.

SPECIFICATION	
30-cm Wurfkörper 42 **Dimensions:** length 1230 mm (48.44 in); body diameter 300 mm (11.8 in) **Weights:** overall 125.7 kg (277 lb);	propellant 15 kg (33.07 lb); explosive 44.66 kg (98.46 lb) **Performance:** initial velocity 230 m (754 ft) per second; range about 4550 m (4,975 yards)

Japanese rockets 20-cm and 44.7-cm rockets

The Japanese recognised the value of the artillery rocket to their under-armed forces and carried out considerable design and development work in order to provide a weapon that could make up for their lack of industrial capacity. Unfortunately for them their results were patchy and well behind the work carried out by the Allies. To add to the lack of Japanese success there were often development programmes carried out in opposition to each other, and typical of these were the projects to develop a 20-cm (7.87-in) rocket by both the army and the navy.
The **Army 20-cm Rocket** may be regarded as the better of the two projects. It was a spin-stabilised rocket using six base vents to impart propulsion and spin, and had an overall resemblance to an artillery

projectile. To fire this rocket the army provided what appeared to be an oversize mortar known as the **Type 4 Rocket Launcher**. The rocket was inserted into the 'barrel' by raising part of the upper section of the barrel and part of the tube base was open. This launcher was supposed to deliver the rocket relatively accurately, but few equipments appear to have been issued and most of these were used for coastal defences.
The **Navy 20-cm Rocket** resembled the army weapon in many respects, but was intended for launching from troughs made from simple wooden planks, or in some cases more sophisticated metal troughs. At times the rockets were simply emplaced to be launched directly from holes dug in the ground. A more conventional launcher used in small

numbers only was a simple barrel on a light artillery-type carriage.

Rocket motor
These 20-cm rockets formed the bulk of the Japanese rocket programmes but there were others. One was the **Type 10 Rocket Motor** which was a simple propulsion unit designed to push aircraft bombs along ramps or troughs to launch them. At least two versions of the Type 10 existed but they were very inaccurate and had a maximum range of only 1830 m (2,000 yards).

The launchers used for these rocket motors were often improvised, and improvisation was also used in at least one case where the conventional fins of an aircraft 250-kg (551-lb) bomb were replaced by a large rocket motor for launching from a simple wooden trough. Some intelligence reports from the period (1945) speak of these launchers mounted on trucks, but no confirmation of this has been found.
The largest of all the Japanese rockets had a diameter of 44.7-mm

(17.6-in), and this **44.7-cm Rocket** was a somewhat crude spin-stabilised design that was used in action on Iwo Jima and Luzon. It had a range of 1958 m (2,140 yards) at best, and was launched from short wooden racks or frames. It was wildly inaccurate, but it did have a warhead weighing 180.7 kg (398 lb).
By the time these rockets were used, Japanese industrial capacity was in such a state that the conventional HE warheads for these rockets often had to be replaced by simple picric acid.

Japan undertook considerable development work on rockets, but lagged behind the other belligerent nations and produced few usable weapons. This 20-cm army rocket was one of the small number to see action.

SPECIFICATION	
Army 20-cm Rocket **Dimensions:** length 984 mm (38.75 in); diameter 202 mm (7.95 in) **Weights:** overall 92.6 kg (44.95 lb); filling 16.2 kg (35.7 lb)	**Navy 20-cm Rocket** **Dimensions:** length 1041 mm (41 in); diameter 210 mm (8.27 in) **Weights:** overall 90.12 kg (198.5 lb); propellant 8.3 kg (18.3 lb); filling 17.52 kg (38.6 lb) **Performance:** range 1800 m (1,970 yards)

M-8 Soviet 82-mm rocket

During the 1920s and 1930s the Soviet Union used a great deal of its research potential to determine exactly how propellants suitable for rockets could be mass produced. Even before 1918 the Russians had been great advocates of the war rocket, and after this the Soviets were determined to remain in the forefront of rocket technology despite the fact that they were hampered by a lack of industrial potential, which in turn led to their selection of the simpler and more easily produced fin-stabilised over the more accurate spin-stabilised rockets. One of their very first designs, produced during the late 1930s, was one of their most famous rockets, namely the 82-mm (3.23-in) **M-8** weapon.

The M-8 rocket was an off-shoot of an aircraft rocket programme. The aircraft rocket was the RS-82, and

such was the state of the Soviet rocket development programme that it actually entered service after the 132-mm (5.2-in) rocket. The M-8 was a small rocket with a maximum range of 5900 m (6,455 yards) that carried a fragmentation warhead. It was carried on and fired from a series of rails carried on 6x6 trucks, and these rail launchers were just one type of the series of weapons known as **Katyusha**. One of the first of these multiple launchers was carried on a ZiS-6 6x6 truck. As this arrangement could carry and launch up to 36 M-8 rockets it was known as the **BM-83-6**, the BM denoting 'combat vehicle' as a cover name.

The BM-83-6 was not the only vehicle that fired the M-8 rocket, for when sufficient US-supplied Lend-Lease trucks became available these too were used as M-8

launcher vehicles: typical of these was the Studebaker 6x6, which was large enough to take rails for 48 rockets and thus became the **BM-8-48**. Being wheeled, these launchers could not always traverse the rough terrain of the Soviet Union or keep up with the tank units they were meant to support. At one point experiments were made to fit single-rail launchers to the sides of tank turrets, but they came to nothing. Instead numbers of the T-60 light tank, which had proved to be of little combat value in its designed role, were converted to take rails for 24 M-8 rockets and the type thus became known as the **BM-8-24**.

Mountain rocketry

There were other launchers for the M-8 rocket, including a special eight-rocket frame intended for use by mountain troops. On all of the M-8 launchers the rockets were fired not in a massed salvo but in ripples under the control of an electrical rotary switch box.

The M-8 rockets had quite an effect on the recipient German troops who had to

Seen here mounted atop a T-70 light tank, the M-8 82-mm rocket had its origins in an aircraft rocket programme; it proved an enormous success and served throughout the war. The Waffen-SS were so impressed that they copied it.

endure the high fragmentation warheads fired into them in large numbers. The Waffen-SS was so impressed that it decided to copy the design direct (along with the launcher rails) as its own 'Himmlerorgel'. The M-8

rocket remained in service throughout the war, but following 1945 they were gradually phased from use in favour of the heavier Soviet war rockets and in particular the 132-mm (5.2-in) and 300-mm (11.8-in) rockets.

SPECIFICATION	
M-8	propellant 1.2 kg (2.645 lb);
Dimensions: length 660 mm	explosive 0.5 kg (1.1 lb)
(26 in); body diameter 82 mm	**Performance:** initial velocity 315 m
(3.23 in)	(1,033 ft) per second; maximum
Weights: overall 8 kg (17.6 lb);	range 5900 m (6,450 yards)

M-30 and M-31 Soviet 300-mm rockets

The **M-30** 300-mm (11.8-in) rocket was introduced during 1942 when it was appreciated that good as the M-8 and M-13 rockets were, a heavier explosive warhead would be an advantage. The M-30 used a modified M-13 rocket motor allied to a bulbous warhead that contained 28.9 kg (63.7 lb) of explosive, which more than met the requirement, although the range was limited to no more than 2800 m (3,060 yards).

The first M-30s were fired from their carrying crates with the aid of a frame known as **Rama**, which was a close copy of the German method of using the Packkiste for launching from the schwere Wurfgerät. These Ramas were cumbersome devices that were laborious to set up close to the front line, and were little liked by the Red Army troops. But they did like the M-30 rocket for its powerful effects, even going to the extent of using the M-30 for ambushes against tanks or for house-to-house fighting. When used in this role the M-30 was simply aimed at the target while still in its carrying crate and fired at very close range.

By the end of 1942 a newer type of 300-mm rocket was ready and this was known as the **M-31** to differentiate it from the earlier model. The M-31 had an improved rocket motor that gave a range of 4300 m

(4,705 yards). This rocket could be fired from the Rama frames in the same manner as the M-30, but later Ramas could take six M-31s or M-30s in place of the original four. By March 1944 the first mobile launchers for the M-31 appeared. These could carry up to 12 M-31s (the short range of the M-30 ruled out their use with the mobile launchers), and the type was thus known as the **BM-31-12**.

Truck launchers

Early versions of this launcher were carried by the ZiS-6 6x6 truck, but most wartime production examples were carried on Lend-Lease Studebaker US-6 6x6 trucks. These American trucks were fitted with steel shutters over the cab windows for protec-

tion against blast when the rockets were fired.

After 1945 the M-31 rockets did not survive for many years as they were essentially short-range weapons, and as such often suffered from counter-battery fire. But the basic M-31 did undergo some development before it was dropped.

There was an **M-31-UK** which used some of the efflux gases to impart a measure of spin for increased stabilisation and hence accuracy. Range was slightly reduced, but the M-13-UK could greatly decrease the area of ground covered by a battery and thus increase the amount of explosive falling

upon a point target.

The M-30 and M-31 rockets were fitted only with HE warheads. They were undoubtedly powerful projectiles, but they lacked range and for much of the war their mobility was virtually nonexistent as they had to be fired

from the static Rama frames. It was not until the later stages of the war that they were provided with mobility in the form of the BM-31-12, a tardiness for which the German troops on the Eastern Front were no doubt grateful.

SPECIFICATION	
M-30	**M-31**
Dimensions: length 1200 m	**Dimensions:** length 1760 mm
(47.24 in); body diameter 300 mm	(69.3 in); body diameter 300 mm
(11.8 in)	(11.8 in)
Weights: overall 72 kg (158.7 lb);	**Weights:** overall 91.5 kg (201.7 lb);
propellant 7.2 kg (15.87 lb);	propellant 11.2 kg (24.7 kg);
explosive 28.9 kg (63.7 lb)	explosive 28.9 kg (63.7 lb)
	Performance: initial velocity
	255 m (836 ft) per second

Entering service in 1942, the M-30 300-mm rocket carried almost six times as much explosive as the M-13, but its heavy payload reduced its range to under 3 km (1.8 miles). The first mobile launchers were introduced in 1944.

M-13 132-mm rocket

The most widely used of all the Soviet war rockets during World War II was the **M-13** 132-mm (5.2-in) weapon. It was designed during the late 1930s, and when the Germans invaded the Soviet Union in 1941 there were only a few production launchers and a small stock of rockets to hand. These were pressed into service as an emergency measure and first went into action on the Smolensk front in July 1941, when they caused near-panic among the hapless German troops. This is hardly surprising, for in a period of under 10 seconds a single M-13 battery could swamp a large area in high explosive to an extent hitherto unseen in warfare.

Katyusha in action

These first M-13 batteries were very much special units. The launchers for the M-13 fin-stabilised rockets were carried by ZiS-6 6x6 trucks with rails for 16 rockets. The rails were known as 'Flute' launchers to the Soviet troops as a result of their perforated appearance, but they soon gained the name **Katyusha** ('Little Katy'), and at one time were known as 'Kostikov guns' after their supposed

designer. For security purposes the launchers were usually shrouded in tarpaulins when not in use, and the crews were culled from Communist Party members in order to maintain tight security. But it was not long before the M-13 launchers were in widespread use and their secrets became common knowledge.

Rocket design

The basic M-13 rocket had a range of about 8000 to 8500 m (8,750 to 9,295 yards). The usual warhead was of the HE fragmentation type, and as always with fin-stabilised rockets accuracy was not of a high order. But as the M-13s were usually used in massed barrages this last mattered only little. Later versions of the M-13 used a form of efflux diversion to introduce more spin for increased accuracy, but this measure reduced the range slightly. As mentioned above, the first launcher type used 16 rails and was known as the **BM-13-16**, but when supplies of Lend-Lease trucks became available they too were used as Katyusha carriers. Several types of truck, including Studebakers, Fords, Chevrolets and

Internationals, were so used, along with STZ-5 artillery tractors and other vehicles. These BM-13-16 launchers had no traverse and only limited elevation,

Above: In for the kill, steel shutters down, Katyushas bombard the last pocket of German resistance near the Reichstag itself in March 1945. Such was the power of the Soviet industry that by 1945 some 10,000 launchers had been produced along with over 12 million rockets.

Shunted off the road and abandoned, this is the most famous of the war rockets: the truck-mounted Katyusha. Because of the distinctive moaning sound the missiles made in flight, the Germans dubbed the weapon 'Stalin's organ'.

Above: Original World War II Katyushas and their modern launchers remained favourites of the Palestine Liberation Organisation into the 1980s. Also, after the Israelis crushed the PLO in Beirut in 1982, they captured many Katyushas that they subsequently used themselves.

Right: M-13 132-mm rocket launchers in action on the outskirts of Berlin. The dreadful noise and clouds of smoke produced by these rockets, combined with the shock effect of mass detonations, frequently induced panic amongst the defenders.

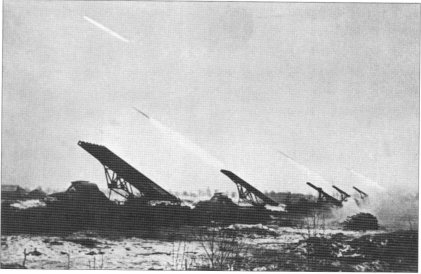

For the awesome barrages that heralded a Red Army offensive, rockets would be massed on static launchers close to the front. Here the first salvoes blast off against the doomed men of the German 6th Army trapped in Stalingrad, January 1943.

and were laid by pointing the carrier vehicle towards the target. Some carrier vehicles used steel shutters to protect the cab and crew in the launching sequence.

Warhead types

As the war progressed more types of M-13 warhead were introduced, including armour-piercing to break up tank formations, flare for night illumination, incendiary and signal. One variation was the **M-13-DD**, which used two rocket motors burning together at launch to produce a possible range of 11800 m (12,905 yards), and this rocket was launched from the upper rails of the launcher only. The M-13-DD had the greatest range of all solid-propellant artillery rockets in World War II.

After 1945 the M-13 rocket batteries remained in Red Army use right up to 1980, when the last examples were finally replaced by later models. However, the M-13 remained in service with many countries after this date, although more modern trucks were used as carriers in place of the old wartime models. In fact the service life of the basic M-13 continued into the 21st century, for the Chinese continue to use the design as a form of minelet-laying device known as the **Type 74**. This system is mounted on the rear of a CA-30A 6x6 truck and incorporates an I-shaped frame system for 10 284-mm (11.2-in) rockets, each carrying 10 anti-tank mines.

SPECIFICATION	
M-13	propellant 7.2 kg (15.87 lb);
Dimensions: length 1.41 m	explosive 4.9 kg (10.8 lb)
(55.9 in); body diameter 132 mm	**Performance:** initial velocity
(5.2 in)	355 m (1,165 ft) per second; range
Weights: overall 42.5 kg (93.7 lb);	8500 m (9,295 yards)

PETER SARSON · TONY BRYAN

Introduced in conditions of great secrecy and crewed by dedicated party members, the first Soviet rocket launchers were tested in combat on 7 July 1941. Called Kostikov guns to conceal their real nature, they were soon nicknamed Katyusha ('Little Katy') after a popular song of the time. Rockets were mounted on a wide variety of vehicles from obsolescent light tanks to ZiS-6 lorries, but one of the most common combinations was the M-13 132-mm rocket on American Studebaker 6x6 trucks. Note the steel shutters over the windscreen to protect the cab from the ferocious backblast.

2-in rocket Anti-aircraft rocket

During the late 1930s the need for improved defence of the United Kingdom against air attack was finally appreciated, but at the time it was thought that to produce enough anti-aircraft guns to meet immediate needs would take too long. Thus the rocket was investigated to see if it could provide a cheap and easily-manufactured alternative to the gun, and among the first designs investigated was a type known as the **2-in Rocket**. As things turned out the later 3-in rocket was to prove more promising, but at the time the smaller rocket seemed quite encouraging and work went ahead on the design with some momentum.

The 2-in (51-mm) rocket was a simple device that used a propellant known as solventless cordite or SCRK.

The overall simplicity of the weapon could be seen in the fact that the earliest designs used a direct-action wind vane on the nose to arm the fuse after firing, with a self-destruct timer to destroy the weapon after it had been in flight for 4.5 seconds, by which time it would have reached a maximum height of about 1370 m (4,500 ft).

Naval applications

In the event the 2-in rocket was used mainly to arm light naval vessels and some merchant shipping. There were many and various simple naval mountings such as the basic vertical launchers that were mounted on each side of the bridge on many light vessels. These were supposed to launch their rockets as a low-flying aircraft attacked the ship. As

the rockets rose they were designed to carry aloft a length of light wire that would enmesh itself in the aircraft's propellers and bring it down. The system never worked and neither did many other similar and somewhat optimistic devices. There was a high explosive version that could carry a 0.25-kg (0.56-lb) warhead, but by the time this was ready it was appreciated that the larger 3-in (76-mm) rocket was much better for this role and relatively few 2-in rockets were produced.

Pillar Box

One naval mounting that was used on land was the one known as the **2-in Rocket Mounting Mk II, Pillar Box**. This was used during the desperate days of 1940-41 to provide at least a measure of coastal AA defence, and could launch up to 20 rockets. The rockets were arranged in two vertical rows of five on each side of a central drum housing in which the aimer operated the simple con-

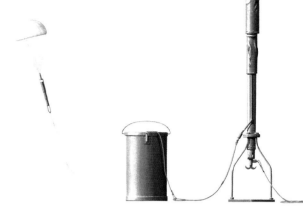

The 2-in Rocket was an ingenious AA rocket, being designed to destroy low-flying aircraft by fouling their propellers with the long wire it left in its wake.

trols. This drum housing gave the Pillar Box mounting its name. The aimer could fire all 20 of the rockets in one salvo or two salvoes of 10 rockets using electrical ignition. Other forms of land-mounted 2-in rocket launchers existed and were used but only in very small

numbers as temporary defensive measures. The 2-in rocket was really too small and light to have any great destructive effect, but the lessons learned in the design and development of these early attempts at war rockets had a good effect on later designs.

SPECIFICATION	
2-in Rocket	warhead 0.25 kg (0.56 lb)
Dimensions: length 914 mm	**Performance:** initial velocity
(36 in); body diameter 57 mm (2 in)	457 m (1,500 ft) per second
Weights: overall 4.88 kg (11 lb);	

3-in rocket Anti-aircraft rocket

Design work on British artillery rockets started as early as 1934, though only on a low-priority basis, and by 1937 had reached the position where a **3-in Rocket** was proposed as an alternative to the anti-aircraft gun; indeed, the rocket used the same warhead weight as the 3.7-in (94-mm) AA shell. Under strict security conditions, development of the new rocket went ahead with the **UP** (**Unrotated Projectile**) cover name. Early firings were made at Aberporth in Wales, and by

1939 the final test firings were being made in Jamaica. Interestingly it was the trial battery at Aberporth that claimed the first 'kill' of a Luftwaffe bomber. These trials led to the establishment of the first operational battery near Cardiff in South Wales, where it was known as a Z battery.

This first Z battery used a single-rail launcher known as the **Projector, 3-in, Mk 1**. It was a very simple, even crude device and it was produced for both the Army and the Royal Navy, although in

Designed originally as an anti-aircraft system, the 3-in rocket achieved modest success as a ground weapon. However, it is better known as an air-to-ground weapon, fired from Hawker Typhoons over Normandy during D-day.

the event most of the Royal Navy's allocation went to the merchant navy. The rocket was a simple fin-stabilised tube containing a motor and the same SCRK cordite used on the 2-in (51-mm) rocket. These early designs were somewhat erratic in performance, and accuracy was such that huge salvoes had to be fired from all the projectors in a Z battery in order to have some chance of hitting an aircraft target. They did have their successes, but they were few and did not improve until the **Projector, Rocket, 3-in, No. 2 Mk 1** came along. This used a two-rail launching system and was produced in some numbers, still firing the 3-in (76-mm) rocket but fitted with more sophisticated fusing systems including early attempts at proximity fusing

and other electro-magnetic devices. Some of these No. 2 projectors saw action in North Africa, including port defence at Tobruk.

Ripple fire

The next improvement in launching methods was the **Projector, Rocket, 3-in, No. 4 Mk 1** and **Mk 2**. This had no fewer than 36 launcher rails to fire nine rockets in a ripple sequence. Again some of these projectors were used in North Africa. The largest of all the British 3-in rocket projectors was the **Projector, Rocket, 3-in, No. 6 Mk 1**, which could fire 20 rockets in four salvoes. This entered service in 1944 and was intended for use in static locations for home defence.

One unexpected offshoot from the AA rocket programme was that the ground-launched 3-in rocket was taken up as an aircraft weapon. Fired from short launcher rails it proved to be a devastating ground-attack missile, especially against tanks, and during 1944 proved to be one of the most powerful of all anti-tank weapons when used by 'cab-rank' Hawker Typhoons over the Normandy battlefields. By the time the war ended the airborne 3-in rocket was even being used to sink U-boats. In a different installation towards the close of the war, the Coldstream Guards even fitted two 3-in aircraft rockets to rails on either side of their tank turrets.

SPECIFICATION	
3-in Rocket	**Performance:** maximum velocity
Dimensions: length 1.93 m (76 in);	457 m (1,500 ft) per second; service
body diameter 82.6 mm (3.25 in)	ceiling 6770 m (22,200 ft);
Weights: overall 24.5 kg (54 lb);	horizontal range 3720 m
propellant 5.76 kg (12.7 lb);	(4,070 yards)
warhead 1.94 kg (4.28 lb)	

The 36-round Projector, Rocket, 3-in, No 4 Mks 1 and 2 was mobile as it was carried on converted 3-in (76-mm) anti-aircraft artillery platform trailers.

LILO Short-range rocket

SPECIFICATION	
LILO rocket (9.53-kg/21-lb warhead)	**LILO rocket (27.2-kg/60-lb warhead)**
Dimensions: length 1.24 m (49 in); body diameter 83 mm (3 in)	**Dimensions:** length 1.32 m (52 in); body diameter 152 mm (6 in)
Weights: overall 17.8 kg (39.25 lb); propellant 1.93 kg (4 lb); explosive 1.8 kg (4 lb)	**Weights:** overall 35.5 kg (78.25 lb); propellant 1.93 kg (4 lb); explosive 6.24 kg (14 lb)

By 1944 the Allies were becoming accustomed to the Japanese tactic of using heavily-protected bunkers to delay Allied advances, not only on the Pacific Islands but also in the land warfare raging in South East Asia. The only effective way to demolish these formidable defensive works was by the use of heavy artillery at close ranges, but the Japanese did not always build their bunkers where such heavy weapons could get at them. The rocket was obviously a relatively portable method of dealing with such obstacles, and thus there emerged a programme known by the cover name **LILO**.

Bunker-buster

LILO was a very simple single-barrel launcher designed to fire a rocket at short range against bunker-type targets. It fired a projectile powered by the Motor, Rocket, 3-in, No. 7 Mk 1 to which two types of warhead could be fitted. Both were HE types, one weighing 17.8 kg (39.25 lb) complete and the other 35.5 kg (78.25 lb) complete. The idea was that the LILO projector could be carried to its firing location by one man, with another carrying a rocket on a suitable backpack. The projector was then set up as close to its intended target as possible and the rocket loaded into the launcher tube from the front. Open sights were used to aim the weapon, the back legs of the launcher being moved for changes in elevation. When all was ready the rocket was fired electrically, using a light 3.4-volt battery.

The LILO rockets were capable of penetrating 3.05 m (10 ft) of earth plus a layer of logs, so they could normally penetrate any Japanese bunker. But the main problem was hitting the target: despite the fact that a degree of spin was imparted to the rocket as it was launched, the inherent inaccuracy of the rocket was such that to ensure a 95 per cent chance of hitting a point target distant only some 45 to 50 m (49 to 55 yards), five rockets had to be fired. This may sound uneconomic but the alternative was to bring up heavy artillery with all its attendant risks and labour.

US equivalent

The Americans also used a short-range rocket for the same purpose as LILO. Their device was known as the **M12 Rocket Launcher** which fired a 4.5-in (114-mm) rocket, and this resembled LILO in many ways apart from the fact that the first launcher tubes used were plastic and were discarded after firing. Such a system proved to be too wasteful, even for the US

As the Allies drove the Japanese back towards their homeland, numerous expedients were tried to knock out the toughly-constructed bunkers that were the hallmark of Japanese positions. One such was LILO – a short-range single-shot 60-lb (27.2-kg) rocket.

war economy, so a later version was developed as the **M12E1** which used a magnesium alloy tube that could be reloaded and reused. These projectors were used during the latter stages of the fighting on Okinawa when the Japanese defenders had to be blasted from their heavily-defended caves.

Land Mattress Artillery rocket

Although early development of the war rocket in the United Kingdom was initially to produce an anti-aircraft weapon, some consideration was also given to producing an artillery rocket. One early attempt at this was a design for a 5-in (127-mm) rocket which was rejected by the Army but adopted by the Royal Navy for use in modified landing craft for the saturation of landing beaches and approaches by massed rocket fire. This eventually evolved as the **Mattress**, but range was limited. However, further trials

SPECIFICATION	
Land Mattress (rocket)	3.18 kg (7 lb)
Dimensions: length 1.77 m (70 in)	**Performance:** maximum velocity 335 m (1,100 ft) per second; maximum range 7.2 km (4.4 miles)
Weights: overall 30.5 kg (67 lb); propellant 5 kg (11 lb); payload	

revealed that the range could be improved by introducing, at launch, a degree of spin which would also improve accuracy, and this was simply achieved by using an aircraft 3-in (76-mm) rocket motor attached to a naval 13-kg (29-lb) warhead. This increased range to a possible 7315 m (8,000 yards), making the artillery rocket a viable proposition once more. Thus Mattress became **Land Mattress**. The first Army launchers for these new Land Mattress rockets had 32 barrels, but a later version had 30 barrels. Demonstrations of this launcher greatly impressed Canadian army staff officers, who requested a 12-launcher battery which in the event was ready for action on 1 November 1944.

First action

This battery went into action during the crossing of the River Scheldt and was a great success, to the extent that more were requested and produced. The Land Mattress launcher was limited in its elevation capabilities to between 23° and 45°, and this not only limited the maximum range to 7225 m (7,900 yards) but also limited the minimum range to 6125 m (6,700 yards). To reduce the minimum range possible, a system of rotary spoilers

Land Mattress was a curious hybrid – an Army weapon constructed from an aircraft rocket motor and a 5-in naval warhead. Early models were severely restricted in performance since elevation was restricted between 23° and 45°.

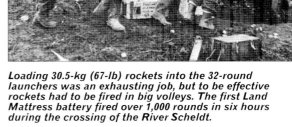

Loading 30.5-kg (67-lb) rockets into the 32-round launchers was an exhausting job, but to be effective rockets had to be fired in big volleys. The first Land Mattress battery fired over 1,000 rounds in six hours during the crossing of the River Scheldt.

over the rocket exhausts was formulated and put into use. The rotary spoiler disturbed the exhaust gases by closing off their efflux by varying amounts, and thus reduced the minimum range to 3565 m (3,900 yards).

For all the success of the Land Mattress, not many equipments were in action before the war ended in Europe in May 1944. By that time many were only just emerging from the factories ready to be sent off to South East Asia, but their use there was very limited, as a result mainly of the weight and bulk of the projectors in the area's jungle conditions. A special 16-barrel version was accordingly developed for towing by a Jeep, but the war was over by the time it was ready for service.

Rocket, HE, 4.5-in, M8 & M16 Fin- and spin-stabilised rockets

When the US entered World War II in December 1941, its armed forces had no rockets at all in service or even in prospect. But with typical energy, the Americans used their considerable technical knowledge and industrial potential to remedy this deficit with great speed. In what seemed like no time at all they had erected huge facilities for the production of rocket propellants of all kinds (the first deliveries being accomplished even before the factories had been completed) and were busy designing and producing rockets for a host of purposes.

Mass production

One of these rockets was a relatively straightforward fin-stabilised weapon known during its development and trials periods as the **T12** but then standardised for service as the **Rocket, HE, 4.5-in, M8**. This 114.3-mm rocket carried a nose-fused warhead and tail-mounted folding fins for stabilisation, and was destined to be manufactured in numbers larger than those for any other World War II artillery rocket with the probable exception of the Soviet 82- and 132-mm (3.23- and 5.2-in) weapons: no fewer than 2.537 million had been produced by the end of World War II in 1945. Used in exactly the same fashion as the M8, the **M8A1**, **M8A2** and **M8A3** were slight variations of the baseline M8, the first having a strengthened motor body for service in a wider range of climates, the second having a smaller warhead with thicker walls providing a superior fragmentation effect, and the third being the M8A2 with slightly modified fins.

Technical details

The M8 was powered by 30 sticks of ballistite propellant exhausting through a single venturi nozzle in the tail, and

When the US entered World War II it had no rocket weapons. A high-speed programme then saw the creation of the M8 and M16 (seen) and their launchers.

was firing by an electrical circuit, or a percussion cap, or a black powder igniter depending on the type of launcher being employed.

Being fin- rather than spin-stabilised, the M8 was inherently inaccurate as any slight trajectory deviation as the rocket left the launcher was amplified by range, and was accordingly used not for the engagement of point targets but for the saturation of large areas. Thus it was used extensively for the mass bombardment of target areas before amphibious landings or as a supplement to massed artillery bombardments. Even at short ranges its accuracy was erratic, so nearly all the launchers used with the M8 were of the multiple type to ensure that the target area was saturated with fire.

Special launcher

Typical of these types was the **T27 Multiple Rocket Launcher**, which fired eight M8 rockets and was carried on the back of a GMC or Studebaker 2.5-ton truck on a mounting that provided an elevation arc of 50 degrees (-5 to +45 degrees) to vary the range. The launcher was moved onto the right bearing by alignment of the truck, and sighting was entrusted to the M6 telescopic sight. There were two variations of this launcher, namely the **T27E1** that could be disassembled for transport and the **T27E2** with capacity for up to 24 rockets in three layers of eight tubes each.

The **T34** or **Calliope** was a large launcher carried over the turret of an M4 Sherman medium tank. The Calliope had no fewer than 60 launching tubes (two upper

Above: Armed with an M1 carbine personal weapon, a US Army soldier loads a 4.5-in (114.3-mm) M8 rocket into its tube on a frame launcher unit.

layers each of 18 tubes and two divided bottom layers each comprising upper and lower six-tube units) and was constructed from plywood as it was a one-shot weapon for use against strongpoints. Measuring some 3.05 m (10 ft) in length, the Calliope was traversed by movement of the turret, and elevated by a link to the gun barrel, and after firing or in an emergency the

whole device could be jettisoned to leave the Sherman unencumbered for its gun tank role. Variants of the T34 were the **T34E1** and the **T34E2**. The former had two 16-tube upper rows and two divided lower rows each comprising seven-tube upper and lower layers. The

T34E1 provided lower dispersion than the T34. The latter had square- rather than round-section tubes.

The **T44** was even larger than the Calliope as it had 120 launcher tubes, and was designed for installation in the cargo area of a DUKW amphibious truck or LVT

Looking toward German positions in front of the Canadian 1st Army's XII Corps in January 1945, a fire controller prepares to unleash part of a barrage.

SPECIFICATION

Rocket, HE, 4.5-in, M8
Dimensions: length 838 mm
(33 in); diameter 114.3 mm (4.5 in)
Weights: overall 17.5 kg (38.5 lb);
propellant 2.16 kg (4.75 lb);

explosive 1.95 kg (4.3 lb)
Performance: maximum velocity
259 m (850 ft) per second;
maximum range 4205 m
(4,600 yards)

Left: This T34 (Calliope) 60-tube launcher for M8 artillery rockets is fitted not on the standard M4 medium tank, but on a captured German halftrack.

Below: A gunner checks the sight of a simple T27 eight-tube launcher, generally mounted in the cargo area of GMC or Studebaker 2½-ton trucks. The M8 was also fired from DUKWs for beach assault.

amphibious vehicle. The T44 was a simple area-saturation launcher, so there was no method of varying elevation or traverse. A similar device known as the **Scorpion** but mounting 144 launcher tubes was used on DUKW amphibious trucks in the Pacific theatre. The **T45** was a twin 14-tube launcher system that could be fitted to the sides of various vehicles, including light trucks, the M24 light tank and the LVT amphibious vehicle: there were no traverse controls, but the paired launders could be elevated between 0 degrees and +35 degrees. Yet another launcher that fired the M8 rocket was the **M12** (developed and trialled as the **T35**) which was a single-shot 'bunker-buster' (also possessing capability against Japanese cave positions) along the lines of the British LILO, with a plastic launcher

tube supported on one rear and two front legs. Complete with one M8 rocket, the equipment weighed 23.6 kg (54 lb). The **M12A1** was an improved M12, while the **M12E1** had a tube made of magnesium alloy rather than plastic and could therefore be reused; the M12E1 also has an adjustable rear leg.

Improved accuracy

Despite the fact that it was made in very large numbers and saw extensive service in the European and Pacific theatres, the M8 was so inaccurate that the rocket was considered inadequate for use as a genuine artillery rocket. Using knowledge gained from trials of captured German rockets, the Americans developed a spin- rather than fin-stabilised weapon known as the **Rocket, HE, 4.5-in, M16**.

This had an overall length of 787 mm (31 in) and a weight of 19.3 kg (42.5 lb) including 2.16 kg (4.75 lb) of propellant and 2.36 kg (5.2 lb) of HE, and its other data included a maximum velocity of 253 m (830 ft) per second and a maximum range of 4805 m (5,250 yards).

Dedicated launcher

The M16 was fired from the **Launcher, Rocket, Multiple 4.5-in, T66**. This was an arrangement of three layers of tubes, each with a circular-section interior and hexagonal- section exterior, carried on a two-wheel carriage towed by a light truck. The launcher was trained in azimuth by movement of its trail, and could be elevated between 0 degrees and +45 degrees. The launcher weighed 544 kg (1,200 lb) empty and 1007 kg (2,220 lb) with its 24 rockets,

which were loaded from the front rather than the rear, which was the case with the M8 rocket's launchers. It took some 90 seconds to load the T66 launcher, and the 24 rockets could then by discharged in a rippled salvo lasting two seconds.

This combination arrived

at the front late in the war and was used during only one engagement in Germany, by the 282nd Field Artillery Battalion of the US 1st Army's VIII Corps, before the end of hostilities in Europe. The M16 weapon was not used at all in the Pacific theatre.

Above: The firing of any artillery rocket weapon is always an impressive sight and sound, all the more so when multiple launchers are used to fire area-saturation salvoes from wheeled or tracked vehicles.

Left: These M4 Sherman medium tanks each carry the 60-tube T34 launcher generally known as the Calliope. Intended for only a few firings at most (the whole launcher was often jettisoned after only one salvo to allow the tank to function in its primary role), the launcher was based on the use of plywood tubes.

25-mm Hotchkiss Mle 1938, 1939 and 1940 light AA guns

Between the world wars the French army retained great weapon stockpiles from World War I, and with them a military philosophy relevant almost only to World War I battles. Thus when it came to considerations of anti-aircraft weapons, it was decided that an updated '75' (the famous 75-mm/2.95-in modèle 1897 field gun) was all that was required, and that a new 12.7-mm (0.5-in) heavy machine-gun would suffice for low-level defence. French armaments manufacturers, including Hotchkiss, thought otherwise, however, and in 1932 brought out a new 25-mm automatic weapon and offered this to the military.

Negative response

The response was negative. The staff planners saw no need for a weapon such as the 25-mm Hotchkiss and were unwilling to consider the type. They did agree to carry out trials with the new gun, but that was all. By the mid-1930s it appeared that the project was defunct, but then came the Spanish Civil War. French military observers quickly noted that there most definitely existed a requirement for a weapon heavier than the machine-gun to counter the activities of ground-attack aircraft. Thus there emerged a rush order to Hotchkiss for large numbers of its 25-mm weapon. But this order was beset with uncertainties

regarding rates of fire, type of carriage, and so on. It was late in 1938 before the order was finally sorted out and by then things had got a bit out of hand, for Hotchkiss had already started production of a model for Romania and the French order meant changes to the design and the production line. Eventually, though, the guns started to flow from the factory.

Pair of models

There were two types of 25-mm Hotchkiss. One was the **Mitrailleuse de 25 mm sur affût universel Hotchkiss modèle 1938**, which was a light weapon transported on a single-axle carriage, and the other was the **Hotchkiss modèle 1939**, which was a heavier weapon intended for static use but capable of being moved if required. Both were basically simple and adequate weapons with a high rate of fire and good ammunition (fed from a 10-round overhead box) that was also intended for use against ground targets if the opportunity arose. Thus an armour-piercing projectile was available. A version for use by the French navy was produced using a pedestal mounting, and just before Germany invaded France in May 1940 Hotchkiss produced a two-barrel variant known as the **Hotchkiss modèle 1940**, which did not get past the trials stage.

The main problem for the

There were two main models of the 25-mm Hotchkiss AA cannon. This is the mle 38 ready for towing but minus the usual flash-hider at the muzzle. Other models used different barrel and sight arrangements.

French army was that the Hotchkiss production lines could not churn out the guns in sufficient numbers. Despite wartime urgency, the Hotchkiss works were beset by industrial troubles and other delays, to the extent that when the Germans invaded France only 1,103 of these Hotchkiss guns were in service, which was very considerably below the numbers required. In the event those that were produced mainly fell into the hands of the Germans. Some were retained by the Vichy French armed forces and some used by the Free French in the Middle East, but the bulk

that survived May 1940 were impressed into German use and issued to units based in France; some were later incorporated into the Atlantic Wall beach

defences. The German designations for these weapons were **2.5-cm Flak Hotchkiss 38** (light mounting) and **2.5-cm Flak Hotchkiss 39** (heavy mounting).

SPECIFICATION	
Hotchkiss modèle 38	per second
Calibre: 25 mm (0.98 in)	**Maximum effective ceiling:**
Length of piece: 1.5 m (59.05 in)	3000 m (9,845 ft)
Weight: in action 850 kg (1,874 lb)	**Rate of fire:** (cyclic) 350 rpm and
Elevation: -5° to +80°	(practical) 175 rounds per minute
Traverse: 360°	**Projectile weight:** 0.29 kg
Muzzle velocity: 900 m (2,953 ft)	(0.64 lb) HE; 0.324 kg (0.714 lb) AP

37-mm Schneider Mle 1930 medium AA gun

The 37-mm Schneider gun was produced initially during the early 1930s, and was at the time rejected by the French army which could then see no reason for obtaining such a weapon; a similar Hotchkiss proposal met with the same response. The Schneider concern decided to go ahead with development of the design as a private venture, and in time these efforts were rewarded by a number of export orders from nations such as Romania. More were taken by the French navy, but the numbers involved were never large.

Radical rethink

The Spanish Civil War changed French official thinking to a radical degree: it was now clear that the bulk of the anti-aircraft weapons used by the French armed forces were at best obsolescent or, in the case of low-level defence weapons, ineffective. Accordingly large production orders were placed for weapons initially to supplement and eventually to replace existing

stocks. But in the case of the 37-mm guns the French staff planners were in something of a quandary, for they had nothing in what they came to regard as the medium-calibre bracket. At the bottom end 12.7-mm (0.5-in) and 25-mm weapons were selected, and at the

upper end of the bracket the old '75' (75-mm/2.95-in) weapons were being updated and new designs were in prospect, but as there was nothing in the medium bracket a rushed procurement programme was established.

The Schneider 37-mm gun

Only a few (some sources say 20) examples of the 37-mm Schneider modèle 30 AA gun were produced for the French army, as the weapon was originally produced for export. It was generally passed over in favour of the Swedish Bofors gun after 1938.

was an immediate candidate for selection, but at the same time it was appreciated that it was not a very

satisfactory weapon. The gun itself had a rather short barrel (resulting in a low muzzle velocity and therefore a lack of range) and its ammunition was also not particularly powerful. It was also considered that the carriage was too heavy and awkward, moreover, and took too long to get into action on its three-legged firing platform. Thus although the Schneider gun was ordered as the **Mitrailleur de 37 mm Schneider modèle 1930**, this order was placed only in parallel with a contract for the Swedish 40-mm Bofors in a form made under licence in

Poland. An order for 700 Schneider guns was placed, with deliveries hopefully extending into 1941. In the event only some 20 of the weapons had been produced by the time the Germans invaded; this handful was emplaced around Paris and never got a chance to take any part in the events of May and June 1940.

Production problems

This delay in delivery was caused mainly by production and other troubles at the

Schneider factories. The 37-mm gun was not easy to manufacture, and it took time to establish the production facilities. In fact things got so far behind schedule that by early 1940 the French army planners actually approached the US with a request for large numbers of Colt 37-mm anti-aircraft guns. Nothing came of this venture before the German invasion.

Thus the Schneider 37-mm gun faded from the scene. The numbers taken

over by the Germans were too small for the weapon to be considered for the usual inclusion in the German inventory, and by the time 1945 came around they had

all apparently vanished into the scrap furnaces. Thus the Schneider gun may be regarded as one of World War II's least successful anti-aircraft weapons.

SPECIFICATION	
Schneider modèle 1930	**Muzzle velocity:** 800 m (2,625 ft) per second
Calibre: 37 mm (1.46 in)	
Length of piece: not recorded	**Maximum effective ceiling:**
Weight: in action 1340 kg (2,954 lb)	3000 m (9,845 ft)
	Rate of fire: (cyclic) 175 rpm
Elevation: -0° to +80°	**Projectile weight:** about 0.55 kg (1.21 lb)
Traverse: 360°	

2-cm Flak 30 20-mm light AA gun

By the time the 'new' German army was ready to re-arm during the early 1930s, the German armament manufacturers had built up a considerable degree of expertise in heavy automatic weapons. This was especially true of the giant Rheinmetall-Borsig concern, and accordingly it was given a contract to produce a light anti-aircraft gun with a calibre of 20 mm, and this was ready for service by 1935. Known as the **2-cm Flak 30**, the term Flak standing for *Fliegerabwehrkanone* (anti-aircraft gun), this light weapon was of the type often known as a cannon, and was the first of a series of weapons that became dreaded by the crews of low-flying Allied aircraft.

Complex weapon

The Flak 30 was for its light calibre a rather complex weapon mounted on a carriage that could be towed on two wheels and in action rested on a ground platform. This platform provided a stable firing base with 360° traverse, and had a seat behind the gun for the firer who used, in the Flak 30's original form, a rather complicated form of reflector sight. This sight became

The 2-cm Flak 30 was a Rheinmetall-Borsig design that entered German service in 1935. Seen here on its triangular firing platform, the weapon was also used on a number of wheeled and tracked self-propelled mountings for greater tactical mobility.

even more complicated when simple predictor systems were built into it, and at one point the small sight had reached the state in which it had to be driven by a clockwork mechanism. In fact the sight became so complicated that the whole idea was dropped and later versions reverted to simple 'cartwheel and bead' iron sights. The gun had a crew of five, but in action was frequently managed by less, especially when the gun was located in a static position. Generally the number was at least four, and usually one man held and operated a stereoscopic rangefinder, though after 1944 this function was

deleted as it was found to be tactically unnecessary.

Ammunition was fed into the gun in 20-round magazines, but for some never fully determined reason the Flak 30 was prone to ammunition jams. Also, although it was perfectly adequate when first introduced, it was later discovered that the equipment's rate of fire was too slow to cope adequately with the increased aircraft speeds that prevailed after 1940. Consequently it was supplanted on the production line by the later Flak 38, but the weapons already in service were not replaced until they became worn out or were lost to enemy action. In light anti-aircraft *Abteilungen* (battalions) of field units there were usually three 2-cm batteries to one 37-cm battery, but as the war continued there were many variations.

Foreign service

The Flak 30 was also used by countries other than Germany, for before 1939 numbers of the weapons were sold to China and the Netherlands. In Germany

A 2-cm Flak 30 is seen in action, using what appears to be a special raised emplacement, probably on a range or on a static firing position. Raising the level of the weapon enabled the crew to serve the gun much more easily, making life less tiring over prolonged periods of constant firing.

Early in World War II, gun crews manhandle their 2-cm Flak 30 weapons into position for towing. Such anti-aircraft guns gave Allied pilots a severe shock.

the Flak 30 was also used by the Luftwaffe for ground defences, and the German navy had many specialised naval mountings. Some saw service for the defence of armoured trains, and the weapon was one of those mounted on several types of halftracks or trucks for

the defence of mobile formations and convoys. The Flak 30 was frequently used in the ground target role, and there was even a special AP40 armour-piercing round for use against tanks. The weapon was also the basis of the KwK 30 tank gun.

SPECIFICATION	
	per second
2-cm Flak 30	**Maximum effective ceiling:**
Calibre: 20 mm (0.787 in)	2200 m (7,218 ft)
Length of piece: 2.3 m (90.6 in)	**Rate of fire:** (cyclic) 280 rpm
Weight: in action 450 kg (992 lb)	**Projectile weight:** 0.119 kg (0.262 lb)
Elevation: -12° to +90°	
Traverse: 360°	
Muzzle velocity: 900 m (2,953 ft)	

2-cm Flak 38 and Flakvierling 38 Light AA guns

By 1940 it was already appreciated that the rate of fire of the 2-cm Flak 30 was too low to cope with the higher speeds of the warplanes of the forthcoming generation. It was therefore decided to increase the rate of fire in order to increase the possible numbers of projectiles hitting the target, and at the same time to redesign the gun to get rid of its inherent jamming problem. The contract for the project was given not to Rheinmetall-Borsig but to Mauser, which came up with a new gun that was outwardly similar to the Flak 30 but internally much was changed to provide a cyclic rate of fire of 420 to 480 rounds per minute. The ammunition, feed system and most of the carriage remained much the same as before. So did the complicated sights which were later simplified, as on the Flak 30.

Service entry

The **2-cm Flak 38**, as the Mauser design was known, entered service late in 1940 and eventually replaced the Flak 30 in production. It served alongside the Flak 30 and was also used by the Luftwaffe and the German navy. For the use of the German army's mountain units there was even a special version that could be broken down into pack

loads. This used the same gun as the Flak 38, but the carriage was much smaller and lighter: it was known as the **2-cm Gebirgsflak 38** and was intended as a dual-purpose weapon for use against ground targets as well as against aircraft.

By 1940 it was appreciated that aircraft targets were getting not only faster but also heavier and better protected against ground and air fire. Undertaken with typical German thoroughness, operational analysis revealed that although the high rate of fire of the Flak 38 was more likely to ensure a target hit, the low explosive payload of the projectile was unlikely to inflict enough damage to ensure a 'kill'. The only easy and immediate way to remedy this was to increase the number of barrels firing from one mounting, and thus the **2-cm Flakvierling 38** was developed. This was the carriage of the Flak 38 modified to accommodate four barrels capable of firing at once. This combination became a dreaded aircraft-killer that constantly exacted a toll of low-flying Allied aircraft right until the end of the war. The first such equipments entered service late in 1940, and there were never enough of them. The mounting was used by the German army, air force and navy, and many self-propelled mount-

The 2-cm Flak 38 was a Mauser design overcoming some of the drawbacks of the Flak 30, which included a low rate of fire and a tendency to jam. It used the same carriage but had a higher firing rate.

ings were improvised or produced to make the mounting more mobile. There was a special version for use on armoured trains, and at one point there was even a version with radar control under development. The Flakvierling 38 required more men (usually six or seven) to serve it in action, but those emplaced on static Flak towers defending large cities often had fewer men on the gun.

For the Germans there were never enough of the weapons, and throughout the Reich many production facilities were devoted to manufacture of the guns, their carriages and ammunition. This last was produced in several forms including high explosive, high explosive with tracer and armour-piercing rounds of various types.

Above: The arrangement of the barrels and reflector sight can be seen in this view of the Flakvierling 38. The 20-round box magazines limited rate of fire.

Below: This 2-cm Flakvierling 38 is mounted on a SdKfz 7/1 halftrack with the crew ready for action. This conversion was first produced late in 1941.

SPECIFICATION	
2-cm Flak 38	**Muzzle velocity:** 900 m (2,953 ft) per second
Calibre: 20 mm	**Maximum effective ceiling:** 2200 m (7,220 ft)
Length of piece: 2.2525 m (88.7 in)	**Rate of fire:** (cyclic) 420-480 rpm
Weight: in action 420 kg (926 lb)	**Projectile weight:** 0.119 kg (0.262 lb)
Elevation: -20° to +90°	
Traverse: 360°	

SPECIFICATION	
2-cm Flakvierling 38	**Muzzle velocity:** 900 m (2,953 ft) per second
Calibre: 20 mm	**Maximum effective ceiling:** 2200 m (7,220 ft)
Length of piece: 2.2525 m (88.7 in)	**Rate of fire:** (cyclic) 1,800 rpm
Weight: in action 1514 kg (3,338 lb)	**Projectile weight:** 0.119 kg (0.262 lb)
Elevation: -10° to +100°	
Traverse: 360°	

3.7-cm Flak 18, 36 and 37 Light/medium AA guns

When it entered service in 1935, the **3.7-cm Flak 18** was regarded by the German army and Luftwaffe as a medium-calibre AA weapon. It had been developed in Switzerland by Rheinmetall to avoid the stipulations of the 1919 Versailles Treaty, and for a time was known as the **ST 10** or **Solothurn S10-100**. When introduced, the Flak 18 suffered from many teething problems, but even in its final form it was not

regarded as much of a success. In original form, the gun and carriage were moved on a heavy twin-axle arrangement, which made getting in and out of action slow. Moreover, carriage traverse was slow and the gun mechanism was so prone to stoppages that crews had to be highly trained to cope with them. Despite these drawbacks, the 3.7-cm Flak 18 was never replaced in service. Some examples were

On the move the 3.7-cm Flak 36 was a compact unit on a two-wheel axle. The Flak 37 differed from these drawbacks, the 3.7-cm Flak 36 only in its use of a clockwork-powered predictor sight.

SPECIFICATION

3.7-cm Flak 36 and Flak 37	
Calibre: 37 mm	**Muzzle velocity:** 820 m (2,690 ft) per second
Length of piece: 3.626 m (142.75 in)	**Maximum effective ceiling:**
Weight: in action 1550 kg (3,417 lb)	4800 m (15,750 ft)
Elevation: -8° to +85°	**Rate of fire:** (cyclic) 160 rpm
Traverse: 360°	**Projectile weight:** 0.64 kg (1.41 lb)

Above: A 3.7-cm Flak 36 is seen as part of the 'Atlantic Wall' in 1940-41 before earthworks were replaced by concrete positions and the range-taker was taken from the crew.

Left: The 3.7-cm Flak on a PzKpfw IV tank chassis was known as the Möbelwagen (furniture van).

exported to China before 1939.

Manufacture of the Flak 18 ceased in 1936, the year in which manufacture of a new gun of the same calibre started. This appeared to be the same design as before, but there were many changes, not least of which was a new type of ammunition with one rather than two driving bands. The carriage was much altered to allow towing on a single axle. The new **3.7-cm Flak 36** retained the same performance as the earlier

weapon, but was more versatile. There was one further variant, the **3.7-cm Flak 37** that differed only in its sight, a complex clockwork-powered predictor unit.

The Flak 36 and 37 were produced in large numbers, and by August 1944 the Luftwaffe alone had 4,211 in service. The German navy used various forms of the basic gun on naval mountings including one for U-boat service. There were also several self-propelled types, some hastily mounted on trucks and converted tank chassis, and some on half-tracks. In action the usual number of men to each gun was seven, one of them operating a portable rangefinder, but after 1944 this crew member was withdrawn. Ammunition was fed into the gun in linked six-round clips.

After about 1940 the Flak

18, 36 and 37 became the standard defence weapons against low-flying aircraft, and were usually organised into nine- or 12-gun batteries. Many were statically emplaced on Flak towers providing good all-round fire close to important target areas. Special Flak trains, which moved around the Reich to protect against the heaviest Allied air attacks, also carried numbers of Flak 36 or 37 guns. The type was also used in the field as an anti-tank weapon, and one weapon developed for use on the Eastern Front was a muzzle-loaded stick bomb fired against tanks using a special blank cartridge.

Production of the Flak 36 and 37 continued right up to the end of the war at three main centres, but the Flak 36 and 37 were not easy or cheap to produce, a fact which led to the introduction of the Flak 43.

3.7-cm Flak 43 and Flakzwilling 43 Light AA guns

By 1942 the threat posed by Allied aircraft over all the various battlefields of Europe and North Africa was reaching the point at which there were never enough air-defence weapons available to the Germans. The 3.7-cm (1.46-in) guns were always in demand as they were the standard weapon against low-flying aircraft, and in 1942 Rheinmetall-Borsig was busy developing a gun to replace the existing Flak 36 and 37 series weapons, which were costly and slow to make. As ever, Rheinmetall-Borsig came up with a novelty, not in the design of the gun or carriage, but in the manner of manufacture: the company decided to adopt methods already in use for small-arms production.

Rheinmetall-Borsig was in competition with Krupp for the new gun contract, and at one point the order was given to the Krupp gun, which used conventional production methods. But at the last moment the Krupp design developed weaknesses and the contract was reallocated to Rheinmetall-Borsig. This immediately resulted in the internal party and factional wrangling that often beset the German wartime industrial dream, so by the time Rheinmetall-Borsig was actually able to go ahead on a new production line, well over a year had passed. Rheinmetall-Borsig

was able to make up part of the leeway through the fact that its gun, known as the **3.7-cm Flak 43**, was produced with stampings, weldings and simply-fabricated components in the same way as sub-machine guns. The production time for a gun was cut by a factor of four, and the overall performance boosted by an increased rate of fire.

Production run

It was at a time early in 1944 before the first of the new guns was ready, and thereafter the type poured off the lines at Dürkopp. In service the Flak 43 proved very successful, but in the initial rush to get the new gun into production it had been decided to retain the barrel design and ammunition types of the original Flak 36 and 37. Thus

the Flak 43 was at a disadvantage from the start, for the increased speeds of low-flying aircraft meant that multiple shell hits were not common and a single hit from a Flak 43 was often inadequate to bring down one of these aircraft, which were better protected than their predecessors. The only possible short-term solution to this firepower deficiency was to multiply the number of barrels on a single carriage, and this led to the **3.7-cm Flakzwilling 43** with two barrels, one above the other, on a single mounting. This made a kill much more likely and the Flakzwilling became preferred over the single-barrel version. In the event both types of weapon were produced until the end of World War II, and at one stage there were even plans

for the creation and manufacture of a four-barrel mounting. There was also a project on which the two barrels were mounted side-by-side.

The single- and twin-barrel Flak 43 guns were potent weapons, but there can be no denial of the fact that the twin-barrel version was somewhat unwieldy to get in and out of action, largely because it was generally top heavy. Fortunately for Allied air crews, the number of Flak

The 3.7-cm Flakzwilling 43 was an attempt to increase the firepower of the Flak 43 mounting by adding another barrel. Relatively few of the weapons were made as the Flakzwilling 43 was high and awkward.

.43 weapons (especially the Flakzwilling 43) available to the German forces was never enough to meet demand. By February 1945 there were 1,032 Flak 43s of both types in service, but of these only 280 were of the twin-barrel version.

In action each type required a six-man crew, and if a gun was to be maintained in action for any length of time more men were needed to supply ammunition to the gun.

SPECIFICATION

3.7-cm Flak 43	
Calibre: 37 mm (1.46 in)	**Muzzle velocity:** 840 m (2,756 ft) per second
Length of piece: 3.3 m (130 in)	**Maximum effective ceiling:**
Weight: in action 1392 kg (3,069 lb)	4800 m (15,750 ft)
Elevation: -7.5° to +90°	**Rate of fire:** (cyclic) 250 rpm
Traverse: 360°	**Projectile weight:** 0.64 kg (1.41 lb)

Wirbelwind and Möbelwagen Self-propelled AA gun mountings

Faced from 1943 by the steady rise of Allied air superiority and close support capability in general, the German army found itself in need of specialised armoured AA vehicles to protect the armoured units that were primary targets for ground attack aircraft. Such vehicles were allocated to the Flugabwehrzug (AA platoons) of Panzer regiments.

'Furniture van'

The German army used the chassis of the PzKpfw IV medium tank two self-propelled mounts for the 20-mm Flakvierling 38 four-barrel anti-aircraft gun. Designed early in 1943, the **Flakpanzer IV (2-cm Flakvierling 38) auf Fgst PzKpfw IV Möbelwagen** which was also known as the **2-cm Flakvierling auf Fgst PzKpfw IV (Sf)**, earned its nickname of 'furniture van' from the hinged slab-sided armoured shields that were designed to drop down as the equipment

Based on the hull of the obsolete PzKpfw IV battle tank, the Wirbelwind provided powerful short-range AA capability despite the fact that the turret and the mounting for the four 20-mm cannon were manually operated.

came into action to provide the gun crew with an exposed working platform.

The equipment had a crew of seven, but a development with a 37-mm cannon was preferred as an interim type as there were severe doubts about the effectiveness of the 20-mm projectile against the current generation of armoured ground attack aircraft.

Altogether more successful was the **Flakpanzer IV (2cm) auf Fgst Pz IV/3 Wirbelwind** ('whirlwind'), of which 86 were created as conversions from PzKpfw IV tank standard by Ostbau (Sagan) between July and November 1944 after a prototype conversion had been completed in May of the same year.

This five-man type was a

Left: Made to the extent of 240 vehicles in the 13 months up to March 1945, the 3.7-cm Flak auf Fgst PzKpfw IV (Sf) was the Mobelwagen revised with a 37-mm gun.

better conceived inasmuch as the gun mounting was installed in an open-topped multi-sided turret of 16-mm (0.63-in) armour that sloped outward at the bottom and then back inward at the top. The hull was protected by armour ranging in thickness between 10 and 80 mm (0.39 and 3.15 in), and retained the 7.92-mm (0.312-in) frontal machine-gun from its original tank configuration. The Wirbelwind carried 16 20-round magazines in the turret and another 15 boxes of clips towed in the hull. As with the Möbelwagen, it was fear about the tactical viability of the 20-mm projectile that led to the conversion of only 86 tanks to this anti-aircraft standard.

Both of the self-propelled equipments were based on the use of the Flakvierling 38 four-barrel mounting that Mauser had developed for the Kriegsmarine. It con-

sisted of four Flak 38 cannon on one mount, and had three seats (one for the gunner who fired the weapon using two pedal triggers) and two for the loaders who handled the curved 20-round box magazines. With four barrels based on the Flak 38 lightened and faster-firing development of the Flak 30, the mount had cyclic and practical rates of 1,800 and 880 rpm respectively. The Flakvierling 38 could be traversed through 360°, and its elevation arc was -10° to +100°, or to +90° on the SP mounting.

Devastating weapon

The muzzle velocity with 0.119-kg (0.2625-lb) HE projectile was 900 m (2,953 ft) per second or 830 m (2,723 ft) per second with the AP ammunition as a devastating short-range weapon, and the effective ceiling was 2200 m (7,220 ft).

Right: The Mobelwagen was rejected for service as it was considered that its armament and protection would be inadequate for the tactical situation likely to prevail from the later part of 1943.

SPECIFICATION	
Flakpanzer IV (2cm) auf Fgst Pz IV/3 Wirbelwind **Type:** self-propelled quadruple 20-mm AA gun mounting **Crew:** 5 **Weight:** 22350 kg (49,272 lb) **Dimensions:** length 5.92 m (19 ft 5 in); width 2.9 m (9 ft 6¾ in); height 2.76 m (9 ft ½ in) **Powerplant:** one Maybach HL 120TRM liquid-cooled V-12 patrol engine developing 224 kW (300 hp) **Performance:** maximum road speed 38 km/h (24 mph); range 200 km (124 miles)	**Fording:** 0.8 m (2 ft 7½ in) **Trench:** 2.3 m (7 ft 6½ in) **Armour:** hull and superstructure front 80 mm (3.15 in); hull and superstructure sides 30 mm (1.18 in); hull and superstructure rear 20 mm (0.79 in); top and bottom 10 mm (0.4 in); turret 16 mm (0.63 in) **Armament:** one 20-mm Flakvierling 38 mounting with 320 ready-use rounds, and one 7.92-mm (0.312-in) MG 34 machine-gun with 1,350 rounds

Ostwind and SdKfz 7/2 Self-propelled AA gun mountings

During World War II the Germans fielded four distinct 37-mm calibre anti-aircraft guns, namely the 3.7-cm Flak 18, 36, 37 and 43 weapons. As the war developed the larger-calibre shell of these weapons found increasing favour since it had a longer range and was more effective against armoured ground-attack aircraft.

For the protection of Panzer unit, the Flak 43 was mounted in the **3.7-cm Flak 43 auf Sf Ostwind** (east wind), otherwise known as the **Flakpanzer IV/3.7-cm Flak**, a 37-mm self-propelled AA gun produced by Ostbau to the extent of 36 PzKpfw IV conversions and seven new-production vehicles between December 1944 and March 1945 after the end of successful trials with a prototype conversion in July 1944. Like the 20-mm SP guns, it used the PzKpfw IV chassis and had a crew of six men.

Basic model

The **mittlerer Zugkraftwagen 8t mit 3.7-cm Flak 36 (SdKfz 7/2)**, otherwise known as the **3.7-cm Flak 36 auf FgZkw 8t**, was a cruder vehicle consisting of the 8-tonne half-track cargo carrier/gun tractor for the 8.8-cm Flak AA gun or 15-cm sFH 18 howitzer with a Flak 36 mounted on its rear deck. The vehicle was later reworked with a lightly armoured cab to protect the driver. The versatile half-track was first built in 1934 and by the end of World War II Borgward, Breda, Büssing-NAG, Daimler-Benz, Hansa-Lloyd, Sauer and Krauss-Maffei had built nearly 8,000 vehicles.

Though the Flak 43 looked externally similar to the earlier guns, it was in fact a ground-based version of the Rheinmetall MK 103 aircraft cannon and as such was a gas-operated weapon with

Seen ready for action with its gun crew closed up and the rangetaker on the ground, this SdKfz 7/2 is of the updated pattern with a cab armoured on an 8-mm (0.315-in) basis. The gun shield offered limited protection to the gun crew.

cyclic and practical firing rates of 250 and 180 rpm, whereas the earlier weapons were recoil-operated with cyclic and practical rates of 160 and 80/120 rpm. The guns were clip-fed from the side and fired HE-Tracer, HE-Incendiary and HEI-T, Armour-Piercing, and HE projectiles.

The Flak 43's weight in action was 1219 kg (2,688-lb), and the mounting could be traversed through 360° with elevation between -7.5° and +90°. The Flak 36 weighed 1550 kg (3,418 lb), and its traverse and elevation arcs were 360° and -8° to +85° respectively. The muzzle velocity was 840 m (2,756 ft) per second with the 0.64-kg (1.4-lb) HE projectile and 770 m (2,526 ft) per second with the AP projectile. The guns had an effective ceiling of 4800 m (15,750 ft) and horizontal range of 6500 m

(7,110 yards). The Flak 36 and 43 were sighted with the aid of the Flakvisier 40 and 43 respectively, and a stereoscopic rangefinder was standard.

The 10-crew SdKfz 7/2, of which 123 were completed up to February 1945, weighed 11550 kg (25,463 lb), was 6.85 m (22 ft 5½ in) long, and with the

104-kW (140-hp) Maybach HL 62TUK engine had a speed of 50 km/h (37 mph) and range of 250 km (155 miles). Ammunition was carried in a two-wheel trailer.

Above: The successor to the Wirbelwind, produced only in small numbers, was the Ostwind, in which the Wirbelwind's quartet of 20-mm cannon were replaced by a single 37-mm Flak 43/1 longer-ranged cannon.

Left: This is the early form of the SdKfz 7/2 without an armoured cab and, in this instance, not even a gun shield to protect the gun crew.

SPECIFICATION	
3.7-cm Flak 43 auf Sf Ostwind **Type:** self-propelled single 37-mm AA gun mounting **Crew:** 6 **Weight:** 25400 kg (55,996 lb) **Dimensions:** length 5.92 m (19 ft 5 in); width 2.95 m (9 ft 8 in); height 3 m (9 ft 10 in) **Powerplant:** one Maybach HL 120TRM112 liquid-cooled V-12 patrol engine developing 203 kW (272 hp) **Performance:** maximum road	speed 38 km/h (24 mph); range 200 km (124 miles) **Fording:** 0.8 m (2 ft 7½ in) **Trench:** 2.3 m (7 ft 6½ in) **Armour:** hull and superstructure front 80 mm (3.15 in); hull and superstructure sides 30 mm (1½ in); hull and superstructure rear 20 mm (0.79 in); top and bottom 10 mm (0.4 in); turret 25 mm (0.98 in) **Armament:** one 37-mm Flak 43 gun with 1,000 rounds, and one 7.92-mm (0.312-in) MG 34 machine-gun

5-cm Flak 41 Medium-altitude AA gun

The 5-cm (1.97-in) Flak 41 was one of the least successful of all the German anti-aircraft guns, for it had excessive recoil and flash and the carriage traversed too slowly. Despite their shortcomings, a total of 50 were built and the type was used until the war ended.

In World War II air warfare terms, there was an altitude band that extended from approximately 1500 m (4,921 ft) to 3000 m (9,843 ft) that existing anti-aircraft guns could cover only with difficulty. Aircraft flying in this band were really too high or too low for small or larger-calibre weapons. What was obviously required was an interim-calibre weapon that could deal with this problem but, as artillery designers in both the Allied and German camps were to discover, it was not an easy problem to be solved.

German designs

The German solution to the interim-altitude band situation was a gun known as the **5-cm Flak 41**, and the best that can be said of it was that it was not a success. It was first produced

in 1936, and was yet another Rheinmetall-Borsig design that was preferred over a Krupp submission. Development of the prototype was carried out with no sense of urgency, for it was 1940 before the production contract was awarded and in the event only 60 guns were completed. The first of them entered service in 1941 and the type's shortcomings soon became apparent.

The main problem was the ammunition: despite its 50-mm (1.97-in) calibre, this was rather underpowered and on firing produced a prodigious amount of muzzle blast and flash that distracted the aimer, even in broad daylight. The carriage proved rather bulky and awkward to handle in action, and despite the characteristics of the expected targets the traversing mechanism was also rather underpow-

ered and too slow to track fast flying targets.

Two versions of the Flak 41 were produced: a mobile type using two axles to carry the gun and carriage, and a static version for emplacing close to areas of high importance such as the Ruhr dams. Despite their overall lack of success the guns were kept in service until the war ended, but by then only 24 were left.

Weapon development

During the war years some development work was carried out using the Flak 41s, not so much to improve the guns themselves but to determine the exact nature of the weapon that was to replace them. In time this turned out to be a design known as the **Gerät 56** (Gerät was a cover name, meaning equipment) but it was not finalised before the

war ended. One Flak 41 development was the formation of one battery operating under a single remote control.

In action the Flak 41 had a crew of seven men. Loading the ammunition was no easy task for it was fed into the gun in five-round clips that were somewhat difficult to handle. Though designed for use against aircraft targets, the Flak 41 was also provided with special armour-piercing projectiles for use against tanks, but this AP round appears to

have been little used as the Flak 41 was one of the few German weapons that was not selected for mounting on a self-propelled carriage.

Allied efforts

If the Germans were unsuccessful in their attempt to defend the interim-altitude band, it has to be stated that the Allies were no more successful. Typical of their efforts was the British twin 6-pdr, a 57-mm (2.24-in) weapon that never got past the trials stage because of its indifferent performance.

SPECIFICATION	
Flak 41	**Traverse:** 360°
Calibre: 50 mm (1.97 in)	**Muzzle velocity:** 840 m (2,756 ft) per second
Length of piece: 4.686 m (184½ in)	**Maximum effective ceiling:** 3050 m (10,007 ft)
Weight: in action 3100 kg (6,834 lb)	**Rate of fire:** (cyclic) 180 rpm
Elevation: -10° to +90°	**Projectile weight:** 2.2 kg (4.85 lb)

20-mm Breda Modello 35 DP gun

One of the two standard Italian 20-mm AA guns was the weapon known to the Italian army as the **Cannone-Mitragliera da 20/65 modello 35 (Breda)**. It was first manufactured in 1931 by the Società Italiana Ernesto Breda of Brescia, a company that was no stranger to weapon production but whose staple activity was building locomotives and trucks. The Breda gun was designed as a dual-purpose weapon for use against ground and aircraft targets, and was taken into service by the Italian army in 1935.

Effective weapon

The 20-mm Breda gun was a very effective weapon, and was much used by the Italian army. It had a rather complicated twin-wheeled carriage that could be towed into action behind a truck, but it was light enough to be manhandled over considerable distances and it could even be broken down into four pack loads for man car-

One very prominent feature of the 20-mm Breda gun was the long sight arm arrangement, which was meant to keep the gun sight in front of the aimer's face at all angles of elevation. It worked very well, but was rather complex and heavy, and elsewhere much simpler design solutions were usually found.

Members of a Slovak division operating with the Wehrmacht are manning a 20-mm Breda. Following the Italian surrender, Germany commandeered much of the equipment of the Italian army, often giving it to their dwindling number of allies.

SPECIFICATION

Breda modello 1935
Calibre: 20 mm (0.787 in)
Length of piece: 1.3 m (51¼ in)
Weight: in action 307.35 kg (678 lb)
Elevation: -10° to +80°
Traverse: 360°

Muzzle velocity: 830-850 m (2,723-2,789 ft) per second
Maximum effective ceiling: 2500 m (8,202 ft)
Rate of fire: (cyclic) 200-220 rpm
Projectile weight: 0.135 kg (0.298 lb)

a self-destruct feature if it did not hit a target. The tripod platform of the gun provided a steady base for firing, and against aircraft the gun proved to be very successful. Against tanks it was less effective, but any weapons captured by the Allies during the North African campaigns were usually mounted on the light armoured cars of the day to provide them with more offensive capability than that provided by the usual machine-guns. The Germans also took over numbers of Breda guns for their own use in North Africa under the designation **2-cm Breda (i)**, and the Italian surrender of

1943 meant that all guns on the Italian mainland immediately changed to German use. Much further afield, some Breda guns were also used by various warring Chinese military factions.

Weapon variations

Apart from the modello 35 there was also a **modello 39**. This was a much more complex weapon: it used the same gun as before, but allied to a static pedestal-type mounting on which the gun itself was suspended below curved arms that carried the sighting system. This version was usually retained for the defence of the Italian mainland.

riage or mule transport. In action the gun required a team of three men: the aimer sat on the gun and used a complex telescopic sight incorporating a predictor function. Ammunition was fed into the gun on 12-round trays, and the feed mechanism contained the

odd Italian feature of placing the spent cartridge case back into the tray once it had been fired. Exactly what function this feature was supposed to impart is uncertain, but it appeared on several Italian automatic weapons and at least had the advantage of keeping

the gun position tidy.
Against ground targets the gun fired armour-piercing rounds. Aircraft targets were engaged with a high explosive projectile that incorporated a very sensitive percussion fuse to operate against light aircraft structures. The projectile also had

Type 98 20-mm Machine Cannon Japanese army DP gun

The **Army Type 98 20-mm Machine Cannon** was a Japanese army weapon introduced into service in 1938, and was designed from the outset as a dual-purpose weapon capable of use against aircraft and armoured ground targets. Thus, it had a rather odd-looking carriage that added to its somewhat archaic appearance. This appearance was deceptive, for the Type 98 was a thoroughly modern weapon with good overall performance.

Gun transportation

The carriage was rather high and mounted on two spoked wooden wheels that were used to move the weapon, either as a towed unit behind a light truck or animal team, or by manhandling. Once in position the trail legs opened to form the rear components of a tripod with another outrigger leg forward. Once the tripod had been deployed the wheels were lifted off the ground to permit 360° traverse with the gunner/aimer behind the gun on a small seat. If required the entire weapon could be broken down into separate loads for animal or man-pack trans-

port. It was possible to fire the gun direct from the wheels but since the weapon had a rather high centre of gravity it soon became unstable; moreover, it took only about three minutes to get the gun into action on its tripod with a two- or three-man crew.
The Type 98 was a very hard-hitting weapon. This was due mainly to its 20-mm ammunition which was similar to that fired from the Type 97 anti-tank rifle, though the Type 98 ammunition used a slightly longer and wider cartridge case. This cartridge enabled the Type 98 projectiles to penetrate 30 mm (1.18 in) of armour at a range of 247 m (270 yards), so the effect of the same projectile against a low-flying aircraft can well be imagined. According to many accounts the Type 98 was used more in the anti-aircraft than anti-tank role, despite the fact that its cyclic rate of fire was rather low (120 rounds per minute), decreased in service by the use of a box magazine holding 20 rounds positioned in a vertical row.
A twin-barrelled version of the Type 98 was produced in small numbers, but this was

not the only other 20-mm weapon used by the Japanese. By 1944 anti-aircraft guns were in great demand and all manner of odd weapons were impressed for the role. Surplus aircraft cannon were one source, and the Japanese navy often gave up

precious weapons for extemporised mountings in the defence of strategic islands. Among these were 25-mm cannon that were lifted direct with their original naval mountings into shore-located weapon pits in single-, double- and triple-barrelled mountings. These **Navy**

Type 96 25-mm Machine Cannon weapons had a performance very similar to that of the Army Type 98 and were used by army personnel. To provide these navy weapons with mobility, some were mounted on simple sledges for towing across level ground.

SPECIFICATION

Type 98
Calibre: 20 mm (0.787 in)
Length of piece: 1.46 m (57½ in)
Weight: in action 268.77 kg (593 lb)
Elevation: -10° to +85°
Traverse: 360°

Muzzle velocity: 830 m (2,723 ft) per second
Maximum effective ceiling: about 3650 m (11,975 ft)
Rate of fire: 120 rpm
Projectile weight: 0.136 kg (0.31 lb)

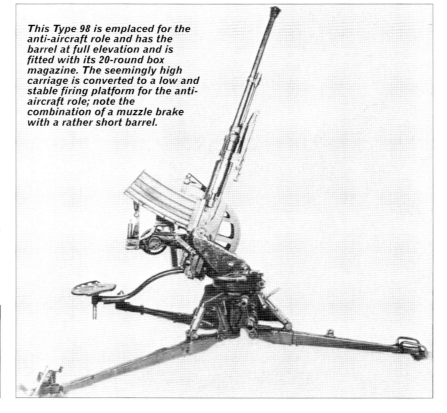

This Type 98 is emplaced for the anti-aircraft role and has the barrel at full elevation and is fitted with its 20-round box magazine. The seemingly high carriage is converted to a low and stable firing platform for the anti-aircraft role; note the combination of a muzzle brake with a rather short barrel.

20-mm Oerlikon Swiss-designed anti-aircraft cannon

The **20-mm Oerlikon** gun has a rather long history, stretching back as far as 1914 when it was produced by Reinhold Becker in Germany. Versions of this gun were used during World War I as German air force weapons, but in 1919 Becker transferred his brain-child to Switzerland, where it was produced by a firm known as SEMAG, until that concern was taken over by the Werkzeug Maschinenfabrik Oerlikon at Oerlikon, still in Switzerland. Under this new concern production of many types of Oerlikon gun expanded greatly (the original Becker weapon as the **Type F**, the SEMAG model as the **Type L** and its own version as the **Type S**), and the usual practice of licence production elsewhere soon followed. France was one early manufacturing location (**2-cm Mitrailleuse C.A. Oerlikon**), and Japan another (**Type 98**). Sales were made worldwide, and Oerlikon aircraft and anti-aircraft guns were a common sight in many nations.

Gas operation

The Oerlikon was a gas-operated gun with the mechanism action assisted by the large coil springs around the barrel that were a recognition feature of the weapon. After 1935 the Oerlikon was produced in the United Kingdom for the Royal Navy so that by 1939 there were considerable numbers of this **Gun,**

The Swiss 20-mm Oerlikon cannon was manufactured in the United Kingdom and many other countries, and was one of the most important weapons of its type in use during World War II. Although used mainly as a naval weapon, many were employed by land forces. This is the British HB Mk 1 mounting.

Below: First introduced in its earliest form in 1914, the Oerlikon 20-mm saw its widest service as a naval weapon. Modern guns by the same firm are in widespread use both at sea and on land.

20-mm, Oerlikon in use. This was just as well, for by 1940 they were being pressed into service on land mountings of all kinds. Some of these British mountings were simple in the extreme but others such as the Haszard semi-mobile mount were much more 'formal'. Later in the war a triple-gun mounting with the three guns one over the other was placed into production and some of these types of mounts were later used on trucks.

The Oerlikon normally used a 60-round drum magazine for the feed system, but a 20-round box magazine was used on some versions, including those used by the Germans, who knew the

Oerlikon as the **2-cm Flak 28** or **Flak 29**, and some of their guns were later passed to the Italians (**Cannone-Mitragliera da 20 Oerlikon**). Over the Atlantic the Americans were producing Oerlikons by 1940 as the **20-mm Automatic Gun Mk IV** originally for the Royal Navy but later for their own use, and the type was particularly useful in the Pacific against Japanese kamikaze attacks. Thus the Oerlikon gun was another of those weapons that started life in a neutral state but ended up being used by all sides, and some of the kamikaze aircraft that attacked US Navy shipping were shot down by Oerlikon guns carried on those same ships, firing back

at aircraft that also carried Oerlikon guns. The same situation prevailed in Europe, for many Luftwaffe aircraft carried Oerlikon guns of one type or another.

Many of the guns used by the UK armed forces had their origins in Royal Navy models, but these were fairly easy to adapt to a number of land mountings. At sea most Oerlikons were

used on simple pedestal mountings whatever navy happened to be using them. Many are still in use today for they continue to be a popular naval weapon, which cannot be bad for a design that can trace its origins to 1914. Since then it is probable that more Oerlikon guns have been produced than any other weapon of their type.

SPECIFICATION

Automatic Gun Mk IV	
Calibre: 20 mm (0.787 in)	**Muzzle velocity:** 831 m (2,725 ft) per second
Length of piece: 2.21 m (87 in)	**Maximum effective ceiling:** 1097 m (3,600 ft)
Weight: (gun only) 66.68 kg (147 lb)	**Rate of fire:** (cyclic) 465-480 rpm
Elevation: -10° to +75°	**Projectile weight:** 0.119 kg (0.2625 lb)
Traverse: 360°	

Twin 20-mm Oerlikons are cleaned aboard the Indian Navy sloop HMIS Naradba late in the war. Still in service at sea after more than 70 years, the Oerlikon is now only very rarely encountered in towed form.

40-mm Bofors Swedish-designed anti-aircraft cannon

The **40-mm Bofors** gun has by now passed virtually into legend as one of the most successful weapons of its type that has ever been produced, and it was used by nearly all protagonists during World War II, and a measure of its effec-

tiveness can be seen by the fact that it is still in service to this day.

The 40-mm Bofors gun had its origins in a 1928 request from the Swedish navy for AB Bofors to design a light anti-aircraft gun. The first weapon was

manufactured in 1930 and was subsequently produced in single- and twin-gun mountings for the navy, and on a mobile ground mounting for the army. It was this latter version that became the most famous, for it was soon

seen to be the best gun of its type available. It had a high muzzle velocity (making it an ideal anti-aircraft weapon), it fired a good-sized projectile with a worthwhile payload that could bring down virtually any aircraft that it hit and

the mounting and carriage were relatively light and manageable to use in action. Within a few years orders were flooding into the AB Bofors factory at Karlskroga but, more importantly at the time, a number of foreign governments

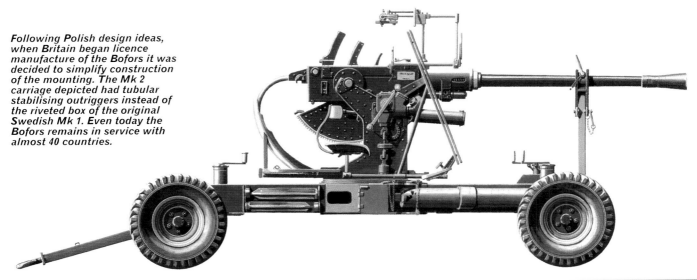

Following Polish design ideas, when Britain began licence manufacture of the Bofors it was decided to simplify construction of the mounting. The Mk 2 carriage depicted had tubular stabilising outriggers instead of the riveted box of the original Swedish Mk 1. Even today the Bofors remains in service with almost 40 countries.

negotiated for licence production of the gun and its ammunition. These nations included Hungary, Poland, Finland, Greece, Norway and many other countries as well. Thus by 1939 the Bofors gun was in production all over Europe for many armies in a bewildering arrangement of cross-deals. For instance the United Kingdom took out a licence, but was in such a hurry to re-arm with the Bofors gun that it also purchased quantities from Poland and Hungary. France wanted to set up a line but purchased guns from Poland.

Some nations, such as Poland, incorporated their own modifications, contributing a lighter carriage (in the **40-mm armata przeciwlotnicza wz 36)** which was later adopted by the British.

Weapon development

Progressive developments to the carriage and sights were gradually introduced, and there were many and various models of naval mountings. Some of these variations are covered separately, though the gun itself changed but little. It used a robust clip-fed mechanism in which the sequence was automatic once the gunner had pressed the trigger. As he did so a round was rammed into the breech, the breech closed and the weapon fired, the spent case being ejected ready for another round to be fed, all in a sequence that continued as long as the trigger

US soldiers in Germany in 1944 jack up a Bofors anti-aircraft gun to attach to a truck in preparation for moving it to a new site for use against the enemy.

was pressed. If the barrel became overheated it could be rapidly changed.

Principal production

After 1940 the main centres of Bofors production were the United Kingdom (**Gun, AA, Mk 1**) and the United States, where the original Swedish design was reproduced virtually unchanged as the **40-mm Gun M1**. On the German side production was continued at the Kongsberg Arsenal in Norway for use by the German army and the Luftwaffe as the **4-cm Flak 28 (Bofors)**. In the Far East weapons captured in the Dutch East Indies were used by the Japanese. The Soviet Union received some numbers of Bofors from the Americans under Lend-Lease, so it can be seen that Bofors guns were in action on all fronts throughout the war.

Few landing craft had any anti-aircraft weapons of their own, or crew to man them, so any units embarked had to use whatever weapons they took with them. Here the crew of a Bofors gun stands ready to take on any target that appears, probably during the run-up to the June 1944 D-Day landings.

SPECIFICATION	
Bofors gun	
Calibre: 40 mm (1.575 in)	**Muzzle velocity:** 854 m (2,802 ft) per second
Length of piece: 2.25 m (88.6 in)	**Maximum ceiling:** 7200 m (23,622 ft)
Weight: in action 2460 kg (5,423 lb)	**Rate of fire:** (cyclic) 120 rpm
Elevation: -5° to +90°	**Shell weight:** 0.89 kg (1.96 lb)
Traverse: 360°	

A Bofors gun in action during the brief Syrian campaign of 1941. The gun is an early model with no crew protection and simple sights, items that were altered later in the production run. Note the open ammunition box in the foreground and the wheels and axles still on the carriage.

Polsten 20-mm light anti-aircraft gun

In many ways the Polsten gun may be regarded as a Polish rather than a British weapon, but it was produced only in the United Kingdom. It had its origins in the fact that although the Oerlikon gun was a highly successful weapon, it was difficult to manufacture and required a large number of machining processes. The Poles decided to make production easier. They took the basic design but introduced changes to make the weapon simpler. They were just about to complete the project when the Germans invaded Poland in September 1939. Subsequently the members of the design team fled to the UK, taking their drawings and experience with them and re-established the team there. They were joined by expatriate Czechs and some British designers and in time their results were placed in production in a weapon known as the **Polsten** ('Pol' after Poland and 'sten' after the British Sten Company, the same company that manufactured the cheap yet effective Sten sub-machine gun).

The Polsten was a remarkable piece of design and production engineering. The Oerlikon gun used 250 components, but the Polsten reduced this to 119 and the costs were considerably reduced as a result, falling from a nominal £320 for the original to between £60 and £70 for the Polsten. Not surprisingly, as soon as the Polsten was ready it was rushed into production. That was in March 1944 and thereafter production of the Oerlikon ceased in favour of the cheaper weapon.

All-round performer

Although the Polsten was cheaper and easier to make it was every bit as effective as the Oerlikon original. The Polsten could fit into any mounting intended for the Oerlikon, so it was used in a diversity of roles ranging from aircraft gun to tank co-axial weapon. On ground mountings it was used as an anti-aircraft gun on a Universal Mounting that could accommodate either an Oerlikon or a Polsten. The same mounting could also accommodate an American Hispano aircraft cannon, also in 20-mm calibre.

One change that was introduced as standard on the Polsten was a new magazine. The old Oerlikon drum magazine proved to be unpopular in service as it was a bulky and awkward item and took some time to load properly. It was also very difficult to make and consumed a large number of machining operations. On the Polsten it was replaced by a vertical box magazine holding 30 rounds arranged in a double-stack configuration that was not only easier to load but which was much easier to change on the gun. It was also far cheaper to make.

Enduring weapon

The Polsten never completely replaced the Oerlikon gun in service, for although the Oerlikon was expensive it was very robustly made and could last for a very long time. Instead the Polsten and the Oerlikon soldiered on side-by-side with the British Army until both were withdrawn some time during the 1950s. Until recently Polstens continued to appear at odd spots around the world, the fact that the ammunition for them and the Oerlikon remained in widespread production ensuring the weapon's longevity.

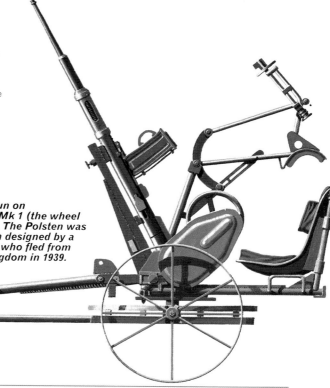

A 20-mm Polsten Mk 1 Gun on the Mounting, Universal Mk 1 (the wheel outline is diagrammatic). The Polsten was a simplified Oerlikon Gun designed by a team of Polish engineers who fled from Poland to the United Kingdom in 1939.

SPECIFICATION	
Polsten (Universal Mounting)	**Muzzle velocity:** 831 m (2,725 ft) per second
Calibre: 20 mm (0.787 in)	**Maximum effective ceiling:**
Length of piece: 2.178 m (85.75 in)	2021 m (6,630 ft)
Weight: (gun) 54.9 kg (121 lb)	**Rate of fire:** (cyclic) 450 rpm
Elevation: -5° to +85°	**Projectile weight:** 0.119 kg
Traverse: 360°	(0.2625 lb)

Maxson Mount 0.5-in light anti-aircraft gun

One of the main American weapons produced as a counter to the low-flying aircraft was not of the same calibre as the other weapons in this study, for instead of using what are normally regarded as cannon calibres, the American solution used heavy machine-guns with a calibre of 0.5 in (12.7 mm). This was the **Maxson Mount**, which used a combination of four 0.5-in Browning M2 heavy machine-guns on a single mounting with two guns on each side of a central pedestal-type housing. The proper service designation for this arrangement was the **Multiple Caliber .50 Machine-Gun Carriage M51**.

Electrical supply

The Maxson Mount was used on a variety of different carriages. One of the most common was a trailer towed by a light truck or even a Jeep. This trailer used twin axles, and in action legs could be lowered to the ground at each corner to provide increased stability when firing. The trailer also carried a number of batteries and a battery-charging set, for the Maxson Mount was electrically powered. The electrical supply was used for elevation and traverse, and the motors used were powerful enough to meet the most demanding calls made upon them by the gunner, who sat on the turret between the two pairs of machine-guns. The motors could move the guns from the horizontal to +60° in one second, and the turret could traverse at the same rate. In order to keep the two main batteries topped up at all times, they were normally kept on constant charge in action.

The combined fire of the four Browning machine-guns was sufficient to bring down most aircraft caught in their fire, despite the fact that the rounds carried no explosive payload. The guns were aimed using a naval reflector sight, but the tracer fired by the guns could also be used to assist aim, and some gunners relied on the tracer alone to make fire-control corrections.

A Maxson Mount is dug in in the Solomons. The quadruple gun layout can be clearly seen, as can the four box magazines outboard of the guns that held up to 200 0.5-in (12.7-mm) rounds. The gunner was seated between the guns and used a reflector sight.

SPECIFICATION	
Maxson Mount	**Muzzle velocity:** 884 m (2,900 ft) per second
Calibre: 0.5 in (12.7 mm)	**Maximum effective ceiling:**
Length: (guns) 1.654 m (65.1 in)	about 1000 m (3,280 ft)
Weight: in action 1087 kg (2,396 lb)	**Rate of fire:** (cyclic, all guns)
Elevation: -5° to +85°	2,300 rpm
Traverse: 360°	

Above: The crew of a Multiple Gun Motor Carriage M16 relax on stand-by close to the famous bridge at Remagen. The crew have toned down the appearance of the vehicle with hessian and a board over the tracks. Note the spare ammunition magazines.

Left: A Multiple Caliber .50 Machine-Gun Carriage M51 is seen in action at Hollandia on New Guinea against low-flying aircraft. This trailer-borne carriage was commonly known as the Maxson Mount and the gunner's helmet can just be seen protruding from between the magazines.

The Maxson Mount was also used on halftracks as well as towed trailers. On both types of carriage the guns were supplied with 200 rounds each, fed from belts carried in enclosed chests mounted outboard of the guns. On some turrets the belts could be fed into the guns under electrical control but the normal gun action was more commonly used.

The Maxson Mounts were normally used to provide protection for convoys or mobile units against air attack, and after 1945 continued to serve with many armies. Many were in use until recently, but later years saw a move away from the retention of the four machine-guns to a new configuration using two 20-mm cannon. Israel adapted all the Maxson Mounts it had in service to this new form, and Brazil was another nation to take the same path. Israel used its modernised Maxson Mounts on halftracks, but there was also a towed version.

37-mm Antiaircraft Gun M1 37-mm light anti-aircraft gun

The development work that led to the **37-mm Antiaircraft Gun M1 on Carriage M3** series started in 1921. It was yet another product of the fertile mind of John M. Browning, who continued to work on the gun until he died in 1926. Development of the project then lapsed until 1934, mainly as a result of defence spending cuts of the period. When work resumed it was not long before the gun was in production, not only for the US Army but for the US Navy (**37-mm AN-M4**) and US Army Air Corps (**37-mm Aircraft Automatic Gun M4** and **M10**) as well. Production started in 1940 under the auspices of the Colt Company, and to some the gun is still known as the **Colt 37 mm**.

Low-value ammunition

The 37-mm gun was an unremarkable design that performed well enough, but it was rather let down by its ammunition which proved to be underpowered and was thus of limited value against low and fast aircraft targets. Various production and carriage changes were introduced until the **M1A2** stage was reached, and at that point the British requested that the Americans should use some of their industrial potential to build Bofors guns for them. A quick perusal of the Bofors gun convinced the Americans that it was much better than their 37-mm design, and they promptly adopted the Bofors in its place. But it was some time before Bofors fabrication could get under way, so the M1A2 continued to roll off the Colt production lines.

Aiming techniques

Somewhere along the line combat analysis revealed that many anti-aircraft gunners were not using the gunsights to aim their weapons, but were instead watching the tracer elements as they fired and correcting the aim onto the target by this means alone. While this was, and still is, a positive way to aim a gun, at calibres of 37-mm and above, it soon becomes an uneconomic practice on any scale. Accordingly, a new **Combination Mount M54** was developed that carried two 0.5-in (12.7-mm) Browning heavy machine-guns, one on each side of the central 37-mm barrel. As the machine-guns were ballistically very similar to the main gun, their tracer could be used as the aiming element and once on target the main gun could be fired. This worked out very well in practice. Most of these combination mounts were used on halftracks or on board US Navy vessels right through and after the war, but there was a drawback as far as the original designers were concerned: far from using the two machine-guns as the aiming elements of the combination, many enthusiastic gunners continued to use all three weapons to fire tracer all the time, thereby negating the original intention.

Ongoing service

During the war large numbers of M1A2 guns and combination mounts were delivered to the USSR as part of the Lend-Lease arrangement. Many of these weapons never found their way back to the United States and during the Cold War continued to appear in odd corners of the world where Soviet influence was paramount. Some even remained in service with Warsaw Pact militia forces long after they had passed from use in the West.

It had been intended that the 37-mm Antiaircraft Gun M1A2 was to be the standard US Army light anti-aircraft weapon, but the superior Bofors Gun took over that role. However, the M1A2 remained in production until there were enough Bofors Guns to hand.

SPECIFICATION	
M1A2 on Carriage M3A1	**Muzzle velocity:** 853 m (2,800 ft) per second
Calibre: 37 mm (1.457 in)	**Maximum ceiling:** 5669 m (18,600 ft)
Length of piece: 1.986 m (78.2 in)	
Weight: in action 2778 kg (6,124 lb)	**Rate of fire:** (cyclic) 120 rpm
Elevation: -5° to +90°	**Projectile weight:** 0.61 kg (1.34 lb)
Traverse: 360°	

8.8-cm Flak 18, Flak 36 and Flak 37 Anti-aircraft guns

The terms of the Treaty of Versailles, signed in 1919, laid down strict limits as to what artillery production could be be carried out in Germany, so the largest of that country's armaments companies, Krupp of Essen, sent a team to Sweden to carry on research and development outside the imposed restrictions. Working with Bofors, the Krupp team worked initially on a 75-mm (2.95-in) anti-aircraft gun using clandestine German army funds, but the army was not particularly happy with the result and asked for something heavier. Thus the 'Swedish' Krupp team produced a new and advanced 88-mm (3.46-in) gun that by 1933 was in series production at Essen as the Nazi party came to power.

This new gun was the **8.8-cm Flak 18** (Flak standing for *Fliegerabwehr- kanone*, or anti-aircraft gun), and it was an immediate success. Based on a long barrel, the gun was set on a pivoted cruciform carriage, which was in turn carried on the move by twin axles that allowed rapid placement of the gun into its firing position. The Flak 18 had a one-piece barrel, but was later supplemented by an improved version, the **8.8-cm Flak 36**, which had a multi-section barrel on which only the most worn part, that nearest the chamber, needed to be changed after extended firing. Then came the **8.8-cm Flak 37**, which was the Flak 36 with a revised system of fire-control data transmission more suited to static use than field use.

In practice the three models were interchangeable to a high degree, and it was not unusual to see a Flak 18 bar-

rel on a Flak 37 carriage. Several changes were introduced to the weapons after they had entered service, including a revised twin-axle carriage arrangement, and the 8.8-cm Flak series was adapted for carriage on a variety of self-propelled mountings, including railway flatcars.

Much-feared weapon

The 8.8-cm Flak series became one of the most celebrated weapons in German service, for it went on to be as famous as an anti-tank weapon as it was as an anti-aircraft gun: following the gun's 'blooding' in the Spanish Civil War and again

Above: This Flak 36 is seen in action during the Soviet campaign. After the tribulations of the bitter winter of 1941, the German army had become more familiar with sub-zero fighting, but 'General Winter' was still a potent contributor to the Soviet war effort.

Left: The 8.8-cm Flak (Sf) auf Zugkraftwagen 18t, of which 14 were created in 1943, was an attempt to boost the Flak 37's mobility by placing it on the Zugkraftwagen 18t halftrack with armour over the engine and crew compartment.

Despite its height, which made tactical concealment difficult, the 8.8-cm Flak guns were decisive anti-tank guns as they fired a potent armour-piercing projectile with the high muzzle velocity that yielded a flat trajectory even over comparatively long ranges.

In an effort to improve the efficiency of Germany's defences against the efforts of Allied bombers, a number of 8.8-cm Flak guns were mounted on railway flatcars so that whole batteries could be moved quickly to any target area that seemed particularly threatened. Allied decimation of Germany's railway system made this concept less useful that it could have been.

in France in 1940, it was discovered that a high muzzle velocity combined with a projectile that was both efficient and heavy to make the weapon ideal as a 'tank killer'. This became very evident first during the North African and later in the Eastern Front campaigns, but the 8.8-cm Flak series was really too high and bulky for the anti-tank role and had to rely on its range and power rather than concealment in action.

Primary AA gun

As anti-aircraft weapons, the guns of the 8.8-cm Flak series were the mainstay of the German field forces and of the defence of the Reich under Luftwaffe control. The type was never replaced by later models as had been planned, and in August 1944 there were 10,704 of all three models in service. Production was undertaken at several centres, and a wide range of ammunition was produced for these weapons, including a high proportion of armour-piercing. By the end of World War II versions for static emplacement only were being produced, but by then the 8.8-cm Flak series had been employed on self-propelled platforms, railway mountings, coast defence locations and ships as well as in experimental forms.

The guns of the 8.8-cm Flak series were also used by the Italian forces, and for a while in late 1944 captured weapons were even used operationally by the US Army along Germany's western border after the American forces' own supply lines had became overextended. Many examples were used by several other armies after World War II, and the Yugoslav army used the 8.8-cm Flak gun as a coast defence weapon into the 1980s.

Above: Resting on a cruciform firing platform after the wheels had been removed from its carriage, the 8.8-cm Flak gun was notably stable when firing, a fact that enhanced its tactical utility to a marked degree.

Above: This 8.8-cm Flak gun carries many 'kill' rings round its barrel. In its Flak 18 form, the gun fired the 9.5-kg (20.9-lb) AP40 armour-piercing projectile with a muzzle velocity of 795 m (2,608 ft) per second.

Right: By the end of World War II the 8.8-cm Flak guns had been overtaken in some respects by larger-calibre weapons, but were still very formidable guns.

SPECIFICATION	
8.8-cm Flak 18	**Elevation:** -3 degrees to +85°
Calibre: 88 mm (3.46 in)	**Traverse:** 360°
Weight: travelling 6861 kg (15,126 lb) and firing 5150 kg (11,354 lb)	**Maximum ceiling:** 8000 m (26,245 ft)
Dimensions: length overall 7.62 m (25 ft); width 2.305 m (7 ft 6¾ in); height 2.418 m (7 ft 11¼ in); length of barrel 4.93 m (16 ft 2 in)	**Shell weight:** HE 9.24 kg (20.34 lb)
	Muzzle velocity: 820 m (2,690 ft) per second

8.8-cm Flak 41 Anti-aircraft gun

By 1939 it was obvious to the long-term German military planners that the expected increases in aircraft performance would render the existing 8.8-cm (3.465-in) and 10.5-cm (4.13-in) Flak weapons obsolete, so they initiated the development of a new 8.8-cm weapon. Rheinmetall was given the contract for this new gun, and the company accordingly attempted to integrate into the design all the various lessons learned from the existing 8.8-cm Flak 18 and Flak 37 series. Thus the new weapon, known initially as the **Gerät 37**, was intended for use not only as an anti-aircraft gun but it also had to be suited for use as an anti-tank weapon and even a field or coastal artillery piece. As an anti-tank weapon, the new gun overcame the disadvantage faced by the Flak 18 and Flak 37 in this role by turning the upright mount arrangement of the earlier models through almost 90° to reduce the silhouette. The new gun also offered a greater muzzle velocity than the earlier 8.8-cm Flak 37 (some 1000 m/3,280 ft per second) by replacing that weapon's L/56 barrel with a new, strengthened barrel of 71 calibres.

Despite operational problems throughout its career, the 8.8-cm Flak 41 was regarded as one of the finest anti-aircraft weapons of World War II. However, relatively few of the weapons were built.

Development

When development of the multi-role Gerät 37 was completed in 1941, a highly complicated weapon was presented to the troops. The Gerät 37 was adopted as the **8.8-cm Flak 41**, but service development took until 1943 as the design was full of minor problems, some of which were never entirely eliminated. An example of this can be quoted as the ammunition, which in typical German style used a long and expensive cartridge case. These cases frequently jammed on extraction after firing, to the extent that special high-grade brass cases had to be manufactured specifically for some of the early examples. Both three- and four-section

barrels were produced, and the weapon even had an automatic fuse setter on the loading mechanism. There were no fewer than three separate firing circuits, and a powered rammer was fitted.

The 8.8-cm Flak 41 could be fired from the travelling position with the cruciform side arms extended, and the twin-wheeled Sonderhänger 202 carriage was adopted as standard for the weapon.

Tunisian campaign

The first production examples were sent to Tunisia during the latter stages of the North African campaign: here their technical troubles continued and they were given little chance to prove themselves in combat. Thereafter they were

assigned to use within the borders of the Reich only, and principally around key industrial areas, where they could be near the very necessary workshop facilities that they constantly demanded. However, it should not be thought that the Flak 41 was an unsuccessful weapon, for when it worked it was an excellent anti-aircraft gun. After the war it was generally regarded as the best of all the German anti-aircraft guns from a technical point of view, but one that required an inordinate amount of maintenance and repair time. When it did work properly it had a rate of fire of up to 25 rounds per minute and had a maximum effective ceiling of 14700 m (48,230 ft).

Compared to the Flak 37, which required an average of 16,000 shells to bring down one high-flying enemy bomber, the Flak 41 required 8,000 rounds. This was still a very disappointing return, and compounded Germany's problems on the Eastern Front, where ammunition – particularly that required for high-velocity anti-tank guns such as the '88' – was in short supply.

The Flak 41 also fired a different range of ammunition compared to the other 8.8-cm anti-aircraft weapons. The rounds fired by the 8.8-cm Flak 41 included Sprenggranate Patrone (high-explosive), Sprenggranate Patrone Gerillt (high-explosive fragmentation) and

Panzergranate Patrone (armour-piercing) types.

Despite the technical promise of the Flak 41, the type was never produced in anything but limited numbers. It consumed a great deal of manufacturing potential, and production was not assisted by the constant attention given by the Allied air forces to the weapon's main production centre at Düsseldorf.

Production delay

Further lengthy production delays were imposed when an attempt was made to switch some production to the Skoda Werke at Pilsen, but for all their efforts the most the Germans could ever field was 318 and that was in January 1945.

10.5-cm Flak 38 and Flak 39 Anti-aircraft gun

As far back as 1933 the German military planners saw a need for an anti-aircraft gun heavier than the 8.8-cm (3.465-in) Flak series, and both Rheinmetall and Krupp were invited to submit designs for a 'shoot-off' contest for 10.5-cm (4.13-in) weapons held in 1935. Rheinmetall won the contract with its Gerät 38, which duly went into production as the **10.5-cm Flak 38**. This model had an electrical control system and a

powered loading mechanism, but was soon replaced in production by the **10.5-cm Flak 39** with a revised electrical and fire-control data system.

Both 10.5-cm (4.13-in) Flak guns were intended for use by the German field armies, but in the event they were almost all employed in the home defence of the Reich. In appearance the Flak 38 and Flak 39 resembled scaled-up Flak 18 guns, but there were many detail

differences and proportionally the Flak 38 and Flak 39 were much heavier and bulkier weapons. In overall terms the Flak 38 and Flak 39 were complex weapons and were made more complex to manufacture by the use of a sectional barrel (for rapid change of the worn portion only after firing) on the Flak 39. Unfortunately, in action they proved to be little better than the 8.8-cm (3.465-in) Flak series as far as overall performance was

concerned, and at one point it was even intended to replace them in production by the 8.8-cm (3.465-in) Flak 41, although this never happened: production of the Flak 41 was so slow that the 10.5-cm (4.13-in) Flak guns were kept on the production lines. When the war ended there were still 1,850 in service, most of these within the borders of the Reich.

Although intended as a field weapon, the Flak 38 and Flak 39 were really too

heavy for the role. They used a scaled-up version of the mobile twin axle carriage of the 8.8-cm (3.465-in) Flak series, but even with the aid of integral winches and pulleys the guns were slow and awkward to emplace. Many were subsequently assigned to static emplacements, and 116 were mounted on special Flak railway trucks that rumbled around the Reich wherever they were needed. Each model needed

The 10.5-cm (4.13-in) Flak 38 and 39 resembled scaled-up versions of the 8.8-cm Flak 18 series, but used an all-electrical control system and a revised loading system. Intended for use by field units, many were later diverted to the Luftwaffe for the defence of the Reich, and many were used on railway mountings.

SPECIFICATION

10.5-cm Flak 39
Calibre: 105 mm (4.13 in)
Weight: travelling 14600 kg (32,187 lb) and firing 10240 kg (22,575 lb)
Dimensions: length overall 10.31 m (33 ft 9.9 in); width 2.45 m (8 ft ½ in); height 2.9 m (9 ft 6 in); length of barrel 6.648 m (21 ft 9.7 in); length of rifling 5.531 m (18 ft 1¾ in)
Elevation: -8°/+90°
Traverse: 360°
Maximum ceiling: 12800 m (41,995 ft)
Shell weight: 15.1 kg (33.3 lb)
Muzzle velocity: 880 m (2,887 ft) per second

a crew of a commander and nine men, though use of the manual loading system required a further two men.

Heavier projectile

The 10.5-cm (4.13-in) Flak series never acquired the fame of the 8.8-cm (3.465-in) Flak series, mainly because it was not widely used in the field and because its bulk and weight meant that it was only rarely used as an anti-armour weapon. Overall its performance was not as good as had been originally hoped, and despite a great deal of development work on a project known as the 10.5-cm Flak 40, which was to have had a longer barrel to fire a heavier projectile, the 10.5-cm (4.13-in) Flak guns were never stretched to the same extent as the other German Flak guns. Instead production went steadily ahead until the war ended.

Right: A 103-cm Flak 39 in action on a special railway truck mounting, here being used for harbour defence. These railway mountings were moved around the occupied territories and the Reich itself.

12.8-cm Flak 40 Heavy anti-aircraft gun

Only six mobile versions of the 12.8-cm Flak 40 were produced before production was switched to static versions. This gun is carried on a Sonderhänger 220 in one load.

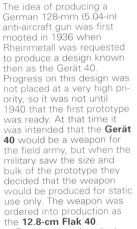

The idea of producing a German 128-mm (5.04-in) anti-aircraft gun was first mooted in 1936 when Rheinmetall was requested to produce a design known then as the Gerät 40. Progress on this design was not placed at a very high priority, so it was not until 1940 that the first prototype was ready. At that time it was intended that the **Gerät 40** would be a weapon for the field army, but when the military saw the size and bulk of the prototype they decided that the weapon would be produced for static use only. The weapon was ordered into production as the **12.8-cm Flak 40**.

By that time plans had already been made for a production-line mobile version, so the first six were produced on mobile carriages. The Flak 40 was so large

that it proved impossible to carry the gun in one load over other than very short distances, so a two-load system was initially employed. Even this proved to be too cumbersome, and was later revised to a single load once again. Later versions were produced for static use only, and such was the overall performance of the Flak 40 that it was carefully emplaced around some of the main production and population centres, such as Berlin and Vienna. Special Flak towers were built in some locations to make best use of these guns, and there was also a special rail-car version to provide these cumbersome guns with some sort of mobility.

Production of the static version began in 1942, but it was a costly and complex gun so by January 1945 there were only 570 in service, all of them within the borders of the Reich.

Mirror loading

Soon after full-scale production began, the Flak 40 was joined by a twin version of the same gun known as the **12.8-cm Flakzwilling 40**. This consisted of two 12.8-cm (5.04-in) Flak guns mounted side-by-side on the same mounting and provided with 'mirror' loading arrangements. These powerful gun combinations were used only

on special Flak towers around the main centres of population within the Reich, and were so costly and difficult to produce that there were never many of them; even by February 1945 there were only 33 in service. The Flakzwilling (zwilling, or twin) was introduced as it was realised that ever heavier anti-aircraft guns would be needed to counter the increasing performance of Allied bombers, and despite strenuous efforts to develop guns with calibres of 150 mm

(5.9 in) and even 240 mm (9.45 in), none got past the prototype stage at best and some failed to get even that far. Thus the twin arrangement of the Flakzwilling 40 was an attempt to produce at least some form of increased firepower to counter the Allied heavy bombers, and in the event it turned out to be a highly effective and excellent anti-aircraft weapon.

As the war ended the original mobile Flak 40s were still in use; many were in use on special trains.

This photograph of a 12.8-cm Flak 40 in the field was taken in 1940 in order to show the might of the German army's anti-aircraft field defences. In fact, only one battery was so used before all production of the gun was switched to the home defence of the Reich. This one battery was also moved out of the field.

SPECIFICATION

12.8-cm Flak 40
Calibre: 128 mm (5.04 in)
Weight: travelling (mobile) 27000 kg (59,524 kg), firing (mobile) 17000 kg (37,478 lb), and firing (static) 13000 kg (28,660 lb)
Dimensions: length overall 15 m (49 ft 2½ in); height 3.965 m (13 ft); length of barrel 7.835 m (25 ft 8½ in); length of rifling 6.478 m (21 ft 3 in)
Elevation: -3°/+87°
Traverse: 360°
Maximum effective ceiling: 14800 m (48,555 ft)
Shell weight: 26 kg (57.3 lb)
Muzzle velocity: 880 m (2,887 ft) per second

French heavy AA guns 75-mm guns

When the problem of anti-aircraft defences arose during World War I the French army reacted in its usual manner, taking the ordnance of the famous '75', the mle 1897 field gun, and placing it on to a simple high-angle mounting. There were several of these mountings, one being a simple arrangement of the gun on a fixed turntable with the carriage knocked up from steel assemblies. This simple arrangement was the **Canon de 75 mm anti-aérien mle 1915**, but a better arrangement was produced by the **Canon de 75 mm anti-aérien mle 1913**, which was an early attempt to produce a self-propelled anti-aircraft gun by mounting a mle 1897 on a truck. Despite the early design date this turned out to be a remarkably good anti-aircraft weapon but it was not the only use of the mle 1897 for the role. There was also a **Canon de 75 mm contre aeronefs mle 1917** which

was a towed piece but one in which all the fire-control instruments were mounted on the carriage; this was a Schneider design.

Weapon upgrade

These three equipments were still in use in appreciable numbers in 1939 when World War II began for the simple reason that there appeared to be no real need to replace them; moreover, funds for new equipment for the French army were scant while the Maginot Line was being constructed. However, by the late 1920s it was appreciated that the old mle 1897 field gun was being rapidly outmoded as an anti-aircraft weapon and that higher-velocity weapons would soon be needed. Thus there started a desultory programme of re-equipping the many old batteries.

Some of the first to be updated were the fixed batteries around such locations as Paris, where the old fixed

mle 1915 equipments simply had their barrels replaced with a more powerful Schneider ordnance to produce the **Canon de 75 mm contre aeronefs mle 17/34**. This new barrel provided a much better performance with less time-of-flight and improved service ceiling. Similar barrels were placed on the old mle 1913 truck-mounted equipments and also on the almost-as-old mle 1917 equipments, but so slow was this gradual rebarrelling programme that many guns still had their original mle 1897 barrels in 1940.

Some completely new equipments were produced during the 1930s. Using the new Schneider barrel a completely new anti-aircraft gun known as the **Canon de 75 mm contre aeronefs mle 1933** was produced during the mid-1930s. This was an odd-looking gun mounted in action on a cruciform platform with the barrel trunnions mounted well down the barrel near the breech; 192 equipments were in service in 1940. Another totally new Schneider weapon was produced in two forms as the **Canon de 75 mm contre aeronefs mle 1932** and **1936**, which differed only in detail. This was a thoroughly modern weapon designed from the outset for mobility. The mle 1932 had a crew of nine men and could fire up to 25 rounds

per minute. On the road it could be towed at speeds of up to 40 km/h (24.85 mph).

Obsolete barrels

When the Germans invaded in May 1940, the French army was still in a state of confusion regarding anti-aircraft guns. The planned programme of replacement of the old weapons was still far from complete, and many guns still had their obsolete mle 1897 barrels. There were really too many types of guns in service for logistical comfort but in the event the advances of May and June 1940 swept the French army away before the anti-aircraft guns could

make any impact on the Luftwaffe. Huge amounts of French 75-mm (2.95-in) anti-aircraft equipment were captured by the Germans, who took over many for their own use – but not the old mle 1897s, which were removed from their carriages and were later used as beach defence weapons in the Atlantic Wall. However, many of the more modern Schneider guns were still in German use in 1944. The designations were **7.5-cm FK 97(f)** for the 75-mm anti-aérien, **7.5-cm Flak M.17/34(f)** for the mle 17, **73-cm Flak M.33(f)** for the mle 1933, and **73-cm Flak M.36(f)** for the mle 36.

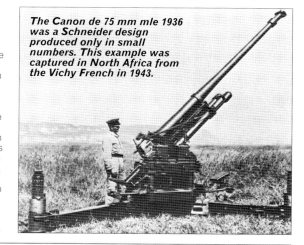

The Canon de 75 mm mle 1936 was a Schneider design produced only in small numbers. This example was captured in North Africa from the Vichy French in 1943.

SPECIFICATION	
Canon de 75 mm contre aeronefs mle 1932 **Calibre:** 75 mm (2.95 in) **Weight:** travelling 5300 kg (11,684 lb) and firing 3800 kg (8,377 lb) **Dimensions:** length travelling 6.95 m (22 ft 9⅔ in); width travelling 1.5 m (4 ft 11 in); length	of barrel 4.05 m (13 ft 3½ in); length of rifling 3.25 m (10 ft 8 in) **Elevation:** +70°/-5° **Traverse:** 360° **Maximum ceiling:** 8000 m (26,245 ft) **Shell weight:** 6.44 kg (14.2 lb) **Muzzle velocity:** 700 m (2,297 ft) per second

Cannone da 75/46 C.A. modello 34 75-mm AA gun

Between the two world wars the Italian armaments industry produced many good designs, but not many got to the hardware stage for the Italian economy was constrained, then as now, by an overall shortage of raw materials of every kind. Thus before any new weapon design was introduced into service it had to be vetted carefully to ensure that it was as good a design as possible to justify the expenditure involved. So when Ansaldo produced a new anti-aircraft gun in 1926 it was examined over a long period before production was authorised, and it was not until 1934 that the gun was actually in service.

The new gun was the **Cannone da 75/46 C.A. modello 34** (75/46 denoting the calibre of 75 mm/2.95

in and the barrel length of 46 calibres). In overall design the 75/46 was a sound though unremarkable effort that owed much to the influence of the contemporary Vickers designs produced in the UK. This was especially apparent in the carriage design, with a central pivot on which the gun saddle swivelled and a folding cruciform platform. On the move, the platform legs were folded together, leaving the pivot resting on a two-wheeled carriage arrangement. When the equipment was ready for emplacement, the legs were swung forward and the wheels removed once the load had been taken by the centre of the carriage. The arrangement of the ordnance on the carriage was very simple and straightforward, and the

fire-control instruments on the carriage were simple but adequate.

Production problems

As always for the Italian armaments industry, the main problem with the 75/46 was one of production. Despite ever-increasing demands from the field, production was slow and erratic. Initially 240 equipments were ordered, but even by the end of 1942 only 226 had been delivered. Not all of these were used primarily as anti-aircraft guns, some being emplaced as dual-purpose anti-aircraft and coastal defence guns at selected points. This meant that many of the rather ancient AA weapons in use at the time had to be retained well past their planned replacement dates.

Despite this dispersion of effort, the 75/46 was spread as thinly as possible for home defence of the Italian mainland and the North African territories. When Italian army units moved to serve on the Eastern Front they took a further 54 guns with them, leaving even fewer to defend Italy. But even these guns were destined

*This **Cannone da 75/46 C.A. modello 34** is in action against Allied aircraft over Libya. This Ansaldo gun was the standard Italian anti-aircraft gun; it was used on all the Italian fronts and was a good all-round performer, but suffered from production problems.*

to follow a varied service career, for in 1943 after the Italian surrender remaining guns were taken over by German occupation forces. The 74/46 then became the **7.5-cm Flak 264/3(i)**, but the type was not used by the Germans outside Italy other than in some of their anti-Yugoslavian partisan

operations. Even this change of hands did not mark the end of the ownership list for the 75/46, for following the Allied invasion of the Italian mainland numbers were captured by the advancing Allied armies and eventually used in a coastal defence role around such ports as Naples.

SPECIFICATION	
Cannone da 75/46 C.A. modello 1934 **Calibre:** 75 mm (2.95 in) **Weight:** travelling 4405 kg (9,711 lb) and firing 3300 kg (7,275 lb) **Dimensions:** length overall 7.4 m (24 ft 3 in); width 1.85 m (6 ft ¾ in); height 2.15 m (7 ft ⅝ in); length of	barrel 3.45 m (11 ft 3¾ in); length of rifling 2.844 m (9 ft 4 in) **Elevation:** +90°/-2° **Traverse:** 360° **Maximum effective ceiling:** 8300 m (27,230 ft) **Shell weight:** 6.5 kg (14.33 lb) **Muzzle velocity:** 750 m (2,461 ft) per second

Cannone da 90/53 90-mm AA gun

Of all the anti-aircraft guns in service with the Italian army from 1941 to 1943, none was better than the **Cannone da 90/53**. It was an excellent weapon that could stand comparison with any of its contemporaries, and it was a good, sound and modern design.

It was another product of the Ansaldo design team and the first examples were produced during 1939. Production was authorised in three main versions.

The most numerous version of the 90/53 was supposed to be the **modello 41P** intended for static emplacement only; 1,087 examples of this version were ordered. A further 660 examples of the towed **modello 41C** were ordered, while another order was for a further 57 guns to be mounted on a variety of heavy trucks (**autocannoni da 90/53**). A later order requested yet another batch of barrels (30) for mounting on self-propelled tracked mountings.

Production shortfalls

Ordering these weapons was one thing, but producing them was quite another, and the final production figures never reached the original optimistic totals. By July 1943 only 539 weapons of all variants had been delivered, but by then the production line was in German hands and continued for German use alone. German formations in North Africa had already had the 90/53 in their service for some time, for they recognised it as a very good gun comparable with their own '88'.

At first sight the 90/53 resembled the 8.8-cm (3.46-in) Flak 18 and Flak 37 weapons, but there were many differences and the similarities were only superficial. The 90/53 had a pivot carriage mounted on a cruciform platform, but on the carriage itself the arrangement of the fire-control instruments was quite different from those of the German guns and the barrel was of one-piece construction instead of the multi-section arrangement of the later German guns.

The Italians used the 90/53 as a multi-purpose weapon on occasion, but some were emplaced as dual-purpose anti-aircraft/coast defence weapons. At times they were used as long-range field guns and the performance of the gun was such that it could match the German '88' as an anti-armour weapon. Numbers were also diverted to the Italian navy. The Germans valued the 90/53 so highly that following the Italian surrender of 1943 they impressed as many 90/53s as they could find. Many of them were sent back to Germany for the defence of the Reich as the **9-cm Flak 41(i)** though the official designation was **9-cm Flak 309/1(i)**, and by December 1944 315 such equipments are mentioned in German records, though many of these would no doubt have been emplaced in Northern Italy. Numbers of 90/53s also fell into Allied hands during their advance north through Italy, and many of these were impressed for the coast defence role by British coastal batteries around the main captured ports.

This Cannone da 90/53 is rendered mobile by mounting it on a Autocarro Pesante Lancio 3/RO heavy truck. The gun is seen here fitted with a protective shield for the gun crew in action, and very noticeable are the outriggers used to stabilise the gun when firing. Only a few of these combinations were made.

SPECIFICATION	
Cannone da 90/53	4.046 m (13 ft 3⅓ in)
Calibre: 90 mm (3.54 in)	**Elevation:** +85°/-2°
Weight: travelling 8950 kg (19,731 lb) and firing 6240 kg (13,757 lb)	**Traverse:** 360°
Dimensions: length 7.6 m (24 ft 11¼ in); width 2.3 m (7 ft 6½ in); height 2.5 m (8 ft 2½ in); length of barrel 4.736 m (15 ft 6½ in); length of rifling	**Maximum effective ceiling:** 12000 m (39,370 ft)
	Shell weight: 10.33 kg (22.77 lb)
	Muzzle velocity: 830 m (2,723 ft) per second

Type 88 75-mm anti-aircraft gun

The 75-mm (2.95-in) **Type 88 Mobile Field AA Gun** was a Japanese army weapon introduced into service in 1928. At that period the Type 88 was as good a gun as any in service, and was well capable of tackling aerial targets of the time. However, it was soon overtaken by increases in aircraft performance to the extent that it could at best be described as an efficient but indifferent performer.

The Type 88 design was chosen after an examination of other current and prospective anti-aircraft guns, and was an amalgam of some of the better points of several weapons. The barrel was a single-piece design with a sliding breech and mounted on the then-fashionable central pivot. The firing platform had five legs that folded fore and aft for transport, and to assist the overall balance on the move the barrel was partially retracted. In action each outrigger leg was supported on an adjustable foot for levelling and there was another adjustable foot under the central pivot. A central pair of wheels was used to tow the gun along roads, these being removed before firing.

Like so many other contemporary Japanese weapons, the Type 88 was difficult to produce as virtually everything on the gun had to be hand-made. It gradually became the standard Japanese army anti-aircraft gun and at one time or another was used by every army field formation, starting in China and Manchuria during the 1930s. It was also widely used during the early Japanese advances in the Pacific. However, once the Japanese mainland came increasingly under threat of air attack from 1943 onwards the Type 88s were gradually withdrawn from the more outlying island garrisons and sent to the home islands.

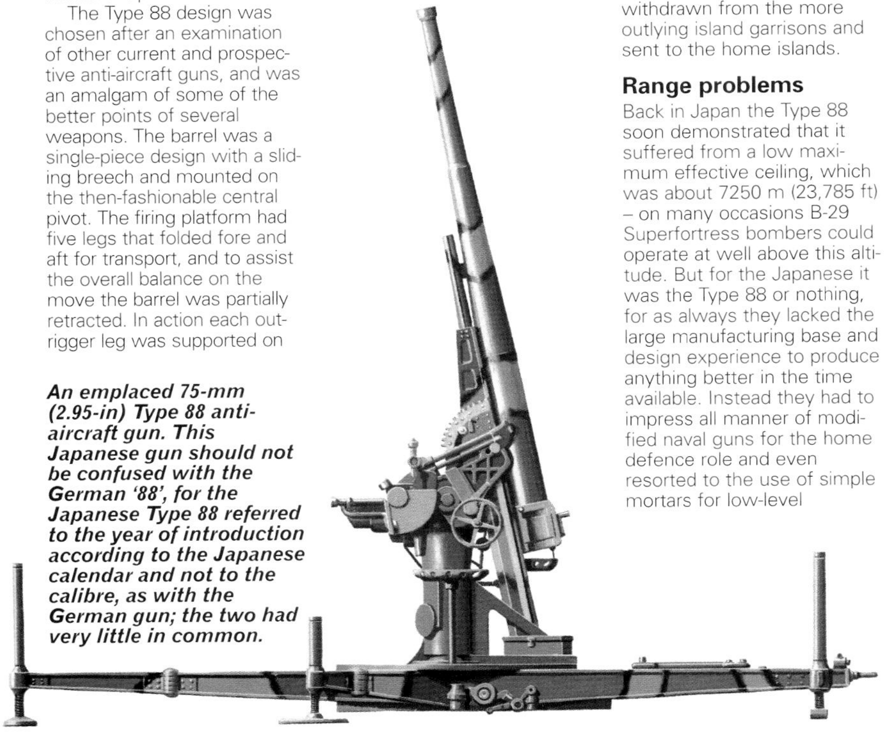

Range problems

Back in Japan the Type 88 soon demonstrated that it suffered from a low maximum effective ceiling, which was about 7250 m (23,785 ft) – on many occasions B-29 Superfortress bombers could operate at well above this altitude. But for the Japanese it was the Type 88 or nothing, for as always they lacked the large manufacturing base and design experience to produce anything better in the time available. Instead they had to impress all manner of modified naval guns for the home defence role and even resorted to the use of simple mortars for low-level defences in some areas.

The Type 88 is mentioned in some Allied intelligence reports as having an anti-armour role, but there appears to be little (if any) evidence of the Type 88 being used in this way. A special armour-piercing projectile known as the Type 95 was produced for use by the Type 88 gun, but the usual high-explosive projectile was the Type 90.

SPECIFICATION	
Type 88	(10 ft 10½ in); length of rifling
Calibre: 75 mm (2.95 in)	2.578 m (8 ft 5½ in)
Weight: travelling 2747 kg (6,056 lb) and firing 2443 kg (5,386 lb)	**Elevation:** +85°/-0°
	Traverse: 360°
Dimensions: length travelling 4.542 m (14 ft 10¾ in); width 1.951 m (6 ft 4¾ in); height 2.019 m (6 ft 7½ in); length of barrel 3.315 m	**Maximum effective ceiling:** 7250 m (23,785 ft)
	Shell weight: 6.58 kg (14.5 lb)
	Muzzle velocity: 720 m (2,362 ft) per second

An emplaced 75-mm (2.95-in) Type 88 anti-aircraft gun. This Japanese gun should not be confused with the German '88', for the Japanese Type 88 referred to the year of introduction according to the Japanese calendar and not to the calibre, as with the German gun; the two had very little in common.

The mount of a captured Type 88 75-mm gun is examined in the Pacific. Notice the five legs of the firing platform and the detached barrel at the bottom left of the photograph.

Bofors 75- and 80-mm Models 1929 and 1930 AA guns

As well as its classic 40-mm guns, Bofors made a larger and quite successful 75-mm (2.95-in) AA gun, possibly due to cross-fertilisation between the Swedish company and the Krupp team based in Sweden to avoid the terms of the Versailles Treaty. At almost the same instant the Krupp team produced a 75-mm gun that led eventually to the famous German '88', and Bofors produced its 75-mm **Model 1929**. The latter differed in many details from the Krupp design, but the weapons had very similar performances, had horizontal breech block mechanisms, used a cruciform carriage with a central traverse (lowered to the ground for firing, in the case of the Swedish weapon, by the removal of the two-wheeled axles used for transport), and had barrels of similar length and construction. Whereas the Krupp gun was used in only limited numbers by the German navy and a few South American states, the Bofors model was adopted by the Swedish forces.

Principal models

The two main models were the Model 29 and **Model 30**. These differed only in detail, but were both produced for export in 75-mm and 80-mm (3.15-in) calibres. Exports were made to Argentina, China, Finland, Greece, Hungary, Iran and Thailand. One of the largest customers was Hungary, which received 80-mm guns; these **8-cm 29 M** guns were used extensively during the period when the Hungarian army was allied with the Germans along the Eastern Front from 1941 to 1944, and more were retained for home defence. Another 80-mm customer was the Dutch East Indies, but few of these weapons survived after 1942.

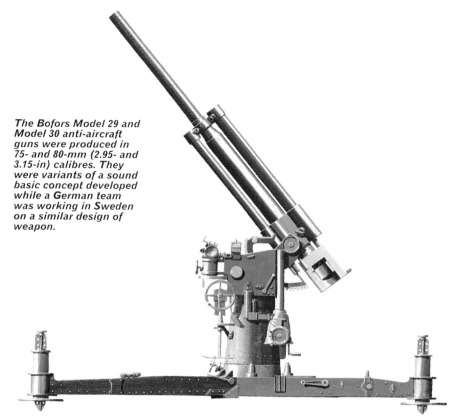

The Bofors Model 29 and Model 30 anti-aircraft guns were produced in 75- and 80-mm (2.95- and 3.15-in) calibres. They were variants of a sound basic concept developed while a German team was working in Sweden on a similar design of weapon.

SPECIFICATION	
8-cm 29 M	
Calibre: 80 mm (3.15 in)	**Elevation:** -3° to +80°
Weight: travelling 4200 kg	**Traverse:** 360°
(9,259 lb) and firing 3300 kg	**Effective ceiling:** 10000 m
(7,275 lb)	(32,810 ft)
Dimensions: barrel length 4 m	**Shell weight:** 8 kg (17.6 lb)
(13 ft 1½ in)	**Muzzle velocity:** 750 m (2,461 ft) per second

Soviet 85-mm weapons Model 1939 and Model 1944 AA guns

By the late 1930s the Soviet armed forces, in common with many other armed forces of the time, decided that the anticipated increases in aircraft performance over the next few years would soon render their current anti-aircraft weapons obsolete. Accordingly they embarked on the search for a more modern anti-aircraft gun with better all-round performance but, in typical Soviet fashion, instead of designing a new weapon they used an old design as the basis for a new weapon. They simply took the 76.2-mm (3-in) Model 1938 and enlarged it all round to become an 85-mm (3.35-in) gun. The new gun was designated as the **85-mm Anti-Aircraft Gun Model 1939**, and is sometimes known as the **KS-12**.

Distinguishing feature

The Model 1939 was very similar to the Model 1938, but could easily be differentiated by its multi-baffle muzzle brake, a feature lacked by the smaller-calibre weapon. A shield was an optional extra. Production of the Model 1939 was just getting under way at Kaliningrad, when the Germans invaded the USSR in 1941, so the entire plant was moved to the Urals for the rest of the war. Once back in production, the Model 1939 became the standard heavy anti-aircraft gun of the Red Army, though it was replaced in production during 1944 by the more powerful **85-mm Anti-Aircraft Gun Model 1944**, otherwise the **KS-18**. This was virtually the same weapon as the Model 1939, but could use a more powerful charge to boost all-round performance with the same projectile as fired by the Model 1939.

Both the Model 1939 and Model 1944 were designed from the outset for secondary capability as anti-tank weapons, in just the same manner as the German '88'. The Soviet guns were so successful in this role that the Germans prized them as war booty and used any captured examples alongside their own '88s' under the designations **8.5-cm Flak M.39(r)** and **8.5cm Flak M.44(r)**. As with the Soviet 76.2-mm guns, captured examples were also shipped back to the Reich for home defence, where they were rebored to the standard German 88-mm (3.47-in) calibre once all captured ammunition stocks had been expended. Most of the guns used in this way by the Germans were

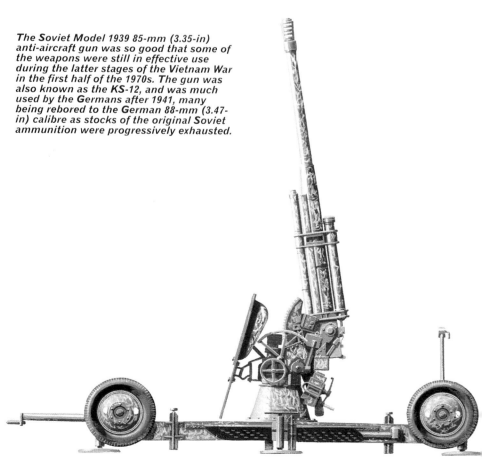

The Soviet Model 1939 85-mm (3.35-in) anti-aircraft gun was so good that some of the weapons were still in effective use during the latter stages of the Vietnam War in the first half of the 1970s. The gun was also known as the KS-12, and was much used by the Germans after 1941, many being rebored to the German 88-mm (3.47-in) calibre as stocks of the original Soviet ammunition were progressively exhausted.

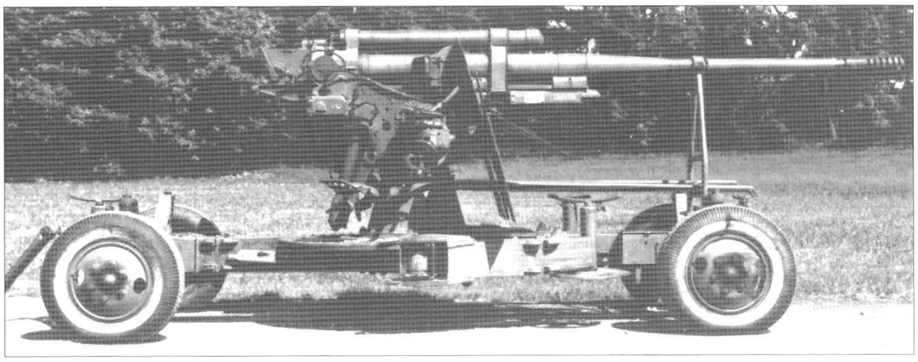

SPECIFICATION

85-mm Anti-Aircraft Gun Model 1939
Calibre: 85 mm (3.35 in)
Weight: travelling 4220 kg (9,303 lb) and firing 3057 kg (6,739 lb)
Dimensions: length travelling 7.049 m (23 ft 1½ in); width 2.15 m (7 ft ½ in); height 2.25 m (7 ft 4½ in); length of barrel 4.693 m (15 ft 4¾ in); length of rifling 3.494 m (11 ft 5½ in)
Elevation: -2° to +82°
Traverse: 360°
Maximum ceiling: 10500 m (34,450 ft)
Shell weight: 9.2 kg (20.29 lb)
Muzzle velocity: 800 m (2,625 ft) per second

The 85-mm (3.35-in) gun was developed from the successful 76.2-mm (3-in) series, and in service proved to be highly effective. Captured weapons were highly prized by the Germans, who used the type for the defence of Germany against Allied bombers.

Model 1939 weapons, which became **8.5/8.8-cm Flak M.39(r)** anti-aircraft guns.

The Model 1939 and Model 1944 were both good anti-aircraft guns, and this is attested to by the fact that limited numbers remained in active service until very recently. Numbers remained in service with some of the Warsaw Pact nations (but not the USSR itself) into the 1980s, and the guns were likely to be encountered in countries as diverse as Sudan and Vietnam. Large numbers were active during the Vietnam conflict against the US air arms. These 'modern' guns usually relied on a centralised fire-control system, usually radar-based, and the original on-carrier fire controls were either removed or little used.

The 85-mm gun itself was used as the basis for other Soviet weapon projects. It was adapted to become the main armament of the SU-85 assault gun and tank destroyer, and it was even adapted for use on a towed anti-tank gun mounting.

Ordnance, QF, 3-in, 20 cwt Anti-aircraft gun

The British 3-in (76.2-mm) anti-aircraft gun has the distinction of being one of the very first, if not the first, gun designed specifically for the anti-aircraft role, the initial examples being in service as early as 1914. From that time the basic design was gradually modified and generally updated, and in 1940 there were still many in service with the designation **Ordnance, QF, 3-in, 20 cwt**. The updating meant that the gun was still a viable weapon for its role, but its overall performance was such that it lacked the power of later designs and it was intended in 1939 that most of them would be replaced by more modern equipments (mainly the 3.7-in/94-mm weapon) by 1941.

In 1939 there were no fewer than eight marks of gun in service, some with sliding breech blocks, some with interrupted thread blocks, some with loose barrel liners, and so on. There was an equally formidable array of carriages in use as well: some of these had four wheels, others had but two and still more were statically emplaced in concrete. By 1940 nearly all in-service anti-aircraft gunners had been trained on the 3-in gun for not only was it the standard weapon of the small regular forces but it was also the main equipment of the growing number of Territorial Army batteries formed during the later 1930s.

The gun was of simple design, being little more than a barrel and recuperator/recoil mechanism slung between two side mounting plates carried on a turntable. The turntable could be either mounted on a heavy cruciform firing platform or carried on a four-wheeled platform, the field army not surprisingly preferring the latter by 1939 as it was more mobile.

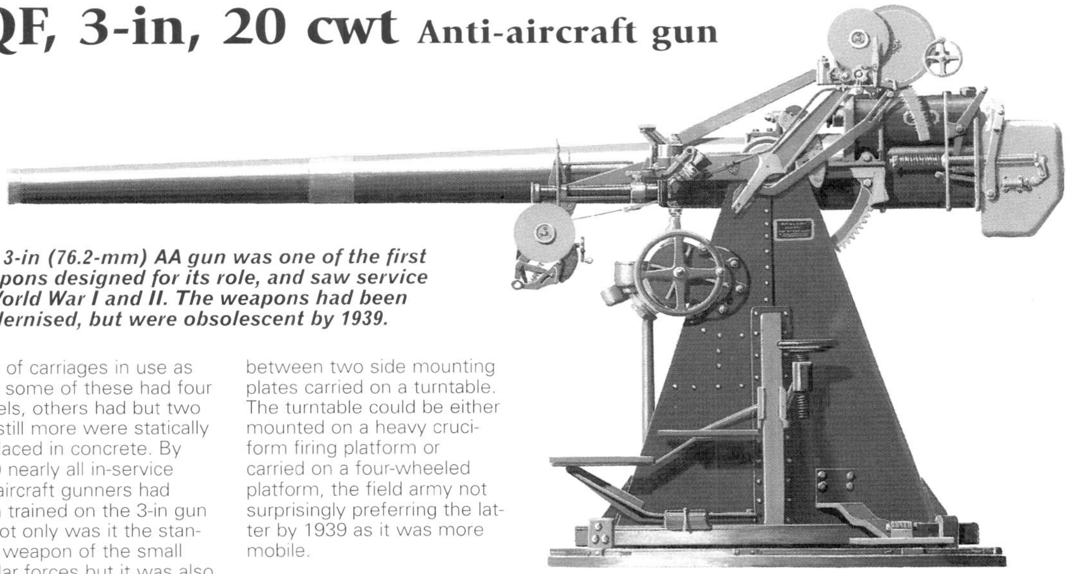

The 3-in (76.2-mm) AA gun was one of the first weapons designed for its role, and saw service in World War I and II. The weapons had been modernised, but were obsolescent by 1939.

At war in France

The gun was the mainstay of the anti-aircraft batteries allocated to the British Expeditionary Force (BEF) in France, for although some batteries had been issued with the newer 3.7-in gun by 1940, they by far preferred the much lighter and more versatile 3-in gun with which they were by now wholly familiar. However, the Dunkirk episode as the remnants of the BEF were evacuated from France put paid to that source of dissent for most of the BEF's 3-in guns were either destroyed or captured by the Germans. The Germans later took these captured weapons into their own service with units based in France, allocating them the designation **7.5-cm Flak Vickers (e)**.

There were few serviceable 3-in guns left in the United Kingdom other than those in the few static installations, but gradually even these were phased out of service as front-line weapons and many of their mobile platform carriages were converted into rocket-launching platforms. The conversion process involved about 100 of these platforms. Of the barrels removed in the conversion process, some were used as the main armament for a tank destroyer using the chassis of the Churchill tank. That project eventually came to nothing, and mystery still surrounds a project to place 50 old 3-in guns onto surplus 17-pdr anti-tank gun carriages for home defence during 1944. There were few of the 3-in anti-aircraft guns left in service by 1945.

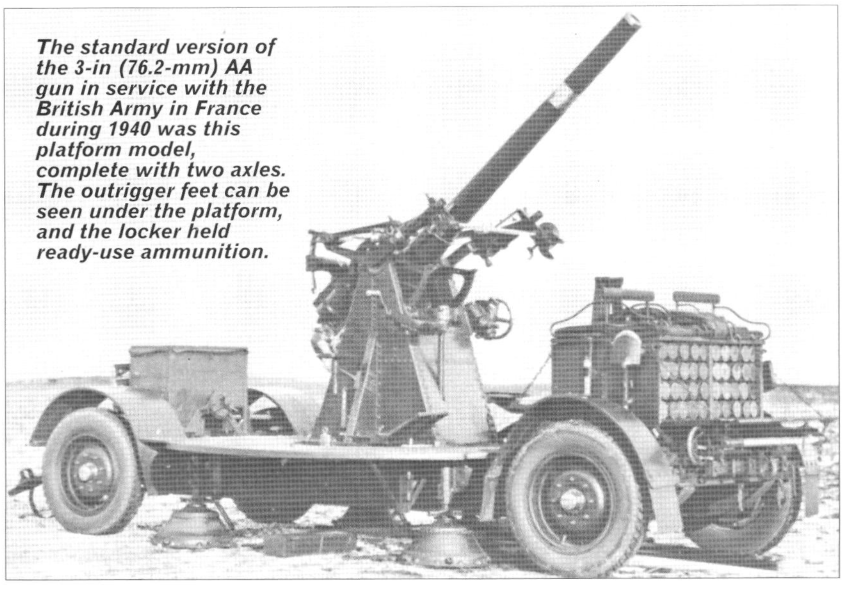

The standard version of the 3-in (76.2-mm) AA gun in service with the British Army in France during 1940 was this platform model, complete with two axles. The outrigger feet can be seen under the platform, and the locker held ready-use ammunition.

SPECIFICATION

Ordnance, QF, 3-in, 20 cwt (on four-wheel platform)
Calibre: 3 in (76.2 mm)
Weight: travelling and complete 7976 kg (17,584 lb)
Dimensions: length travelling 7.468 m (24 ft 6 in); width travelling 2.311 m (7 ft 7 in); height 2.794 m (9 ft 2 in); length of barrel 3.551 m (11 ft 7¾ in); length of rifling 2.977 m (9 ft 9¼ in)
Elevation: -10° to +90°
Traverse: 360°
Maximum ceiling: 7165 m (23,500 ft)
Shell weight: 7.26 kg (16 lb)
Muzzle velocity: 610 m (2,000 ft) per second

Ordnance, QF, 3.7 in Anti-aircraft gun

The static version of the British 3.7-in (94-mm) anti-aircraft gun was the Mk II, of which there were three slightly different versions. This version had a power rammer and had a characteristic counterbalance weight over the breech to compensate for the long barrel.

Soon after the end of World War I it was suggested that something heavier and more powerful than the existing 76.2-mm (3-in) anti-aircraft gun would be required by the UK to meet anticipated increases in aircraft performance, but at that time (1920) the report was simply shelved as there was then no prospect of any funding for even initial research into such a project. Thus it was not until 1936 that Vickers produced a prototype of a new gun with a calibre of 3.7 in (94 mm). The design was approved for production as the **Ordnance, QF, 3.7 in**, but initial progress toward this goal was so slow that it was not until 1938 that the pilot production models were issued for development trials.

The main reason for this slow progress was the gun's carriage. While the gun was a fairly straightforward but modern component, the car-riage was complex to what seemed an extreme. The gun was intended for use in the field by the army and thus had to be fully mobile, but the final assembly was what can only be classed as 'semi-mobile'. The gun and its cradle and saddle rested on a large firing platform which in action rested on four outriggers. In action, the front wheels were raised off the ground in order to provide some counter-balance for the weight of the gun mass, and the rear (towing end) axle was removed.

Production of the carriage soon proved to be a time-consuming bottleneck, to the extent that production began of what was to be a purely static carriage for emplacement in concrete. As time went on the car-riage was re-engineered into a unit of somewhat more manageable form.

Three carriages

Thus the first production carriage was the Mk I, the static carriage the Mk II and the final production version the Mk III; there were sub-marks of all of these.

When the equipment was first issued the gunners did not take kindly to it as they by far preferred the handier and familiar 3-in gun, but they soon came to appreci-ate that the performance of the 3.7-in ordnance by far exceeded that of the older gun. In fact the 3.7-in gun

Right: A complete battery of 12 3.7-in (94-mm) AA guns fires a victory salute in May 1945, on Salisbury Plain, to mark the end of World War II in Europe.

had excellent all-round per-formance, even if emplacing and moving it was some-times less than easy. As more equipments entered service they were gradually fitted with improved and centralised fire-control sys-tems and extras such as power rammers and fuse setters. By 1941 the type formed the mainstay of the army's anti-aircraft defences, and went on through the rest of the war to prove itself to be an excellent weapon.

Anti-tank role

The 3.7-in gun was impressed into use as an anti-armour weapon in the Western Desert campaigns,

Left: The 3.7-mm (94-mm) AA gun was a highly effective piece of ordnance somewhat hampered by its various carriages, which were difficult to make.

Right: The 3.7-in AA gun fired fixed ammunition whose size and weight meant that loading was greatly facilitated by a powered rammer.

A 3.7-in AA gun sited in a desert sangar formed by filling old Italian ammunition boxes with stones. The barrel is fitted with makeshift sights as the gun was no doubt operating away from its normal position.

SPECIFICATION	
Ordnance, QF, 3.7 in, Mk III on Carriage Mk III	0.95 in)
Calibre: 3.7 in (94 mm)	**Elevation:** -8°/+80°
Weight: complete 9317 kg	**Traverse:** 360°
(20,541 lb)	**Maximum effective ceiling:**
Dimensions: length overall	9755 m (32,000 ft)
travelling 8.687 m (28 ft 6 in); width	**Shell weight:** HE 12.96 kg
2.438 m (8 ft); height 2.502 m (8 ft	(28.56 lb)
2½ in); length of barrel 4.7 m (15 ft	**Muzzle velocity:** 792 m (2,600 ft)
5 in); length of rifling 3.987 m (13 ft	per second

but its weight and bulk made it less than effective in this role although it could still knock out any tank set against it. Instead it was retained for what it was best suited, the anti-aircraft role, and thus the 3.7-in never really got a chance to prove itself as the British equivalent of the German '88'. It was used on occasion as a long-range field piece and was even at one stage of the war used as a coastal defence gun. However, its use in this role was in the hands of the Germans, who had captured some of the type at Dunkirk. They appreciated the effectiveness of the weapon they termed the **9.4-cm Flak Vickers M.39(e)** so much that they went to the trouble of manufacturing their own ammunition for them for use in both the Flak and coastal defence roles. In the latter they were particularly effective at Walcheren, where such guns sank several Allied landing craft.

Long life
The gun soldiered on in British use until Anti-Aircraft Command was disbanded during the 1950s. Many were sold or handed over to other nations, and some survived in use in such locations as South Africa and Burma into the 1980s.

Ordnance, QF, 4.5 in, AA Mk II Anti-aircraft gun

The British 4.5-in (114-mm) anti-aircraft gun was not created as an easily transportable weapon, for it was originally a naval gun. In order to move these guns across the country a special transporting carriage was produced, but even so moving the gun was a slow and awkward process.

The gun that was to become the British Army's 4.5-in (114-mm) anti-aircraft gun had a rather muddled provenance, for it was actually a naval gun intended for use on board heavy vessels. It was undergoing acceptance trials in 1936 when it was decided that it would make an ideal anti-aircraft weapon for the army, and after some inter-service discussion the Admiralty agreed to divert some of its anticipated production to the army, but only on the understanding that the guns would be emplaced for the local defence of naval dockyards and other such installations. More muddle ensued when it was discovered by the army that the naval guns (actual calibre 113 mm/4.45 in) were intended for mounting in pairs. The army wanted single mountings, so time was lost while the necessary changes were made and tested.

Service

When the type did eventually enter service, as the **Ordnance, QF, 4.5 in, AA Mk II**, in time for the difficult days of 1940 when the UK faced the possibility of a German invasion under heavy air support, it was emplaced as a static weapon only. Some measure of mobility could be provided by using a special heavy transporter trailer, but such moves were both difficult and lengthy, and required a great deal of preparation. Once emplaced, the guns demonstrated their naval origins by the retention of a turret-type mounting that rested on a base of heavy steel plate. The turret-type shelter over the gun had only limited protective value against steel splinters or falling shrapnel, but was welcome on some of the bleak gun sites at which the weapons were located.

The gun had all the usual naval attributes, namely items such as a power rammer, a heavy counterweight over the breech and a fuse setter on the loading tray. The ammunition handling equipment was very necessary, for the complete round weighed 38.98 kg (85.94 lb) and the movement of such weights over even a short period would soon have exhausted the ammunition handlers.

By 1941 the need to locate the guns around Admiralty-significant areas had been relaxed somewhat, allowing some of the guns to be relocated on stretches of coast. They could be used in a dual anti-aircraft/coastal defence role, but the numbers of guns involved were never large as most of the guns remained in their static emplacements. These guns were issued with a special armour-piercing ammunition, but the projectiles generally fired were of the HE type, although there was a special but little-used shrapnel projectile intended for local defence against low-flying aircraft.

By 1944 it was intended that the gun should be phased out in favour of the more powerful 5.25-in (133.4-mm) weapon, but this did not happen and some of these obsolescent 4.5-in anti-aircraft guns were still in their static emplacements as late as 1951.

Right: Originally produced as secondary armament for major warships, the 4.5-in (114-mm) AA retained some naval characteristics.

Below: The demands of handling many rounds quickly made the provision of a powered rammer essential.

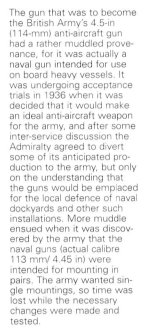

SPECIFICATION	
Ordnance, QF, 4.5 in, AA Mk II	8½ in); length of rifling 4.341 m
Calibre: 4.45 in (113 mm)	(14 ft 2⅔ in)
Weight: emplaced 16841 kg	**Elevation:** +0/80°
(37,128 lb)	**Traverse:** 360°
Dimensions: height of muzzle	**Maximum ceiling:** 12985 m
above ground emplaced (0°	(42,600 ft)
elevation) 2.438 m (8 ft) or (80°	**Shell weight:** 24.7 kg (54.43 lb)
elevation) 7.163 m (23 ft 6 in);	**Muzzle velocity:** 732 m (2,400 ft)
length of barrel 5.086 m (16 ft	per second

3-in Anti-aircraft Gun M3 Heavy AA gun

When the United States decided to adopt an anti-aircraft gun during World War I it saved a great deal of development time by taking a number of existing 3-in (76.2-mm) coastal defence guns and adapting them for the new task. Two main versions emerged from this operation, one a static gun and the other a mobile gun using a basic form of platform mounting. In time the mobile mounting was used as the basis for a more modern mobile equipment, and starting in the mid-1920s a great deal of experimental and development work was carried out, the original M1918 coastal defence guns still being used as the basis for the new anti-aircraft weapon.

Radical redesign

By the time that this development work had been completed, the original gun was virtually unrecognisable. The rifling had been changed and practically every other item on the gun was altered to some degree as well. The main trouble was that the gun itself proved to be far too difficult to manufacture and required a great deal of machining to very close tolerances. Some redesign resulted in the **3-in Antiaircraft Gun M3**, which also had a semi-automatic breech block. It was this gun that was standardised for use with the new mobile platform, itself the result of a great deal of development work. The original World War I platform had been very much a 'rushed' job, and as such left much to be desired in the eyes of the US Army, which sought an ideal solution. In time this emerged

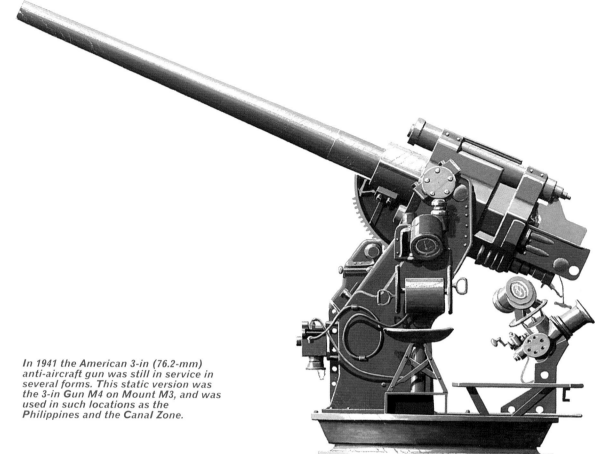

In 1941 the American 3-in (76.2-mm) anti-aircraft gun was still in service in several forms. This static version was the 3-in Gun M4 on Mount M3, and was used in such locations as the Philippines and the Canal Zone.

as the carriage known as the M2 or 'Spider Mount'. This was a pedestal mounting with a number of long outrigger legs over which a thick mesh platform was laid for the gun crew. The arrangement was certainly practical but the long outrigger legs, which folded upwards to the centre, took up a great deal of ground

space.

By the mid-1930s it was obvious that the days of the M3 were coming to an end, and the basic design was once again revamped in an effort to secure better performance. An entirely new 90-mm (3.54-in) design was already on the way, however, and thus the revamped M3 did not

prosper. Instead the existing equipments were gradually withdrawn from front-line use as the new 90-mm guns appeared. This took time, and when the United States entered the war in 1941 the old M3 was still in use for the defence of the Philippine Islands, where the weapons were used as long as the islands held out against the Japanese invaders. Some of these 3-in weapons lingered on for a while in other Pacific areas, and during early 1942 some were even paraded through US west coast towns and cities in a programme to boost civilian morale. These west coast guns were culled mainly from training stocks, for by early 1942 the M3 was in use as a training gun only. Many of the gunners who then went on to man the

subsequent 90-mm guns started their service training using up the existing ammunition stocks for the M3 guns. Once this training role had been completed the old guns still found a use, for many were removed from their Spider Mountings and renovated for use as the barrels for the M5 anti-tank gun. For this role the breech of the 105-mm (4.13-in) M2 howitzer was used, and thus the old anti-aircraft guns went on to a new service career.

At one point in the days immediately after the evacuation of the British Expeditionary Force from Dunkirk in 1940 there were plans to sell numbers of M3 guns to the United Kingdom to replenish AA guns lost in France, but in the event none made the Atlantic crossing.

At the time of the United States' entry into the war in 1941 the M3 was largely relegated to home defence, as many of the guns dated back to World War I. Some did see action in the Far East during 1942, however.

SPECIFICATION	
3-in Antiaircraft Gun M3 on Mount M2A2	length of barrel 3.81 m (12 ft 6 in)
Calibre: 3 in (76.2 mm)	**Elevation:** +80°/-1°
Weight: complete 7620 kg (16,800 lb)	**Traverse:** 360°
Dimensions: length travelling 7.62 m (25 ft); width 2.108 m (6 ft 11 in); height 2.87 m (9 ft 5 in);	**Maximum ceiling:** 9510 m (31,200 ft)
	Shell weight: 5.8 kg (12.8 lb)
	Muzzle velocity: HE 853 m (2,800 ft) per second

90-mm Gun M1 and M2 Heavy AA guns

Once it was realised that the old 3-in (76.2-mm) anti-aircraft guns were coming to the end of their service life during the late 1930s, it was decided by the US Army to produce a weapon not only with a better all-round performance but one capable of firing a heavier projectile. Since a 90-mm (3.54-in) calibre projectile was considered the upper weight limit of what a soldier could handle manually this was fixed as the new calibre, and design work began in 1938. By 1940 the prototypes were approved for service use as the **90-mm Gun M1 on Antiaircraft Mount M1A1**, and production commenced with a high-priority cachet.

Complex carriage

The M1 was a handsome but rather complex weapon which proved difficult to produce. The gun assembly itself was straightforward enough, but the carriage was another matter. It was designed to be towed on a single axle with two pneumatic tyres on each side and in action it stood on a cruciform mounting with the crew standing around the gun on a folding platform. The problem was to get all this carriage and platform folded onto the single axle. The result can be described only as complicated.

Soon after the M1 gun was placed in production it was supplemented by the **M1A1**, which had provision for the fitting of a spring rammer. In practice this rammer proved to be more trouble than it was worth and was usually removed, but another change was on the way. In July 1941 it was decided that in future the 90-mm gun and carriage combination would have to

The 90-mm Antiaircraft Gun M2 was a much revised version of the earlier M1, but used a new carriage with a turntable, a power rammer, fuse setter and other changes. This resulted in an excellent gun, but one that was slow and expensive to produce.

be capable of engaging sea and land targets as well as aerial threats. This meant a revision of the carriage as on the M1 carriage the gun could not be depressed below 0°, and the opportunity was taken to incorporate a radical redesign. The M2 carriage had a totally different design with a low firing platform carried on four outrigger legs when firing. It was much easier to handle and quicker to get into action, and some versions also had a small shield fitted. The main change, however, was to the gun which became the **M2** in which the ammunition feed for a new fuse setter and rammer was added, this making fuse setting much more rapid and accurate, and also raising the rate of fire to a possible 27 rounds per minute. Yet more accuracy and lethality was added in late 1944 when the 90-mm gun was used as one of the first weapons on land to fire the new proximity-fused round, one of the most advanced weapon developments of

the war years. Using this fuse one gunner managed to shoot down an Fw 190 fighter with a single shot as the unfortunate aircraft attempted to intervene in the Ardennes campaign. The 90-mm gun and the proximity fuse were also instrumental in the destruction of the V-1 flying bombs over southern England.

Coastal defence

The 90-mm gun in all its forms was manufactured in large numbers. By August 1945 a total of 7,831 of all types had been produced. This total included some guns intended for static

mounting only, and some guns were indeed used around the coasts of the continental United States in a dual anti-aircraft/coastal defence role.

The 90-mm gun was also used in a purely coastal-defence mounting in a special armoured turret, and at one stage it was proposed that these turrets would even have their own automatic loaders, thus

removing the need for men to crew them in action as they would be aimed and fired by remote control. The 90-mm gun was also used in M36 tank destroyers mounted on Sherman medium tank chassis, and there were several advanced designs involved in the production of a towed 90-mm anti-tank gun. None of these designs saw service, however.

Below: The M2 gun (seen here in its travelling configuration) gave a stout defence, most interestingly against the V-1 'Doodlebug' flying bombs launched from the Low Countries. The weapon was also a highly versatile coastal defence system as well as being the gun which was used on the 90-mm M36 tank destroyer.

Left: This 90-mm M1 anti-aircraft gun is dug in to take part in beach defences. Other emplacements can be seen in this image, including one at the left rear containing the battery's rangefinder and other related fire-control equipment. In this instance, the gun mount is the M1A1 model; the later M2 mount used a turntable.

SPECIFICATION	
90-mm Gun M2 on Mount M2	(14 ft 9 in)
Calibre: 90 mm (3.54 in)	**Elevation:** +80°/-10°
Weight: complete 14651 kg	**Traverse:** 360°
(32,300 lb)	**Maximum ceiling:** 12040 m
Dimensions: length travelling	(39,500 ft)
9.021 m (29 ft 7 in); height 3.073 m	**Shell weight:** 10.6 kg (23.4 lb)
(10 ft 1 in); wheelbase 4.166 m	**Muzzle velocity:** 823 m (2,700 ft)
(13 ft 8 in); length of barrel 4.5 m	per second

Modèle 50 155-mm howitzer

The **modèle 50** 155-mm (6.1-in) howitzer was the standard towed howitzer of the French army from the early 1950s, and has also been made under licence by Bofors of Sweden for the Swedish army under the designation **15.5-cm Field Howitzer Fr**. In the French army it has been largely replaced by the 155-mm TR towed gun, which has an integral auxiliary power unit and a much longer range, while in the Swedish army it has been replaced by the Bofors 155-mm FH-77A. The modèle 50 howitzer, which is also called the **OB-156-50 BF** by the French army, was also exported to Israel, Lebanon (where some were captured from the PLO by Israel during the fighting of summer 1982), Morocco and Switzerland.

The barrel of the modèle 50 is 4.41 m (14 ft 5⅓ in) long, and has an unusual multi-baffle muzzle brake, a hydro-pneumatic recoil system that varies with elevation, and a screw breech mechanism. The carriage is of the split-trail type with two rubber-tyred road wheels located on each side of the forward part of the carriage. When being towed by a truck the ordnance is locked to the trails by a locking device which is situated in the rear

part of the cradle. To enable the equipment to be towed at high speeds on roads, the modèle 50 has a brake system operated by compressed air from the towing vehicle.

When in the firing position, the forward part of the carriage is supported by a circular pivot plate underneath and by the ends of each trail.

The modèle 50 is operated by an 11-man crew, and in French service is normally towed by a Berliet GBU 15 6x6 truck, which also carries the crew and ammunition. The ammunition is of the separate-loading type, the HE projectile weighing 43 kg (94.8 lb) and having a maximum muzzle velocity of 650 m (2,135 ft) per second to give a range of 18000 m (19,685 yards). Illuminating and smoke projectiles can also be fired. Subsequently Brandt developed a rocket-assisted HE projectile with a maximum range of 23300 m (25,480 yards). The maximum rate of fire is between three and four rounds per minute.

To meet the requirements of the Israeli army, the French Etablissement d'Etudes et Fabrications d'Armement de Bourges fitted the modèle 50 howitzer to a much modified Sherman

chassis, and this entered service with the Israeli army in 1963 as the 155-mm self-propelled howitzer **Model 50** (or **M-50**). This equipment is now used only by reserve units, and will shortly be retired completely. The modifications to the chassis were extensive, and included moving the engine to the front of the vehicle on the right-hand side with the driver to its left. The 155-mm howitzer is mounted at the rear of the hull in an open-topped compartment, over which a tarpaulin cover can be fitted in wet weather. Stowage boxes are provided externally above the tracks. When the vehicle is in the firing position the rear of the hull folds down and doors open on each side to reveal ammunition stowage. The loaded weight of the M-50 is 31 tonnes, and the crew consists of eight men including the driver. Several of these systems were captured by the Egyptians in the heavy fighting around Suez in the 1973 Middle East War.

Above: In firing position, the modèle 50 howitzer has the weight of the ordnance and carriage supported by a turntable and the rear of the opened trails.

An interesting feature of the modèle 50 is its multi-baffle muzzle brake to reduce the forces imposed on the equipment's recoil system.

SPECIFICATION	
modèle 50	(8 ft 2½ in)
Calibre: 155 mm (6.1 in)	**Elevation:** -4° to +69°
Weight: travelling 9000 kg	**Traverse:** total 80°
(19,841 lb), firing 8100 kg (17,857 lb)	**Maximum range:** 18000 m
Dimensions: length, travelling	(19,685 yards) with standard round
7.8 m (25 ft 7 in); width, travelling	and 23300 m (25,480 yards) with
2.75 m (9 ft); height, travelling 2.5 m	rocket-assisted projectile

OTO-Melara modello 56 105-mm pack howitzer

The mountainous terrain of northern Italy is defended by specialist Alpine brigades, and these and the sole Italian airborne brigade required a 105-mm (4.13-in) howitzer that could be disassembled for easy movement across the mountains and, in assembled form, still be light enough to be airdropped or carried slung underneath a helicopter. To meet this requirement the Italian arma-

ments manufacturer OTO-Melara (now Otobreda) at La Spezia designed a weapon that became known as the **modello 56** 105-mm pack howitzer. This entered production in 1957, and was soon adopted by more than 30 countries all over the world. By a time early in the 21st century more than 2,500 of the weapons had been delivered, and the type has seen combat use in

SPECIFICATION	
modello 56	travelling 1.5 m (4 ft 11 in); height,
Calibre: 105 mm (4.13 in)	travelling 1.93 m (6 ft 4 in)
Weight: travelling 1290 kg	**Elevation:** -5° to +65°
(2,844 lb)	**Traverse:** total 36°
Dimensions: length, travelling	**Maximum range:** 10575 m
3.65 m (11 ft 11¾ in); width,	(11,565 yards)

A Royal Artillery unit attached to the Royal Marine Commandos carry 105-mm pack howitzers in Norway. The normal towing vehicle for the pack howitzer in British Army service was the Swedish Bv 202, which was successfully used in the Falklands towing the more modern 105-mm Light Gun.

many areas. The British used it in the South Yemen and during the Borneo confrontation, while the Argentines used it in the Falklands campaign of 1982. By today's standards the modello 56 howitzer has a short range, and in British service the Royal Artillery has replaced it with the Royal Ordnance 105-mm Light Gun, which has a maximum range of 17000 m (18,590 yards) compared with only 10575 m (11,565 yards) for the modello 56 which, however, is a much lighter equipment.

Muzzle brake

The modello 56 has a very short barrel with a multi-baffle muzzle brake, a hydraulic buffer and helical recuperator, and a vertical sliding-wedge breech block. The carriage is of the split-trail type and fitted with rubber tyres for high-speed towing. An unusual feature of the modello 56 is that its wheels can be fitted in two different positions: in the normal field position the wheels are overslung, the weapon then having an elevation of +65° and a depression of -5°, and a total traverse of 36° (18° left and right); but for the anti-tank role the wheels are underslung and the weapon has an elevation of +25° and a depression of -5°, total traverse remaining 36°. The main advantage of having the wheels underslung is

that the height is reduced from 1.93 m to 1.55 m (6 ft 4 in to 5 ft 1 in), so making the weapon much easier to conceal, a valuable asset in the anti-tank role.

The modello 56 can be dismantled into 11 sections for transport across rough country, and in peacetime the shield is often removed to save weight. The weapon is manned by a seven-man crew, and can be towed by a long-wheelbase Land Rover or similar vehicle. It can also be carried slung under a UH-1 or

similar helicopter.

Another advantage of the modello 56 is that it fires the same ammunition as the American M101 and M102 105-mm towed guns, and this ammunition is manufactured all over the world. Types of ammunition fired include a 21.06-kg (46.4-lb) HE projectile with a muzzle velocity of 472 m (1,550 ft) per second, as well as smoke, illuminating and HEAT, the last weighing 16.7 kg (36.8 lb) and capable of penetrating 102 mm (4 in) of armour.

Above: The light weight and excellent portability of the OTO-Breda modello 56 105-mm howitzer commended the type to units faced with operations in difficult terrain. The weapon is here seen in service with the Italian army, the shield removed in order to reduce its weight further.

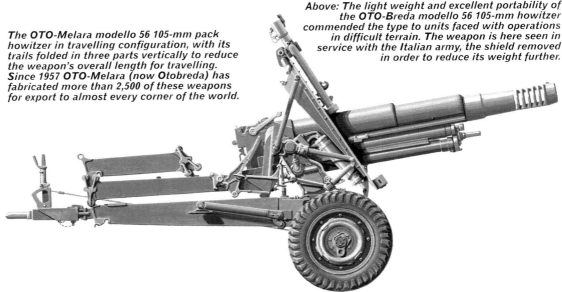

The OTO-Melara modello 56 105-mm pack howitzer in travelling configuration, with its trails folded in three parts vertically to reduce the weapon's overall length for travelling. Since 1957 OTO-Melara (now Otobreda) has fabricated more than 2,500 of these weapons for export to almost every corner of the world.

5.5-in Gun Medium field gun

After 1945 the 100-lb (45.4-kg) projectile for the **5.5-in Gun**, a 140-mm medium weapon went out of fashion and was replaced for all fire missions by an 80-lb (36.3-kg) HE projectile with a longer maximum range of 16460 m (18,000 yards) using a five-part propellant charge system. This gun/projectile combination proved so versatile that it remained in service with many armed forces for decades after 1945. Post-war

Royal Artillery gunners manhandle one of a 5.5-in Gun's spade-equipped trails. The gun was introduced into service in 1942 to fire separate-loading ammunition, and in addition to its two HE projectiles could also fire smoke and illuminating rounds.

alliances and arrangements resulted in 5.5-in Guns surplus to British requirements being distributed to many nations, including Burma, Greece, New Zealand, Pakistan and Portugal, while the gun remained as a front-line equipment with the British Army until the last was retired in 1978. Even then a few were retained at the Royal School of Artillery at Larkhill to fire off remaining ammunition stocks for

artillery burst-spotting purposes. The last of these training veterans was not retired until the mid-1990s. A project of the 1950s to produce a self-propelled combination of the 5.5-inch Gun and a Centurion tank chassis was unsatisfactory.

One of the most involved post-1945 users of the 5.5-in Gun was the South African army, which knew the type as the **140-mm G2**. By the late 1970s, with troubles accumulating on South Africa's northern borders and UN arms sanctions in place, it was discovered that the old G2 was outranged by opposing Soviet-supplied

The British World War II-era 5.5-in Gun was known as the G2 in South African service and an example is pictured here undertaking a night-firing exercise.

artillery. As a short-term measure, a local concern (Naschem) developed a new high-fragmentation projectile with a base-bleed unit to extend the maximum range to 21000 m (22,965 yards), but this was little used after the new 155-mm (6.1-in) G5 and G6 indigenous artillery equipments became avail-

able. Naschem also developed an updated smoke projectile with a maximum range of 15400 m (16,840 yards).

The 10-crew 5.5-in Gun has been withdrawn from service by all but Myanmar (Burma), but until recent years remained a reserve weapon in Pakistan.

SPECIFICATION	
5.5-in Gun	2.62 m (8 ft 7 in)
Calibre: 5.5 in (140 mm)	**Elevation:** -5° to +45°
Weight: 5851 kg (12,900 lb) in	**Traverse:** total 60°
travelling and firing orders	**Maximum range:** 16460 m
Dimensions: length, travelling	(18,000 yards) with the 80-lb
7.52 m (24 ft 8 in); width, travelling	(36.3-kg) HE projectile
2.54 m (8 ft 4 in); height, travelling	

M101 105-mm howitzer

The **M101** 105-mm (4.13-in) howitzer is one of the most successful guns ever produced. Between 1940 and 1953, production totalled 10,202 for delivery to large numbers of armies, of which 60 still field the type at the start of the 21st century. Development of a weapon known as the **M1** started as early as 1920, but only trial numbers were completed, and in 1934 there appeared the **M2** development able to fire a fixed shrapnel round. This was standardised as the **M2A1** in March 1940 on the two-wheel Carriage M2. After World War II the M2 and M2A1 were reclassified as the **M101** and **M101A1** respectively. The barrel is short, which contributes to the howitzer's modest range, but it has a life of 20,000 rounds. A horizontal sliding breech block is used with a percussion firing mechanism. The hydro-pneumatic recoil system, mounted over and under the barrel, is of the constant recoil length type.

The M1 ammunition system was designed for this howitzer and later became a standard NATO ammunition

usable by a number of later equipments. The M101 series fires semi-fixed ammunition, and the HE projectiles included the unitary M1 and the M444 with 18 M39 grenades. There was also a HESH round able to penetrate 102 mm (4 in) of armour at a range of 1500 m (1,640 yards). Among experi-

mental rounds were CS, anti-personnel and HEAT. Two rocket-assisted projectiles were developed, one being standardised as the 17.46-kg (38.5-lb) M548 with a range of 14600 m (15,965 yards) by comparison with the 11270 m (12,325 yards) of the standard 21.06-kg (46.5-lb) M1 HE round.

In many ways obsolete, especially in terms of its projectiles' ranges, the M101 is still in widespread service as it is rugged and reliable, and was readily available from stocks of US surplus weapons.

Various impact and time fuses were also developed.

The layout of the carriage is simple. The box-section, split-trail legs are straight and carry recoil stresses to inbuilt spades. The gun fires off its road wheels, above which the elevating mass is mounted at its centre of gravity. The crew is eight.

Modified weapons have included the **M3** for South-

East Asian use with a shorter barrel and a 75-mm (2.95-in) field howitzer carriage, the **HM 2** French M101A1 fitted with the barrel of the AMX-105/50 or AMX-105B SP howitzer, the Canadian **C1** with a new auto-frettaged monobloc barrel, and the German **FH 105(L)** with a single-baffle muzzle brake and a longer barrel.

SPECIFICATION	
M101A1	
Calibre: 105 mm (4.13 in)	**Elevation:** -5° to +66°
Weight: (travelling and firing)	**Traverse:** 46°
2258 kg (4,978 lb)	**Maximum range:** with M1
Dimensions: (travelling) length	projectile 11270 m (12,325 yards) or
5.99 m (19 ft 9 in); width 2.16 m (7 ft	with M548 projectile 14600 m
1 in); height 1.574 m (5 ft 2 in)	(15,965 yards)
	Rate of fire: 10 rounds per minute

The M101 can be fitted with a shield, but is seldom seen with this type of crew protection. The maximum rate of fire is 10 rounds per minute, declining to three rounds per minute for sustained firing.

M102 105-mm howitzer

For many years the standard 105-mm (4.13-in) howitzer of the US Army was the M2, which was standardised in 1940 as an improved version of the original M1. A total of 10,202 such weapons had been built by the time production ended in 1953. After World War II the M2 became the M101, which is still in large-scale service all over the world. The main drawbacks of the M101 series are its weight of 2030 to 2258 kg (4,475 to 4,978 lb) depending on the

An M102 of the US 82nd Airborne Division is seen in action during the 1983 invasion of Grenada. Note the gun's unusual carriage configuration.

model, and its lack of all-round traverse.

In 1955 a requirement was issued for a new 105-mm howitzer which would fire the same range of ammunition and yet be lighter than the M101. The Rock Island Arsenal designed a new weapon with the prototype designation **XM102**, of which the first was completed in 1962. Following trials, the weapon was classified as standard during the following year with the service designation **M102**. The first production examples of the M102 were completed in January 1964, and only a few months later the weapon was deployed to South Vietnam, where a major build-up of US armed strength was beginning to

aid the South Vietnamese against local insurgents and North Vietnamese regular forces.

After so short a development period, technical and reliability problems were inevitably encountered with early M102 howitzers, but these were soon rectified. The M102 was issued on the scale of 18 howitzers per battalion, each of the battalion's three batteries having six weapons. Now in reserve, the M102 was latterly allocated primarily to airborne and air-mobile divisions, for whom low weight rather than great range was the most important factor. The M102 is also used in modest numbers by Brazil, El Salvador, Guatemala, Honduras, Jordan, Lebanon,

Malaysia (reserve), Philippines, Saudi Arabia (national guard), Thailand and Uruguay.

The M102 comprises four main components, namely the M137 cannon, the M37 recoil system, the M31 carriage, and the fire-control equipment. The M137 cannon has a vertical sliding-wedge breech mechanism but is not fitted with a muzzle brake. The recoil system is of the hydro-pneumatic type and variable, so eliminating the need for a recoil pit. The most unusual feature of the M102 is the two-wheel box-type carriage, which is constructed of aluminium for the minimum possible weight. When the weapon is deployed in the firing posi-

tion, a circular baseplate is lowered to the ground from its stowed position under the forward part of the base, and then the two rubber-tyred road wheels are lifted clear of the ground to ensure the highest possible level of firing stability. A roller located at the rear of the trail assembly allows the complete carriage to be traversed through 360° on the baseplate. This facility

proved to be of considerable importance in South Vietnam, where M102 howitzers had to engage targets in different directions at only a moment's notice.

As a result of its longer barrel, the M102 fires the same ammunition as the M101 at a higher muzzle velocity and therefore to greater range: the M1 HE projectile reaches 11500 m (12,575 yards), for instance.

SPECIFICATION	
M102	**Elevation:** -5° to +75°
Calibre: 105 mm (4.13 in)	**Traverse:** 360°
Weight: (firing and travelling) 1496 kg (3,300 lb)	**Maximum range:** with M1 projectile 11500 m (12,575 yards) or with M548 projectile 15100 m (16,515 yards)
Dimensions: (travelling) length 5.182 m (17 ft); width 1.962 m (6 ft 5¼ in); height 1.59 m (5 ft 2¾ in)	**Rate of fire:** 10 rounds per minute

M114 155-mm howitzer

The 155-mm (6.1-in) howitzer now known as the **M114** was developed in the US before World War II, standardised in May 1941 and first issued in 1942 as the **M1** successor to the 155-mm M1918 howitzer, the US-made counterpart of the French-made M1917. The origins of the M1 can be traced to 1934, when work started on the design and development of a new split-trail carriage for the M1918. It was then decided that rather than seek to improve an existing ordnance, it would make better long-term sense to create an entirely new equipment, whose design was entrusted to the Rock Island Arsenal.

Different carriage

It was also decided that the new howitzer would use the carriage designed for a new heavy gun, in the process offering reduced design, development and manufacturing costs as well as opening the way for the US Army to field a pair of artillery equipments that were well matched in tactical terms. The gun had originally been schemed as a 4.7-in (119-mm) weapon, but was then finalised as a 114-mm weapon so that it could fire the same range of ammunition as the British 4.5-in gun.

Meanwhile, production of the M1 howitzer exceeded 6,000 units, and after World War II the weapon was redesignated as the M114 or, on a slightly modified carriage, **M114A1**.

Operated by an 11-man crew, the M114 comprises the M1 or M1A1 cannon, the M6 series recoil mechanism, and the M1A1 or M1A2 carriage. The differences are that the M1A1 cannon is built of stronger steel than the M1, and the M1A1 carriage has a rack-and-pinion firing jack while the M1A2 carriage has a screw-type fir-

ing jack. The breech block is of the stepped thread/interrupted screw type, and the recoil mechanism is of the hydro-pneumatic variable type. The carriage has split trails, and there is provision for a small shield on each side of the barrel, the top of the left-hand unit folding down in the firing position.

In the firing position the equipment is balanced on three points (the firing jack and both trails). For travelling the jack is forward of the shield, and the trails (with rear spades for enhanced firing stability) are locked together before attachment to the prime mover.

There is also an **M114A2** model with a revised and

slightly lengthened barrel incorporating a 1/20 rather than 1/12 rifling twist to promote projectile range.

Ammunition variants

There have been seven types of projectile (including two smoke, one practice and the Copperhead laser-guided types), but the most important of these types of separate-loading rounds, fired with a muzzle velocity of 564 m (1,850 ft) per second, are the 42.9-kg (94.6-lb) M107 HE and the 43.09-kg (95-lb) M449 carrying 60 anti-personnel grenades.

There have also been several upgraded models created in Europe, Israel and South Korea. Early in the

The howitzers of the M114 series saw large-scale service with the US and allied forces in the Vietnam War. Such equipments were often sited in strategically located fire bases where they could be supplied by road or, failing that, by air in their efforts to interdict communist supply routes.

21st century the M114 howitzer family is still in service with 37 countries, some

using large numbers of these obsolescent but reliable and effective weapons.

SPECIFICATION	
M114	**Traverse:** 24° left and 25° right
Calibre: 155 mm (6.1 in)	**Maximum range:** with M107 or M449 projectile 14600 m (15,965 yards)
Weight: (travelling) 5800 kg (12,787 lb) and (firing) 5760 kg (12,698 lb)	**Rate of fire:** 2 rounds in the first 30 seconds, 8 rounds in the first 2 minutes, 16 rounds in the first 60 minutes, and 40 rounds per hour in the sustained-fire role
Dimensions: (travelling) length 7.315 m (24 ft); width 2.44 m (8 ft); height 1.803 m (5 ft 11 in)	
Elevation: -2° to +63°	

M-46 130-mm field gun

The M-46 130-mm (5.12-in) field gun has a distinctively long barrel with a muzzle brake of the pepperpot type. It has been in service for 50 years, but has a long range that was only recently matched by Western artillery weapons firing RAPs (rocket-assisted projectiles).

The **M-46** 130-mm (5.1-in) field gun is believed to have been developed from a naval weapon, and was first seen in public during the 1954 May Day parade. For this reason the M-46 is sometimes designated **M1954**. Despite its age, the gun remains an effective weapon with exceptional range, and has been used in combat in the Middle East and Vietnam. In the latter only the US M107 175-mm (6.9-in) self-propelled gun, with a range of 32700 m (35,760 yards), could outrange the M-46.

Foreign operators

In addition to being used by the USSR, the M-46 has been operated by more than 50 countries. The Indians took the weapon off its normal carriage and installed it on the chassis of the Vickers Mk 1 MBT, which was built as the Vijayanta self-propelled gun. In the Soviet army the M-46 was deployed at the army-level artillery regiment, which included two battalions each with 18 M-46s (three batteries each with six weapons). The regiment also had an HQ and service battery, a target-acquisition battery and a battalion of 18 D-20 152-mm (6-in) gun/howitzers. The artillery division, allocated at front (army group) level, included two regiments each with 54 M-46s, each regiment having three battalions of 18 weapons. The Chinese have made a different model of the M-46 field gun called the **Type 59-1**, and the gun was also manufactured in Egypt.

'Pepperpot' muzzle

The M-46 has a barrel 7.6 m (24 ft 11.2 in) long and fitted with a very distinctive 'pepperpot' muzzle brake and a horizontal sliding-wedge breech mechanism. The recoil system consists of a hydraulic buffer and a hydropneumatic recuperator below and above the barrel.

The M-46 130-mm (5.12-in) guns of a Soviet battery are camouflaged during training. When travelling, the gun has its barrel withdrawn out of battery to the rear to reduce overall length, and a two-wheel limber is used to support the closed ends of the trails.

To reduce travelling length, the barrel is withdrawn out of battery to the rear and locked in position between the spades. The carriage is of the split-trail type and is provided with a two-wheel limber at the rear. For travelling the two spades are removed and carried on the tops of the trails. The M-46 has a nine-man crew, takes four minutes to bring into action, and can be towed by a variety of vehicles including the AT-S, ATS-59 and M1972 unarmoured artillery tractors as well as the AT-P tracked armoured artillery tractor.

The ammunition fired by the M-46 is of the separate-loading type and includes HE-FRAG (HE fragmentation) and APC-T (armour-piercing capped tracer). The former weighs 33.4 kg (73.63 lb)

with a 4.63-kg (10.2-lb) bursting charge, and the maximum muzzle velocity is 1050 m (3,445 ft) per second. The 33.6-kg (74.07-lb) APC-T projectile, with a 0.127-kg (0.26-lb) bursting charge, has the same muzzle velocity and can penetrate 230 mm (9.05 in) of armour at a range of 1000 m (1,095 yards). Other types of projectile available include illuminating and smoke, and a rocket-assisted projectile was introduced in the late 1960s. This last was first used by Syria during the

1973 Middle East war. In Iranian service the M-46 uses a locally developed base-bleed round, which increases the range to 37000 m (40,465 yards). Norinco in China also manufactures cargo rounds and an ERFB BB (extended-range full-bore base-bleed) projectile extending the range to 38000 m (41,555 yards). Further ammunition types for the M-46 are manufactured in at least 12 countries, including Finland and South Africa.

Although no longer manu-

factured in Russia, the M-46 remains in widespread service and has seen extensive action: in the Iran-Iraq War of the 1980s the gun was deployed by each side.

The M-46 has also been subject to various upgrades including a 155-mm (6.1-in) L/45 barrel. Such efforts have been made by China (**GM-45**), India, Israel, the Netherlands and Yugoslavia. The Indian project is at the prototype stage, but is intended to upgrade around 750 M-46s that remain in Indian service.

SPECIFICATION

M-46
Calibre: 130 mm (5.12 in)
Weight: travelling 8450 kg (18,629 lb) and firing 7700 kg (16,975 lb)
Dimensions: (travelling) length

11.73 m (38 ft 5.8 in); width 2.45 m (8 ft ½ in); height 2.55 m (8 ft 4⅓ in)
Elevation: +45°/-2.5°
Traverse: 50°
Maximum range: 27150 m (29,690 yards)

Rugged, reliable and possessed of excellent range with a high level of accuracy, the M-46 is still a capable and effective weapon despite the fact that it was designed in the immediate aftermath of World War II.

S-23 180-mm gun

For most of the Cold War this weapon was able to outrange virtually all NATO towed and self-propelled artillery weapons. It was first seen in public during a 1955 Moscow parade, and for many years was thought to be a 203-mm (8-in) weapon that was known in the West as the **M1955** gun/howitzer. This is believed to have entered service several years before 1955 and to have been a development of a naval weapon. During the Middle East War of 1973 a number of these weapons were captured and then taken back to Israel for detailed evaluation by intelligence personnel. It was then discovered that the weapon's actual calibre is 180 mm (7.09 in) and that its correct Soviet designation is **S-23**.

In the Soviet army the S-23 was issued on the scale of 12 weapons in the heavy artillery brigade of every artillery division. Subsequently, the Soviet artillery division no longer had S-23s and instead consisted of an HQ, an anti-tank regiment with 36 T-12/MT-12 towed anti-tank guns, an MRL brigade with four battalions of BM-27s (total of 72 launchers), a target-acqui-

sition battalion, a signal company, a motor transport battalion, two regiments of 130-mm (5.1-in) M-46 field guns (total of 108 equipments) and two regiments of 152-mm (6-in) D-20 gun/howitzers or M1973 self-propelled gun/howitzers (total of 108 equipments).

Export operators
The S-23 has seen service with a number of other countries including Egypt, India, Iraq and Syria, and other likely operators also include Cuba, Ethiopia, North Korea, Libya, Mongolia and Somalia. The weapon was normally towed by an AT-T heavy tracked artillery tractor, which also carried the 16-man crew and a small quantity of ready-use ammunition.

The S-23 has a barrel some 8.8 m (28 ft 10.46 in) long with a pepperpot muzzle brake and a screw breech mechanism, and the recoil system is under the barrel. To reduce overall length for travelling, the barrel can be withdrawn out of battery to the rear and linked to the trails. The carriage is of the split-trail type, with two twin rubber-tyred road wheel units at the front and a two-wheel dolly at the rear.

The S-23 fires a bag-type variable-charge separate-loading 84.09-kg (185.4-lb) OF-43 HE projectile with a maximum muzzle velocity of 790 m (2,590 ft per second). as well as the 97.7-kg (215.4-lb) G-572 concrete-piercing projectile, and could formerly also fire a 0.2-kT tactical nuclear projectile.

RAP projectile
After the weapon had been in service for some time an HE rocket-assisted projectile (RAP) was introduced: with a muzzle velocity of 850 m (2,790 ft) per second, this has a maximum range of 43800 m (47,900 yards) compared with 30400 m

An S-23 180-mm gun in travelling configuration with the dolly attached to the rear. For many years this was thought to be a 203-mm (8-in) weapon, but examination of weapons captured by Israel in 1973 showed that it was in fact of 180-mm (7.09-in) calibre.

SPECIFICATION	
S-23	
Calibre: 180 mm (7.09 in)	**Elevation:** +50°/-2°
Weight: in action 21450 kg (47,288 lb)	**Traverse:** 44°
Dimensions: (travelling) length 10.485 m (34 ft 4¾ in); width 2.996 m (9 ft 9¾ in); height 2.621 m (8 ft 7¼ in)	**Maximum range:** 30400 m (33,245 yards) with the HE projectile and 43800 m (47,900 yards) with the rocket-assisted projectile

(33,245 yards) for the original projectile. Because of the shell's heavy weight, the S-23 has a relatively slow

rate of fire (one round per minute), dropping to one round every two minutes in the sustained-fire role.

D-20 152-mm gun/howitzer

Although it was designed shortly after the 'Great Patriotic War' of 1941-45, the **D-20** 152-mm (6-in) gun/howitzer was not seen in public until 1955, and as a result was long known in the West as the **M1955**. In accord with standard Soviet artillery design practice, the ordnance of the D-20 was placed on the carriage of an existing design, in this case the D-74 122-mm (4.8-in) field gun. Also in accord with Soviet practice, the D-20 proved to be a sound and

rugged design with good all-round performance. Despite its age, the Russian armed forces are reported as still fielding more than 1,000 D-20s as front-line equipment.

Chinese variant
Although it is no longer manufactured in what was the USSR, the D-20 is still available from Norinco of the People's Republic of China, where it is known as the **Type 66**. The gun can thus be encountered all over the world.

The barrel of the D-20 is 5.195 m (17 ft ½ in) long and features a double-baffle muzzle brake and a semi-automatic vertical sliding wedge breech. Protection for the breech end of the barrel and the recoil mechanisms is provided by an optional shield, while the split-trail carriage can be placed on a firing pedestal lowered from under the cradle. The firing pedestal permits a full 360° traverse. For short moves each trail leg has a castor wheel. At

one time the D-20 was towed by a special AT-S tracked medium tractor, although the more usual prime mover is now a Ural-375 6x6 heavy truck.

The main projectile fired by the D-20 is a TNT-filled HE-fragmentation (HE-FRAG) shell weighing 43.51 lb (95.92 lb). This can be fired to a range of 17410 m (19,040 yards), while the special RAP can reach 24000 m (26,245 yards). The latter is now little used due to its variable accuracy. Several types of HE-FRAG projectile are available, as are concrete-piercing, smoke and illuminating. Variable bagged propellant charges are employed. For an anti-armour capability the D-20 can fire either solid AP-T (with a unitary propellant charge) or a hollow-charge projectile. One unusual projectile contains flechettes for use against massed personnel while another contains several anti-tank mines scat-

tered as the projectile is still in flight. A similar projectile containing anti-personnel mines has been withdrawn. It is understood that the D-20 can also fire the Krasnopol laser-guided projectile. The ordnance used on the 152-mm 2S3 self-propelled gun/howitzer is a development of the D-20.

The D-20 was distributed wherever Soviet influence extended, so it is likely to be encountered as far afield as the former Congo and Finland. It saw considerable action during the Iran-Iraq conflict and is still held by Syria. The Chinese Type 66 has also been widely exported to nations such as North Korea and Bolivia.

The Chinese Type 66 differs from the D-20 in few respects. At one time the former Yugoslavia designed and manufactured a variant of the D-20 with an L/39 barrel as the **M-84**, although it is no longer available for export sales.

The D-20 can fire a 48.78-kg (107.54-kg) AP projectile with a muzzle velocity of 600 m (1,969 ft) per second to penetrate 124 mm (4.88 in) of armour at 0° at a range of 1000 m (1,095 yards).

SPECIFICATION	
D-20	
Calibre: 152 mm (6 in)	**Elevation:** +65°/-5
Weight: travelling 5700 kg (12,566 lb) and in action 5650 kg (12,456 lb)	**Traverse:** 58° on carriage
Dimensions: (travelling) length 8.1 m (26 ft 7 in); width 2.35 m (7 ft 8½ in); height 2.52 m (8 ft 3¼ in)	**Maximum range:** 17410 m (19,040 yards) with the HE-FRAG projectile and 24000 m (26,245 yards) with the rocket-assisted projectile

Mk 61 105-mm self-propelled howitzer

The development of the AMX-13 light tank by the Atelier de Construction d'Issy-les-Moulineaux during the late 1940s laid the basis for one of the largest families of tracked vehicles ever developed. At an early stage the French army issued a requirement for a 105-mm (4.13-mm) self-propelled howitzer, and it was decided to base this **Mk 61** equipment on a modified AMX-13 tank chassis. After trials with prototype vehicles, the equipment was placed in production at the Atelier de Construction Roanne in the late 1950s under the designation **Obusier de 105 Modèle 50 sur Affût Automoteur** for the French army. The type was later supported by Creusot-Loire (now GIAT) after this company had taken over responsibility for the AMX-13 and its derivatives.

In addition to being used by the French army, the Mk 61 was also purchased by Israel, Morocco and the Netherlands, the equipments for the last having a longer L/30 barrel. The first to phase the type out of service was Israel, where the Mk 61 was replaced by the 155-mm (6.1-in) M109A1; in the French army it was replaced by the 155-mm

GCT self-propelled weapon.
The vehicle was of all-welded steel construction providing the crew with protection from small arms fire and shell splinters. The engine and transmission were at the front, the driver on the left side and the fully enclosed gun compartment at the rear. Access hatches were provided in the roof and rear, and the commander had a cupola with periscopes for all-round observation. The suspension was of the well-proven torsion-bar type, and on each side comprised five rubber-tyred road wheels and three track-return rollers, together with the drive sprocket at the front and the idler at the rear. Hydraulic shock absorbers were fitted at the first and last road wheel stations. The tracks were steel, but could be fitted with rubber pads to reduce damage to the road surface.

Ordnance details
The 105-mm howitzer had a double-baffle muzzle-brake, and could be elevated between -4° 30' and +66°, while traverse was 20° left and right; elevation and traverse were both manual. Various types of separate-loading ammunition could be fired, including an HE

projectile weighing 16 kg (35.3 lb) to a maximum range of 15000 m (16,405 yards) and a HEAT projectile which could penetrate 350 mm (13.8 in) of armour at an incidence of 0°, or 105 mm (4.13 in) of armour at 65°. A total of 56 rounds of ammunition was carried, and of these six were normally HEAT rounds. A 7.62- or 7.5-mm (0.3- or 0.295-in) machine-gun was mounted externally on the roof for AA defence; a similar weapon was carried inside the vehicle for use in the ground role; 2,000 rounds of ammunition were carried for these weapons.

The Mk 61 did not have an NBC system, and lacked any amphibious capability. Another drawback was the

The Mk 61 was based on the AMX-13 light tank chassis. The lack of a true turret and fitting of a medium-calibre gun soon rendered the type obsolete.

limited traverse of the Mk 61's ordnance.

There appeared prototypes, some of them purchased by Switzerland, of a similar vehicle with a turret that could be traversed through 360°. By the time the turret version was ready most countries had decided

to replace their 105-mm equipments with more effective 155-mm weapons. The Mk 61's chassis was also used for prototype trials with the Roland SAM system and as a minelayer; a similar chassis was used for the AMX-13 DCA twin 30-mm self-propelled AA gun.

SPECIFICATION	
Mk 61	petrol engine delivering 186 kW (250 hp)
Crew: 5	
Weight: 16500 kg (36,375 lb)	**Performance:** speed 60 km/h (37 mph); range 350 km (217 miles)
Dimensions: length 5.7 m (18 ft 8½ in); width 2.65 m (8 ft 8¼ in); height 2.7 m (8 ft 10¼ in)	**Gradient:** 60 per cent
	Vertical obstacle: 0.65 (2 ft 2 in)
Powerplant: one SOFAM 8Gxb	**Trench:** 1.6 m (5 ft 3 in)

Mk F3 155-mm self-propelled gun

In the period immediately after World War II the standard self-propelled howitzer of the French army was the US 155-mm (6.1-in) M41 Howitzer Motor Carriage, essentially the M24 Chaffee light tank chassis fitted with a slightly modified version of the standard M114 towed howitzer. This was replaced in the 1960s by the 155-mm **Mk F3** self-propelled gun, which is basically a shortened AMX-13 light tank chassis with a 155-mm gun, based on the Modèle 50 towed weapon, mounted at the rear of the hull. In addition to deliveries to the French army, which knew the type as the **Canon de 155 mm Modèle F3 Automoteur** and replaced it with the 155-mm GCT in the 1980s, the Mk F3 was also sold to Argentina, Chile, Cyprus, Ecuador, Kuwait, Morocco, Peru, Qatar, Sudan, the United Arab Emirates and Venezuela.

Production of the Mk F3, along with other members of the AMX-13 light tank family, was originally undertaken at the Atelier de Construction Roanne, a French government facility. As this plant tooled up for production of the AMX-30 family of MBTs and other vehicles and also of the

AMX-10P family, however, production of the whole AMX-13 family, including the Mk F3, was transferred to Creusot-Loire at Châlon-sur-Saône, now part of GIAT, which still supports the series.

Gun elevation
The 155-mm ordnance is mounted at the very rear of the chassis and can be elevated from 0° to +67°, with a traverse of 20° left and right up to an elevation of +50° and of 16° left and 30° right from +57° upward. Elevation and traverse are both manual. When travelling, the ordnance is held in a travel lock and traversed 8° to the right. The L/33 barrel has a double-baffle muzzle-brake and a screw breech mechanism.

The ammunition is of the separate-loading type, and the following can be fired: HE with a maximum range of just over 20000 m (21,875 yards), illuminating and smoke to a range of 17750 m (19,410 yards) and a rocket-assisted projectile to range of 25330 m (27,670 yards). The rate of fire for the first few minutes is three rounds per minute, but when the Mk F3 is used in the sustained-fire role the rate is one round a minute. Before firing commences

Above: The Mk F3 155-mm self-propelled gun in the firing position with the two rear-mounted spades lowered to stabilise the system. The total lack of gun and crew protection is self evident.

Right: In 2003, the Mk F3 remained in service with 11 nations, the most recent deliveries being made from French stocks to the largest operator, Morocco, in 1997.

Developed in the 1950s, the Mk F3 can fire a range of ammunition, including the Mk 56 HE projectile, smoke and illuminating shells and the M107 round.

SPECIFICATION	
Mk F3	**Powerplant:** one 186-kW (250-hp)
Crew: 2	SOFAM 8Gxb petrol engine
Weight: 17400 kg (38,360 lb)	**Performance:** speed 60 km/h
Dimensions: length (gun forward)	(37 mph); range 300 km (185 miles)
6.22 m (20 ft 5 in); width 2.72 m	**Gradient:** 40 per cent
(8 ft 11 in); height 2.085 m (6 ft	**Vertical obstacle:** 0.6 m (2 ft)
10 in)	**Trench:** 1.5 m (4 ft 11 in)

two spades are manually released at the rear of the hull and the vehicle then reversed backward onto them to create a more stable firing platform.

A major disadvantage of the Mk F3, in addition to the total lack of protection for the gun and its crew, is that only the driver and commander can be carried in the actual vehicle. The other members of the gun crew are carried in an AMX VCA (Véhicule Chenillé d'Accompagnement, or tracked support vehicle) or a 6x6 truck which also carries 25 projectiles, charges and associated fuses. The VCA can also tow a 2-tonne F2 ammunition trailer carrying an additional 30 projectiles and charges.

The Mk F3 can ford to a depth of 1 m (3 ft 3 in) but has no NBC system; active or passive night-vision equipment can be installed and all vehicles have direct and indirect sights, and a loudspeaker and cable. The basic vehicle is powered by a petrol engine, but in many examples has been replaced by a General Motors Detroit Diesel 6V-53T delivering 209 kW (280 hp). This produces a slightly higher road speed and, importantly, an increase in operational range from 300 to 400 km (185 to 250 miles).

Israeli self-propelled artillery M-50, L33, Romach and Doher

In the 1950s Israel used many types of towed artillery weapons to support their mechanised units, but found that such weapons could not keep up with these highly mobile forces when they deployed to the desert, where roads were non-existent. Despite the fact that they felt, as did most members of NATO at that time, that the 155-mm (6.1-in) projectile was much more effective than the 105-mm (4.13-in) shell because of the former's greater HE payload, Israel bought quantities of the US World War II Priest and French Mk 61 105-mm self-propelled howitzers.

Service
The first self-propelled weapon of 155-mm calibre to enter service with the Israeli army was the **M-50** developed in France by the Etablissement d'Etudes et Fabrications d'Armement de Bourges for a service debut in 1963. This system was essentially a Sherman tank chassis rebuilt with the engine moved forward to the right of the driver to make it possible for a French Modèle 50 howitzer, already used by Israel in its towed form, to be mounted in an open-topped compartment at the rear of the hull.

When the vehicle was deployed in action, the two doors opened to each side of the hull rear revealing horizontal ammunition racks, and a tailgate folded down to provide space for the crew to operate the howitzer. Additional ammunition storage space was provided under the mount, and external stowage compartments were provided in each side of the hull. The howitzer fired a 43-kg (95-lb) HE projectile to a maximum range of 17600 m (19,250 yards). The howitzer's maximum elevation was +69°, but the traverse was very limited. The M-50 had a crew of eight and weighed 31000 kg (68,340 lb) fully loaded. The main drawback of the system, which was used for the first time in the 1967 Six-Day War, was the lack of any overhead protection for the crew.

The M-50 was followed in Israeli service by the **L33** (named after the length of the ordnance in calibres), which was developed in Israel by Soltam, and this saw action for the first time in the 1973 Yom Kippur War. This is based on the M4A3E8 Sherman chassis, which has HVSS (Horizontal Volute Spring Suspension) rather than the VVSS (Vertical Volute Spring Suspension) of the M-50 and gives a much improved ride across country. The original petrol engine has since been replaced by a Cummins diesel for a much increased operational range.

Proven ordnance
The 155-mm M-68 gun/howitzer is almost identical to the standard towed weapon, and is mounted in the forward part of the superstructure with an elevation arc between -3° and +52°, and traverse 30° left and right. Weapon elevation and traverse are manual. The ordnance has a single-baffle muzzle-brake, a fume extractor, a barrel travel lock and a horizontal sliding semi-automatic breech block.

Powered rammer
To assist in maintaining a high rate of fire and in loading the ordnance at any angle of elevation, a pneumatic rammer is installed. The weapon fires the 43-kg HE projectile to a range of 21000m (22,965 yards) at maximum charge; smoke and illuminating projectiles can also be fired. A total of 60 projectiles and charges is carried, 16 of which are for ready use. A 7.62-mm (0.3-in) machine-gun is roof-mounted for local and anti-aircraft defence.

The hull is of all-welded steel construction and protects the crew from small arms fire and shell splinters. Entry doors are provided on each side of the hull, and ammunition resupply doors are fitted in the hull rear; ammunition can be loaded via these doors when the weapon is still firing. The driver is seated at the front on the left with the commander to his rear, and the machine-gunner is in a similar position on the opposite side: each of these crew members is provided with a roof hatch and bulletproof windows to their front and side for observation.

Unlike the earlier M-50 conversion, which entailed moving the engine forward, the L33 has its engine at the rear, power being transmitted to the transmission at the front of the hull by a two-part propeller shaft.

Israel also operates two US self-propelled artillery systems, the 175-mm (6.9-in) M107 gun and 155-mm M109 howitzer, and has upgraded many of these equipments to the **Romach** and **Doher** standards, respectively. The former fires a locally-designed Extended Range Sub Calibre Mk 7 Mod 7 projectile to a range of 40 km (24.9 miles) and carries an additional 7.62-mm machine-gun. The IDF's Doher howitzer features many improvements in order to suit local requirements.

The crew of a 155-mm (6.1-in) L33 man their vehicle during an exercise. Based on the M4A3 tank chassis, the L33 was extensively used in combat during the 1973 Arab-Israeli War and incorporates the armament of the M-68 towed gun/howitzer system.

The first 155-mm (6.1-in) self-propelled gun to enter service with the IDF was the M-50. This entered service in 1963 and first saw action in the Six-Day War of 1967.

SPECIFICATION	
Soltam L33	8-460-Bi liquid-cooled diesel
Crew: 8	delivering 343 kW (460 hp)
Weight: 41500 kg (91,490 lb)	**Performance:** maximum road
Dimensions: length (gun forward)	speed 36.8 km/h (23 mph);
8.47 m (27 ft 9½ in) and (hull)	maximum range 260 km (162 miles)
6.47 m (21 ft 2¾ in); width 3.5 m	**Gradient:** 60 per cent
(11 ft 6 in); height 3.45 m (11 ft	**Vertical obstacle:** 0.91 m (3 ft)
3¾ in)	**Trench:** 2.3 m (7 ft 6½ in)
Powerplant: one Cummins VT	

ASU-57 Airborne self-propelled anti-tank gun

The **ASU-57** (ASU being the Soviet designation for airborne assault gun and 57 for the calibre of the gun) was developed in the 1950s specifically for use by the Soviet airborne divisions and was seen in public for the first time during a parade held in Red Square, Moscow, during 1957. The gun itself was a development of the World War II ZIS-2 (M1943) anti-tank gun while the engine was from the Pobeda civilian car.

Limited protection

The hull of the ASU-57 was of welded aluminium construction with a uniform thickness of only 6 mm (0.24 in), making it very vulnerable. The engine was at the front on the right with the cooling system on the left and transmission at the very front. The open-topped crew compartment was at the rear with the driver and loader on the right, and the commander, who also acted as the gunner, on the left. Forward of the driver and commander was an armoured flap which contained two vision blocks; when the vehicle was not in the combat area this flap could be folded forwards to provide improved vision. The top of the ASU-57 could be covered by a tarpaulin cover, and an unditching beam was often carried at the rear, the latter being a common feature on Soviet armoured vehicles.

The torsion-bar suspension consisted of four single rubber-tyred road wheels with the drive sprocket at the front and the fourth road wheel acting as the idler; there were two track-return rollers. The ASU-57 could ford to a depth of 0.7 m

An ASU-57 airborne self-propelled anti-tank gun, armed with a 57-mm (2.24-in) Ch-51M gun with a double-baffle muzzle brake. For many years this was the main self-propelled anti-tank gun of the Soviet airborne divisions but it was replaced by the ASU-85, which had a bigger gun and much improved armour protection.

(28 in), but had no NBC protection system.

The vehicle was armed with a Ch-51 or Ch-51M rifled gun offset slightly from the vehicle's centre-line. The Ch-51 was the first model to enter service and had a long barrel with a multi-slotted muzzle brake. This was followed by the Ch-51M, which had a shorter barrel with a double-baffle muzzle brake.

Both weapons had a vertical sliding breech-block and hydro-spring recoil system, and fired the following types of fixed ammunition: HE fragmentation (muzzle velocity 695 m/2,280 ft per second), AP-T (muzzle velocity 980 m/3,215 ft per second and capable of penetrating 85 mm/3.35 in of armour at 0° at a range of 1000 m/1,094 yards), and HVAP (capable of penetrating 100 mm/3.94 in of armour at 0° at a similar range). A total of 30 rounds of ammunition was carried, and it was estimated that a well-trained crew could fire a maximum of 10 rounds per minute. The gun had manual elevation and traverse, the former being from -5° to +12°, and the latter 8° left and 8° right.

The vehicle was often

used to carry four para-troops, and a 7.62-mm (0.3-in) machine-gun was carried. This could be dismounted for use in the ground role.

Deployment

Each Soviet airborne division had three rifle regiments, and each of these had one battalion each with three six-gun batteries with ASU-57s, giving the division a total of 54 such weapons. In the USSR the ASU-57 was used for training after it has been replaced in front-line use by the ASU-85, which not only had a more powerful gun but also much improved armour protection.

It is interesting to note that the ASU-57 was developed at roughly the same time as the American M56

An ASU-57 advances across the snow while in the background an 85-mm (3.35-in) auxiliary propelled anti-tank gun is positioned. Note the undtiching beam carried on the left side of the hull of the ASU-57, and the driver's head in an exposed position.

self-propelled anti-tank gun with its 90-mm (3.54-in) gun.

When originally introduced, the ASU-57 was packed in a special container and two of these could be carried under a Tupolev Tu-4 transport, one under each

wing. On the Antonov An-12 introduced in the late 1950s, two ASU-57s could be carried internally on individual pallets. The pallets were provided with parachutes and a retro-rocket system to soften the landing impact.

SPECIFICATION	
ASU-57 (with Ch-51M gun)	**Powerplant:** one 41-kW (55-hp)
Crew: 3	M-20E 4-cylinder petrol engine
Weight: 3.35 tonnes	**Performance:** maximum road
Dimensions: overall length	speed 45 km/h (28 mph); maximum
4.995 m (16 ft 4⅔ in); hull length	road range 250 km (155 miles)
3.48 m (11 ft 5 in); width 2.086 m	**Gradient:** 60 per cent
(6 ft 10 in); height 1.18 m (3 ft	**Vertical obstacle:** 0.5 m (20 in)
10½ in)	**Trench:** 1.4 m (4 ft 7 in)

ASU-85 Airborne self-propelled anti-tank gun

For many years the standard self-propelled anti-tank gun of the Soviet airborne division was the ASU-57. This weighed only 3.35 tonnes and was armed with a long-barrel 57-mm (2.24-in) gun. In addition to the lack of penetration provided by the 57-mm ammunition, the ASU-57 had very thin armour protection and the crew compartment was not provided with any serious overhead protection.

ASU-57 successor

In the late 1950s the more capable **ASU-85** self-propelled anti-tank gun was developed and this entered service with the Soviet airborne divisions in 1960 and also saw service with Poland. Compared to the older ASU-57, the ASU-85 had improved armour, firepower and mobility. The

Soviet ASU-85s parade through Moscow. The ASU-85 was not widely exported, but saw action during the 1968 occupation of Czechoslovakia.

85-mm (3.35-in) SD-44 gun was mounted in a well-sloped glacis plate with a total traverse of 12° and with elevation from -4° to +15°; traverse and elevation were manual. The gun fired fixed-type ammunition including HE armour-piercing and HVAP; a total of 40 rounds of ammunition was carried. A 7.62-mm (0.3-in) PKT machine-gun was mounted co-axially. Some vehicles were also fitted with a roof-mounted 12.7-mm (0.5-in) DShKM machine-gun for air defence purposes.

The hull of the ASU-85 was of all-welded steel armour with the highest level of protection over the frontal arc. The vehicle could be carried inside a tactical transport aircraft such as the An-12, and could be dropped by parachute.

Standard equipment included night-vision devices, and additional fuel drums were normally mounted on the hull rear to extend the operational range of the vehicle. The ASU-85 was phased out of Soviet service without a direct replacement, and the airborne units' long-range anti-tank capability was subsequently entrusted to anti-tank guided missile systems and the gun- and missile-armed BMD series of vehicles.

A column of ASU-85 self-propelled guns is seen on the move while on exercise, with local air defence provided by 14.5-mm (0.57-in) ZPU-1 anti-aircraft guns.

SPECIFICATION	
ASU-85	developing 179 kW (240 hp)
Crew: 4	**Performance:** maximum road
Weight: 15.6 tonnes	speed 45 km/h (28 mph); maximum
Dimensions: overall length 8.49 m	road range 260 km (162 miles)
(27 ft 10¼ in); hull length 6 m (19 ft	**Fording:** 1.1 m (3 ft 7 in)
8 in); width 2.8 m (9 ft 2¼ in);	**Gradient:** 70 per cent
height 2.1 m (6 ft 10¾ in)	**Vertical obstacle:** 1.1 m (3 ft 7 in)
Powerplant: one V-6 diesel engine	**Trench:** 2.6 m (8 ft 6 in)

SU-100 Tank destroyer

During World War II, the Soviets developed a number of tank destroyers based on tank chassis. These included the SU-85 and **SU-100** based on the T-34, and the SU-152 based on the KV heavy tank chassis. These were quicker and easier to produce than tanks and were built in large numbers.

The SU-85 and SU-100 were very similar in appearance with the main difference being in the calibre of the weapon: 85 mm (3.35 in) for the SU-85 and 100 mm (3.94 in) for the SU-100. The SU-100's fighting compartment was at the front of the vehicle with the main D-10S armament carried in a ball-type mount in the front of the well-sloped hull and with limited manual traverse and elevation.

The SU-100 carried a total of 34 rounds of main-gun ammunition, with the HE armour-piercing projectile capable of penetrating over 180 mm (0.7 in) of armour at a range of 1000 m (1,904 yards). Other types of ammunition that could be fired included OF-412 HE fragmentation projectiles.

Wartime use

Used in combat for the first time in Hungary in January 1945, the prime role of the SU-100 was to engage enemy tanks but it could also be used in the direct fire support role which proved very useful in urban fighting towards the end of World War II.

By the end of the war some 3,037 SU-100 tank destroyers had been built and in the post-war period large numbers of these weapons were exported, especially to the Middle East where some of these saw action with Egypt and Syria.

The SU-100 remained in service within the armies of most of the members of the Warsaw Pact for many years after the end of the war and was also manufactured in Czechoslovakia during the 1950s. In mid-2004, SU-100s remained in service in a few countries.

When eventually withdrawn from front-line service with the Soviet army, many SU-85 and SU-100 assault guns were converted into armoured recovery vehicles. Some SU-100s were also used in the command post role for which they were fitted with additional communications equipment.

Above: The SU-100 was similar in configuration to the T-34, sharing almost 75 per cent of its components. Although based on a common hull, the frontal armour of the SU-100 was increased from 45 mm (1.77 in) to 75 mm (2.95 in) compared to the earlier SU-85.

The SU-100 tank destroyer began to enter service in December 1944 and remained in Warsaw Pact use until the late 1970s. Meanwhile, the type also saw action during wars in the Middle East and Angola.

SPECIFICATION	
SU-100	engine developing 388 kW (520 hp)
Crew: 4	**Performance:** maximum road
Weight: 31.6 tonnes	speed 55 km/h (34 mph); maximum
Dimensions: overall length 9.45 m	road range 300 km (186 miles)
(31 ft); hull length 6.19 m (20 ft	**Fording:** 1.3 m (4 ft 3 in)
3¾ in); width 3.05 m (10 ft); height	**Gradient:** 60 per cent
2.245 m (7 ft 4¼ in)	**Vertical obstacle:** 0.73 m (29 in)
Powerplant: one V-2-34M diesel	**Trench:** 2.5 m (8 ft 2 in)

M37 and M44 Self-propelled howitzers

The design origins of the **Howitzer Motor Carriage M37** can be traced back to the end of World War II. The vehicle was based on the chassis of the M24 Chaffee light tank and carried the 105-mm (4.13-in) howitzer in an open-topped compartment. In layout the M37 resembled the earlier M7 'Priest' and carried over the same 'pulpit' type of housing, to the right of the howitzer, for the 0.5-in (12.7-mm) M2 machine-gun used for local and AA defence. The combat compartment was larger than that of the M7, however, with provision for up to 90 105-mm rounds.

Originally known as the **T76**, the M37 did not enter US Army service until the end of 1945. The M37 saw action during the Korean War, but was gradually phased out of service thereafter as the dangers of nuclear fall-out, to which the open-topped M37 was notably vulnerable, came to be appreciated more fully.

The howitzer was the M4, a modified version of the 105-mm M1 towed weapon.

It could fire a 14.97-kg (33-lb) projectile to 11160 m (12,200 yards).

The **Howitzer Motor Carriage M44**, rushed into production during the Korean War period, carried a 155-mm (6.1-in) howitzer on a chassis based on that of the M41 light tank. The original intention was to provide the production versions with a limited traverse turret having an armoured roof, but this was later changed to a completely open-top fighting compartment, somewhat forgetful of the need for fall-out protection. The rush to production proved unfortunate, for numerous technical problems remained with the M44 as it entered service, most especially with the advanced but complicated and troublesome fire-control system.

Production was halted to allow the problems to be solved, and some early production models had to be updated to the corrected form. The type entered service in 1954, some going to the new German army. The 155-mm howitzer could fire its 43-kg (95-lb) projectile to 9700 m (10,600 yards).

Above: Seen at the Aberdeen Proving Ground in 1954, this is an M44 155-mm (6.1-in) self-propelled howitzer. The equipment was based on the chassis of the M41 light tank with a powerplant based on one 373-kW (500-hp) petrol engine.

Above: US Army M44 155-mm (6.1-in) self-propelled howitzers are caught by the camera on the move during June 1955. The crew comprised of six men.

Left: The M44 was 6.17 m (20 ft 3 in) long, 3.25 m (10 ft 8 in) wide and 3.12 m (10 ft 3 in) high, and the open-topped fighting compartment was a poor feature.

SPECIFICATION	
M37	**Powerplant:** two Cadillac water-cooled V-8 petrol engines each developing 82 kW (110 hp)
Crew: up to 7	
Weight: about 18144 kg (40,000 lb)	
Dimensions: length 5.54 m (18 ft 2 in); width 3.02 m (9 ft 11 in); height 2.235 m (7 ft 4 in)	**Performance:** maximum road speed 56 km/h (35 mph); maximum range 241 km (150 miles)

M52 105-mm self-propelled howitzer

The **Howitzer Motor Carriage M52** was a self-propelled 105-mm (4.13-in) equipment that was developed specifically to meet the requirements of the US Field Artillery in the period immediately after World War II, and used many automotive components of the M41 light tank. Production started in 1951 at the Detroit Tank Arsenal under the designation **T98E1**, and the vehicle was later standardised as the M52. From the early 1960s the equipment was replaced by the 105-mm M108, which itself was soon replaced by the 155-mm (6.1-in) M109 self-propelled howitzer, which was based on the same chassis as the M108. The main reasons for the replacement of the M52

and M108 by the M109 was the latter's 155-mm projectile, which is much heavier and has a greater HE content, and is therefore considerably more effective. It also has the longer range of 14000 m (15,310 yards) and can fire a wider selection of ammunition, eventually including tactical nuclear ammunition.

Extended life

For some years after it had been replaced in US Army service by the M108 and M109, the M52 was retained by the armies of countries such as Belgium, Greece, Italy, Japan, Spain and Turkey. It has now disappeared from service.

The hull and turret of the M52 were of 12.7-mm

(0.5-in) welded steel armour, with the engine and transmission at the front of the hull and the turret at its rear. The suspension was of the

Although replaced in US Army service by the altogether superior M109 series of 155-mm (6.1-in) self-propelled howitzers, the M52 could be found for some time after this in continued service with a number of NATO and Far Eastern countries.

The extensive stowage spaces for reserve ammunition and the turret-mounted revolver-type 'Lazy Susan' 21-round ready-use rack can clearly be seen in this rear view of a US Army M52. It was about to fire during an exercise in 1959.

SPECIFICATION

M52
Crew: 5
Weight: 24040 kg (53,000 lb)
Dimensions: length 5.8 m (19 ft 0.3 in); width 3.149 m (10 ft 4 in); height 3.316 m (10 ft 10.25 in) with AA machine-gun
Powerplant: one Continental AOS-

895-3 6-cylinder petrol engine developing 373 kW (500 hp)
Performance: maximum road speed 56 km/h (35 mph); maximum range 100 miles (161 km)
Gradient: 60 per cent
Vertical obstacle: 0.91 m (3 ft)
Trench: 1.83 m (6 ft)

torsion-bar type, and consisted on each side of six road wheels, of which the rearmost acted as the idlers. The drive sprockets were at the front, and there were four return rollers. Located at the vehicle's rear, the fully enclosed turret was unusual in that it accommodated the driver.

Manual operation
The turret could be traversed 60° left and right, and the main armament consisted of the 105-mm M49 howitzer with an elevation arc between -10° and +65°. Both turret movement and ordnance elevation were manual. The M49 howitzer had a very short barrel, and a total of 102 rounds of ammunition was carried, of which 21 rounds were located in a vertically-mounted revolver-

type rack (commonly called the 'Lazy Susan') at the left rear of the turret. More ammunition was stowed in the turret and under the hull at the rear. The 105-mm howitzer had a maximum range of 11270 m (12,325 yards), and was cleared to fire the following types of ammunition: chemical, anti-personnel, HE, HE plastic, HE rocket-assisted (with a range of 15000 m/16,405 yards), leaflet, illuminating, smoke and tactical CS.

Two sights
Both direct-fire and indirect-fire sights were fitted, although the former would only be used as a last resort for anti-tank purposes. A 0.5-in (12.7-mm) Browning M2 machine-gun was mounted on the commander's cupola for anti-aircraft and local

defence use; 900 rounds of ammunition were carried for this weapon.

Standard equipment on the M52 self-propelled howitzer included a heater, a turret-mounted ventilator of the type essential for the removal of howitzer fumes from the turret when the

ordnance was being fired, an auxiliary generator so that the batteries would not be quickly run down when the main engine was not being operated to conserve fuel and keep noise to a minimum, a bilge pump and a fixed fire-extinguishing system.

The M52 lacked any NBC system, and also was not amphibious, although it was capable of fording to a water depth of 1.22 m (4 ft). As a retrofit to improve their operational capabilities for nocturnal operations, some of the vehicles were fitted with infra-red driving lights.

M53 and M55 Self-propelled artillery pieces

The **M53** and **M55** were based on the much-modified chassis of the M47 medium tank. The vehicles were basically similar except for the types of ordnance carried and related items such as ammunition stowage. The M53 carried the 155-mm (6.1-in) M46 gun and the M55 the 8-in (203-mm) M47 howitzer. Both were intended to withstand the rigours of nuclear warfare, so the ordnance was installed in a fully enclosed armoured turret at the rear of the hull, while the forward part of the hull carried the engine and transmission. Each of the vehicles was manned by a crew of six men, all of them accommodated in the turret.

The first prototypes were ready for trials during 1952, but assorted technical troubles delayed their service debuts until 1956, by which time the US Army had decided not to adopt the M53 (originally the **T97**),

so M53 production vehicles went to the US Marine Corps, with whom the type saw its only active service during the early phases of the Vietnam conflict. Thus the US Army fielded only the 8-in model, originally known as the **T108**.

Heavy platforms
The 155-mm M46 gun fired the M107 HE projectile weighing 43 kg (95 lb) to 23515 m (25,700 yards), while the 8-in M47 howitzer fired the M106 projectile weighing about 90 kg (198 lb) to 16925 m (18,500 yards). In each vehicle type the turret could be traversed through 60° left and right, and before firing began, an auxiliary engine lowered a large recoil spade at the rear of the vehicle. A 0.5-in (12.7-mm) Browning M2 machine-gun was usually carried next to the commander's roof hatch.

Both vehicles were large

Above: The M53 carried its 155-mm (6.1-in) M46 gun in a large turret whose rear opened upward, and was stabilised in firing position by a rear spade.

and heavy platforms, so heavy that they soon fell out of favour when more emphasis was placed on the need to transport combat equipments overseas rapidly to almost anywhere in the world. The 155-mm M53 weighed 45545 kg

Left: Armed with an 8-in (203-mm) M47 howitzer, the M55 self-propelled gun was used by the US Army for the heavy indirect-fire role with a 90-kg (198-lb) projectile.

(96,000 lb), so movement had to be by sea rather than air. When lighter air-transportable SP artillery became available, the M53 and M55 faded from the scene.

SPECIFICATION

M55
Crew: 6
Weight: 44452 kg (98,000 lb)
Dimensions: length overall 7.9 m (25 ft 11 in); width 3.58 m (11 ft 9 in); height 3.56 m (11 ft 8 in)

Powerplant: one Continental AV-1790-5B liquid-cooled V-12 engine developing 525 kW (704 hp)
Performance: maximum road speed 48 km/h (30 mph); maximum range 257 km (160 miles)

M50 Ontos Tank destroyer

In the early 1950s the US Marine Corps issued a requirement for a highly mobile tank destroyer, and in October 1951 authorisation was given for the building of no less than five prototype vehicles, all of which had various numbers of recoilless rifles as their main armament. These were built and tested, and in February 1953 approval was given for the procurement of 24 examples of the **T165**, which was armed with six 106-mm (4.2-in) recoilless rifles. Trials with the first of these vehicles showed that some work was required with the mounting, fire-control system and suspension. The remaining vehicles were built to a slightly modified design and designated the **T165E2**. Following trials with the latter vehicles, and more modifications, the vehicle was finally accepted for service with the US Marine Corps and in 1955 was standardised as the **Rifle, Multiple, 106-mm Self-Propelled, M50** or, as it was normally called, the

Ontos (Greek for 'the thing'). In August 1955 Allis Chalmers was awarded a production contract for 297 vehicles, all of which had been completed by November 1957. At a later date it was decided to replace the original General Motors petrol engine with a Chrysler petrol engine developing 134 kW (180 hp) and subsequently, in June 1963, the original manufacturer was awarded a contract to rebuild 294 M50 vehicles to this new configuration, known as the **M50A1**; at the same time a number of other minor improvements were made to the vehicle.

Ontos in combat

The M50 was used in South Vietnam and in the Dominican Republic, but it was retired from service with the US Marine Corps without a direct replacement, although ground-and vehicle-launched TOW ATGWs carry out a similar function.

The vehicle was armed with six M40A1C recoilless

The M50 Ontos tank destroyer as used by the US Marine Corps. Note the 0.5-in spotting rifles above the top four 106-mm recoilless rifles. The crew had to leave the vehicle to reload the latter.

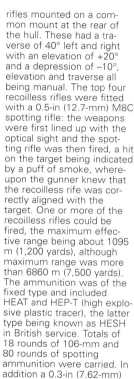

rifles mounted on a common mount at the rear of the hull. These had a traverse of 40° left and right with an elevation of +20° and a depression of –10°, elevation and traverse all being manual. The top four recoilless rifles were fitted with a 0.5-in (12.7-mm) M8C spotting rifle: the weapons were first lined up with the optical sight and the spotting rifle was then fired, a hit on the target being indicated by a puff of smoke, whereupon the gunner knew that the recoilless rife was correctly aligned with the target. One or more of the recoilless rifles could be fired, the maximum effective range being about 1095 m (1,200 yards), although maximum range was more than 6860 m (7,500 yards). The ammunition was of the fixed type and included HEAT and HEP-T (high explosive plastic tracer), the latter type being known as HESH in British service. Totals of 18 rounds of 106-mm and 80 rounds of spotting ammunition were carried. In addition a 0.3-in (7.62-mm)

The M50's six recoilless rifles had a maximum effective range of around 1095 m (1,200 yards) but could reach targets at a distance of up to 6860 m (7,500 yards).

M1919A4 machine-gun was fitted above the mount for local protection.

The driver was seated at the front of the hull on the left, with the engine to his right and the very cramped crew compartment at the rear; entry to the last was effected via two doors in the hull rear. The engine was coupled to a General Motors

Corporation (Allison Division) XT-90-2 cross drive transmission that delivered power to the drive sprockets at the front of the hull.

The M50's chassis was also used for a number of experimental vehicles but none of these, including several armoured/infantry carriers, entered production or service.

An M50 Ontos is seen here in action in South Vietnam, providing a good view of the vehicle's potent arrangement of 106-mm recoilless rifles.

SPECIFICATION	
M50 Ontos	GMC Model 302 petrol engine
Crew: 3	**Performance:** maximum road
Weight: 8640 kg (19,050 lb)	speed 48 km/h (30 mph); maximum
Dimensions: length 3.82 m (12 ft	range 240 km (150 miles)
6 in); width 2.6 m (8 ft 6 in); height	**Gradient:** 60 per cent
2.13 m (6 ft 11 in)	**Vertical obstacle:** 0.762 m (30 in)
Powerplant: one 108-kW (145-hp)	**Trench:** 1.42 m (4 ft 8 in)

M56 Scorpion 90-mm airborne self-propelled anti-tank gun

Apart from hand-held weapons, the most important anti-tank weapon used by US airborne forces in World War II was the Jeep-towed 57-mm (2.24-in) M1 anti-tank gun, which was essentially the British 6-pdr made in the United States. After the war a requirement was issued for a highly mobile self-propelled anti-tank gun that could be air-dropped by parachute during the initial phases of any airborne operation and have a firepower similar to that of a tank. Two proto-

types of a vehicle called the **T101** were built by the Cadillac Motor Car Division of the General Motors Corporation. Further development resulted in the improved **T101E1** which was eventually standardised as the **Gun, Anti-tank, Self-Propelled, 90-mm M56**, or more commonly the **Scorpion**. Production was undertaken by the Cadillac Motor Car Division between 1953 and 1959. In the US Army the M56 was issued only to the 82nd and 101st Airborne Divisions, but was

The M56 90-mm self-propelled anti-tank gun, or Scorpion, was created specifically for the US 82nd and 101st Airborne Divisions. Its main drawback was the lack of armour protection, apart from the small shield, for the gun crew.

One of the T101 prototypes for the M56 is seen shortly after the 90-mm gun has fired, showing the gun recoiling to the rear and the forward part of the chassis lifting clear of the ground. The dust often obscured the gunner's line of sight for the next shot.

supplied power to the final drives on each side. The suspension was of the torsion-bar type with four rubber-tyred road wheels, the idler at the rear and the drive sprocket at the front; there were no track-return rollers. The track consisted of a steel-reinforced endless rubber band.

Muzzle brake

The main armament was a 90-mm (3.54-in) M54 gun fitted with a muzzle brake and a vertical sliding breech block. Manually controlled, the gun had an elevation of +15° and depression of -10°, and a traverse of 30° left and right. A total of 29 rounds of fixed ammunition was carried under and to the rear of the gun; AP-T, APC-T, HE-T, HEAT, HEAT-T, HEP-T, WP, TP-T, HVAP-T and HVTP-T rounds could be fired. The main drawback of the M56, which had much better firepower than the M41 light tank with its 76-mm (3-in) gun, was that the chassis was too light and when the

90-mm gun was fired the vehicle often moved several feet and the target was obscured by dust from the muzzle blast.

Another drawback was the complete lack of armour protection for the crew, apart from the very small shield. The driver, who was equipped with a steering wheel, was seated to the left of the gun with the gunner to the rear; the latter was provided with a sight with a magnification of x4.1 or x8. A box on the left-hand side of the driver's station held the vehicle's radio. The commander sat on top of the radio. The other two and unluckier members of the

crew were positioned on the right-hand side of the vehicle, near the exhaust pipe which was situated opposite their station.

The chassis of the M56 was also used as the basis for a number of other vehicles including an armoured personnel carrier with a much higher superstructure incorporating a rear troop compartment, 81-mm (3.2-in) and 107-mm (4.2-in) self-propelled mortar carriers, a 106-mm (4.17-in) M40 recoilless anti-tank gun carrier, a missile launcher and an anti-aircraft vehicle fitted with four 0.5-in (12.7-mm) M2HB machine-guns; none of these entered production.

replaced in the 1960s by the M551 Sheridan Armored Reconnaissance/Airborne Assault Vehicle. A few M56s were supplied to Spain and Morocco, and some were also deployed by the US Army in Vietnam, where they were used mainly in the fire-support role.

The hull of the M56 was

of welded and riveted aluminium construction, with the engine and transmission at the front, gun in the centre and the crew area at the rear. The engine was coupled to a General Motors Corporation (Allison Division) transmission with one reverse and two forward ranges which in turn

SPECIFICATION	
M56 Scorpion	6-cylinder petrol engine developing
Crew: 4	149 kW (200 bhp)
Weight: 7030 kg (15,500 lb)	**Performance:** maximum road
Dimensions: length (including gun)	speed 45 km/h (28 mph); maximum
5.841 m (19 ft 2 in) and (hull)	road range 225 km (140 miles)
4.555 m (14 ft 1 in); width 2.577 m	**Gradient:** 60 per cent
(8 ft 5 in); height 2.067 m (6 ft 9 in)	**Vertical obstacle:** 0.762 m (30 in)
Powerplant: one Continental	**Trench:** 1.524 m (5 ft)

M107 175-mm self-propelled gun

In the 1950s the standard 203-mm (8-in) self-propelled howitzer of the US Army was the M55, which had the chassis and turret of the M53 155-mm (6.1-in) self-propelled gun. The main drawbacks of both these weapons were that at a weight of about 45 tons they were too heavy for air transport and their petrol engines gave them an operating range of only 260 km (160 miles). In the mid-1950s a decision was taken to design a new family of self-propelled artillery that would share a common chassis and mount, be airportable, and come into and be taken out of action quickly. Prototypes were built by the Pacific Car and Foundry Company as the **T235** 175-mm (6.89-in) self-

propelled gun, T236 203-mm self-propelled howitzer, and T245 155-mm self-propelled gun. Further development, including the replacement of the petrol engines by diesels for increased operational range, resulted in the T235 being standardised as the **M107** and the T236 as the M110. The chassis of the family was also used as the basis for a number of armoured recovery vehicles (ARVs), but only the T120E1 was placed in production as the M578 light ARV; this has served with many countries including the United States.

Production of the M107 was undertaken initially by the Pacific Car and Foundry Company; the first vehicles were completed in 1962, with the first battalion forming at Fort Sill (home of the

A US Army M107 in travelling order. All of these vehicles were subsequently converted to the M110A2 configuration by replacing the 175-mm (6.89-in) gun.

An M107 on the move. This weapon was deployed throughout the NATO area, and fired a 66.78-kg (147-lb) HE shell at a muzzle velocity of 914 m (2,998 ft) per second. The M107 was also used to provide long-range fire support from up to 30 km (18.6 miles) during the Vietnam War.

US Field Artillery) in early 1963. At a later date production was also undertaken by FMC, and between 1965 and 1980 by Bowen-McLaughlin-York.

The US Army deployed the 175-mm M107 in 12-gun battalions at corps level but all of these weapons were later converted to the 203-mm M110A2 configuration as this could fire the somewhat heavier 203-mm HERA (HE rocket assisted) round to a range only slightly reduced to just over 29000 m (31,715 yards). The M107 was exported to Greece, Iran, Israel, Italy, South Korea, the Netherlands, Spain, Turkey, the UK and West Germany; many of these countries also converted their M107s to the M110A2 configuration.

The chassis of the M107 is fully described in the entry for the M110. The 175-mm gun had an elevation of +65° and a depression of -2°, and the traverse of 30° left and right. Traverse and elevation were pow-

ered, with manual controls provided for emergency use. Only one round was ever standardised for US Army use – the M437A1 or M437A2 HE type which, with a charge three propellant, had a maximum range of 32700 m (35,760 yards), although a special round was used by Israel with a range of some 40000 m (43,745 yards). To assist the crew in loading the 66.78-kg (147-lb) projectile, a rammer and loader assembly was mounted at the rear of the chassis. This lifted the pro-

jectile from the ground and then rammed it into the chamber. The charge was loaded and the ordnance fired. Only two projectiles and charges were carried on the M107, which had a crew of 13, of whom five (driver, commander and three gunners) travelled on the M107. The remainder were carried in the M548 tracked cargo carrier that carried the bulk of the ammunition. Some countries used 6x6 trucks to support the M107, but often these offered poor cross-country mobility.

SPECIFICATION	
M107	Detroit Diesel Model 8V-71T diesel
Crew: 5+8	**Performance:** maximum road speed
Weight: 28168 kg (57,690 lb)	56 km/h (35 mph); maximum range
Dimensions: length (gun forward)	725 km (450 miles)
11.256 m (36 ft 7 in) and (hull)	**Gradient:** 60 per cent
5.72 m (18 ft 9 in); width 3.149 m	**Vertical obstacle:** 1.016 m (3 ft
(10 ft 4 in); height 3.679 m (12 ft)	4 in)
Powerplant: one 302-kW (405-hp)	**Trench:** 2.326 m (7 ft 9 in)

Pluton and Hades French battlefield missiles

Conceived in the early 1960s, the **Pluton** missile system entered service in 1974 with the French army. The missile was designed as a short-range, road-mobile system armed with a single nuclear warhead. The missile was 7.64-m (25-ft) long, with a diameter of 0.65 m (2 ft 1½ in). It had a 2423-kg (5,342-lb) launch weight and was powered by a single-stage solid propellant motor, which gave the missile a 120-km (75-mile) range, while the internal guidance system made Pluton accurate to within 150 m (492 ft) of its target. Pluton could carry a variable-yield nuclear warhead. The 10-kT device was designed to be used against forward area targets, such as front-line troops or armoured columns. The 25-kT warhead would be used for 'counterforce' strikes on rear installations such as tank parks, supply dumps or command and control facilities. Alternatively, the system could be used against 'countervalue' targets such as railway junctions and bridges.

Pluton was designed to deliver a 'nuclear warning' to an aggressor. Although the missile was deployed on French territory in peace-

time, it would be moved to the French Second Army Corps in the south west of Germany during a crisis. This was controversial in West Germany, given that the country was only 300 km (186 miles) wide where the Second Army Corps were stationed. Pluton's maximum range was 150 km, meaning that even missiles launched from the front-lines would still land on targets in West Germany. However, the then French President François Mitterrand gave Bonn the assurance that Pluton would not be fired on West German territory, during a visit in 1987.

The missile itself was carried on a heavily modified AMX-30 tank chassis. The chassis included a large box atop of the body. The entire system was designed to work with sophisticated command and control equipment. This included a 'real time' targeting datalink, which received information from a CT-20 drone. A total of 70 Pluton missiles served with the French Army. In total, 30 of the AMX-30 launchers were deployed together with missiles, reloads and batches of alternative warheads. The Pluton missile was in French Army service until 1993.

The land component of the French nuclear deterrent, the Pluton (shown above) and Hades system gave the French Army a powerful battlefield missile system.

Like Pluton, **Hades** was also a single warhead solid propellant missile fielded on a road-mobile chassis. The Hades programme was initially intended to deploy 120 missiles, some of which were to be armed with high explosive (HE) warheads, and some to be armed with nuclear warheads. Hades carried the TN-90 nuclear warhead, which had an explosive yield of 80 kt.

The missile was designed to follow a low-angle trajectory, to allow the aerodynamic control fins at the back of the missile's body to make course alterations during its flight; this allowed it to undertake evasive manoeuvres if targeted by anti-ballistic missile (ABM) defences. Hades was originally designed as a SRBM system with a range of

250 km (155 miles) although in 1983, this was increased to 480 km (298 miles). In 1993, reports indicated that the system had its range downgraded to 250 km once more. Furthermore, the system was fitted with a Global Positioning System (GPS) inertial navigation system. A TV/digital scene-matching system was also considered, which would have increased the missile's accuracy to within 5 m (16 ft 5 in) of the target. Unlike Pluton, Hades was designed for transport on wheeled, articulated TELs. Each trailer would carry two missiles in containers, which also acted as launch boxes. While the original programme called for

the construction of 120 missiles and 60 launchers, this requirement was revised for 30 missiles and 15 launchers. The first Hades regiment was deployed at Suippes, eastern France, on 1 September 1991. However, due to the end of the Cold War, the French government announced that the Hades force would be mothballed, although 20-25 missiles were retained at Luneville for use in case of national emergencies. On 23 February 1996, French President Jacques Chirac announced that the Hades missile system would be dismantled, and on 23 June 1997, the last Hades missile was scrapped.

SPECIFICATION	
Hades	**Range:** 480 km;
Dimensions: Length: 7.5 m;	**Payload:** kT-range thermo-nuclear
Diameter: 0.53 m	warhead
Weight: 1850 kg;	

SPECIFICATION	
Pluton	**Range:** 120 km;
Dimensions: Length: 7.64 m;	**Payload:** kT-range thermo-nuclear
Diameter: 0.65 m; Weight: 2423 kg	warhead

Prithvi and Hatf-2/Shadoz Indian/Pakistani missiles

Development of the **Prithvi** ('Earth') missile began in 1983. It was first test-fired on 25 February 1988. This ongoing project is overseen by India's Integrated Guided Missile Development Programme (IGMDP), which has designed three versions of the missile for India's navy, army and air force. The Indian army uses the 150-km/1000-kg (93-mile/2,205-lb) payload **Prithvi-1**. The **Prithvi-2** has a 250-km (155-mile) range and a 500-kg (1,102-lb) payload, and will eventually enter service with the Indian air force. The reduced payload of Prithvi-2 increases the missile's range. The IGDMP is also thought to be develop-

ing a 350-km (217-mile) range **Prithvi-3** for the Indian Navy. Prithvi can deploy both conventional and nuclear warheads. The IGMDP has already performed test flights of a missile, fitted with a conventional, pre-fragmented warhead. However, only the army's Prithvi-1 missile is believed to have the sufficient 'throw-weight' to deliver a nuclear warhead. Alternatively, the missile can deploy cluster munitions, sub-munitions, fuel-air explosives (FAE) and incendiary devices. The missile's accuracy is thought to be within 150-1500 m (492-4,921 ft) of its target, and it is fuelled by a highly volatile mixture of red fuming nitric acid,

Developed in tight secrecy and inspite of international sanctions, Pakistan's 'Hatf' series of missiles are developed for both nuclear and conventional missions.

Seen here during India's Republic Day celebrations, India's Prithvi missiles form the backbone of its fledgling nuclear and battlefield missile force.

xylidienne and triethylamine. The Indian army raised the 333rd Missile Regiment, based near Jodhpur, northern India, to field the system. The force will eventually deploy 100 missiles, transported on several specially designed Kolos Tatra 8x8 TEL vehicles. The 333rd regiment received 20 missiles in October 1995. The Indian Army will also raise the 444th and 555th regiment for Prithvi deployment. Each company of missiles will include four missile carrier vehicles, re-supply and reloading vehicles, a propellant tanker and a command and control post.

It is thought that the Indian Army has decoy missile convoys available for dispersal to the countryside, along with active units to confuse enemy targeting. Moreover, Prithvi missile convoys are ordered to keep changing their location to frustrate and minimise the chance of attack by the enemy.

Pakistan's SRBMs
Designed to counter India's Prithvi system, Pakistan's **Hatf-2/Shadoz** ('Sword of the Prophet'/'King Hawk') system has a range of between 280-450 km (174-280 miles). Reportedly based on the French Eridan

Sounding (testing) rocket, Pakistan's College of Electrical and Mechanical Engineering at Rawalpindi, and the Space and Upper Atmosphere Research Commission (SUPARCO) in Karachi were responsible for development of the Hatf-2/Shadoz system. Pakistan is also thought to have received Chinese help to turn Eridan technology into a workable SRBM.

Although the solid-propellant engine bears a close resemblance to the French system, Washington has been convinced that the Hatf-2 system owes its development to the Chinese M-11 system. Pakistan is believed to produce M-11 missiles under license. Development of the missile

Although now obsolete from Cold War defence planning, SRBM systems are attractive to states wishing to develop a comprehensive missile force.

is thought to have begun in the 1980s, with the first test flights taking place in February 1989; the existence of Hatf-2 was revealed by the Pakistan government in 1989. Like India's Prithvi system, the missile is road-mobile and it was displayed in Rawalpindi, during March 1989, travelling on an ex-British World War II anti-aircraft gun carrier. The missile entered service with the Pakistan army in 1996. Hatf-2 is thought to be capa-

ble of delivering a 100-200 kt nuclear device along with alternative high explosive or chemical warheads. However, the current status of the Hatf-2 programme is unknown, and the programme may have stalled. Reports have circulated concerning problems with the missile's guidance and control systems. If so, the engine may have been salvaged to form part of a future multi-stage space-launch vehicle.

India's Prithvi system has formed the basis for its longer-range Agni system, which is designed as an intermediate range nuclear delivery system.

SPECIFICATION	
Prithvi	**Hatf-2**
Length: 8.5 m (27 ft 10½ in)	**Length:** 9.75 m (31 ft 11½ in)
Diameter: 1 m (3 ft 3 in)	**Diameter:** 0.82 m (2 ft 8 in)
Weight: 4,500 kg (9,921 lb)	**Weight:** 5500 kg (12,125 lb)
Range: 150-250 km (93-155 miles)	**Range:** 280 km (174 miles)
Payload: 500-1000 kg (1,102-2,205 lb)	**Payload:** 500 kg (1,102 lb)

Jericho 1 Israeli missiles

First test fired in 1968, Israel's **Jericho 1** SRBM was developed with extensive French assistance. A deal with France to supply

SRBMs was first discussed by Shimon Peres, Israel's Deputy Minister of Defence, and the French government in 1957. The

Israelis were anxious to secure a missile system from the French with the 260-km (162-mile) range sufficient to hit Cairo. France signed a contract with Israel in 1965 and supplied it with Marcel

Dassault MD-600 500-km (311-mile) missiles.

Israel developed its own version of the weapon – the Jericho 1 – in the late 1960s after France imposed an embargo on arms exports to Tel Aviv. Israel

was thought to have deployed its Jericho missiles during the October 1973 Arab-Israeli war, and Jericho was thought to have become nuclear capable during the same year.

SS-1 'Scud' Short-Range Ballistic Missile system

First brought to the attention of the world's TV audiences during the Iraqi missile attacks in Operation Desert Storm, this missile was not in fact a new phenomenon. Designed by the Korolyev Design Bureau (OKB-1), it was based on the German A4/V-2, but was half the size. A test firing of a proto-type missile occurred on 18 April 1953.

Prototype problems

Some problems were experienced with the prototype's kerosene fuel and propellant leakages, and the first version of the missile, the **SS-1b 'Scud-A'** entered service in July 1955. Known to the Soviets as the **R-11** and **8K11**, the missile was classed as an operational- and tactical-level weapon by its originators. The SS-1b's range was limited to 180 km (111 miles), and it was fitted with a 50-kT nuclear war-head. The missile had a circular error of probability (CEP) of 3 km (1.8 miles) and was carried on an IS-2 tank chassis.

In 1962 an improved version of the previous model was produced, known in the West as the **SS-1c 'Scud-B'** and to the Soviets as the **R-17 Elbrus** and **8K14**. This weapon had a greatly improved guidance system, using a rudimentary inertial system which included three gyroscopes. The missile's improved fuel mixture consisted of Unsymmetrical Dimethyl Hydrazine (UDMH) and Inhibited Red Fuming Nitric Acid. The 'Scud-B' was also deployed on an eight-wheeled MAZ-543P Transporter-Erector-Launcher (TEL) for greater mobility. The missile could also be fitted with an assortment of war-heads including chemical, nuclear or conventional muni-tions. By 1970 the 'Scud-B' constituted three-quarters of

the 300 'Scud' launchers deployed.

The above weapons were supplemented by the **SS-1d 'Scud-C'**, which carried a lighter 600-kg (1,323-lb) war-head, which separated from the rest of the vehicle at motor burn-out, over a range of some 550 km (342 miles). However, it is unclear if this version ever entered service. The **SS-1e 'Scud-D'** of the later 1980s had an improved guidance package, possibly incorporating active radar ter-minal guidance, and a wider choice of warheads and a range of 700 km (435 miles). It may not have entered Soviet service.

A navalised version of the missile was also developed as the **R-11FM**, developed from 1955 at Kapustin Yar. Three experimental launches of the missile were con-ducted from an R-11 missile launcher. Between September and October

1955, tests of the missile was conducted from a Project 611 submarine in the White Sea. The navalised version had a range of 150 km (93 miles), was accepted for naval deploy-ment in 1959, but was never deployed operationally.

In Soviet service the 'Scud-B' and 'Scud-C' were deployed at army and army group levels in brigades con-sisting of an HQ battery with three firing batteries each of three launcher vehicles and three reload vehicles carrying single missiles.

The 'Scud-A' and 'Scud-B' were exported to all the Warsaw Pact nations in addi-tion to Egypt, Syria, Libya, Iraq and South Yemen. Libya was probably the only opera-tor of the 'Scud-C', and was the largest operator of the weapon outside the USSR,

Above: The MAZ-543 TEL can ready a missile for launching in one hour, allowing for the adoption of the so-called 'shoot and scoot' tactic. The missile would be launched and the vehicle would move rapidly to another location, reload, and launch once more.

Right: This photograph shows four 'Scud-A' missiles in about 1962. Carried on a very heavy IS-2 tank chassis, 'Scud-A' was one of the largest battlefield mobile weapons with a length of 11.25 m (36 ft 11 in) and a launch weight of 4400 kg (9,700 lb). The range of the weapon was up to 180 km (112 miles).

Below: The MAZ-543 has been used for several types of Soviet tactical missile, and here this vehicle is seen as the TEL for the 'Scud' system, with its missile load in the firing position. Far left is the baseline 'Scud-A'.

R-17 (SS-1c 'Scud-B')
Length: 11.25 m (36 ft 11 in)
Diameter: 0.88 m (34.65 in)
Weight: 5900 kg (13,007 lb)
Warhead weight: 985 kg
(2,171 lb)
Warhead types: 50-kT nuclear,
HE, chemical and training
Minimum range: 80 km (50 miles)
Maximum range: 180 km

(111 miles) with nuclear warhead,
and 300 km (186 miles) with HE or
chemical warhead
CEP: 450 m (490 yards) at 180 km
(111 miles) decreasing with further
range
Launch vehicle: MAZ-543P 8x8
wheeled TEL
Propellant type/guidance:
liquid/inertial

and undertook the first missile attack on mainland Europe since World War II in 1986 when it launched two 'Scud-B' missiles at a US Navy facility on the Italian island of Lampedusa in response to the US attack of that year. However, the missiles fell short of their target.

Desert 'Scuds'
On 17 January 1991, an Iraqi 'Scud-B' missile slammed into Tel Aviv. Iraqi President Saddam Hussein had used this vintage missile to respond to the Allied military campaign to end his occupation of Kuwait. Terror gripped Israeli citizens who quickly donned chemical and biological protection masks. The missiles were armed with conventional explosives, however, but no one was sure if Iraq, which had used chemical weapons during the Iran-Iraq war, would fit the missiles with something much more terrifying and deadly.

Iraq's gamble was that Israel would then enter the war, and split the Allied Coalition which included Saudi Arabia, Egypt and Syria. The exclusion of chemical or bacteriological agents might have been a deliberate tactical calculation by the Iraqi leader. The inclusion of such warheads could have bought an Israeli retaliation with nuclear weapons.

This was not the first time that Iraq had used the 'Scud' in combat, having fired it against Tehran during the Iran-Iraq war.

During the first night of the

Seen here in the form of a trio of weapons during a parade in Red Square, the 'Scud-A' was carried by a TEL based on the chassis of the IS-2 heavy tank. This model remained in Soviet service until at least 1972.

1991 Gulf War, eight 'Scud' missiles exploded in Israel. One hit Tel Aviv, two hit Haifa, three landed in unpopulated areas, and one at an undisclosed location. During the first night, Iraq also began to attack Saudi Arabia with missiles.

By the time the war had finished, 86 Iraqi 'Scud' missiles (40 fired at Israel and 46 fired at Saudi Arabia) had killed around 30 people. The missiles may have been less effective than Saddam had wished, yet the 'Scud' had landed firmly in the public consciousness around the world. Few of Iraq's 'Scud' missiles were destroyed during the war, and the missile remains a potential weapon of mass destruction.

SS-12 'Scaleboard' Short-Range Ballistic Missile system

The **SS-12 'Scaleboard'**, which carried the Soviet designations **TR-1 Temp-S** and **9M76**, was introduced to Soviet army service in the mid-1960s as an operational- and strategic-level missile system designed to hit targets in Central Europe. Deployed only at Front (army group) level in brigades of one headquarters battery and three firing batteries each of three erector-launcher vehicles and three reload vehicles carrying single missiles, the 'Scaleboard' provided the Front commander with his only organic nuclear system capable of hitting both the enemy corps and army group rear areas. The only other Soviet systems tasked with strikes into the army rear areas were held by the Strategic Rocket Forces and by Long-Range Aviation. The

single-stage 9700-kg (21,384-lb) 'Scaleboard' was an inertially guided missile carried enclosed in a ribbed split casing on a MAZ-543 eight-wheeled vehicle similar in appearance to that carrying the 'Scud-B' and 'Scud-C' missiles.

Nuclear warhead
The 'Scaleboard' was elevated to the vertical shortly before the firing of its solid-propellant rocket motor, and the warhead had a yield of 500 kT. The CEP at the maximum range of 800 km (497 miles) was estimated to be 400 m (440 yards). The peak number of 'Scaleboard' missiles deployed was 120 throughout the mid-1970s.

The Intermediate Nuclear Forces Treaty of December 1987 signed the death knell for the 'Scaleboard' and all

nuclear-tipped ground-launched cruise and ballistic missiles with ranges of between 500 km (310 miles) and 5500 km (3,417 miles). All SS-12 missiles and their accompanying vehicles and support infrastructure were destroyed at Stan'kovo from 1 August 1988. Destruction was completed on 25 July 1989. However in 1997, reports emerged from Avaro Prendez, a top Cuban military defector, that Fidel Castro, the Cuban president was attempting to use his five Soviet-made SS-22 missiles to deliver biological weapons. However, the authenticity of his reports was doubted as Cuba is not known to have such weapons.

A modernised version of

Above: A 'Scaleboard' in its TEL-carried ribbed container negotiates the streets of Moscow during one of the city's massive military parades.

the weapon, carrying the unconventional Western designation **SS-12M 'Scaleboard-B'**, and previously referred to as the **SS-22**, became available in the early 1980s with a CEP of 200 m (220 yards) and range of 900 km (559 miles). This allowed the Soviet army to cover even more of continental Europe with its potent umbrella of nuclear-tipped missiles.

Above and below: A powerful battlefield mobile weapons with a range of 800 km (500 miles), the SS-12's life came to an abrupt end in 1988 when the system was destroyed as a product of the INF Treaty, together with its later variant, the 'Scaleboard-B'.

SS-12 'Scaleboard'
Length: 12.4 m (40 ft 8 in)
Diameter: 1.01 m (39.76 in)
Weight: 9700 kg (19,400 lb)
Warhead weight: 1250 kg
(2,756 lb)
Warhead type: 500-kT nuclear
Minimum range: 220 km

(138 miles)
Maximum range: 800 km
(497 miles)
CEP: 400 m (440 yards)
Launch vehicle: MAZ-543 8x8
wheeled TEL
Propellant type/guidance: solid/
inertial

FROG series Artillery rocket systems

The **FROG** (**Free Rocket Over Ground**) weapons are described by the Russians as tactical missile systems. First deployed in 1955, the FROG series has undergone an extensive development programme that has resulted in seven versions of the missile, known by the NATO designations FROG-1 to FROG-7. Of these the tracked vehicle-mounted **FROG-1** (**3R2 Filin**) to **FROG-5** (**3R10 Luna-2**) are obsolete, the **FROG-6** was a non-operational training round, and the **FROG-7** (**9M21 Luna-M**) was the final variant accepted into service in 1964. The FROG-7 is carried on a 9P113 wheeled TEL (transporter-erector-launcher) vehicle and was allocated at divisional level in both the Soviet and Warsaw Pact armies. Each tank division and motorised rifle division had a FROG battalion (a headquarters battery with four three-rocket reload vehicles and two firing batteries each with two TELs).

Two variants of the FROG-7 were fielded. The FROG-7a series included the 9M21F rocket with a conventional warhead filled with 441 lb (200 kg) of HE, 9M21B with three types of nuclear warhead with yields in the range 3-200 kT, 9M21G with a chemical warhead (VX persistent nerve or other agents), 9M21A with a leaflet warhead, 9M210F with a warhead carrying 42 4.5-kg (9.9-lb) anti-personnel submunitions, and two training rockets. The **FROG-7b**

system introduced in 1968 is based on the **R-70** or **Luna-Z** rocket with a longer warhead section increasing overall length from 8.96 m (29 ft 4.75 in) to 9.4 m (30 ft 10 in). This was fitted with a pair of air brakes that could be locked open to reduce the rocket's range. The accuracy of this rocket was less than that of the FROG-7a, whose figure is 400-600 m (435-655 yards), and thus did not enter major service.

Extensive service

The FROG was extensively exported and has also been widely used in combat. The Egyptians used convention-

ally armed FROG-3 and FROG-7 rockets in the 1973 war with Israel. Fired initially against fixed targets in the Sinai and then against the Israeli bridgehead over the Suez Canal, the missiles caused relatively little damage. The Syrians used FROG-2 and FROG-3 missiles during their assault on the Golan Heights, but because of their inaccuracy the rockets impacted mainly on civilian areas. The most recent use of the FROG was by Iraq against Iran in the Gulf War of 1980-88, when the FROG-7 was employed as a long-range bombardment system targeted against Iranian cities immediately behind the lines.

In the first years of the 21st century, the FROG-5 and FROG-7 were still fielded in small numbers by CIS and ex-WarPac states as well as Afghanistan, Algeria, Bosnia, Cuba, Egypt, Iraq, Libya, North Korea, Syria, Yemen and Yugoslavia.

Below: Seen in Polish service, the three-round BAZ-135L4 transporter-loader vehicle has an onboard hydraulic crane to facilitate the offloading of rockets.

Above: Seen unloading from an An-22, the FROG-5 artillery rocket system was carried on the 2P16 TEL based on a PT-76 amphibious light tank chassis.

Below: The TEL of the FROG-7 system offers greater mobility and speed. Each battery also has a trailer-carried meteorological radar and a command vehicle.

SPECIFICATION	
Luna-M (FROG-7a)	(7.46-9.32 miles)
Length: 8.96 m (29 ft 4.75 in)	**Maximum range:** 68 km
Diameter: 0.544 m (1 ft 9.4 in)	(42.25 miles)
Weight: 2432-2450 kg	**CEP:** 400-600 m (435-655 yards)
(5,362-5,401 lb) depending on	but highly variable with range
specific warhead type fitted	**Propellant type:** solid
Warhead types: 3-, 5-, 10-, 20-	**Guidance:** none
and 200-kT nuclear, HE, cluster,	**Launch vehicle:** 9P113 8x8
chemical and training	transporter-erector-launcher (TEL)
Minimum range: 12-15 km	**Crew:** 7

The FROG-5 system had an 11-man crew who needed 11 minutes to ready and fire the rocket. The system weighed 18800 kg (41,446 lb), and the TEL had a speed of 40 km/h (25 mph).

SS-20 'Saber' Mobile IRBM system

Design of the **SS-20 'Saber'** (Soviet designation **RT-21M Pioneer**) as an operational/strategic-level mobile IRBM system began in about 1967 as the long-term replacement for the SS-4 and SS-5 missiles. The programme was allocated to the Moscow Institute of Thermal Technology under the leadership of A. D. Nadiradzye; this organisation already had some experience in developing mobile IRBM systems as it had been involved with the briefly deployed SS-14 'Scapegoat' and SS-15 'Scrooge' IRBM systems.

The SS-20 was basically the first two stages of the SS-16 'Sinner' solid-propellant ICBM, and was first test-fired in September 1974 for deployment from March 1976 and initial operational capability from August of the same year within the Strategic Rocket Forces. The

The SS-20 'Saber' IRBM (right) was carried by a substantial MAZ-547V six-axle wheeled TEL, and elevated to the vertical position before being launched. Some 72 of the missiles were disposed of by launching, of which all were successful.

missile was soon on the strength of this force's six 'rocket armies', being deployed in six major base groupings distributed in western USSR, the area just east of the Ural mountains, and the Soviet Far East. The mobile launchers were grouped in brigades of nine launcher-transporter vehicles situated at a central maintenance and control base. In times of crisis, the launchers were intended to move by road to any of 440 widely dispersed launch sites that had been surveyed to ensure minimal error in the inertial guidance launch co-ordinates.

Wheeled mobility

Each SS-20 was carried on the rear of a wheeled vehicle in a tubular container that had to be elevated to the vertical

for firing. Three other wheeled vehicles completed the SS-20 system, one carrying a reload round and the other two carrying the control, test, generating and communication gear.

By July 1981 the number of SS-20 systems deployed was about 250, of which 175 were targeted against NATO nations. By June 1988, when the implementation of the previous year's INF Treaty demanded the elimination of the SS-20, the number was 954 missiles and 509 launchers at 48 bases.

There were three SS-20 variants. The first of these

was the **SS-20 Mod 1**, carrying a single 1-MT nuclear warhead. In the same year there came the principal **SS-20 Mod 2 (Pioneer-UTTH)** version with a payload of three 150-kT MIRVs and, according to Soviet sources, a slightly inferior CEP figure. Finally, in 1980 there came the modernised and slightly lengthened **SS-20 Mod 3** (subsequently designated **SS-28**) with the ability to carry either the single warhead or the three MIRVs over a range of 7500 km (4,660 miles). All missiles were eliminated by 1991 under the INF Treaty.

SPECIFICATION	
Pioneer (SS-20 'Saber')	(3,107 miles); Mod 2 5500 km
Length: Mods 1 and 2 16.49 m	(3,418 miles); Mod 3 7500 km
(54 ft 1 in); Mod 3 17 m (55 ft 9¼ in)	(4,660 miles)
Diameter: 1.79 m (5 ft 10½ in)	**CEP:** Mod 1 1300 m (1,422 yards);
Weight: 37000 kg (81,570 lb)	Mod 2 1000 m (1,094 yards)
Warhead types: Mod 1 single	**Propellant type/guidance:**
1-MT RV; Mod 2 three 150-kT	solid/autonomous inertial
MIRVs; Mod 3 single 1-MT RV or	**Launch vehicle:** wheeled TEL
three 150-kT MIRVs	**Launch:** cold with reload capability
Range: Mod 1 5000 km	

SS-21 'Scarab' and SS-23 'Spider' Tactical SRBM systems

In the late 1960s the Soviets decided to start the process of developing a guided successor to the unguided artillery rocket known to the West as the FROG-7, and the result was the **9M79 Tochka** that entered service in 1976 and gained the Western designation **SS-21 'Scarab'**.

This is a solid-propellant missile of the single-stage type, and is carried on and fired from the highly mobile 9P129 6x6 wheeled TEL with the crew compartment at the front and the missile element at the rear. The TEL is supported by transloader and missile transporter trailers.

The basic missile has a range of 70 km (43.5 miles), while the **9M79-1**

The SS-21 'Scarab' SRBM is based on the 9P129 6x6 TEL, which is supported in the field by the 9T218 tactical transloader and by the 9T238 missile transporter trailer towed by a ZIL-131 truck.

The SS-21 'Spider', as the Tochka SRBM is known in the West, is a highly effective weapon whose modest range is in effect magnified by the TEL's speed, range and mobility.

Tochka-U has an improved composite propellant boosting the range to 120 km (74.6 miles). The SS-21 can carry a number of tactical warhead types including 9N123F HE-fragmentation type with 120 kg (265 lb) of explosive with a terminal guidance package (radar and terrain-comparison) yielding a CEP of 30 m (33 yards). Other warheads are the AA60 tactical nuclear, 9N123K carrier with 'smart' submunitions,

and chemical.

The SS-21 remains in service with several CIS countries formerly part of the USSR, and was exported without terminal guidance for a CEP of 300 m (330 yards) to Czechoslovakia, East

Germany, Hungary, Poland, Syria, Yemen and probably Libya. At least two examples were used during Russia's war in Chechnya.

Designed to supersede the SS-1c 'Scud-B', with the poor reaction time of about 90 minutes, the

9K714 Oka (Western designation **SS-23 'Spider'**) was designed from the early 1970s as a single-stage weapon with a low-maintenance solid-fuel rocket motor. The 4700-kg (10,362-lb) inertially guided weapon was carried by an 8x8 TEL, could be readied and fired in under 30 minutes, and was capable of delivering a conventional or nuclear warhead to a range of 500 km (311 miles) with considerable accuracy. Based with Soviet units in Czechoslovakia and East Germany some 239 examples of the SS-23 were eliminated by 1989 under the INF Treaty.

SPECIFICATION	
Tochka-U (SS-21 'Scarab')	**CEP:** 30 m (33 yards) with terminal
Length: 6.4 m (21 ft)	guidance package and 300 m
Diameter: 0.65 m (2 ft 1½ in)	(330 yards) without terminal
Weight: 2000 kg (4,409 lb)	guidance package
Warhead types: nuclear, 'smart'	**Propellant type/guidance:**
submunition, unitary HE with or	solid/inertial
without terminal guidance package,	**Launch vehicle:** 9P129 6x6 TEL
and chemical	**Launch:** hot
Range: 120 km (74.6 miles)	

English Electric Blue Water Tactical precision missile

Like almost all the dozens of British military aircraft and missiles of 1955-65, the excellent **English Electric Blue Water** tactical missile had the misfortune to be British. Because of the political environment this practically guaranteed that nothing would be done with it, even though it was technically far in advance of similar weapons in other countries. Its development was authorised in 1958, to meet a War Office requirement for what was called a Corps-Support Rocket (CSR). This was to replace the obsolete Corporal, and it was logical to give the job to English Electric Aviation at Stevenage, which had been foster parent to Corporal in the British Army, and had developed the Army's Thunderbird SAM. The specification was much more severe than that of the contemporary Sergeant, calling for numerical maximum/minimum ranges, immunity to countermeasures, harsh demands on air-portability, and very low bulk, system price and cost. The Blue Water missile was particularly small for its task, and after trials with a special triple-launcher vehicle it was found possible to put the entire weapon sys-

tem aboard a standard Bedford 3-ton truck, except for a small self-checking digital computer. The whole system could be slung under a Belvedere helicopter. When a target was identified the computer vehicle drove up on one side and fed in trajectory, motor cut-off time and warhead burst height, while a theodolite set up the inertial platform by looking through a hole at a mirror inside the missile. The whole procedure took about two minutes, after which the missile could be elevated to the correct angle and fired. Trials went outstandingly well, and this should obviously have become a standard NATO weapon, the Standing Group having announced a European need for just such a missile. In 1962 British political ineptitude resulted in the Blue Water being cancelled in favour of the Sergeant, which had greater circular error, was a far less convenient system weighing three times as much and possessing a reaction time nine times longer, at five times the cost. Intentions for joint production of the Blue Water missile with West Germany also came to nothing.

Above: Developed from 1958 to meet the War Office's CSR requirement for a Corporal replacement, the English Electric Blue Water battlefield missile could be set up for launch in two minutes.

Right: One of the finest tactical missiles ever produced, Blue Water was extremely accurate, with advanced propulsion and guidance. It was cancelled in favour of the much less effective, much heavier and much slower-reacting Sergeant, which had the good fortune to be an American system.

SPECIFICATION

Blue Water
Propulsion: high-impulse dual-thrust solid-propellant motor
Performance: cut-off/burn-out velocity typically 2414 km/h (1,500 mph); maximum range 100 km (62 miles)
Weight: launch 1361 kg (3,000 lb)

Dimensions: length 7.62 m (25 ft); diameter 0.61 m (2 ft)
Warhead: three quick-change heads, normally travelling with 2-kT nuclear
Guidance: strapdown inertial
Control: four moving wings around mid-section

Firestone Corporal Tactical artillery missile

Originally known by the US Army designation **M2**, the **Firestone Corporal** was the first ballistic (wingless) missile to go into service outside Nazi Germany. It stemmed from a research vehicle named **Corporal E** built in 1947-50 to test propulsion and guidance systems, and particularly rocket engines that did not use cryogenic (refrigerated) liquids. In 1951 this

extremely slender vehicle was hurriedly developed, mainly by the Firestone company, into a military weapon with the US Army and US Navy designation **SSM-A-17** (17th Army SSM model). In effect it was planned as a modernised V-2 operated in the field as a piece of super artillery with a calibre of 762 mm (30 in), large enough for the warhead to be a

kiloton-range nuclear device if necessary – the 20-kT W7 warhead being the basic load. Inevitably, the entire weapon system was large and cumbersome, weighing over 100 tonnes (220,000 lb) and riding on or in 15 vehicles. Each battalion had a personnel strength of more than 250, and after the launch decision a delay of from four to (usually) seven hours had to precede the actual firing command. This was largely occupied in preparing a launch site, surveying, setting up the

guidance and getting the parts of the system dismounted and connected together. The result was often impressive: at a demonstration at White Sands (New Mexico) Proving Ground in July 1958 an improved **M2A1** impacted 14.6 m (48 ft) to the left and 3.6m (12 ft) short of its target at a range

of 50 km (31 miles). Several hundred rounds served with US Army battalions from 1954, two being based in Italy, while the British Army's 47th GW Regt, Royal Artillery, used Corporal between 1956-66. From 1962 onwards the US designations for the Corporal were **MGM-5A** (M2) and **MGM-5B** (M2A1).

Concurrent with US programmes to develop strategic missiles, the US Army also produced tactical guided missiles. The first to enter service since World War II was the Firestone Corporal. It could be armed with an HE or tactical nuclear warhead.

SPECIFICATION

Corporal
Propulsion: one 9072-kg (20,000-lb) thrust Ryan rocket engine burning RFNA (red fuming nitric acid) and aniline
Performance: speed at burn-out about 4281 km/h (2,660 mph); maximum range 113 or 138 km (70 or 86 miles) depending on warhead
Weight: launch (typical) 5443 kg (12,000 lb)
Dimensions: length 14.02 m

(46 ft); body diameter 0.76 m (2 ft 6 in); fin span 2.13 m (7 ft)
Warhead: 1500-kg (3,307-lb) HE or nuclear
Guidance: Gilfillan system based on launch azimuth, radar Doppler velocity measurement and launch-site computation of trajectory
Control: electro-hydraulic power units driving refractory jet vanes and four aerodynamic control fins

Sperry Sergeant Second-generation tactical artillery missile

As in any new technical field, early missiles had hardly been created before it could be seen that they were obsolete. This was certainly the case with the Corporal. Basic research and planning for the Corporal had been done by the Jet Propulsion Laboratory (JPL) of the California Institute of Technology, which by 1955 had designed a second-generation system with a new missile (briefly designated **SSM-A-27**), unjammable guidance and totally new ground equip-

ment. In early 1956 JPL handed this **Sergeant** system over to Sperry Rand for production, with the US Army guided artillery missile designation **XM15**. The missile was shorter than the Corporal, had a Thiokol cast polysulphide solid rocket motor and self-contained inertial guidance. A firing battery travelled on three semi-trailers and a standard truck which among other items carried sealed containers housing the motor, guidance section and conical warhead, as well as the four fins with powered controls. These had to be assembled under the girder forming the launch rail, after which the missile would be checked out by two truck-mounted test stations. The launcher would then be pointed exactly towards the

target and the missile launched at 75° elevation. There was no provision for thrust cut-off, range being determined by opening air-brakes around the guidance section. By the time the first test under battlefield conditions took place in September 1961 the Sergeant, then about to be redesignated **MGM-29A**, could be seen to have become obsolete. A far better new-generation missile was the British Blue Water, but British political 'clout' was non-existent so the Blue Water was cancelled and the Sergeant deployed by the US and West German armies in 1962-78. About 500 missiles were produced for the US Army, and both services replaced Sergeant with the MGM-52 Lance.

Left: Test firing of Sergeant under battlefield conditions proved that even though ground handling equipment and the guidance systems were greatly improved over the Corporal, the pace of technological change had made the Sergeant obsolescent.

Smaller than the preceding Corporal, the road-mobile solid-fuelled Sergeant had a similar range. The warhead could be conventional high-explosive, chemical, or nuclear of up to 60 kT yield.

SPECIFICATION

Sergeant
Propulsion: one Thiokol M53 solid-propellant rocket motor with a thrust of 21948 kg (55,000 lb)
Performance: burn-out speed 3701 km/h (2,300 mph); operational range 45 to 140 km (28 to 87 miles)
Weight: launch 4500 kg (9,920 lb)
Dimensions: length 10.6 m (34 ft

10 in); body diameter 0.79 m (2 ft 7 in); fin span 1.8 m (5 ft 11 in)
Warhead: nuclear up to 60 kT, chemical or conventional
Guidance: primitive inertial over pre-computed trajectory
Control: four jet vanes, four aerodynamic fins and timed airbrake deployment

Honest John Short-range tactical battlefield support missile

The **MGR-1 Honest John** missile first entered service in its **M31** form (subsequently **MGR-1A**) in 1953. In 1960 the improved **M50** (later **MGR-1B**) was introduced, and this served with most NATO countries until replaced by the Lance sys-

tem in the 1970s. The first eight US Army batteries were fully equipped in June 1954, making the Honest John the first US tactical nuclear weapon to enter front-line service.

The final NATO operators were Greece (three battal-

ions with 12 launchers) and Turkey (four battalions with a total of 18 launchers), which retained the weapon until the mid-1980s, as did South Korea (two battalions with a total of 12 launchers). Honest John also served with the armies of Belgium, Denmark, France, Italy, Japan, the Netherlands, the UK, the US and West Germany. France replaced Honest John with Pluton, while Denmark and Japan did not introduce any replacement system.

Launch vehicle

The highly-mobile Honest John was individually launched from a rail on its own six-wheeled truck launcher-transporter. At one stage, a lightweight launcher was used for underslung carriage by an H-37 Mojave

The Honest John-Nike-Nike was one of a number of experimental sounding rockets using a first stage based on the original artillery missile. A test launch for the Planetary Entry Parachute Program is seen at White Sands Missile Range, New Mexico, in October 1967.

A clumsy artillery rocket, Honest John was carried singly on a truck which had to be aimed at the target, range being determined by the elevation of the launch rail. The weapon could also be launched from a ground-mounted tripod.

helicopter, this was known as the **M33 Chopper John**. The Mach 1.5 missile was

powered by a solid-propellant motor and was unguided, being ballistically aimed at its target. The warhead was either a HE, chemical or variable-yield nuclear type. An alternative cluster munition warhead was also developed and was sold to South Korea in 1977. Both Greece and Turkey had access to NATO nuclear warheads for Honest John, although these were in American custody under a dual-key arrangement.

SPECIFICATION

MGR-1B Honest John
Propulsion: one 584-mm (23-in) solid-propellant motor
Performance: minimum range 7.2 km (4.5 miles); maximum range 37 km (23 miles); CEP 830 m (910 yards)
Weight: 2136 kg (4,710 lb)
Dimensions: length 7.57 m (24 ft

10 in); body diameter 0.76 m (2 ft 6 in)
Warhead: (weight) 680-kg (1,500-lb) nuclear or conventional, or 564-kg (1243-lb) chemical, (payload) 5- to 25-kT nuclear, HE, cluster munition or training
Guidance: none
Control: spin stabilised

CITEFA Model 77 155-mm howitzer

During the late 1970s, Argentina purchased a number of members of the AMX-13 family of light tracked vehicles from France as well as undertaking the assembly of a quantity of vehicles. These included the AMX-13 light tank armed with a 90-mm (3.54-in) gun, the AMX VCI armoured personnel carrier, and the 155-mm (6.1-in) Mk F3 self-propelled gun.

M114 replacement

At that time the standard 155-mm towed howitzer of the Argentine army was the American M114, which dated back to World War II and had a maximum range of 14600 m (15,967 yards). To replace the M114 the Instituto de Investigaciones Científicas y Tecnicas de las Fuerzas Armadas (CITEFA) designed a new bottom carriage that would take the complete top carriage (barrel, cradle, recoil system and equilibriators) of the Mk F3 self-propelled gun.

Following trials, this new weapon was accepted for service with the Argentine army under the designation **155-mm Howitzer L33 X1415 CITEFA Model 77**, L33 referring to the length of the ordnance in calibres and Model 77 to the year of acceptance. A later version, the **Model 81**, differs in minor details and also has a barrel of Argentine rather than French manufacture.

Falklands combat

Together with the OTO Melara 105-mm (4.13-in)

The CITEFA Model 77 155-mm (6.1-in) howitzer in travelling configuration with trails together. Under the rear part of the trails can be seen one of the small rubber-tyred road wheels that assist the crew in bringing the weapon into action.

In order to assist the crew in bringing the Model 77 into and out of action, an additional road wheel is mounted on each leg of the split-trail carriage.

Model 56 pack howitzer, the Model 77 was deployed to the Falklands where all of these equipments were subsequently captured by the British, some of them being shipped to the UK for trial and display purposes.

The barrel of the Model 77 is 5.115 m (16 ft 9.4 in) long, and is provided with a double-baffle muzzle brake and a screw breech mechanism. The top carriage is of welded steel construction and contains the traverse mechanism and elevating brackets. The former is mounted inside the lower part and forms the connection with the cradle trunnion attachment and the bottom carriage. The bottom carriage is of the split-trail type, and is also of welded construction. Each trail leg is provided with a small rubber-tyred road wheel, and at the end of each trail is a spade. When the equipment is in the firing position the carriage wheels are raised clear of the ground, support then being provided by a circular steel base attached to the carriage by a ball socket. When the equipment is being towed, the

A circular steel base plate fixed to the underside of the carriage supports the gun in the firing position; this helps to compensate for the effects of rough ground.

support is raised, giving ground clearance of 0.3 m (12 in). Maximum rate of fire is four rounds per minute, with a sustained rate of fire of one round per minute.

Ammunition types

The equipment fires an HE projectile weighing 43 kg (94.8 lb) with a maximum muzzle velocity of 765 m (2,510 ft) per second to a maximum range of 22000 m (24,059 yards); there are also illuminating and smoke projectiles. A rocket-assisted projectile is available, but as far as is known such a projectile was not used in the Falklands campaign.

SPECIFICATION	
Model 77	**Elevation:** +67°
Calibre: 155 mm (6.1 in)	**Traverse:** total 70°
Weight: travelling 8000 kg (17,637 lb)	**Maximum range:** with normal
Dimensions: (travelling) length	ammunition 22000 m (24,059 yards)
10.15 m (33 ft 3.6 in); width 2.67 m	and with rocket-assisted projectile
(8 ft 9 in); height 2.2 m (7 ft 2.6 in)	23300 m (25,481 yards)

GHN-45 155-mm gun/howitzer

In the 1970s PRB of Belgium, a well-known manufacturer of ammunition, and Space Research Corporation of Canada jointly established a company called SRC International with its headquarters in Brussels.

This company developed a gun/howitzer called the **GC-45**, of which 12 were subsequently ordered by the Royal Thai Marines, as well as a conversion kit for the 155-mm (6.1-in) M114 howitzer. The first two GC-45s were built in Canada while the remaining 10 were built in Canada but assembled in Austria by Voest-Alpine.

Austrian development

Further development by Voest-Alpine resulted in the **GHN-45** 155-mm (6.1-in) gun/howitzer, of which 200 were ordered by Jordan. Production of these weapons started in 1981, the first examples being delivered during the following year. Some of these weapons were transferred from Jordan to Iraq and used against Iran during the Gulf War in the 1980s. The original weapons supplied to Thailand were used in action on the Thai border against Kampuchea.

The basic version of the GHN-45 is normally towed by a standard 10-tonne 6x6 truck if required. A model fitted with an auxiliary power unit on the front of the carriage was also developed. This enables the weapon to propel itself on roads at a maximum speed of 35 km/h (22 mph), and the 80-litre (17.6-Imp gal) fuel tank provides a range of 150 km (93

miles). In normal practice the system is moved from one firing position to another by a truck with the ordnance traversed over the trails and locked in position to reduce its overall length, the APU then being used for final positioning and for bringing the weapon into and out of action.

The GHN-45 has a standard L/45 barrel fitted with a triple-baffle muzzle brake, and can fire a standard US M107 high-explosive projectile to a maximum range of 17800 m (19,466 yards) or an M101 projectile to a maximum range of 24000 m (26,247 yards). With the extended-range full-bore (ERFB) projectile manufactured by PRB, a range of

30000 m (32,808 yards) can be achieved, while the ERFB projectile with base bleed goes out to 39000 m (42,651 yards). With such long ranges, however, target acquisition and projectile dispersion are major problems.

Projectile options

The ERFB projectile, developed from the earlier extended-range sub-bore and extended-range sub-calibre projectiles, is longer and more streamlined than a conventional projectile, and therefore has reduced aerodynamic drag and thus increased range. The ERFB base-bleed is the basic projectile with a different 'boat' tail containing the base-bleed unit, which reduces

A Voest-Alpine GHN-45 155-mm (6.1-in) gun/howitzer in the travelling position with ordnance locked over the trails. This Austrian-produced weapon first saw service with the Jordanian army and was used with notable success by Iraq during its combat with Iran.

drag at the rear of the projectile, which thus decelerates more slowly, so increasing range. The basic HE ERFB projectile weighs 45.54 kg (100.4 lb), of which 8.62 kg (19 lb) is the

Composition B explosive. Other projectiles include smoke, illuminating, smoke base-ejection and a cargo round which can carry 13 kg (28.7 lb) of M42 grenades.

SPECIFICATION	
GHN-45	**Elevation:** +72°/-5°
Calibre: 155 mm (6.1 in)	**Traverse:** total 70°
Weight: 8900 kg (19,621 lb)	**Maximum range:** with ERFB
Dimensions: (travelling) length	ammunition 30000 m (32,808 yards)
9.068 m (29 ft 9 in); width 2.48 m	and with ERFB base-bleed
(8 ft 1.6 in); height 2.089 m (6 ft	ammunition 39000 m (42,651 yards)
10¼ in)	

Modern Chinese towed artillery Types 85, 59-1, 83, 66 and 89

For many years almost all of the towed artillery pieces used by China's People's Liberation Army (PLA) were copies of Soviet equipment: the 122-mm (4.8-in) **Type 85** towed howitzer was derived from the Soviet D-30

The Type 89 155-mm (6.1-in) gun/howitzer reflects a gradual move within the PLA from Soviet- to Western-standard calibres. The WAC-021 version illustrated is fitted with an APU to provide limited self-propelled mobility.

(M1963), while the 130-mm (5.12-in) **Type 59-1** field gun is a direct copy of the Soviet M-46 but mounted on a lightened carriage.

Using existing Soviet designs as a basis, China then developed more modern towed artillery. More recent types include the 152-mm (6-in) L/52 **Type 83** gun developed in the early 1980s and deployed in small numbers. The widely used 152-mm **Type 66** gun/howitzer is essentially a copy of the Soviet D-20, with a modified carriage and a much longer barrel.

Until recently, most of the PLA artillery was standardised around the established Soviet-standard calibres of 122 mm, 130 mm and 152 mm, but in recent years a move has been made to the widely deployed 155-mm (6.1-in) calibre.

To meet the requirements of the PLA and potential export customers, the 155-mm L/45 **Type 89**

towed gun/howitzer was developed, and was based on Western rather than Soviet technology.

This weapon is similar in appearance to the Austrian GHN-45 (technology relating to the European weapon was passed from Austria to China in the early 1980s) and the South African G5 155-mm L/45 systems. The Type 89 is marketed in the standard towed version or fitted with an auxiliary power unit that assists in bringing the weapon into action more quickly; the latter weapon is designated **WAC-021**. The **GM-45** uses the same armament combined with the two-wheeled carriage of the Type 59-1.

The Type 89's carriage is of the conventional split-trail type, and when deployed in the firing position the weapon is supported on its spades and a firing plate under the carriage.

A flick rammer is provided to increase the rate of fire and reduce fatigue to the gun crew, and a sustained rate of fire of two rounds per minute can be achieved by a well-trained crew. All types of 155-mm ammunition can be fired, including ERFB base-bleed rounds. A typical Type 89 company within the PLA comprises six gun/howitzers and one command and control vehicle with a computerised fire-control system.

SPECIFICATION	
Type 89	(8 ft 10 in); height 3.048 m (10 ft)
Calibre: 155 mm (6.1 in)	**Maximum range:** with HE
Weight: 9700 kg (21,384 lb)	ammunition 24000 m (26,247 yards)
Dimensions: (travelling) length	and with ERFB base-bleed
13.512 m (44 ft 4 in); width 2.69 m	ammunition 39000 m (42,651 yards)

TR 155-mm towed gun

While the UK, Italy and West Germany elected to develop a 155-mm (6.1-in) towed howitzer first (FH-70) and then a self-propelled model (SP-70), France decided to do the reverse. The 155-mm GCT self-propelled gun on an AMX-30 MBT chassis entered production for Saudi Arabia in 1977, first production vehicles being completed during the following year, but the type was not formally adopted by the French army until 1979. It was subsequently also ordered by Iraq.

The prototype of the **TR** 155-mm towed gun was revealed for the first time in 1979 and, following trials with eight prototypes, production started in 1989. The French army bought an initial batch of 105 systems to replace the older towed 155-mm modèle 50 howitzer.

Weapon design

The TR 155-mm towed gun has a barrel 6.2 m (20 ft 4 in) long, a double-baffle muzzle brake, a hydro-pneumatic recoil system and a horizontal-wedge breech mechanism. The carriage is of the split-trail type, with an auxiliary power unit located on the forward part. The 29-kW (39-hp) engine drives three hydraulic pumps, one for each of the main road wheels and the third to provide power for elevation, traverse, and raising the suspension, trail wheel jacks and projectile-loading mechanism. The APU enables the weapon to propel itself around the battery position or on the road at a maximum speed of 8 km/h (5 mph). When being towed or travelling under its own power, the TR 155-mm

gun has its barrel traversed 180° and locked in position over the closed trails. The projectile-loading system makes possible firing rates of three rounds in the first 18 seconds, six rounds per minute for the first two minutes and 120 rounds per hour thereafter. In the event of breakdown of the loading system manual loading is possible. In any Cold War European battlefield scenario such a weapon would have had to be redeployed in a very short time as its position would be quickly determined by the enemy, resulting in counter-battery fire.

Ammunition types

The TR 155-mm towed gun was designed to be able to use any standard NATO or French 155-mm round, and has been used to fire several types of ammunition: the older model 56/59 HE projectile to a range of 19250 m (21,050 yards), the more recent Cr TA 68 HE projectile weighing 43.2 kg (95.25 lb) to a range of 24000 m (26,245 yards), the 155-mm illuminating projectile (providing 800,000 candelas of light) to a range of 21500 m (22,515 yards), a smoke incendiary projectile to a range of 21300 m (23,295 yards), and a Brandt rocket-assisted projectile to a range of 30500 m

(33,355 yards). Other ammunition types fired include several cargo rounds, variously able to dispense six anti-tank mines or 63 anti-personnel bomblets. Most recently the weapon has been used to fire the Franco-Swedish BONUS round, jointly developed by GIAT and Bofors, which has entered service with the French and Swedish armies. BONUS carries a pair of anti-armour sensor-fused submunitions. These destroy hard and semi-hard targets by a 'top attack' on the target roof where the armour is thinnest.

The TR 155-mm gun has an eight-man crew, and is towed by the TRM 10000 (6x6) truck, which also carries 48 projectiles, charges and fuses and is equipped with a crane for handling artillery pallets. The TR can also be towed by other prime movers.

Right: The TR 155-mm gun has an auxiliary power unit on the front of the carriage. This not only provides the power required to propel the weapon around on its own, but also to bring the weapon into and out of action as well as running the projectile loading mechanism.

A TR 155-mm gun in the firing position during Desert Storm. The French army took delivery of its TR systems to replace the 155-mm Modèle 50 howitzer, which had been in service for 30 years.

SPECIFICATION	
TR	1.65 m (5 ft 5 in)
Calibre: 155 mm (6.1 in)	**Elevation:** +65°/-5°
Weight: travelling and firing 10650 kg (23,479 lb)	**Traverse:** total 65°
Dimensions: length, travelling 8.25 m (27 ft ¾ in); width, travelling 3.09 m (10 ft 1½ in); height, firing	**Maximum range:** with standard projectile 24000 m (26,245 yards) and with rocket-assisted projectile 30500 m (33,355 yards)

Soltam M-68 and M-71 155-mm gun/howitzers

The only manufacturer of towed artillery in Israel is Soltam. The **M-68** 155-mm (6.1-in) gun/howitzer was developed as a private venture in the late 1960s, the first prototype being completed in 1968 and the first production models following two years later. As far as is known, the towed model is used only by Singapore and the Thai Marines, although the Soltam L-33 self-propelled gun/howitzer uses the ordnance, elevation and traverse system of the M-68. The L-33 entered service with the Israeli army in time to take part in the 1973

The Soltam M-68 155-mm gun/howitzer in the travelling position with ordnance traversed to the rear and locked in position over the trails. The Israeli army has used this weapon mounted on a rebuilt Sherman tank chassis in the self-propelled role.

Above: The Soltam M-68 155-mm gun/howitzer in travelling configuration, being towed by a truck. Over the last 30 years, the M-68 has provided the basis for several generations of improved guns.

Above: The 155-mm M-68 gun/howitzer in the firing position with trails firmly staked into the ground. The split-trail carriage was unusual for its time, having four rubber-tyred road wheels, each of which has a hydraulic brake operated from the towing vehicle.

Middle East campaign.

The ordnance of the M-68 is 5.18 m (17 ft) long and is fitted with a single-baffle muzzle brake, fume extractor and a horizontal breech mechanism. The recoil system is below the barrel and the counter-recoil system above, the pneumatic equilibrators being located on the sides of the barrel. When travelling, the top carriage is traversed to the rear so that the ordnance is over the closed trails. The carriage is of the split-trail type. Two rubber-tyred road wheels are mounted on each

side; each wheel is fitted with a hydraulic brake, and a maximum towing speed of 100 km/h (62 mph) is thus possible. When in the firing position the carriage is supported by a screw-type firing jack. Four spades are carried, one of these being attached to the end of each trail for firing when the weapon is brought into action. The other two are carried to enable the eight-man crew to change direction and open fire again without taking out the original spades.

Projectiles

The M-68 fires a standard NATO HE projectile weighing 43.7 kg (96.3 lb) to a maximum range of 21000 m (22,965 yards), as well as smoke and illuminating projectiles. The weapon can also fire Soltam-designed projectiles with a higher muzzle velocity (820 m/2,690 ft per second compared with 725 m/2,380 ft per second) to a maximum range of 23500 m

(25,700 yards).

The Soltam M-68 is no longer in volume production, although it could be placed back in production if sufficient numbers were ordered. It was followed by the **M-71** howitzer, which uses the same carriage, breech and recoil system as the M-68 but is fitted with a longer L/39 barrel. Mounted on the right trail of the M-71 is a rammer powered by a compressed air cylinder, enabling the weapon to be loaded at all angles of elevation and so making possible a short-period fire rate of four rounds per minute. The M-71 is known to be service with the Israeli army, and fires an HE projectile to a maximum range of 23500 m (25,700 yards).

For trials purposes one M-71 has been fitted with an auxiliary power unit on the left trail and an ammunition handling crane on the right trail. The APU enables this weapon, called the **Model 839P**, to travel on roads at a maximum speed of 17 km/h (10.6 mph). The product-improved **Model 945** has in turn been superceded by the new 155-mm **TIG** gun/howitzer, which is air-transportable in the C-130 and has barrels of 39, 45 or 52 calibres. These can easily be replaced in the field.

SPECIFICATION	
Soltam M-68	2.58 m (8 ft 5½ in); height,
Calibre: 155 mm (6.1 in)	travelling 2 m (6 ft 6¾ in)
Weight: travelling 9500 kg	**Elevation:** +52°/-5°
(20,944 lb) and firing 8500 kg	**Traverse:** total 90°
(18,739 lb)	**Maximum range:** standard HE
Dimensions: length, travelling	projectile 21000 m (22,965 yards)
7.2 m (23 ft 7½ in); width, travelling	

FH2000 155-mm gun/howitzer artillery system

The 155-mm (6.1-in) **FH2000** towed gun/howitzer was developed in Singapore from the earlier 155-mm FH-88 howitzer, the first example appearing during early 1990. The FH2000 differs from the the earlier weapon in that the barrel of the FH-88 is 39 calibres long, while that of the FH2000 is 52 calibres long to provide greater range. FH2000 development lasted until late 1992 and by mid-1995 the Singapore defence forces had 18 examples in service. This was a remarkable performance by a small city state, for those FH2000s were the first 52-calibre artillery equipments, towed or self-propelled, to enter service anywhere in the world. As far as is known the FH2000 has not yet been exported.

In most other respects, the FH-88 and FH2000 are similar overall, although the FH2000 has been elevated in status to an artillery system with items such as matched projectiles being manufactured locally. The system is manufactured by Singapore Technologies Kinetics (STK) who also manufacture the ammunition.

The L/52 barrel provides a maximum possible range of 40000 m (131,234 ft) using an advanced Extended Range, Full Bore, Base Bleed

The FH2000 was the first in-service gun with a long 52-calibre barrel, which is rapidly becoming a common feature on modern long-range artillery. An electronically-controlled rammer ensures a high rate of fire and can operate in four modes: automatic, automatic back-up, electric manual and hydraulic manual.

(ERFB-BB) projectile. The range using a standard M107 HE projectile is 19000 m (62,336 ft). The ERFB-BB projectile weighs approximately 46.7 kg (103 lb) and contains a nominal 8 kg (17.63 lb) of TNT, the high-quality steel body providing enhanced fragmentation effects. Also available, apart from similar smoke and incendiary projectiles, is an

ERFB-BB cargo round carrying 64 dual-purpose bomblets. The cargo projectile and its contents were designed in Singapore and it has entered service.

The FH2000 carriage includes a 53-kW (71-hp) auxiliary power unit (APU) which provides the system with a degree of self-propulsion around the firing area as well as providing

hydraulic power for lowering the firing platform and opening and closing the split-trail

legs. Time in and out of action can be as low as two minutes.

SPECIFICATION	
FH2000	travelling 2.80 m (9 ft 5 in); height,
Calibre: 155 mm (6.1 in)	(with display unit) 2.55 m (8 ft ½ in)
Weight: travelling 13500 kg	**Elevation:** +70°/-3°
(29,762 lb)	**Traverse:** 30° each side
Dimensions: length, travelling	**Maximum range:** ERFB-BB
10.95 m (35 ft 9 in); width,	projectile 40000 m (131,234 ft)

FH-70 155-mm Towed howitzer

This FH-70 155-mm howitzer is illustrated as it would appear in firing position. The weapon fires a standard high-explosive projectile out to a maximum range of 24 km (15 miles).

In 1968 a Memorandum of Understanding (MoU) was signed between the UK and West Germany for the joint development of a 155-mm (6-in) howitzer which would replace the British 5.5-in gun and the American-supplied M114 155-mm howitzer.

The main requirements the new weapon had to meet included a high rate of fire with a burst fire capability, increased range and lethality together with a new family of ammunition, high mobility and a minimum of effort for deployment.

The UK was team leader for this weapon, which became known as the FH-70, while West Germany became team leader for the abortive self-propelled equivalent, the SP-70.

Italian partner

Nineteen prototypes of the FH-70 were built, and in 1970 Italy joined the project as a full partner. In 1976 the FH-70 was accepted for ser-

vice, the first production weapons being completed in 1978. Production lines were established in all three countries. The UK ordered 71 equipments, West Germany 216 and Italy 164. The weapon entered service with Saudi Arabia, and has been manufactured under licence in Japan for the Ground Self Defence Force.

The 6.02-m (19-ft 9-in) long barrel of the FH-70 has a double-baffle muzzle brake and a semi-automatic wedge-type breech mechanism. The carriage of the FH-70 is of the split-trail type, with an auxiliary power unit mounted on the forward part. This enables the FH-70 to propel itself on roads and across country at a maximum speed of 16 km/h (10 mph).

In addition the APU provides power for steering, and for raising and lowering the main and trail wheels. When travelling, the ordnance is traversed to the rear and locked in position over the closed trails.

To achieve the requirement for burst-fire a semi-automatic loading system is fitted, and this operates at all angles of ele-

vation. The loading system includes a loading tray that presents the projectile to the chamber. A burst rate of three rounds in 13 seconds can be achieved, while the normal sustained rate of fire is six rounds per minute.

Ammunition

The FH-70 has been cleared to fire most NATO standard 155-mm ammunition, includ-

ing guided and extended-range rocket-assisted, but generally is limited to three main types: HE with a weight of 43.50 kg (96 lb) smoke (base ejection), and illuminating. The last provides one million candelas for one minute.

The FH-70 has an eight-person crew. It is usually towed into action by a 6x6 truck.

SPECIFICATION

FH-70 field howitzer
Calibre: 155 mm (6 in)
Weight: travelling and firing 9300 kg (20,503 lb)
Dimensions: length, travelling 9.80 m (32 ft 1¾ in); width, travelling 2.20 m (7 ft 2¾ in); height,

travelling 2.56 m (8 ft 4¾ in)
Elevation: +70°/-3°
Traverse: total 56°
Maximum range: with standard round 24 km (15 miles) and with rocket-assisted projectile 30000 m (32,810 yards)

In addition to its original developers in Britain (illustrated), Germany and Italy, the FH-70 is used by the Saudi Arabian army and the Japanese GSDF.

Bofors FH-77 155-mm Towed howitzer

The Bofors FH-77A 155-mm field howitzer in travelling position. The auxiliary power unit mounted in the front of the gun carriage enables the gun crew to move the ordnance into position or to change positions easily and rapidly.

In the late 1960s the Swedish army carried out a series of studies to determine its future artillery requirements. It decided to develop a new 155-mm (6-in) towed weapon that would have superior cross-country performance, a high rate of fire, and a good range with more effective ammunition. At that time Bofors was building the 155-mm (6-in) Bandkanon 1A self-propelled gun, which is fully armoured and has a high rate of fire as it is fitted with an automatic loader for 16 rounds of ready-use ammunition. Its main drawback, however,

was, and is, its size and weight (53 tonnes), which limit its movement in certain parts of Sweden as well as making it difficult to conceal.

Bofors was awarded the development contract for the new towed weapon, which subsequently became known as the **FH-77A**

155-mm field howitzer, for which the first orders were placed by the Swedish army in 1975.

The FH-77A has a barrel 5.89 m (19 ft 4 in) long, fitted with a pepperpot muzzle brake and a vertical sliding breech mechanism. The split-trail carriage has an aux-

iliary power unit mounted on the front, enabling the FH-77A to propel itself on roads and across country. The equipment is normally towed by a Saab-Scania (6x6) truck, which also carries ammunition in pallets and the six man crew consisting of commander, gunner, two

ammunition handlers, loader and crane handler.

Cross-country

When the truck and the FH-77A encounter very rough country the main wheels of the howitzer can be engaged from the cab of the truck, so giving an 8x8 combination at a maximum speed of 8 km/h (5 mph). When this speed is exceeded the main wheels of the FH-77A are disengaged automatically.

Elevation and traverse of the FH-77A is hydraulic, though manual controls are provided for emergency use. Mounted on the right side of the FH-77A is the loading tray, on which clips of three projectiles can be placed.

A typical firing sequence is that the cartridge case is placed on the loading tray followed by the projectile, which is fed from the loading table. When the projectile has slipped down into the neck of the cartridge case the projectile and charge are rammed, the breech is closed and the weapon is fired. Three rounds can be fired in six to eight seconds, though normal sustained fire is six rounds fired every other minute for 20 minutes.

The Bofors-developed NY77 projectile weighs 42.40 kg (93½ lb), has a muzzle velocity of 774 m (2,540 ft) per second and goes out to a maximum range of 22 km (14 miles). It is believed that Bofors is currently developing a base-bleed projectile which will have a maximum range of between 27 and 30 km (17 and 19 miles).

Export guns

Bofors developed the **FH-77B** for export, with a longer barrel, increased elevation of +70°, mechanised loading system and a number of other major improvements. The FH-77B has been supplied to Nigeria, India and others, though the Indian order for 410 units was tainted by a major bribery scandal.

To meet the requirements of the Swedish coastal artillery, Bofors has developed the **CD80**, essentially the carriage of the FH-77A fitted with a 120-mm (4.72-in) ordnance.

SPECIFICATION

Bofors FH-77A field howitzer
Calibre: 155 mm (6 in)
Weight:: travelling 11500 kg (25,353 lb)
Dimensions: length, travelling 11.60 m (38 ft ¼ in); width, travelling 2.64 m (8 ft 8 in); height, travelling 2.75 m (9 ft ¼ in)
Elevation: +50°/+3°
Traverse: total 50°
Maximum range: 20 km (14 miles)

Armscor G5 155-mm Towed gun/howitzer

Inspired by the eccentric but supremely capable artillery designer Gerald Bull, the G5 incorporated features from several different artillery pieces. The result outperformed all of its progenitors, proving to be one of the longest-ranged and most accurate 155-mm weapons ever built and sent into action.

For many years after World War II, the mainstays of South African field artillery units were the British 5.5-in (140-mm) medium gun with a maximum range of 16.46 km (10 miles) and the 25-pdr (88-mm) field gun with a maximum range of 12.25 km (8 miles).

Outranged

During operations in Angola the South Africans found themselves outranged by Soviet-supplied artillery and rockets. This led to the development of two indigenous systems, since at that time no Western country would supply South Africa with the arms it required.

The **G5 155-mm gun/howitzer** and the 127-mm (5-in) 24-round multiple rocket system were developed and put into production in time to have seen combat during raids into Angola.

The G5 owes much to the Canadian Space Research Corporation GC 45 155-mm (6-in) weapon. However, so many additional features have been incorporated into the G5 that it is in essence a completely new weapon.

The G5 has a 45-calibre barrel fitted with a single-baffle muzzle brake and an interrupted-thread breech mechanism. To the rear of the breech is a pneumatically operated rammer to ram projectiles into the chamber at all angles of elevation; this is powered by an air bottle mounted on the right trail. The bagged charges are loaded by hand.

On the forward part of the split trail carriage is the auxiliary power unit, which consists of a 51-kW (68-hp) diesel engine. In addition to providing power to the main driving wheels, the APU also supplies power for raising and lowering the circular firing platform under the carriage, for opening and closing the trails, and for raising and lowering the trail wheels. To reduce the overall length of the G5 for travelling, the ordnance is normally traversed through 180° and locked in position over the trails.

Rate of fire

The ordnance has a total traverse of 84° below 15° of elevation, and 65° above that. Maximum rate of fire over a 15-minute period is three rounds per minute, with two rounds per minute possible in the sustained fire role. The G5 is operated by an eight-person crew.

The G5 can fire five types of ammunition, also manufactured in South Africa. The standard HE projectile weighs 45.50 kg (100 lb), and is of the Extended-Range Full Bore (ERFB) type. The HE base-bleed (HE BB) type is slightly heavier because of the base-bleed attachment, but has a range of 37000 m (40,465 yards) at sea level, though greater ranges are attained when the G5 is fired at altitude. The other three projectiles are illuminating, smoke and white phosphorus.

To operate with the G5, South Africa developed a complete fire-control system including a muzzle-velocity measuring device, AS 80 artillery fire-control system with a 16-bit minicomputer, S700 meteorological ground station and a complete range of communications equipment. South Africa has also developed a 155-mm (6-in) self-propelled 6x6 howitzer called the **G6**, which has an ordnance based on the G5 weapon and uses the same ammunition.

In addition to South Africa, the G5 has been sold to at least four other armies. Saddam Hussein's Iraq used the type during the occupation of Kuwait in 1990, but most were destroyed in the Gulf War which followed.

SPECIFICATION

G5 gun/howitzer
Calibre: 155 mm (6 in)
Weight: travelling 13500 kg (29,762 lb)
Dimensions: length, travelling 9.10 m (29 ft 10¼ in); width, travelling 2.50 m (8 ft 2½ in); height, travelling 2.30 m (7 ft 6½ in)
Elevation: +73°/-3°
Traverse: total 84° (but see text)
Maximum range: with standard ammunition over 30000 m (32,810 yards) and with base-bleed projectile 37000 m (40,465 yards

The G5 was designed to be towed into action behind a SAMIL 100 6x6 10-tonne truck. The vehicle also carries the gun crew and the weapon's ammunition.

105-mm L118 Light Gun

The Royal Ordnance 105-mm (4.13-in) Light Gun was designed in the later 1960s as successor to the OTO-Melara Pack Howitzer of the same calibre, and was accepted for service in 1973. Since that time the weapon has been used successfully in action, and more than 1,000 such weapons have been delivered to the UK and export customers, including Australia and the US among a total of 19 operators.

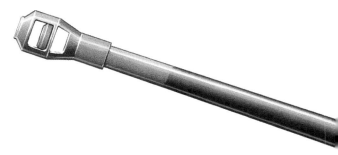

Land Rover tractor

The L118A1 Light Gun weighs 1860 kg (4,100 lb) in travelling order, and to tow this useful piece of what is now in effect light artillery, the British Army opted for the 1-tonne Land Rover, a 4x4 vehicle able to tow the Light Gun and also carry its crew and some ready-use ammunition. Powered by a Rover V-8 petrol engine delivering 95 kW (128 bhp), the Land Rover has a maximum road speed of 120 km/h (74 mph) and carries two personnel (driver and one passenger) in the cab as well as eight crew in its rear (four on each of two bench seats along the sides) under the weather protection afforded by a canvas tilt. In the illustration below, the Light Gun is seen in its long-distance towing position, with the barrel rotated through 180° and clamped to the trail. This is achieved in a one-minute process: the equipment is jacked up (using a jack stowed on the trail), the quick-release wheel and traverse gear pin are removed, the barrel is clamped and the wheel is replaced.

Firing platform

A circular unit of lightweight construction, the Light Gun's firing platform provides a firm base and a high level of gun stability under all operating conditions. The tyres of the gun's carriage run round the outer edge of the platform, providing for rapid changes of gross azimuth, and the platform is connected to the underside of the gun by an assembly of four wire stays.

Elevating mass

The elevating mass of the Light Gun comprises the ordnance (complete with a multi-baffle muzzle brake that can easily be removed for cleaning), recoil system, cradle with trunnions, balancing gear and electrical firing system. The breech is based on a vertical sliding breech block actuated by a lever mounted at the top. Mounted on a lightweight fabricated cradle, the recoil system is of the hydro-pneumatic type with a separate recuperator, and the buffer is fitted with a cut-off to shorten the recoil as the ordnance's elevation is increased.

Major elements

The major elements of the Light Gun, seen to the left in firing position, are the elevating mass, the saddle and controls, the trail and spades, the platform, the suspension and the sighting system. The Light Gun has the same weight in firing position as in travelling order, and its overall length in firing position at 0° elevation is 7.01 m (23 ft). Indirect and direct sights are fitted, these being used by the layer while seated. Indirect sighting was simplified by the omission of a separate setting for angle of sight. The quadrant elevation is set on the elevation scale. Direct fire is undertaken with the aid of a telescopic sight incorporating a moving illuminated graticule adjustable for lead when firing at longer ranges against a moving target. There is also a direct-fire night sight, and all scales and graticules are illuminated by Trilux activated light sources, removing the need for onboard electrical batteries.

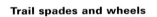

Trail spades and wheels

The trail of the Light Gun carries any of three different types of spade (combined rock and digger spade for use on firm ground, field spade for use on soft ground, and snow spade for use in Arctic conditions). The wheels have large-section 9.00x16 tyres and incorporate hydraulically-operated overrun brakes for safe high-speed towing by light vehicles.

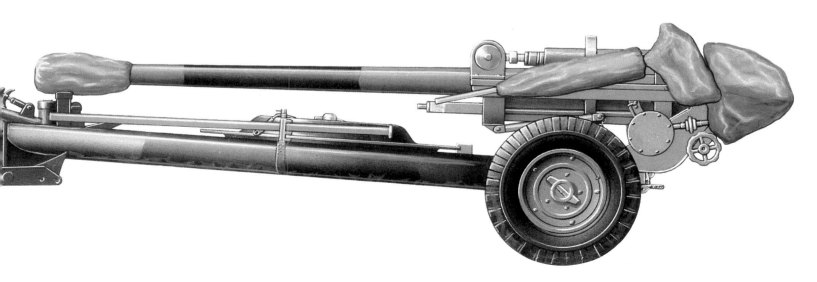

Artillery in the Falklands

The Light Guns of the five Royal Artillery batteries deployed during the 1982 Falklands campaign played a major role, completely outranging and outshooting the Argentine 105-mm Pack Howitzers.

The artillery battle of the Falklands campaign of 1982 was fought between the flexible and co-ordinated firepower of five Royal Artillery batteries of 4.13-in (105-mm) Light Guns, supported by the 4.5-in (114-mm) guns of Royal Navy ships, and an Argentine force of five six-gun batteries of 105-mm OTO-Melara modello 56 105-mm pack howitzers and a single four-gun battery of 6.1-in (155-mm) CITEFA modello 77 howitzers.

Included in the San Carlos landings of 21 May were the three six-gun batteries of the 29th Commando Regiment, Royal Artillery, and one battery of the 4th Field Regiment with their L118A1 Light Guns. A further battery and regimental HQ of the 4th Field Regiment was landed at the beginning of June. The first battery in action was the 8th (Alma) Commando Battery of the 29th Commando Regiment, which initially used three of its guns from a position established at Camilla Creek House in support of the 2nd Battalion, The Parachute Regiment, during the latter's actions at Darwin and Goose Green; the other three guns were brought forward by helicopter on the morning of 29 May for the final attack. Throughout the battle the Argentines harassed the attackers with a group of four pack howitzers and six 120-mm (4.72-in) mortars from the garrison at Port Stanley, but most of their rounds failed to explode in the soft ground.

Difficult movement

With the way cleared, the advance to Port Stanley began. The sinking of the Atlantic Conveyor removed three-quarters of the Chinook heavy-lift helicopter force to lift the ammunition supplies for the batteries, leaving only one Chinook and a number of Sea King medium-lift helicopters for the purpose.

Once the area of Mount Kent had been secured on the night of 30 May, the Light Gun batteries were brought forward and emplaced in built-up earth revetments on flat terrain, gunpits being impractical because of the boggy ground. The ground was so soft that the guns tended to sink in during prolonged firing, so after only a very few rounds the gunners had to drag the gun out and re-bed it. This, in combination with the humping of projectiles from the distant points where the helicopters had dropped the ammunition pallets to the immediate-use ammunition dumps and then to the guns themselves, added considerably to gun crew fatigue.

Within range of Port Stanley

During the attacks on 11/12 June against Mount Longdon, Two Sisters and Mount Harriet, the British forces very often found themselves following close behind the supporting fire from the artillery and naval guns. They also found themselves under considerable enemy fire from the Argentine guns in and around Port Stanley. Both the 2nd and 3rd Battalions, The Parachute Regiment, received a large number of ground- and air-burst shells from the 155-mm howitzers.

A Royal Navy Sea King lifts a 105-mm Light Gun from ship to shore. The difficult terrain on the Falklands meant that artillery and ammunition had to be helicopter-portable to be of any use.

For the final assault on 13 June against Tumbledown, Wireless Ridge and Mount William the British fired over 6,000 rounds in something like 12 hours. Although once again under accurate counter-battery fire, the Argentine artillery replied to this barrage.

As the Argentines fell back, it was the Light Guns that helped to break up the only counter-attack attempted during the whole war, when a platoon-sized force attempted to assault the positions held by the 2nd Battalion, The Parachute Regiment. The artillery also engaged the retreating Argentine forces until they surrendered. The surviving Argentine artillery pieces were then claimed as war trophies and a number of them, including examples of the modello 77 howitzer, were sent back to the UK.

Mortar support

Although much of the artillery support had been supplied by the Royal Artillery and Royal Navy, the infantry had been able to provide some of its own support in the form of mortar fire. Each of the Royal Marine Commandos and army battalions had an integral mortar unit with six 81-mm (3.2-in) L16A1 mortars with maximum and minimum ranges of 5650 and 180 m (6,180 and 195 yards) respectively, firing 4.47-kg (9.85-lb) high explosive, white phosphorus, smoke and illuminating bombs. The lack of extensive helicopter or suitable vehicle transport meant that these weapons had to be man-packed across East Falkland together with first-line ammunition and, moreover, they had to be dug out of the ground every so often as recoil forces forced them into the soft soil. To alleviate this problem a simple device, called the Raschen Bag after its inventor, was used. This was simply a canvas bag filled with whatever soil, stones or other suitable material was to hand, and placed under the baseplate to spread the recoil forces over a much wider area, thus reducing the sinking rate.

This Italian OTO-Melara modello 56 105-mm pack howitzer was captured by the British in the 1982 Falklands campaign. The Argentines deployed five six-gun batteries of these weapons to the islands, together with four 155-mm howitzers.

105-mm Light Gun

Lightweight fire support

The 105-mm Light Gun is ideally suited for the support of mobile forces operating in many types of third-world conditions: rugged and reliable, it can provide modest fire support over tactically useful ranges.

Though its projectiles lack the range and explosive effect of the shells fired by larger-calibre weapons, the British 105-mm (4.13-in) L118A1 Light Gun is a very useful weapon for forces operating in adverse conditions (especially soft terrain of any sort) and without the support of heavier vehicles, including both trucks and helicopters, for the movement of the guns and their ammunition.

L118A1 Light Gun

1 Barrel
2 Breech ring
3 Breech block: an electric firing needle assembly (3a) within the breech block completes a contact when the breech is closed
4 Firing mechanism: actuated by the firing lever (4a)
5 Electric contact in breech block
6 Breech mechanism lever lowers and raises the breech block as required. Opening breech breaks mechanical lock, retracts electrical firing needle, lowers breech block, engages extractor levers (not shown) and pulls spent case from breech
7 Cradle, in which barrel assembly slides, providing anchorage for the recoil system. This consists of hydraulic recoil buffer (7a) and compensating cylinders, and a hydro-pneumatic recuperator (7b) with its air reservoir (7c), which returns the barrel to its starting point after firing
8 Saddle-pintle mounted allowing 5° traverse left and right
9 Trail assembly
10 Traversing wheel
11 Elevating gears
12 Torsion-bar suspension
13 Suspension arm
14 Damper

15 Brake drum
16 Balancing gear
17 'A' frame (supports front end of cradle when towing in firing position)
18 Wire ropes (secure suspension to firing platform)
19 Firing platform (enables 360° traverse on wheels)
20 Gun layer's seat (sights are fitted to the left side of the saddle)
21 Separate-loading ammunition (comprises direct action and graze fuse)
22 HE shell containing exploder (22a), main filling (22b), and driving band which engages rifling in the barrel (22c)
23 Normal propellant charge containing colour-coded propelling charge increments and an electric primer (fired by the electric firing needle in the breech block). A fibre holder (23b) is used to hold an extra increment of charge

Left: Designed by the Royal Armament Research and Development Establishment at Fort Halstead in Kent, the Light Gun was manufactured by Royal Ordnance Nottingham, later taken over by British Aerospace (now BAE Systems). Deliveries for British use totalled 168 guns including a number of reserve and training weapons; total production amounts to over 400 for the home and export markets. The weapon is pictured in the firing position: the 105-mm Light Gun has among the longest range of any weapon of its type.

Below: A 105-mm (4.13-in) L118A1 Light Gun of the British Army is caught by the camera during an exercise in Norway. Part of the UK's NATO commitment is to the defence of northern Norway, where light and mobile artillery is a major asset.

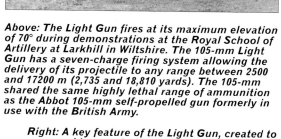

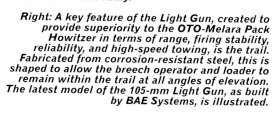

Above: The Light Gun fires at its maximum elevation of 70° during demonstrations at the Royal School of Artillery at Larkhill in Wiltshire. The 105-mm Light Gun has a seven-charge firing system allowing the delivery of its projectile to any range between 2500 and 17200 m (2,735 and 18,810 yards). The 105-mm shared the same highly lethal range of ammunition as the Abbot 105-mm self-propelled gun formerly in use with the British Army.

Right: A key feature of the Light Gun, created to provide superiority to the OTO-Melara Pack Howitzer in terms of range, firing stability, reliability, and high-speed towing, is the trail. Fabricated from corrosion-resistant steel, this is shaped to allow the breech operator and loader to remain within the trail at all angles of elevation. The latest model of the 105-mm Light Gun, as built by BAE Systems, is illustrated.

SPECIFICATION

105-mm L118 Light Gun

Barrel

Calibre: 105 mm (4.13 in)
Length: 3.175 m (10 ft 5 in)

Muzzle brake

Double baffle

Recoil system

Hydro-pneumatic type
Recoil length: 1.07 m (42.125 in) at 0° and 0.33 m (13 in) at 70°

Breech

Vertical sliding type

Weights

In travelling and firing orders: 1860 kg (4,100 lb)
Elevating mass: 1066 kg (2,350 lb)

Dimensions

Length travelling with gun forward: 6.629 m (21 ft 9 in)
Length travelling with gun over trail: 4.876 m (16 ft)
Length firing with ordnance at 0°: 7.01 m (23 ft)

Width 1.778 m (5 ft 10 in)
Height travelling with gun forward 2.63 m (8 ft 2 in)
Height travelling with gun over trail 1.371 m (4 ft 6 in)
Ground clearance 0.5 m (19.75 in)
Track 1.4 m (4 ft 7 in)

Elevation

-5.5° to +70°

Traverse

Total on carriage: 11°
Total of platform: 360°

Rate of fire

12 rounds per minute for 1 minute
6 rounds per minute for 3 minutes
3 rounds per minute sustained

Range

Minimum: 2500 m (2,735 yards)
Maximum: 17200 m (18,810 yards)

Projectile types

16.1-kg (35.5-lb) L31 HE, 10.49-kg (23.125-lb) L42 HESH, 15.88-kg (35-lb) L37, L38 and L45 Smoke, and L43 Illuminating

Above: A 1-tonne Land Rover moves off towing an L118A1 Light Gun, in this instance with its elevating mass in the firing position rather than rotated through 180° back over the trail. With the gun crew and some ready-use ammunition carried in the Land Rover, the combination is well optimised for 'shoot and scoot' tactics.

Left: Royal Artillery 105-mm Light Guns in action at the Royal School of Artillery, Larkhill, Wiltshire. In addition to being used by the Royal Artillery, the Light Gun has also seen service with many overseas countries, including Australia (where it has been built under licence), Brunei, Ireland, Kenya, Malawi, Oman and the United Arab Emirates.

Below: A Light Gun in action. With weight reduction paramount in the design of this weapon, features such as a gun shield were omitted even though this leaves the crew somewhat vulnerable to shell splinters. The Light Gun has a limited but adequate number of projectile types, and adequate minimum and maximum ranges.

M198 155-mm towed howitzer

The M198 155-mm (6.1-in) howitzer is seen in one of its two travelling configurations. This is now the standard 155-mm howitzer of the US Army and Marines, and replaced the old 155-mm M114. The gun has been the subject of a Product Improvement Program to ensure its viability into the 21st century.

For many years the standard 155-mm (6.1-in) towed howitzer of the US Army was the M114. This had been developed in the 1930s and, by the end of World War II, some 6,000 had been built. Like the 105-mm (4.13-in) M101 towed howitzer, the M114 suffered the major drawback of having limited range and traverse capabilities. Following the issue of a formal requirement for a new 155-mm howitzer, Rock Island Arsenal started design work in 1968, its first development prototype being completed two years later.

Prototype weapons

A total of 10 prototypes were built under the designation **XM198** and, after trials and the usual modifications, the new howitzer was adopted for service as the **M198**. Production started at Rock Island Arsenal in 1978, with the first battalion of 18 M198 howitzers forming at Fort Bragg in the following year. Each battalion has three batteries each with six M198s. In addition to being used by the US Army and US Marine Corps, the M198

was also ordered by Australia (an initial batch of 36 to replace the British 5.5-in gun) and a number of other countries, notably in the Middle East.

Air mobility

In the US Army and US Marine Corps the M198 is towed by a 5-ton 6x6 truck which also carries the ammunition and nine-man crew, although the weapon can be towed by a variety of other tracked and wheeled vehicles. It is air portable, and can be carried slung underneath US Army CH-47C Chinook and US Marine Corps CH-53E Super Stallion helicopters.

The M198 is normally issued to US infantry, airborne and air assault divisions, while mechanised infantry and armoured divisions have the 155-mm M109 self-propelled howitzer. The M198 was first used operationally by the US Marines in Lebanon in 1983.

Principal parts

The main components of the M198 are the carriage, recoil system, fire-control equipment and cannon (or

ordnance, as the British prefer to call it). The carriage is of the split-trail type and fitted with a two-position rigid suspension. When the weapon is in the firing position, a firing platform is lowered to the ground under the forward part of the carriage and the wheels are raised clear of the ground. The cradle has the elevation and traverse system, while the top carriage has the assembly cradle, equilibrators and recoil guides. The recoil mechanism is of the hydro-pneumatic type with a variable recoil length. The M199 cannon has a double-baffle muzzle brake, thermal warning device and a screw-type breech mechanism. The fire-control equipment includes an M137 panoramic telescope, two elevation quadrants, and an M138 elbow telescope.

Travelling position

When in the travelling position the ordnance is normally traversed to the rear and locked in position over the trails. Unlike most modern European 155-mm towed guns (including the multi-national FH-70, the

French TR and the Swedish FH-77), the M198 does not have an auxiliary power unit to enable it to be moved under its own power. The M198 can fire all types of current US/NATO 155-mm separate-loading ammunition, including anti-tank (carrying mines),

Copperhead laser-guided, high explosive, high explosive with various grenades (including dual-purpose and anti-personnel), rocket-assisted, illuminating and smoke projectiles and also, before the end of the Cold War, tactical nuclear and chemical agent projectiles.

Above: This M198 howitzer is in firing position with its firing crew in attendance. A crew of nine is required to fire the weapon. The M198 has been used operationally in both Lebanon and the Middle East.

A laser-guided projectile departs the barrel of an M198 howitzer during a firing exercise at the White Sands Missile Range in New Mexico. These shells are designed to hit either stationary or moving targets with a single round.

SPECIFICATION	
M198	
Calibre: 155 mm (6.1 in)	**Elevation:** -5° to +72°
Weight: travelling and firing 7163 kg (15,790 lb)	**Traverse:** total 45°
Dimensions: (travelling) length 12.34 m (40 ft 6 in); width 2.794 m (9 ft 2 in); height 2.9 m (9 ft 6 in)	**Maximum range:** with M107 projectile 18150 m (19,850 yards) and with M549A1 rocket-assisted projectile 30000 m (32,810 yards)

Above: This M198 is seen in the static fire position, with sand bags providing a measure of protection. The weapon has been sold to a number of other operators including Australia and some Middle Eastern armies.

Modern US towed artillery M777 and M119A1 howitzers

Three separate trends can be detected on the current US towed artillery scene, although one of them is not, in fact, towed. Two of the trends can be seen in the introduction into service of the 155-mm (6.1-in) **M777 Joint Lightweight Howitzer** and the retention of the 105-mm (4.13-in) **M119A1 Lightweight Towed Howitzer**, which was at one time scheduled to be phased out of service. The third trend is associated with the M777, as it is the adoption of a lightweight artillery system to augment the fire of the M777. This system is known as the High Mobility Artillery Rocket System (HIMARS), and is in essence one six-rocket pod in place of the two normally used by the Multiple Launch Rocket System (MLRS). To reduce weight for air transport, the HIMARS is carried on a 6x6 truck chassis.

US Army troops are seen on exercise somewhere in Europe with their 105-mm (4.13-in) M119A1 Lightweight Towed Howitzer. This weapon has been reprieved from retirement and is to receive a series of new extended-range projectiles.

Upgrade programme

At one time it was scheduled that the US Army's M119A1 (which is a US version of the British Royal Ordnance 105-mm Light Gun design) would be phased out of service in favour of new equipments such as the M777. However, the greater importance of high-mobility operations and special forces applications, coupled with range-enhancing ammunition developments, now makes the 105-mm weapon more attractive than before. Various updating options are being studied to enhance the M119A1, which fires the standard suite of US/NATO ammunition such as the M1 HE round. For the most part these enhancements are concentrated on more streamlined projectiles with rocket assistance that can extend the existing M119A1 range of about 11500 m (12,575 yards) to more than 17100 m (18,700 yards).

These improvements are still pending, with other equipments being investigated, the most intriguing being the South African 105-mm Lightweight Experimental Ordnance (LEO) with its standard range of 24000 m (26,245 yards) or 30000 m (32,808 yards) with base-bleed ammunition, combined with a high-fragmentation projectile which, when air burst, has a lethal radius performance similar to standard 155-mm projectiles. In the meantime, the M119A1 seems destined for retention.

Future projects

The M777 Joint Lightweight Howitzer will replace all US Marine Corps cannon systems and become that service's primary direct-support weapon. The US Army will use the weapon for the general support of light forces and as a direct-support weapon for the Light Cavalry Regiment, replacing all M198 towed howitzers.

The M777's L/39 cannon is similar to that used by the the M109A6 Paladin. The M777 is only now entering service, but is already scheduled for a whole raft of improvements mainly connected with fire control and ergonomic handling. Yet the replacement for the M777 is already being investigated under the heading of Future Combat Systems (FCS) Non Line Of Sight Cannon (NLOS-C). A technology demonstrator has already been test-fired using an M777 barrel. One planned version will also have a band track for improving mobility.

The British army has a similar re-equipment programme to the US NLOS-C known as the Lightweight Mobile Artillery Weapon System or LIMAWS (G). Both the M777 and the HIMARS are candidates for this project, hence the designation of the M777 Joint Lightweight Howitzer.

SPECIFICATION

M777
Calibre: 155 mm (6.1 in)
Weight: 3745 kg (8,256 lb)
Dimensions: (travelling) length 9.275 m (30 ft 3 in); width 2.77 m (9 ft 1 in); height 2.26 m (7 ft 5 in)

Elevation: -5° to +70°
Traverse: total 45°
Maximum range: with standard projectile 24690 m (27,000 yards) and with rocket-assisted projectile 30000 m (32,808 yards)

The British Ministry of Defence is contemplating the M777 towed howitzer as a solution to its requirement for a Lightweight Mobile Artillery Weapon System. Several systems are being evaluated and a procurement decision was scheduled for 2004.

The M777's lightweight carriage includes two forward stabilisers, and two split trails fitted with self-digging spades and dampers. The standard crew is seven.

D-30 122-mm towed howitzer

This is the D-30 122-mm (4.81-in) towed howitzer in firing position with its wheels raised and its trail opened into the three units that provide firing stability when staked at their ends.

The **D-30** 122-mm (4.81-in) howitzer was designed by the F.F. Petrov Design Bureau at Artillery Plant No. 9 at Sverdlovsk to replace the 122-mm M1938 (M-30) howitzer, introduced into Soviet service shortly before World War II. The D-30 entered service in the early 1960s and offered several significant advantages, including a range of 15400 rather than 11800 m (16,840 rather than 12,905 yards) and traverse of 360° rather than 49°. The weapon is still in service with 65 countries, and the 2S1 Gvozdika self-propelled howitzer has an ordnance based on the D-30. Other SP versions of the D-30 were developed in Syria and for Egypt.

Soviet issue

In Soviet service the D-30 was issued on the scale of 36 per tank division (one regiment of two 18-weapon battalions each of three six-gun batteries), and 72 per motor rifle division (each motorised rifle regiment having a battalion of 18 D-30s and the artillery regiment two 18-gun battalions). The Soviets later increased the battery from six to eight guns: each battalion thus had 24 rather than 18 D-30s.

The D-30 has a 4.875-m (16-ft) barrel with a multi-baffle muzzle brake and a semi-automatic vertical sliding wedge breech mechanism, the recoil system being mounted over the ordnance. The weapon is towed muzzle first, the three trails being clamped in position under the ordnance. On arrival at the firing position, the crew first unlock the barrel travel lock, which then folds back onto the central trail. The firing jack under the carriage is then lowered to the ground, so raising the wheels, and the outer trails are each spread through 120°. The firing jack is raised until the trail ends are on the ground to provide a stable firing platform after they have been staked to the ground. The D-30 has a small shield, and is normally towed by a ZIL-157 or Ural-375D 6x6 truck, or an MT-LB tracked vehicle.

The D-30 fires case-type separate-loading ammunition including FRAG-HE, HEAT-FS (able to penetrate 460 mm/ 18.1 in of armour), smoke, chemical, illuminating and, later, a rocket-assisted projectile for a range of up to 21000 m (22,965 yards).

The **D-30M** has a revised double-baffle muzzle brake and a square rather than round baseplate. The **D-30A** has other improvements including a new cradle and a modified recoil system.

Top and above: The D-30 122-mm (4.81-in) howitzer was produced in very large numbers in the USSR, and was also made in China, Croatia, Egypt, Iran, Iraq and Yugoslavia. Substantial numbers are still in service.

Right: Three Soviet D-30 122-mm (4.81-in) howitzers in firing position. For many years the Soviet D-30 was the backbone of Soviet artillery regiments, but was succeeded by the 2S1 Gvozdika SP equipment.

SPECIFICATION

D-30
Calibre: 121.92 mm (4.8 in)
Weight: travelling 3210 kg (7,077 lb) and firing 3150 kg (6,944 lb)
Dimensions: (travelling) length 5.4 m (17 ft 8¼ in); width 1.95 m (6 ft 4¾ in); height 1.66 m (5 ft 5¼ in)

Elevation: -7° to + 70°
Traverse: 360°
Maximum range: 15400 m (16,840 yards) with HE projectile and 21000 m (22,965 yards) with rocket-assisted HE projectile

2A36 152-mm towed gun

The **2A36** 152-mm (6-in) towed long-range gun was originally developed during the 1970s at the Perm Machine Works as successor to the old (and heavy) M-46 130-mm (5.12-in) gun. When it first appeared it was known in the West as the **M1976** although the Soviet armed forces named it the **Giatsint-B** (hyacinth-B). The Giatsint-S self-propelled equivalent did not proceed past the prototype stage.

Production

The 2A36 was not shown in public until 1985, but production is understood to have started in 1976. Production continued into the late 1980s, although marketing for potential export continued until the late 1990s. Production totalled about 1,500, the only confirmed export orders from outside the former USSR being for Finland (24) and Iraq (an undetermined quantity).

The L/49 barrel of the 2A36 is 8.187 m (26 ft 10½ in) long and the weapon's primary projectile is an HE-FRAG type whose effect (high blast or high fragmentation) is set by adjustment of the fuse before firing. This projectile weighs 46 kg (101.4 lb) and can be fired to 27000 m (29,530 yards). A special rocket-assisted projectile can reach 40000 m (43,745 yards). An armour-piercing (AP-T) projectile is available for direct fire against armoured targets. With the latter the muzzle velocity is about 800 m (2,625 ft) per second. At one time a special 2A36 nuclear

Characterised by useful range and accuracy with an HE-FRAG shell that can be pre-set for maximum blast or high fragmentation, the 2A36 is used mainly in the counter-battery role.

projectile was reported, but this has long been withdrawn from service. Other projectiles available include smoke, concrete-piercing and incendiary.

Deployment

The guns are usually deployed in batteries of six or eight weapons, so marketing material has emphasised that a single battery can place more than 1 tonne of projectiles on a target in one minute.

References have been made to an improved version of the 2A36 Giatsint-B having

an L/53.8 barrel, but it appears this project did not progress far as it was the later 2A65 152-mm (6-in) gun that was selected for service.

The 2A36 has a crew of eight, some of them partially protected by a shield. The loading of the gun is greatly assisted by a loading tray that aligns with the horizontally opening breech when the latter is opened. The projectile is then hydraulically rammed and a fixed charge in a cartridge case is then inserted. Using this system the maximum rate of fire can be as high as five or six rounds per minute for short periods. Each gun is intended to be taken into action with 60 ready-use rounds.

The 2A36 is normally towed by a KrAZ-260 9-tonne 6x6 truck, although vehicles of similar capacity, including tracked prime movers, can be used. When on tow the gun carriage is supported by a four-wheel (two wheels on each side) walking beam suspension, permitting the gun to be towed over rough terrain at speeds of up to

30 km/h (18.6 mph). In firing position the trail legs are split and the gun rests on a circular jack under the forward part of the carriage. This arrangement allows a traverse of 25° to left and right. Several types of trail spade are available to suit the season, the 'summer' spades being larger for the use of the gun in softer ground.

SPECIFICATION	
2A36	2.788 m (9 ft 1¾ in); height 2.76 m
Calibre: 152.4 mm (6 in)	(9 ft ⅝ in)
Weights: travelling 9800 kg	**Elevation:** -2.5° to +57°
(21,605 lb) and firing 9760 kg	**Traverse:** 25° left and right
(21,517 lb)	**Maximum range:** 27000 m
Dimensions: length (travelling)	(29,530 yards) or, with RAP,
12.92 m (42 ft 4⅝ in); width	40000 m (43,745 yards)

The 2A36 has a multi-baffle muzzle brake and a semi-automatic horizontal sliding breech mechanism. The carriage allows high-speed cross-country towing.

Russian anti-tank guns T-12/MT-12 and 2A45M Sprut-B

While many armed forces have come to rely on guided missiles for anti-armour warfare, Russia has always retained specialised anti-tank guns, considering them reliable and more versatile than the 'one-shot' guided missile. While any Russian artillery piece can be regarded as a potential anti-tank weapon, the Russian armoury still contains two main types of dedicated-to-role towed anti-tank gun.

The oldest of this pair dates from 1961 and is the 100-mm (3.9-in) **T-12** (otherwise known as the **2A19**) and the related **MT-12** (**2A29**). The main difference between the two is that the more numerous MT-12 has a modified carriage to reduce the chances of the carriage overturning while on tow. Most of these guns now likely to be encountered are MT-12s.

Smooth-bore barrel

The 100-mm barrel is smooth-bored to enhance the muzzle velocity and thus the kinetic energy of the armour-piercing, fin stabilised, discarding sabot (APFSDS) projectile. This weighs 4.55 kg (10.03 lb) and is fired at a muzzle velocity of 1548 m (5,079 ft) per second. The projectile has a maximum operational range of about 3000 m (3,281 yards) and it can penetrate 215 mm (8.47 in) of armour at 1000 m (1,094 yards). Another specialised anti-armour round is the 9M117 Kastet (knuckleduster) laser-guided missile. The latest model of this missile is the 9M117M with a tandem shaped-charge warhead

capable of penetrating 550 mm (21.7 in) of armour at any direct-fire range. Both the T-12 and MT-12 can also fire conventional shaped-charge (HEAT) projectiles. Increasing their versatility, the guns are provided with indirect-fire sights and HE projectiles to enable their deployment as field guns.

It has been estimated that the Russian armed forces maintain over 6,000 of these guns. Although no longer in production in the former USSR, the gun is available from Norinco of China as the **Type 73**. Norinco have exported their product, so the T-12 and MT-12 are likely to be encountered almost anywhere around the globe.

The second Russian gun model is the 125-mm (4.92-in) **2A45M Sprut-B**

(octopus). First seen during the late 1990s, the 2A45M combines the main attributes of the 125-mm D-81 tank gun and cradle, normally mounted on tanks such as the T-72, and the triple-trail 360° traverse carriage of the 122-mm (4.8-in) D-30 towed field howitzer. It was originally designed as the long-term replacement for the 100-mm T-12/MT-12 series but up to the time of writing production has been confined to trial batches.

APFDS projectile

The 125-mm 2A45M has an L/51 smoothbore barrel with a double-baffle muzzle brake and fires the same ammunition as the D-81. This includes an APFSDS projectile weighing 7.05 kg (15.54 lb) and fired at a

Crew and combat equipment for the T-12/MT-12 and 2A45M anti-tank guns are transported by the MT-LB tracked prime mover or Ural-4320 6x6 truck. Here East German army MT-LB vehicles tow 100-mm T-12 guns.

SPECIFICATION	
MT-12	**2A45M Sprut-B**
Calibre: 100 mm (3.9 in)	**Calibre:** 125 mm (4.92 in)
Weight: in action 2750 kg (6,063 lb)	**Weight:** in action 6575 kg (14,495 lb)
Dimensions: length, travelling 9.48 m (31 ft 1¼ in)	**Dimensions:** length, travelling 7.12 m (23 ft 4½ in)
Elevation: -6°/+20°	**Elevation:** -6/+25°
Traverse: total 54°	**Traverse:** 360°
Maximum range: 3000 m (3,218 yards)	**Maximum range:** 2100 m (2,297 yards)

muzzle velocity of 1700 m (5,577 ft) per second to a maximum effective range of about 2100 m (2,297 yards). At that range it can penetrate almost 250 mm (9.84 in) of armour. The 2A45M can also fire the laser-guided 9M119M Svir (sabre) projectile that can penetrate 700 mm (27.56 in) of armour at any direct-fire range up to 5000 m (5,468 yards) by employing a shaped-charge warhead. As with other Russian anti-tank guns, the 2A45M can

also fire conventional HEAT and HE projectiles.

One of the main reasons why the 2A45M has yet to enter full-scale production is its weight, 6575 kg (14,495 lb) in the firing position. To assist short moves the carriage is provided with an APU that drives the carriage wheels. In this mode the maximum speed is limited to 14 km/h (8.7 mph) for short distances only. Longer moves are made with the gun towed by a heavy 6x6 truck or tracked prime mover.

Krasnopol-M Cannon-launched guided projectile

Perhaps the most significant of all recent Russian artillery developments has been the introduction of standard NATO-calibre 155-mm (6.1-in) models to render existing Russian-derived 152-mm (6-in) artillery ammunition more attractive to overseas markets. The 152-mm calibre has few adherents outside the former Warsaw Pact bloc (and China) so any move towards 155-mm ammunition could be important.

Westernised CLGP

One of the most attractive types of ammunition already modified to 155-mm calibre is the **Krasnopol-M** cannon-launched guided projectile (CLGP). This differs from the standard 152-mm **9K25 Krasnopol** CLGP in being entirely re-engineered to fit into NATO-pattern stowage racks and handling equipment, but the guidance

techniques remain the same. These techniques rely on laser target indication from a forward position within visual range of the intended target. The gun firing the projectile is laid towards the approximate direction of the target and the barrel elevation set as usual. Once the Krasnopol-M has been fired the target is subjected to laser energy from a ground-based, tripod-mounted target designator system. Some of this energy is reflected from the target and detected by a sensor mounted in the projectile nose. The appropriate trajectory corrections can then be made using an on-board electronic computer that introduces changes to the tailfin surfaces – the tailfins spring out into position only after the projectile has left the gun muzzle. In this way the projectile homes onto the target at a steep angle, the target often being

Above: In Russian service, the 152-mm Krasnopol CLGP is associated with the D-30 towed howitzer. A forward observer illuminates the target for the Krasnopol using a tripod-mounted 1D22 laser target designator with an integral rangefinder.

Right: The semi-active laser-guided Krasnopol-M in 155-mm calibre can be fired from Western systems such as the M109 and G6 self-propelled guns. The projectile makes a top attack on its target's upper armour, striking at an angle between +35° and +45°.

as small as a tank.

Each Krasnopol-M is 955-mm (37.6-in) long overall and weighs 45 kg (99.2 lb) complete. Of this, 20 kg (44.09 lb) is formed by the high-explosive fragmentation (HE-FRAG) warhead containing 6 kg (13.23 lb) of explosive. The maximum range is in the order of 22000 m (24,059 yards), while the maximum range of the laser target

designator is about 7000 m (7,655 yards) for static targets (less for moving targets).

Export success

The 155-mm Krasnopol-M has reportedly been sold to India and it has been tested by France and South Africa, primarily to expand their suites of 155-mm projectiles already on offer. Norinco of China is under-

stood to be producing the type under licence.

Other recent types of Russian artillery projectile have included a cargo projectile that dispenses radio jammer bodies in place of the more usual explosive sub-munitions. Regarding Russian sub-munitions, their cargo projectile offerings contain much heavier sub-munitions than in the West. For instance, one Russian

152-mm cargo projectile contains eight dual purpose sub-munitions, each weighing 1.4 kg (3.09 lb). By

contrast, the standard NATO M864 contains 72 'bomblet' sub-munitions, each weighing about 210 g (7.41 oz).

M-56 105-mm howitzer

With the German surrender in Yugoslavia at the end of World War II, large quantities of German artillery were abandoned and much of this was taken over by the Yugoslav army. Some 40 years later, numbers of German 88-mm (3.46-in) guns were still in service in the coastal-defence role, while the 105-mm (4.13-in) towed M18, M18M and M18/40 howitzers continued to be used by reserve units. In the immediate post-war period the United States supplied Yugoslavia with considerable amounts of towed artillery, including 155-mm (6.1-in) M114 and 105-mm (4.13-in) M101 howitzers, and 155-mm (6.1-in) M59 'Long Tom' guns. Some of these remained in service until the disintegration of the Yugoslav state in the early 1990s, together with a copy of the M114 called the M-65. Yugoslavia also designed and built two weapons to meet its own requirements, these being the 105-mm (4.13-in) howitzer **M-56** and the 76-mm (3-in) mountain gun M-46, the latter developed to meet the specific requirements of Yugoslav mountain units.

M-56 carriage

The M-56 has a barrel 3.48 m (11 ft 5 in) long with a multi-baffle muzzle brake, a hydraulic recoil buffer and hydro-pneumatic recuperator above and below the barrel, and a horizontal sliding-wedge breech mechanism. The carriage is of the split-trail type, with a spade attached to each end of the pole-type trail. The M-56 has a split shield that slopes to the rear and sides. Some carriages have been observed with American-type road wheels and tyres similar to that fitted to the M101, which allows the weapon to be towed up to 70 km/h (43.5 mph), while

A Yugoslav M-56 105-mm howitzer in its travelling configuration. This particular model has wheels with solid rubber tyres similar to those fitted to German 105-mm howitzers also used by the Yugoslav army following World War II.

Seen in service with El Salvador, the M-56 105-mm howitzer bears a strong resemblance to the US 105-mm M101 howitzer that was supplied to Yugoslavia in the years after World War II. The M56, however, is fitted with a larger shield and has a multi-baffle muzzle brake.

others have wheels with solid tyres similar to those fitted to the German 105-mm (4.13-in) howitzers of World War II. When the latter are fitted the weapon cannot be towed at high speed.

Fire-control equipment consists of a panoramic telescope with a magnification

of x4, a direct-fire anti-tank telescope with a magnification of x2, and a gunner's quadrant.

Projectile types

Ammunition is of the semi-fixed type (e.g. projectile and a cartridge case containing the bagged charge). The following projectiles can be fired at a maximum rate of 16 rounds per minute for a short period: HE projectile weighing 15 kg (33.1 lb) with a muzzle velocity of 570 m (1,870 ft) per second, smoke projectile weighing 15.8 kg (34.8 lb), armour-piercing tracer, and high-explosive squash head tracer (HESH-T). The HESH-T projectile

weighs 10 kg (22.05 lb), and when it hits an armoured vehicle the 2.2 kg (4.85 lb) of explosive flattens itself against the armour before exploding, when it can penetrate up to 100 mm (3.9 in) of armour plate at an angle of 30°.

An unusual feature of the M-56 is that in an emergency it can be fired before the trails are spread, although in this case total traverse is limited to 16° and elevation to +16°. The M-56 has a crew of 11 men and is normally towed by a TAM 1500 (4x4) truck. It was initially thought to be in service only with the Yugoslav army and its antecedents, but some have

been observed in El Salvador, in this instance towed by American 2½-ton (6x6) trucks, and also in Cyprus. Further examples of the M-56 were exported to Iraq, these weapons seeing action during the 1990 Iraqi invasion of Kuwait and the ensuing Operation Desert Storm. The M-56 howitzer was also widely used by various parties during the Yugoslavian civil wars of the 1990s. During these conflicts artillery played a major role, for example in the three-month bombardment of the Croatian city of Dubrovnik by Yugoslavian army forces in 1991, and during the siege of Sarajevo between 1992-96.

2S1 Gvozdika (M1974) 122-mm self-propelled howitzer

In the period after World War II the Soviet Union placed its main emphasis on the continuing development of towed artillery whereas NATO emphasised self-propelled weapons. Although the latter are much more expensive to build, maintain and operate they do have many advantages over their towed counterparts, including increased cross-country mobility, full armour protection for the crew and ammunition, the possibility of an NBC system, and a reduction in the time necessary for the equipment to be brought into and taken out of action. The Soviet Union did continue to develop specialised tank destroyers, but it was not until 1974 that the first 122-mm (4.8-in) self-propelled howitzer made its appearance during a parade in Poland, although it had entered service with the Soviet Union and Poland in 1972. NATO calls this 122-mm (4.8-in) self-propelled howitzer the **M1974**, this being the year when it was first seen, while the Soviet designation is **2S1**. The system has also been used by Algeria, Angola, Bulgaria, Cuba, Czechoslovakia, Ethiopia, East Germany, Finland, Hungary, Iran, Iraq, Libya, Romania, Syria, Toga, Uruguay, Yemen and

Yugoslavia and its antecedents. Licensed production took place in Bulgaria and Poland and the type is used by most former Soviet states. In the Soviet army the M1974 was employed on the scale of 36 per motorised rifle division and 72 per tank division.

Configuration

The layout of the M1974 is similar to that of the M109 with the engine, transmission and driver at the front and the fully enclosed turret at the rear. The suspension is adjustable, and consists of seven road wheels with the drive sprocket at the front and the idler at the rear; there are no track-return rollers. When operating in the snow or swampy areas the normal 400-mm (15.75-in) wide tracks can be replaced with 670-mm (26.4-in) wide tracks to reduce the vehicle's ground pressure. Standard equipment includes an NBC system and a full suite of night-vision equipment for the driver and commander. The M1974 is fully amphibious, being propelled in the water by its tracks at a speed of 4.5 km/h (2.8 mph).

The turret is fitted with a modified version of the standard 122-mm D-30 towed howitzer, which has an elevation of +70° and depression

of -3°; turret traverse is 360°. Turret traverse and weapon elevation are electric, with manual control for emergency use. The ordnance has a double-baffle muzzle brake, a fume extractor and a semi-automatic vertical sliding breech block; an ordnance travel lock is mounted on top of the hull. The howitzer fires an HE projectile weighing 21.72 kg (47.9 lb) to a maximum range of 15300 m (16,730 yards), and can also fire chemical, illuminating, smoke and HEAT-FS projectiles. The last is used to engage tanks and will penetrate 460 mm (18.1 in) of armour at an incidence of 0° at a range of 1000 m (1,095 yards). An HE/RAP round is available, and this has a maximum range of 21900 m (23,950 yards). The 2S1 can also fire the Kitolov-2 laser-guided artillery projectile with a 12000-m (13,123-yard) range. A normal ammunition load consists of 40 projectiles: 32 HE, six smoke and two HEAT-FS. It is believed that a power rammer is fitted to permit a higher rate of fire (five rounds per minute) and also to enable the ordnance to be loaded at any angle of elevation.

The chassis of the M1974 is based on that of the MT-LB and is also used for a large number of armoured com-

The M1974 received the Soviet designation 2S1 Gvozdika (carnation) and is fully amphibious, unlike the 2S3 Akatsiya. The chassis is also used for the MT-LBus (or Artillery Command and Reconnaissance Vehicle in NATO circles), the MTK-2 mineclearing vehicle, and for the RKhM chemical warfare reconnaissance vehicle. This is a Finnish 2S1.

SPECIFICATION	
2S1 Gvozdika	diesel developing 224 kW (300 hp)
Crew: 4	**Performance:** maximum road
Weight: 15700 kg (34,612 lb)	speed 61.5 km/h (38 mph);
Dimensions: length 7.3 m (23 ft	maximum range 500 km (311 miles)
11½ in); width 2.85 m (9 ft 4 in);	**Gradient:** 77 per cent
height 2.4 m (7 ft 10½ in)	**Vertical obstacle:** 0.7 m (2 ft 3 in)
Powerplant: one YaMZ-238N V-8	**Trench:** 3 m (9 ft 10 in)

mand and reconnaissance vehicles (ACRVs) fitted with the artillery/mortar-locating radar, a chemical reconnaissance vehicle and a mine-clearing vehicle.

2S19 152-mm self-propelled artillery system

The 152-mm (6-in) **2S19 (MSTA-S)** self-propelled gun was designed to combine the assets of the 2S3 152-mm howitzer and the 2S5 gun into a single self-propelled equipment. The 2S19 therefore combines the long 152-mm ordnance of the 2S5 self-propelled gun with a new hull employing both T-72 and T-80 tank components, with the gun fully enclosed within a large, steel armour turret mounted over the centre of the hull, the turret having a full 360° traverse.

Under the codename of Ferma (farm) work on the 2S19 began during 1985 at the same Uraltransmash facility at Ekaterinburg that manufactured the 2S5 gun. Initial 2S19 production began at Uraltransmash during 1988 before the production line was transferred to the Sterlitamak Machine Construction Factory (STEMA) at Bashkiriya. The Soviet army accepted their first examples during 1989 but subsequent production was slow by the usual Soviet standards, with only about 650 having been manufactured by 2002. Belarus and Ukraine also operate the type in small numbers.

As the 152-mm 2A64 ordnance is the same as that for the 2S5 the ballistic perfor-

mance remains as before. The maximum range is 24700 m (27,012 yards) with standard 152-mm HE-FRAG projectiles and 28900 m (31,605 yards) with base-bleed HE projectiles. Each standard HE projectile weighs 43.56 kg (96 lb) and the 2S19 can also fire the 50-kg (110-lb) 9K25 Krasnopol laser-guided projectile with a range of 15000 m (16,404 yards). An advanced onboard land navigation and fire-control system enables each 2S19 to operate as an independent unit should the need arise.

The 2S19 has a crew of five; commander, driver, gunner and two loaders. A further two personnel from a reload vehicle are required when ammunition is fed to the gun from an external source (as is carried out whenever possible to keep the onboard load ready for future use). A hydraulic crane arm is provided to assist this operation and also to reload the turret. All the ammunition stowage and semi-automatic handling systems for 50 projectiles and propellant charges are located within the turret. The ammunition handling capacity is efficient enough to permit burst fire rates of up to eight rounds each minute. For local and air

defence a 12.7-mm (0.5-in) heavy machine gun is carried on the turret roof.

High performance

Compared to many earlier self-propelled artillery equipments the 2S19 has excellent performance, mainly due to the provision of a V-12 diesel power pack capable of delivering 626 kW (840 hp) for a maximum road speed of 60 km/h (37 mph).

From 1993 onwards the Uraltransmash marketing forces made considerable sales efforts to sell the 2S19 for export sales, with no results. Development work is therefore being directed towards a 155-mm (6.1-in) version initially developed for a Russian army requirement but now firing NATO stan-

SPECIFICATION	
2S19	**Performance:** maximum road
Crew: 5	speed 60 km/h (37 mph); road
Weight: 42000 kg (92,592 lb)	range 500 km (311 miles)
Dimensions: length 11.9 m (39 ft);	**Fording:** 1.2 m (3 ft 11 in) without
width over skirts 3.58 m (11 ft 9 in);	preparation
height 2.985 m (9 ft 9½ in)	**Gradient:** 47 per cent
Powerplant: One V-84A V-12	**Vertical obstacle:** 0.5 m (1 ft 7 in)
diesel developing 626 kW (840 hp)	**Trench:** 2.8 m (9 ft 6 in)

dard projectiles and charges for export operators. Known as the **2S19M1** or **MSTA-S-155**, this export model has a 52-calibre barrel providing a range of 30000 m (32,808 yards) using NATO-standard L15A1 155-mm HE projectiles. Enhanced-range

base-bleed projectiles can be expected to achieve 41000 m (44,838 yards) and smart projectiles including the BONUS can also be fired. It is understood that by early 2003 prototypes of the 2S19M1 had been completed but had yet to be demonstrated.

The 2S19 was developed as a replacement for the 152-mm 2S3 Akatsiya and the 155-mm 2S5 Giatsint artillery and is normally deployed in six-gun batteries.

2S3 Akatsiya (M1973) 152-mm self-propelled gun/howitzer

The **M1973** 152-mm (6-in) self-propelled gun/howitzer was known as the **2S3** in the Soviet Union, and was issued on the scale of 18 per tank division and a similar number per motorised rifle division. The equipment has also been operated by Algeria, Angola, Bulgaria, Cuba, East Germany, Iraq, Libya, Syria, Vietnam and former Soviet states. Its chassis is a short-ened version of that used for the Krug (SA-4 'Ganef') sur-face-to-air missile system and GMZ armoured minelayer.

The M1973 has three compartments, that for the driver at the front, that for the engine to its right and that for the turret at the rear, the last being slightly forward of the very rear as it has such a large overhang. The torsion-bar suspension consists of six road wheels, with a dis-tinct gap between the first and second and the third and fourth road wheels; the drive sprocket is at the front with the idler at the rear, and there are four track-return rollers.

The commander's cupola

is on the roof of the turret, on the left side, and this is fitted with a 7.62-mm (0.3-in) machine-gun for local and anti-aircraft defence. This is the only hatch in the roof, but there is also a hatch in the right side of the turret. In the hull rear is a large hatch that opens downwards and on each side of this is one circu-lar hatch. These, and the two square openings in the turret rear, are used for the rapid loading of projectiles and fuses.

The ordnance is based on the 152-mm D-20 gun/how-itzer but with a bore evacuator, which helps stop fumes from entering the crew compartment when the breech is opened, to the rear of the double-baffle muzzle-brake. The ordnance fires an HE-FRAG projectile weighing 43.5 kg (95.9 lb) to a maxi-mum range of 18500 m (20,230 yards). Other projec-tiles that can be fired include HEAT-FS, AP-T, HE-RAP (Rocket-Assisted Projectile with a range of 24000 m/26,245 yards), illu-minating, smoke, incendiary,

Above: Known as the 2S3 Akatsiya (acacia) in Soviet army service, this vehicle forms the basis for a standard chassis design used for other purposes, including the 'Ganef' launcher and the GMZ minelayer.

flechette, scatterable anti-tank or anti-personnel mines, the Krasnopol laser-guided projectile and 2-kT tactical nuclear. A total of 45 projec-tiles and charges is carried, and maximum rate of fire is four rounds per minute. The ordnance has an elevation of +60° and a depression of -4°; turret traverse is 360°.

Unlike the 122-mm (4.8-in) M1974 self-propelled how-itzer, the M1973 does not

The 2A33 152-mm gun adopted by the 2S3 is ballistically identical to that used on the D-20 towed artillery piece and shares ammunition commonality.

have amphibious capability, although it can ford to a depth of 1.5 m (4 ft 11 in). The M1973 is fitted with an

NBC system, and with infra-red night-vision equip-ment for both the commander and the driver.

SPECIFICATION	
2S3 Akatsiya	developing 388 kW (520 hp)
Crew: 4	**Performance:** maximum road
Weight: 27500 kg (60,626 lb)	speed 60 km/h (37 mph); maximum
Dimensions: length (gun forward)	range 500 km (311 miles)
8.4 m (27 ft 6⅔ in); length (hull)	**Gradient:** 60 per cent
7.8 m (25 ft 7 in); width 3.2 m (10 ft	**Vertical obstacle:** 0.7 m (3 ft 7 in)
6 in); height 2.8 m (9 ft 2¼ in)	**Trench:** 3 m (9 ft 10 in)
Powerplant: one V-59 V-12 diesel	

2S5 Giatsint 152-mm self-propelled gun

The self-propelled gun that was to become the **2S5 Giatsint** (hyacinth) had its design origins during the late 1960s, the prototypes appearing during 1972. Production preparations at what is now the Uraltransmash facility at Ekaterinburg began during 1976, the first examples being delivered to the Soviet army during 1980. The inten-tion was to produce a long-range gun to partner the 2S3 152-mm (6-in) self-pro-pelled gun/howitzer, both sharing the same hull and suspension design. However, the gun installation of the 2S5

was left completely open with no protection for the lim-ited traverse gun and crew. It was probably felt that the long-range capabilities of the gun enabled them to be fired from well to the rear. The maximum range is 28400 m (31,059 yards) with standard 152-mm projectiles and 37000 m (40,464 yards) with HE projectiles of an advanced aerodynamic form.

The steel hull armour is 15 mm (0.59 in) thick to pro-vide some measure of protection against shell splin-ters and small arms fire when travelling. For travelling the driver and gun commander

are located under armour at the hull front, the commander behind the driver as the 388 kW (520-hp) diesel engine is located to the right of the driver. The other three members of the crew of five travel under armour in a sepa-rate compartment at the hull rear.

Into action

Time into and out of action is about three minutes. To bring the gun into action a stabiliser spade is lowered from the hull rear. Some examples have been seen with a front-mounted dozer blade to clear battlefield obstacles or for digging in without specialised engineering support. When travelling, the long barrel of the 2A37 gun, which is pro-vided with a multi-baffle muzzle brake, is secured in a clamp which has to be released when preparing for firing.

The 2S5 can carry 30 pro-

jectiles and charges ready for use, the separate-loading rounds being delivered from a vertical stowage, carousel type magazine to the breech using a conveyor system. Loading and ramming the rounds into the breech are semi-automatic and powered. These arrangements enable up to six rounds to be fired in one minute, the vertical slid-ing breech opening and ejecting the spent case auto-matically after each firing. It is claimed that a six-gun 2S5 battery can have 40 projec-tiles in the air before the first of them impacts on the tar-get area. Each 2S5 artillery battalion has three batteries.

Each standard HE-FRAG projectile weighs 46 kg (101 lb), the propellant charge and case weighing a maxi-mum of 34 kg (75 lb). The

2S5 is one of the equipments that can fire the 9K25 Krasnopol laser-guided projec-tile.

Production of the 2S5 ceased after just over 2,000 had been manufactured. Sales were made to Finland (18) in 1994 but that was the only export success, the rest of the output being delivered to various states within the old Soviet Union. The 152-mm 2S19 self-propelled gun is now replacing many of those examples remaining in Russian service. However, the 2S5 production line is still in existence as efforts have been made to market it on the open defence market as recently as 2002. Further operators of the 2S5 com-prise Belarus, Georgia, Ukraine and (although uncon-firmed) Uzbekistan.

The 2S5 can be supplied with ammunition either from onboard the rear of the vehicle or from the ground. A total of 30 projectiles and charges are carried in the vehicle.

SPECIFICATION	
2S5 Giatsint	388 kW (520 hp)
Crew: 5	**Performance:** maximum road
Weight: 28200 kg (62,170 lb)	speed 63 km/h (39 mph); maximum
Dimensions: length 8.33 m (27 ft	road range 500 km (311 miles)
3½ in); width 3.25 m (10 ft 8 in);	**Fording:** 1.05 m (3 ft 5 in)
height 2.76 m (9 ft)	**Gradient:** 58 per cent
Powerplant: one V-59 V-12	**Vertical obstacle:** 0.7 m (3 ft 7 in)
supercharged diesel developing	**Trench:** 2.5 m (8 ft 2 in)

Abbot 105-mm self-propelled gun

After the end of World War II the standard self-propelled gun of the British Royal Artillery was the 25-pounder Sexton, which was designed and built in Canada. Prototypes of various self-propelled guns were built on a modified Centurion tank chassis, including one with a 25-pounder gun and the other with a 5.5-in (140-mm) gun. By the 1950s these calibres were not standard within NATO, which was standardising on 105-mm (4.13-in) and 155-mm (6.1-in) rounds. To meet the Royal Artillery's immediate requirements for SP weapons of the latter calibre, quantities of American M44 self-propelled howitzers were supplied while development in England concentrated on a 105-mm self-propelled gun which used the engine, transmission and suspension of the FV432 series of APC.

New contract

Vickers of Elswick was awarded a contract to build 12 prototypes, of which six were powered by a petrol engine and six by a diesel engine. Following trials with these prototypes the company was awarded a production contract, series vehicles being built between 1964 and 1967. In the British Army the **FV433 Abbot** 105-mm self-propelled gun was used by the Royal Artillery in regiments of three batteries, each battery having eight Abbots. The Abbot was deployed in West Germany with the British Army of the Rhine, while a few served with the Royal School of Artillery at Larkhill, Wiltshire, and at the British Army Training Area in Suffield, Canada. The **Value Engineered Abbot**, which

Used in the Field Regiments of the Royal Artillery, the Abbot was supported by the amphibious 6x6 Alvis Stalwart High Mobility Load Carrier with pre-packed ammunition pallets, and was capable of operating in an NBC environment.

was the basic vehicle without such luxuries as flotation screen, powered traverse, NBC system and night-vision equipment, was produced for India although the British Army also adopted a few.

Armour protection

The hull and turret of the Abbot were of all-welded steel, providing the four-man crew with complete protection from small arms fire and shell splinters. The driver was seated at the front on the left, with the engine to his right. The turret was mounted at the very rear of the hull, with the commander and gunner on the right and the loader on the left. In addition to the commander's cupola and loader's roof hatches a large door was provided in the hull rear which was also used for ammunition supply. The Abbot was fitted with an

NBC system, infrared driving lights and, when originally introduced into the British Army, with a flotation screen; the last was later removed.

Main armament consisted of a 105-mm gun manufactured by the Royal Ordnance Factory Nottingham, a 0.3-in (7.62-mm) Bren light machine-gun at the commander's station for use in the anti-aircraft role, and one bank of three electrically-operated smoke dischargers

on each side of the turret. The 105-mm gun had a double-baffle muzzle brake, a fume extractor and a semi-automatic breech. Traverse was powered through 360°, while elevation was manual from -5° to +70°. The gun had a maximum range of 17000 m (18,600 yards) and fired the following types of separate-loading ammunition: HE, HESH, practice, smoke (three types) and illuminating. A total of 40 projectiles was carried.

The ammunition of the Abbot is also used in the Royal Ordnance Factory Nottingham (now BAE Systems) 105-mm Light Gun, whose ordnance was developed from the L13A1 gun of the Abbot.

Replacement of the Abbot by the 155-mm M109A2 started in the early 1980s, but the Abbot was not retired from the Royal Artillery until the early 1990s, when it was replaced by the AS90 and MLRS.

SPECIFICATION

Abbot	6-cylinder diesel developing 179 kW (240 hp)
Crew: 4	**Performance:** maximum road speed 47.5 km/h (30 mph); maximum range 390 km (240 miles)
Weight: 16556 kg (36,500 lb)	
Dimensions: length (gun forward) 5.84 m (19 ft 2 in); length (hull) 5.709 m (18 ft 8¾ in); width 2.641 m (8 ft 8 in); height (without armament) 2.489 m (8 ft 2 in)	**Gradient:** 6 per cent
	Vertical obstacle: 0.609 m (2 ft)
	Trench: 2.057 m (6 ft 9 in)
Powerplant: one Rolls-Royce	

Originally planned for replacement in the late 1980s by the abortive SP-70 155-mm (6.1-in) gun, the Abbot was not fitted with the flotation screen during the latter part of its career.

AS90 155-mm self-propelled gun/howitzer

The fully-tracked 155-mm (6.1-in) **AS90** self-propelled gun/howitzer started life as a Vickers Shipbuilding and Engineering private venture that gained acceptance by the British Army after the intended international 155-mm SP-70 programme was terminated during 1986. Changing what was essentially then a simple-to-use equipment intended for a Third World market into the

advanced artillery system demanded by the Royal Artillery took some years, the first deliveries of an ordered batch of 179 being made during 1993.

AS90 has undergone several significant changes since 1993, some of which are still in progress. Perhaps the most significant change has been the replacement of the original 155-mm L/39 barrel by a completely new barrel

with a length of 52 calibres. This considerably enhances the maximum range, originally 24700 m (27,012 yards) but now 30000 m (32,808 yards) with a slightly modified L15 pattern high-explosive projectile as fired from the old FH-70. Using enhanced-range ammunition, the re-barrelled AS90 can reach over 40000 m (43,744 yards). Both long and short barrels can fire all

existing NATO standard projectiles. At present only 96 of the British Army's equipments are scheduled to carry the new L/52 barrel, although others may follow.

To make the best use of this range performance, numerous computer-based systems have been added to the AS90, covering all manner of operations from electrical barrel and turret drives to land navigation and

communications. Also involved is a new ammunition handling system to operate with the modular propellant charges of South African origin employed in place of the original bagged charges.

Sufficient on-platform data processing and fire-control equipment is provided to make each individual AS90 an independent combat unit, although the equipments are normally deployed in batteries of eight. Each gun can fire bursts of three rounds in 10 seconds, or a steadier rate of 18 rounds in three minutes. Ammunition stowage is provided for 48 rounds.

Two AS90 variants have been developed for the export market, both containing the systems and long barrels developed for the British Army's AS90. One is for general sales and is named **Braveheart**, while the **Desert AS90** is intended for operations under extreme conditions as it features extra cooling arrangements and similar modifications to suit desert environments. The turret and L/52 barrel intended for the Braveheart have been selected by Poland for mounting on a locally-developed tracked chassis. The Polish model is known as the **Krab** (crab).

Although its onboard systems are arguably as advanced as those of the German PzH 2000, the AS90 has met with little export success, sales being limited to the British Army.

Left: The AS90 was initially fitted with an L/39 barrel, but a conversion programme has introduced an L/52 barrel. This modification offers greater range and improved ballistic performance. Barrel-laying is fully electrical.

SPECIFICATION	
AS90	diesel developing 492 kW (660 hp)
Crew: 5	**Performance:** maximum road
Weight: 45000 kg (99,208 lb)	speed 55 km/h (34 mph); maximum
Dimensions: length 9.9 m (32 ft 5 in); width 3.4 m (11 ft 1 in); height 3 m (9 ft 9 in)	road range 370 km (229 miles)
	Gradient: 60 per cent
	Vertical obstacle: 0.88 m (2 ft 9 in)
Powerplant: one Cummins V-8	**Trench:** 2.8 m (9 ft 2 in)

PzH 2000 155-mm self-propelled howitzer

Following the termination of the trilateral SP-70 program in 1986, the **Panzerhaubitze 2000** 155-mm (6.1-in) self-propelled howitzer was developed for the German army by Krauss-Maffei Wegmann (KMW), with Rheinmetall Landsysteme as the main sub-contractor. By the end of 2002, the **PzH 2000** had been ordered by Germany (185 systems delivered), Greece (24), Italy (70) and the Netherlands (57).

Main armament

The PzH 2000 is armed with a newly developed Rheinmetall L/52 main armament that is compatible with all current NATO shells and charges. This offers an effective range of 30000 m (32,808 yards) using conventional L15A2 ammunition, or up to 41000 m (44,838 yards) using various assisted rounds. Typical of these is the Rheinmetall RH 40 base-bleed ammunition, fired with a modular charge system.

Electrically controlled, the gun can be automatically elevated between -2.5° and +65° and is capable of 360° traverse. In order to lay the gun barrel precisely and at high speed, the PzH 2000 is equipped with a GPS navigation system. An onboard ballistic computer with a radio datalink to an external fire-control command post enables missions to be undertaken autonomously, using unprepared firing positions, after having received target position and ammunition data. The position of the gun is checked after each round fired and if

The total German army requirement for the PzH 200 is expected to be around 450 units, and the type has also been ordered by the Italian, Dutch and Greek armies, making it something of a European standard for self-propelled artillery.

necessary it is relayed automatically using fire-control data provided by the ballistic computer. The gun is capable of multiple-round simultaneous impact (MRSI) firing and has demonstrated a five-round MRSI on a target at a range of 17000 m (18,600 yards).

The fully automatic ammunition loading system includes different semi-automatic and manual back-up modes, and allows a rate of fire of 10 rounds per minute (increased to 12 during tests with an improved autoloader).

A sustained rate of fire of three rounds per minute can be maintained until the ammunition is spent. The vehicle carries a total of 60 projectiles in the centre of the chassis and 288 modular charges (or equivalent bagged charges). Complete replenishment by two crewmembers takes under 12 minutes. A crew of five is normally maintained, although only three are required for normal operations. A 7.62-mm (0.3-in) machine-gun is carried to

SPECIFICATION	
PzH 2000	Ka-500 diesel V-8 diesel developing 736 kW (987 hp)
Crew: 3 + 2	
Weight: 55330 kg (121,981 lb)	**Performance:** maximum road
Dimensions: length (gun forward) 11.669 m (38 ft 3 in); length (hull) 7.92 m (25 ft 1 in); width 3.58 m (11 ft 8 in); height (to turret roof) 3.06 m (10 ft 0 in)	speed 61 km/h (37 mph); cruising range 420 km (260 miles)
	Gradient: 50 per cent
	Vertical obstacle: 1 m (3 ft 3 in)
Powerplant: one MTU MT881	**Trench:** 3 m (9 ft 9 in)

provide a measure of local and AA defence.

The PzH 2000 has recently undergone trials in Sweden for use as a coastal artillery system, and successfully engaged moving targets at sea.

Bandkanon 1A 155-mm self-propelled gun

Bofors has long been known for its expertise in the design, development and production of guns (and their associated ammunition systems) for both land and sea applications. This work was put to good use in the development of the **Bofors Bandkanon 1A** 155-mm (6.1-in) self-propelled gun for the Swedish army. The first prototype was completed in 1960, and after extensive trials and some modifications the equipment was manufactured between 1966 and 1968. The Bandkanon 1A has the distinction of being the first fully automatic self-propelled gun to have entered service. It is also the heaviest and slowest, which makes the equipment very difficult to conceal and of limited tactical mobility.

The hull and turret are of all-welded steel construction between 10 and 20 mm (0.4 and 0.8 in) thick. The vehicle uses many automotive components of the

Bofors S-tank, including the powerpack and suspension. The engine and transmission are at the front of the hull, with the driver seated to the immediate front of the turret. The suspension is of the hydro-pneumatic type and consists on each side of six road wheels, with the drive sprocket at the front and the last road wheel acting as the idler. To provide a more stable firing platform the suspension can be locked.

Turret mounting

The turret is mounted at the rear of the hull, and is a two-part assembly with the 155-mm ordnance mounted between the parts. In the left part are the commander, gun layer and radio operator, while in the right part are the loader and 7.62-mm (0.3-in) AA machine-gunner. Turret traverse is manual, 15° left and right with the ordnance above 0° in elevation, reducing to 15° left and 4° right with the ordnance

below 0°. Elevation is electric from +2° to +38° and manual from -3° to +40°.

The 155-mm ordnance has a pepperpot muzzle-brake, no fume extractor and a semi-automatic wedge breech block that opens downward. An unusual feature of the ordnance is that it has a replaceable liner. When travelling, the ordnance is held in position by a lock pivoted at the front of the hull. The ammunition is fed from a 14-round clip carried externally in an armoured magazine at the rear of the hull. This clip consists of seven compartments, each of which contain two rounds of ammunition,

Operated only by Sweden, the Bandkanon 1A is heavy and slow, but its L/50 ordnance fires a comparatively heavy shell to a tactically useful range.

these being fed to the breech by a loading tray before being rammed into the breech by a rammer. The loading tray and rammer are operated by springs that are cocked by the run-out of the gun. The first round has to be manually loaded but after this the sequence is fully automatic and the gunner can select single shots or fully automatic. The empty cartridge cases are ejected rearward from the breech. Once the clip of ammunition has been expended a fresh

clip is brought up by truck, the ordnance is elevated to +38°, covers on the magazine are opened vertically, a hoist on the upper part of the turret slides along the slide bar before picking up the clip and placing it in the magazine, the doors are then closed and the hoist is returned to travelling position. This sequence takes two minutes.

The standard HE projectile weighs 48 kg (105.8 lb) and has a range of 25600 m (28,000 yards).

SPECIFICATION

Bandkanon 1A
Crew: 5
Weight: 53000 kg (116,845 lb)
Dimensions: length (gun forward) 11 m (36 ft 1 in); length (hull) 6.55 m (21 ft 6 in); width 3.37 m (11 ft ⅞ in); height (including AA MG) 3.85 m (12 ft 7½ in)
Powerplant: one Rolls-Royce

diesel developing 179 kW (240 hp) and one Boeing gas turbine developing 224 kW (300 shp)
Performance: maximum road speed 28 km/h (17.4 mph); maximum range 230 km (143 miles)
Vertical obstacle: 0.95 m (3 ft 1½ in)
Trench: 2 m (6 ft 6¾ in)

Palmaria 155-mm self-propelled howitzer

The **Otobreda Palmaria** 155-mm (6.1-in) self-propelled howitzer was developed by what was then OTO-Melara for the export market, and shares many components with the OF-40 MBT, which is in service with Dubai. The first Palmaria prototype was completed in 1981, and production vehicles were completed in the following year. The type has so far been ordered by Argentina (20 turrets), Libya (210) and Nigeria (25 or possibly 50).

The layout of the Palmaria (named after an Italian island) is similar to that of a tank, with the driver at the front of the hull, the turret in the centre, and the engine and transmission at the rear. The major difference between the chassis of the Palmaria and that of the OF-40 MBT is that the for-

Specifically developed for export, the Palmaria has now been bought by Libya and Nigeria, while 20 turrets were delivered to Argentina for local installation on the chassis of the TAM tank. Palmaria is based on the chassis of the OF-40 MBT.

mer has thinner armour and is powered by a V-8 diesel developing 559 kW (750 hp) whereas the OF-40 has a V-10 diesel developing 619 kW (830 hp).

The 155-mm (6.1-in) L/41 barrel is fitted with a fume extractor and a multi-baffle muzzle-brake. The turret has 360° traverse and the ord-

nance can be elevated from -4° to +70° hydraulically, with manual controls for emergency use. An unusual feature of the Palmaria is the installation of an auxiliary power unit to provide turret power, thus conserving fuel for the main engine. The Palmaria is available with a normal manual loading system or a semi-automatic loading system. With the latter, a three-round burst can be fired in 30 seconds and then one round every 15 seconds can be maintained until the 23 ready-use projectiles have been fired; a further seven projectiles are stowed elsewhere in the hull. Once the ordnance has fired, it automatically returns

to an elevation of +2°, the breech opens, the projectile is loaded with power assistance, the charge is loaded manually, the breech is closed and the ordnance can be fired.

A complete range of ammunition has been developed for the Palmaria by Simmel: the range consists of five rounds, each weighing 43.5 kg (95.9 lb). The standard HE, smoke and illuminating projectiles have a range of 24700 m (27,010 yards), the HE LT projectile 27500 m (30,075 yards), and the HE rocket-assisted projectile 30000 m (32,810 yards). The extra range of the RAP has a penalty, however, in as much

as it is achieved only at the expense of HE content, which is 8 kg (17.6 lb) compared with 11.7 kg (25.8 lb) in the standard and LT projectiles. A 7.62-mm (0.3-in) machine-gun is mounted at the commander's station on the right side of the turret roof, and four electrically operated smoke dischargers can be fitted on each side of the turret. Much optional equipment can be fitted, including passive night vision equipment and an NBC system, and the standard equipment includes a hull escape hatch, bilge pumps and a fire-extinguishing system. Track skirts help to keep down dust during cross-country travel.

SPECIFICATION

Palmaria
Crew: 5
Weight: 46000 kg (101,410 lb)
Dimensions: length (gun forward) 11.47 m (37 ft 7¾ in); length (hull) 7.4 m (24 ft 3½ in); width 2.35 m (7 ft 8½ in); height (without MG) 2.87 m (9 ft 5¼ in)

Powerplant: one V-8 diesel developing 559 kW (750 hp)
Performance: maximum road speed 60 km/h (37 mph); maximum range 400 km (250 miles)
Gradient: 60 per cent
Vertical obstacle: 1 m (3 ft 3 in)
Trench: 3 m (9 ft 10 in)

ZTS vz 77 Dana 152-mm self-propelled gun/howitzer

The Czechoslovak (now Czech and Slovak) **ZTS vz 77 Dana** was the first wheeled self-propelled howitzer to enter modern service. Self-propelled artillery of the wheeled type has several advantages over its more common tracked counterpart: it is cheaper and easier to manufacture and to maintain, and has much greater strategic mobility as almost without exception wheeled armoured vehicles are much faster than their tracked counterparts and have a greater operational range.

The Dana, which entered service in 1981, is based on the Tatra T815 8x8 truck, which probably has the best off-road performance of any truck in existence. The crew compartment is at the front, the fully enclosed two-part turret in the centre, and the engine compartment at the rear. The armour is of all-welded steel and provides the crew with complete protection from small arms fire and shell splinters. The crew normally travel in the front compartment, entering the turret only for action.

The engine is coupled to a manual gearbox with 10 forward and two reverse gears, which in turn transmits power to a two-speed transfer box, so giving a total of 20 forward and four reverse gears. Steering is power-assisted on the front four wheels, and a central tyre pressure-regulation system allows the driver to adjust the pressure to suit the ground being crossed.

Before firing can begin, three hydraulically operated stabilisers (one at the rear of the hull under the engine compartment and one on each side between the second and third axles) are lowered to the ground to provide stability. The turret can be traversed 225° left and right, and the 152-mm (6-in) ordnance (with a muzzle brake but without a fume extractor as the ordnance is carried between the two sealed turret halves) fires Czechoslovak and Russian ammunition, and can be ele-

Above: The vz 77 Dana is based on the Tatra T815 8x8 truck chassis, and its centrally mounted turret carries the ordnance between two sealed outer halves.

vated from -4° to +70°.

The ordnance is supplied by a hydraulically powered automatic loading system, and the gunner can select single-shot or fully automatic fire from the maximum 60 but more normal 40 separate-loading rounds carried in the system. The maximum rate is five rounds per minute, while the sustained rate is 30 rounds in seven minutes. The ordnance can fire two types of HE round, each weighing 43.56 kg (96 lb), the standard type to 18700 m (20,450 yards) and the base-bleed type to 20080 m (21,960 yards). There is also the EKK dispenser round carrying 42 anti-tank bomblets. Equipment includes NBC and air-conditioning systems, and on the right side of the turret roof a 12.7-mm (0.5-in) NSV

By early 1994 over 750 units of the Dana had been produced but more recent development has focused on the 155-mm ZTS Zuzana on a similar chassis.

machine-gun for local and AA defence. Built in the Slovak Republic, the Dana system has been sold to Libya, Poland and to both the parent countries.

SPECIFICATION

vz 77 Dana
Crew: 5
Weight: 29250 kg (64,484 lb)
Dimensions: length (gun forward) 11.156 m (36 ft 7¼ in); width 3 m (9 ft 10 in); height (turret roof) 2.85 m (9 ft 4¼ in)

Powerplant: one Tatra V-12 diesel developing 257 kW (345 hp)
Performance: maximum road speed 80 km/h (50 mph); maximum range 740 km (460 miles)
Vertical obstacle: 0.6 m (24 in)
Trench: 2 m (6 ft 7 in)

G6 155-mm self-propelled gun/howitzer

Ever since its appearance in prototype form during 1981, the 155-mm (6.1-in) self-propelled gun/howitzer created by Denel, but now known as the **LIW G6**, has been the subject of a seemingly endless series of enhancements and updates. These have covered just about every aspect of the G6 system, only the basic 6x6 automotive platform having remained essentially without change over the years.

When the G6 first appeared it had an L/45 barrel, the same as that employed on the G5 towed howitzer. Using the ammunition then available, the maximum range was just under 40000 m (43,745 yards). In its latest developmental form, using an L/52 barrel firing enhanced-range ammunition, this range can be increased to more than 53000 m

(57,960 yards). Work in progress is expected to result in a range of over 70000 m (76,555 yards), the projectile incorporating ramjet propulsion. A trajectory-correction system will be included to maintain accuracy at extreme ranges.

Together with these range enhancements, the fire-control system has undergone numerous changes, while the turret interior has been revised to include improved turret-drive and gun-laying systems. Improved communication suites have been installed as well as a land navigation system, the commander being provided with a gun management system that displays data relating to command, fire orders, communications, navigation and general ballistic information dealing with the gun.

Despite all these changes the crew of the G6 remains

at six, and the number of projectiles carried is still 45. The original bagged charges have now been replaced by easier to handle modular charges.

The projectiles are of a type known as ERFB (Extended-Range Full Bore) with the option of attaching a BB (Base Bleed) motor to break up the drag-inducing eddies behind the projectile base. The HE projectile weighs 45.3 kg (99.9 lb), increased to 47.7 kg (105.2 lb) with the BB motor in place. Other projectiles include Smoke, Illuminating, Incendiary, Leaflet and Radar Echo. The enhanced-range HE projectile is the Velocity-enhanced Long-Range Artillery Projectile (VLAP). As this projectile combines both BB and rocket assistance to extend the range to more than 53000 m the HE payload is less than the usual 8.7 kg (19.2 lb).

The G6 can be fired from its wheels, but better stability is achieved by lowering four

The G6 offers an attractive combination of capability and low cost. South Africa took 43 vehicles, and Oman and the UAE received 24 and 78 respectively.

outrigger legs. During firing the barrel can be traversed under power control through 90° to each side, and elevation is -5° to -75°. The standard rate of fire is four rounds per minute for 15

minutes, though three rounds in 25 seconds is possible with a semi-automatic rammer assisting the loading processes. The G6 is operated by Oman and the UAE in addition to South Africa.

The most remarkable aspect of the G6's capabilities is the exceptional range offered by its ordnance in either its original L/45 or more recent L/52 forms.

SPECIFICATION

LIW G6
Crew: 6
Weight: 47000 kg (103,616 lb)
Dimensions: length (gun forward) 10.34 m (33 ft 11 in); length (hull) 9.2 m (30 ft 2¼ in); width 3.4 m (11 ft 2 in); height (turret top) 1.9 m (6 ft 3 in)

Powerplant: one air-cooled diesel developing 386 kW (518 hp)
Performance: maximum road speed 90 km/h (56 mph); maximum range 700 km (435 miles)
Fording: 1 m (3 ft 3 in)
Vertical obstacle: 0.5 m (20 in)
Trench: 1 m (3 ft 3 in)

GCT 155-mm self-propelled gun

To replace the 155-mm (6.1-in) Mk F3 and 105-mm (4.13-in) Mk 61 in French service, during the late 1960s a new self-propelled gun was developed as the **GCT** (*Grande Cadence de Tir*, or great weight of fire) on a slightly modified AMX-30 MBT chassis. The first prototype was completed in 1972, and after trials with a pre-production batch of 10 vehicles, production got underway in 1977. For a number of reasons Saudi Arabia was the first country to deploy the GCT, ordering an eventual 63 systems plus a complete fire-control system. The French army designates the GCT as the **155 AUF1**, and deploys most of its 273 systems in regiments of 20 weapons (four five-gun batteries). Later orders were placed by Iraq and Kuwait for 86 and 18 systems respectively.

The GCT is manufactured by Giat Industries. The all-

welded turret is fitted with a 155-mm L/40 barrel fitted with a multi-baffle muzzle brake and a vertical sliding-wedge breech block. Elevation is from -4° to +66°, and traverse 360°. Turret traverse and gun elevation are hydraulic, with manual controls for emergency use. The major feature of the GCT is the automatic loading system for 42 projectiles and a similar number of cartridges carried in racks in the turret rear. The ammunition mix depends on the tactical situation, but can consist of 36 (six racks of six) HE and six (one rack of six) smoke projectiles.

Reloading

Access to the ammunition racks for reloading purposes is via two large doors in the turret rear. The crew can reload the GCT in 15 minutes. The auto-loader enables a rate of eight rounds per minute, and the

Although developed as a successor to the Mk F3 and Mk 61 SP guns in French army service, the GCT was first deployed by Saudi Arabia, since when it has also been adopted by Iraq and Kuwait. The auto-loader enables the 155-mm GCT to fire at a rate of up to eight rounds per minute.

gunner can select single shots or six-round bursts, the latter taking just 45 seconds. The GCT can fire HE (four types including a base-bleed type with a range of 29000 m/31,715 yards), illuminating, smoke and carrier projectiles. A 7.62- or 12.7-mm (0.3- or 0.5-in) machine-gun is mounted on the roof.

The later **155 AUF1 T** had a number of improvements, and 174 French systems are being upgraded to **155 AUF2** standard with an L/52 ordnance able to fire the base-bleed projectile to 40000 m (43,745 yards), and a Mack E9 diesel engine. The L/52 turret is also available for use on other 40-tonne class MBT chassis.

The GCT's equipment includes night vision and ventilation equipment, while options include an NBC system and muzzle velocity measuring gear.

SPECIFICATION	
155 AUF1	fuel engine developing 537 kW (720 hp)
Crew: 4	**Performance:** maximum road speed 60 km/h (37 mph); maximum range 450 km (280 miles)
Weight: 42000 kg (92,595 lb)	
Dimensions: length (gun forward) 10.25 m (33 ft 7½ in); width 3.15 m (10 ft 4 in); height 3.25 m (10 ft 8 in)	**Gradient:** 60 per cent
	Vertical obstacle: 0.93 m (37 in)
Powerplant: one Hispano-Suiza HS 110 water-cooled V-12 multi-	**Trench:** 1.9 m (6 ft 3 in)

Slammer 155-mm self-propelled howitzer

The **Slammer** 155-mm (6.1-in) self-propelled howitzer was developed to meet an Israeli army requirement and was first revealed during 1990, although the first of the two prototypes completed to date was ready during mid-1983. However, no orders for the Slammer (known locally as the **Sholef**) have been announced, although it is marketed for possible export as being ready for production.

To assist Israeli armed forces logistics, the Slammer consists of a 155-mm howitzer and turret on a chassis derived from that of the Merkava MBT. The fully traversing welded steel turret and its L/52 howitzer were developed and manufactured locally by Soltam Systems. The howitzer has an elevation arc of -3° to +75° and, firing enhanced-range

155-mm projectiles, has a maximum range of over 40000 m (43,745 yards). Combined with the howitzer is a computer-controlled Loader Control System (LCS) that permits nine rounds to be loaded automatically and fired in one minute. Bursts of three rounds in 10 seconds are possible. The LCS also selects and sets the projectile fuses and inserts the propellant charge primer. Using the LCS only two ammunition handlers are needed in the turret, the commander controlling and monitoring all processes from a control panel. The remaining member of the four-man crew is the driver. Full NBC protection is provided, while night driving systems are standard.

For normal self-propelled fire missions the Slammer

carries 60 projectiles and propellant charges, all readily accessible by the LCS. A further 15 projectiles are carried at various stowage points around the interior. For more static fire missions, ammunition can be fed into the system from an external stockpile, projectiles being passed into the turret via an elevator. In an emergency the LCS can be replaced by manual operation, although the fire rate is reduced. The LCS, including the complete ordnance, can be retrofitted into existing SP systems, the M109 being mentioned in marketing

material as a likely recipient. Various auto-nomous fire control and land navigation systems can be installed according to choice.

Modified ordnance

The Slammer's 155-mm ordnance is a modified version of that proposed for a towed model, the TIG 2000. The same ordnance has been proposed for the ATMOS 2000 on a modified Tatra 6x6 truck chassis. For travelling, the barrel is firmly held in a remotely controlled external clamp. It is provided with a double-baffle muzzle brake and a fume evacuator.

Though based on that of the Merkava, the Slammer chassis has some role-specific modifications, but has the same diesel powerpack coupled to an automatic transmission. Though lighter than the Merkava (the exact weights have not been released), the Slammer thus has a road range of about 400 km (248 miles) and a speed of 46 km/h (28.5 mph). It is anticipated that any production Slammers would be made to the latest Merkava standard and thus have better all-round automotive performance.

The Slammer has a number of very advanced features as well as a capable ordnance that can fire projectiles to a considerable range, but it has not been ordered.

SPECIFICATION	
Slammer	developing 671 kW (900 hp)
Crew: 4	**Performance:** maximum road speed 46 km/h (28.5 mph); maximum range 400 km (248 miles)
Weight: not released	
Dimensions: length (gun forward) 11 m (36 ft 1 in); width 3.7 m (12 ft 1½ in); height 3.4 m (11 ft 2 in)	**Fording:** 1.3 m (4 ft 3 in)
	Gradient: not released
Powerplant: one General Dynamics AVDS-1790-6A liquid-cooled V-12 diesel engine	**Vertical obstacle:** not released
	Trench: not released

Type 75 155-mm self-propelled howitzer

When the Japanese Ground Self-Defence Force was formed in the 1950s, all of its artillery was of the towed type and supplied by the US. With increased mechanisation taking place in the 1960s, the US also supplied 30 105-mm (4.13-in) M52 and 10 155-mm (6.1-in) M44 self-propelled howitzers. In the later 1960s development of indigenous 105-mm and 155-mm self-propelled howitzers started in Japan, the former eventually being standardised as the Type 74 and the latter as the **Type 75**. Only 20 of the Type 74 were built as a decision was taken to concentrate on the more effective 155-mm Type 75 system. Production lasted into the later 1980s and amounted to 201 systems: Mitsubishi Heavy Industries was responsible for the hull and final assembly, and Japan Iron Works/Nihon Seiko for the gun and turret.

M109 similarities

In many respects the Type 75 is similar to the M109 operated by the US Army and a large number of other forces, with the engine and transmission at the front and the fully enclosed turret at the rear. The six-man crew consists of the commander, layer, two loaders and radio operator in the turret, and

the driver in the front of the hull. The hull and turret are constructed of all-welded aluminium to a thickness that provides the crew with complete protection from small arms fire and shell splinters. The suspension is of the torsion-bar type, and on each side comprises six road wheels, of which the rear unit serves as the idler; the drive sprocket is at the front, and there are no track-return rollers.

The L/30 barrel has a breech block of the interrupted screw type, a fume extractor and a double-baffle muzzle brake. When the Type 75 is travelling the barrel is normally held in a travel lock mounted on the glacis plate. The ordnance has an elevation of +65° and a depression of -5°, and the turret can be traversed through 360°. The elevation of the weapon and the traverse of the turret are both hydraulically powered, with manual controls provided for emergency use. Before fire is opened, two spades are manually lowered to the ground at the rear of the hull to provide a more stable firing platform.

The Type 75 can fire 18 rounds in three minutes, such a rate being achieved by the use of two drum-type magazines (one on each side

The Type 75 self-propelled howitzer is essentially a Japanese-designed and Japanese-built counterpart to the ubiquitous M109 SP howitzer of US origin.

of the turret and containing nine projectiles each), a two-part extending loading tray and a hydraulic rammer. Once the gun has been fired, it returns automatically to an elevation angle of +6° for reloading, the breech is opened, the extending loading tray is positioned, the projectile and charge are then loaded with the aid of the hydraulic rammer, the breech is closed, the loading tray is returned to the normal position, and the weapon is ready to be fired once more. The drum magazines are rotated electrically or manually, and can be reloaded from outside the vehicle via two doors/hatches in the turret rear.

In action the Type 75

would probably fire 12 or 18 rounds before moving off to a new fire position before the enemy could return fire. In addition to the 18 projectiles in the two magazines, a further 10 projectiles are carried internally, as are 56

fuses and 28 bagged charges. Mounted externally at the commander's station, for anti-aircraft and local defence purposes, is a standard 0.5-in (12.7-mm) M2HB heavy machine-gun provided with a shield.

SPECIFICATION	
Type 75	water-cooled 6-cylinder diesel
Crew: 6	developing 336 kW (450 hp)
Weight: 25300 kg (55,775 lb)	**Performance:** maximum road
Dimensions: length (gun forward)	speed 47 km/h (29 mph); maximum
7.79 m (25 ft 6½ in); width 3.09 m	range 300 km (185 miles)
(10 ft 1¾ in); height (without MG)	**Gradient:** 60 per cent
2.545 m (8 ft 4 in)	**Vertical obstacle:** 0.7 m (27 in)
Powerplant: one Mitsubishi	**Trench:** 2.5 m (8 ft 2 in)

Chinese self-propelled artillery PLZ45 and Types 54-1, 83 and 85

Over the years the Chinese defence industry, centred on Norinco, has developed several types of self-propelled artillery for export and domestic use. One recent export success has been the 155-mm (6.1-in) **PLZ45** sold to Kuwait, which took 27 systems. The PLZ45 is thoroughly modern with an L/45 barrel firing ERFB (extended-range full-bore) projectiles, with or without base-bleed units, the latter weighing 47.6 kg (104.9 lb) and reaching 39000 m (42,650 yards) after being fired with a muzzle velocity of 903 m (2,963 ft) per second. The PLZ45 resembles the US M109, but there are numerous differences. The PLZ45 was first displayed publicly in 1988, and is also in service with the Chinese army.

Basic weapon

Another export success was made by the **Type 54-1**, a basic and elderly equipment with the Soviet 122-mm (4.8-in) howitzer of 1938 in a limited-traverse, forward-firing mounting on a modified YW531 APC. Despite the limited ballistic performance of its short-barrel howitzer (maximum range of 11800 m/12,905 yards with a 21.76-kg/48-lb projectile), the Type 54-1 was bought by Bolivia

(18), and large numbers remain in Chinese service. The Type 54-1 is a sturdy and reliable equipment, but is no longer in production.

Another low-cost and basic equipment also based on the YW531 is the **Type 85** with the 122-mm Soviet-designed D-30 howitzer mounted in a semi-open limited-traverse mounting firing forward. Its standard 21.76-kg projectile reaches 15300 m (16,770 yards) and an enhanced-range projectile 21000 m (22,965 yards); the enhanced-range projectile includes some cargo-carrier types. As far as is known, no Type 85 equipments have been exported. It is no longer in production, although marketing continues.

Returning to a larger calibre, Norinco also continues to market the **Type 83**, a design with close affinities to the Soviet 2S3 and mounting an almost identical 152-mm (6-in) gun/howitzer manufactured in China as the Type 66. As with the PLZ45, the immediate visual similarities are misleading as the Type 83 employs an entirely new tracked chassis design which has also been adapted for other vehicles, including a trench digger. The Type 83 can fire a Type 66 HE projectile, weighing 43.56 kg

The Type 83 is based on a new fully tracked chassis and carries heavy ordnance in the form of a derivative of the 152-mm (6-in) Type 66 towed howitzer.

(96 lb), to a range of 17230 m (18,845 yards) at a steady rate of four rounds per minute. Although extensively marketed by Norinco, the Type 83 is in service only with China. A 130-mm (5.12-in) gun is offered as an alternative to the 152-mm ordnance, while one variant, the PTZ89 deployed as a tank destroyer, carries a 120-mm (4.72-in) high-velocity gun. Production of the Type 83 is complete.

SPECIFICATION	
PLZ45	L413FC air-cooled diesel engine
Crew: 5	developing 391 kW (525 hp)
Weight: 33000 kg (72,751 lb)	**Performance:** maximum road
Dimensions: length (gun forward)	speed 56 km/h (35 mph); maximum
10.15 m (33 ft 3½ in); width	range 336 km (450 miles)
3.236 m (10 ft 7½ in); height	**Gradient:** 58°
3.502 m (11 ft 6 in)	**Vertical obstacle:** 0.7 m (27 in)
Powerplant: one Deutz BF12	**Trench:** 2.7 m (8 ft 10 in)

M109 155-mm self-propelled howitzer

The **M109** 155-mm (6.1-in) self-propelled howitzer is the most widely used weapon of its type in the world. Its development can be traced to 1952, when a requirement was issued for a new SP howitzer to replace the 155-mm (6.1-in) M44. At that time the 110-mm (4.33-in) T195 self-propelled howitzer was already being designed, and it was decided to use its hull and turret as the basis for the new weapon, which would be armed with a 156-mm (6.14-in) howitzer. But in 1956 it was decided to stick to a 155-mm (6.1-in) calibre for commonality within NATO, and in 1959 the first prototype was completed under the designation **T196**. There were numerous problems, and much redesign work had to be carried out to improve its reliability.

Diesel power

At the same time a decision was taken that all future US armoured vehicles would be powered by diesel engines for greater operating range, so the vehicle was redesignated T196E1 with such a powerplant. In 1961 this was accepted for service as the M109 SP howitzer, and the first production vehicles were completed late in 1962 at the Cleveland Army Tank Plant, this facility being run by the Cadillac Motor Car Division but later run by Chrysler. In the 1970s all production of the M109 series was taken over by Bowen-McLaughlin-York (now United Defense).

In the US Army the M109 is issued on the scale of 54 per armoured and mechanised division (three battalions each of 18 vehicles, each battalion having three batteries of six M109s). In addition to the US Army and US Marine Corps, the M109 is still used by 29 other countries, and a few countries have given it up in recent years. The weapon has been used in action in conflicts in the Middle East and the Far East.

Layout

The hull and turret of the M109 are of all-welded aluminium construction. The driver is seated at the front on the left, with the engine compartment to his right, and the turret is at the rear. The suspension is of the well-tried torsion-bar type, and on each side consists of seven road wheels with the drive sprocket at the front and the idler at the rear; there are no track-return rollers. Standard equipment includes IR driving lights and an amphibious kit enabling the vehicle to propel itself across slow-flowing rivers with its tracks.

The M109 has a 155-mm M126 howitzer with an elevation arc of -5° to +75° in a 360° traverse turret. Both gun elevation and turret traverse are powered, with manual controls available for emergency use. The ordnance has a large fume extractor, large muzzle brake and a Welin-step thread breech block. Normal rate of fire is one round per minute,

but for short periods three rounds per minute can be attained. The weapon has been qualified to fire a wide range of projectiles including HE (maximum range 14320 m/15,660 yards), illuminating, tactical nuclear, smoke, tactical CS and Agents VX or GB; 28 projectiles and charges are carried. A 0.5-in (12.7-mm) M2HB machine-gun, for which 500 rounds are provided, is mounted on the comman-

der's cupola for local defence.

One of the reasons that the M109 has been in production for so long is that its basic chassis has proved capable of constant updating and of accepting longer-barrelled ordnance that fires projectiles to a greater distance.

The main variants have been the M109 baseline model, **M109A1** with the longer M185 ordnance,

M109A2 with a redesigned rammer and 22 more rounds, upgraded **M110A3**, **M109A4** conversion of two earlier variants with NBC protection, **M109A5** upgraded M109A4, and **M109A6 Paladin**. The last is the production model in the first part of the 21st century (957 ordered for the US Army), and incorporates a host of tactical and reliability improvements reducing the crew from six to four.

The basic M109 self-propelled howitzer mounted the short-barrel M126 weapon. The M109 series is the most widely used of all self-propelled weapons and has seen extensive combat service throughout the world, as well as seeing constant adaptation and updating.

Steady development has kept the M109 series fully capable of effective use in modern operations, the adoption of longer ordnances increasing projectile ranges most usefully.

M110 203-mm self-propelled howitzer

The **M110** 203-mm (8-in) self-propelled howitzer uses the same chassis and mount as the 175-mm (6.89-in) M107 self-propelled gun, and details of its development are given in the entry for the M107. The M110 was one of a complete family of self-propelled weapons developed by Pacific Car and Foundry for trials as the T235 175-mm (6.9-in) gun, **T236** 203-mm howitzer and T245 155-mm (6.1-in) gun.

The M110 entered service with the US Army Field Artillery in 1963, and was issued on the scale of one battery of four M110s per infantry division and one bat-

talion of 12 for each armoured and mechanised division. Production was originally completed in the late 1960s, but was resumed in the 1970s by Bowen-McLaughlin-York, which later merged with FMC to create United Defense. In addition to being used by the US Army and US Marines, the M110 has been or still is operated by the armies of Bahrain, Belgium, Germany, Greece, Iran, Israel, Italy, Japan, Jordan, Morocco, the Netherlands, Pakistan, Saudi Arabia, South Korea, Spain, Taiwan, Turkey and the UK. In many cases, and especially in Europe, the M110s

were upgraded with the aid of US-supplied kits.

The chassis of the M110 is of all-welded steel construction with the driver seated under armour at the front on the left, with the engine compartment to his right and the howitzer on its mount on top of the chassis at the rear. The suspension is of the torsion-bar type and consists on each side of five large road wheels with the rearmost acting as the idler; the drive sprocket is at the front and there are no track-return rollers. When the M110 is in firing position, the suspension can be locked to provide a more stable firing

platform.

The 203-mm M2A2 howitzer was developed well before World War II and is located on the M158 mount, this allowing an elevation arc between -2° and +65°; the traverse arc of 30° left and right. Elevation and traverse are hydraulically powered, with manual controls for emergency use. The M2A2 has no muzzle brake or fume extractor, and has an interrupted screw breech block. At the rear of the chassis is a loader and rammer assembly to lift the projectile from the ground, position it and ram it into the chamber. The following projectiles can be

fired: 92.53-kg (204-lb) HE to a maximum range of 16800 m (18,375 yards), HE carrying 104 or 195 grenades, Agents GB or VX, and tactical nuclear. Only two projectiles and charges are carried on the M110, others being provided from the M548 carrier that also transports the remainder of the crew. The complete crew of the M110 consists of 13 men, of whom five (commander, driver and three gunners) are on the M110.

One of the main drawbacks of the M110 is the complete lack of any protection for the gun crew from

shell splinters, small arms fire and NBC agents. A protection kit was developed but not fielded.

All US M110s were upgraded to **M110A1** or **M110A2** standards. The M110A1 has a longer M201 ordnance firing the M106 HE projectile to a maximum of 22860 m (25,000 yards) or the M650 HE rocket-assisted projectile to 29990 m (32,800 yards); other rounds

An M110A2 of the US Army. This differs from previous M110 versions in having a long, muzzle-braked barrel. All of the M110 series equipments in the US Army were to have been fitted with a crew shelter and NBC system, but in the end were not so fitted.

were the M404 Improved Conventional Munition carrying 104 anti-personnel grenades, the M509A1 ICM carrying 180 anti-personnel/materiel grenades, Agents GB or VX, Binary or tactical nuclear.

The M110A2 is almost identical to the M110A1 but has a muzzle-brake which enables it to fire charge nine of the M118A1 propelling charge, whereas the M110A1 can go only up to charge eight and thus

offers a reduced maximum range capability by comparison with the definitive weapon.

SPECIFICATION	
M110A2	Model 8V-71T liquid-cooled diesel developing 302 kW (405 bhp)
Crew: 5 + 8	
Weight: 28350 kg (62,500 lb)	**Performance:** maximum road speed 54.7 km/h (34 mph); maximum range 523 km (325 miles)
Dimensions: length (gun forward) 10.73 m (35 ft 2½ in); width 3.15 m (10 ft 4 in); height 3.14 m (10 ft 3¾ in)	**Gradient:** 60 per cent
	Vertical obstacle: 1.016 m (40 in)
Powerplant: one Detroit Diesel	**Trench:** 2.36 m (7 ft 9 in)

Crusader 155-mm self-propelled howitzer

Although the **Crusader** 155-mm (6.1-in) self-propelled artillery project is no more, the programme suffering final cancellation in 2002, it still provides an indication of the state-of-the art for future field artillery. The Crusader was innovative in many ways, not the least being that it was a two-part system, comprising the howitzer unit itself plus an ammunition carrier/reload system.

The howitzer component was the **XM1001 Self-Propelled Howitzer** (SPH), and the other component was the **XM1002 Resupply Vehicle** (RSV). The two vehicles were to operate on a one-to-one basis, the two being virtually joined together for the ammunition and fuel resupply operation. Throughout the system computer-controlled automation was employed. For instance all ammunition and fuse selection, handling and loading on the SPH was mechanical, the crew of three not even seeing the processes involved. The crew of three on the RSV could transfer fresh rounds within seconds, again without human intervention other

than monitoring. The SPH could carry 48 rounds and charges, with another 100 on the RSV.

Liquid cooling

The 155-mm XM297E2 howitzer barrel was an L/56 unit, enabling a maximum range with suitable projectiles of over 40000 m (43,745 yards) or 50000 m (54,680 yards) or more with enhanced-range projectiles such as the XM982. It was planned that the barrel would be able to fire at a rate of up to 10 rounds per minute so the barrel featured liquid cooling. Time in and out of action was planned as about 30 seconds, with high-speed moves powered by a Honeywell/General Electric gas turbine engine driving via an Allison automatic transmission.

Development reached the test turret and chassis stage before changing priorities led to cancellation as, with each vehicle exceeding 45 tonnes, the system was becoming too heavy. Some Crusader technology may be used in future but lighter projects. Pending another system, the US Army is continuing to field the 155-mm M109A6 Paladin system.

Above: In firing trials, the Crusader SPH confirmed that it could start firing within 40 seconds of coming to a halt, and that burst rates of 10-12 rounds per minute were possible. The powerplant was originally to have been based on a Perkins CV-12 diesel engine from the UK, but in 2000 it was decided to standardise the gas turbine of the M1A2 Abrams MBT.

Left: The Crusader was based on a hydro-pneumatic suspension system, there being six dual rubber-tyred road wheels on each side, together with a front idler, rear drive sprocket and unspecified number of track-return rollers.

SPECIFICATION	
XM1001 Crusader	**Powerplant:** one Honeywell/General Electric LV-100-5 gas turbine developing 1118 kW (1,500 shp)
Crew: 3	
Weight: 43630 kg (96,186 lb)	
Dimensions: length (gun forward) 7.01 m (23 ft); width 3.33 m (10 ft 11 in); height 2.92 m (9 ft 7 in)	**Performance:** maximum road speed 67 km/h (41.5 mph)

On the gunline with the M109

The M109 self-propelled gun will go down in the history of armament as one of the best, most long-lived and important contributions to the defence of the NATO alliance.

The M109 is far less costly than any of its counterparts. It has enabled standardisation of medium artillery within NATO, and has offered countries which would not otherwise have been able to afford it the possibility of purchasing a large arsenal of self-propelled guns, and to modernise them at minimum cost. Germany, Italy and Switzerland have developed their own M109 versions, all with enhanced gunnery systems. The German M109G has a new breech-block and sights and offers increased range in concert with locally-developed ammunition. The Italian variant, built under licence by OTO Melara, has a lengthened barrel to accept ammunition originally designed for the FH-70. Using standard ammunition, this has a range of 24000 m (26,247 yards). The Swiss, with an eye to fire and movement rather than range, fitted a semi-automatic loader to their M109U, increasing the rate of fire to six rounds per minute.

From the outset it was obvious that measures would have to be taken to update the M109 to provide a stopgap until the introduction of more advanced weapons. To this end the M109A1 was introduced, the first model entering service with the British Army in 1978. The M109A1 is in

Above: Towards the end of the Cold War, the British Army of the Rhine had about 100 M109s in service. These provided a powerful reserve of firepower to support the infantry and armour but would have had to 'shoot and scoot' to avoid enemy counter-battery fire.

essence the M109 fitted with the much longer M185 155-mm cannon. This new gun has an effective fume extractor preventing propellant gases from entering the turret after firing, takes a bigger charge and offers a greater maximum range of 18000 m (19,685 yards) compared with 14600 m (15,967 yards) of the standard M109.

Further improvements

The M109A2 has an improved shell rammer and recoil mechanism, an M178 modified gun mount and other minor improvements. By the late 1980s there were 101 M109A1s/A2s in service with Royal Artillery Medium Regiments, based mainly in West Germany.

The M109A4 combines the improvements of the M109A2 with new NBC equipment. The gun traverse mechanism is improved and a combat override switch allows for emergency starting.

The United States Government awarded a contract for the production of the M109A5 model under its Howitzer Improvement Programme (HIP). Numerous improvements have been made to the M109. A new aluminium armoured turret has additional storage for 36 charges and the new M284 howitzer is capable of a burst fire rate of three rounds in 15 seconds, followed by a sustained rate of 8 rpm. The M109A5 has a normal firing range extended to 22000 m (24,059 yards). Equally important, the NBC protection system operates during firing; earlier models were forced to fire with the rear door open.

The M109A6 Paladin is the latest development and is equipped with onboard navigation and automatic fire-control systems. A Kevlar-lined chassis and pressurised crew compartment protects against NBC threats and the Paladin is capable of operating on the modern battlefield with a high degree of autonomy.

Above left: Used throughout NATO, the M109 has been modernised to serve well into the 21st century. National rivalry within NATO seems to rule out a multinational replacement for this veteran self-propelled gun.

Left: Original M109s can be distinguished by the stubby L/23 barrel with the prominent smoke extractor behind the muzzle brake. It fires the basic HE round to 14,600 metres (47,900 feet).

M109 Family

The first production model of the M109 (identified by its short gun barrel with a double-baffle muzzle brake and a large fume extractor) was completed by the Cadillac Motor Car Division of General Motors in 1962. By the end of the Cold War in excess of 3,700 models had been completed, 1,800 for United States Army service, the rest for export to over 15 countries throughout Europe and the Middle East, making the M109 the most widely used self-propelled howitzer in the world. During the latter stages of the Cold War, the M109 played a key role in the defence of Western Europe. Highly mobile to avoid enemy counter-battery fire, its 155-mm (6.1-in) gun continues to provide vital support for NATO infantry. Used by most NATO armies, the example illustrated belongs to the US Army. The M109A2 variant introduced a new lengthened gun barrel, together with a number of additional improvements, and increased the range of the howitzer to 18000 m (19,685 yards).

Above: A US Army M109 in action during Operation Desert Storm. The M109A2, A3 and A4 models share the M185 L/23 gun, which is replaced by the M284 L/39 weapon on the M109A5 and M109A6 Paladin, with a subsequent increase in range. The M284 howitzer fires a 44-kg (98-lb) projectile to a distance of 22 km (13.7 miles). Note the travel lock for the howitzer in the folded position at the front of the hull. The M109A6 Paladin introduces a remotely-operated travel lock for its gun, which is coupled to the M182 gun mount.

Left: The M109 series of self-propelled howitzer is capable of both direct (line of sight) firing and indirect fire operations. The 155-mm firing assembly is capable of 360° traverse.

Below: Germany, Italy and Switzerland have produced their own variants of the original M109, in each case with an improved gunnery system. The German M109G (an M109A3G variant is illustrated) has a Rheinmetall horizontal sliding breech-block and locally-produced sights, enabling it to fire domestically produced ammunition to an increased range of 18500 m (20,232 yards).

Left: The top of the M109's turret mounts a panoramic telescope shield and indirect fire telescope in addition to the 0.5-in (12.7-mm) machine-gun carried on an M178 (M109A2/A3/A4) or M182 (M109A5) installation. This M109, seen during the 1991 Gulf War, is 'dug in' and partially covered by camouflage netting.

Czech 2S1 self-propelled howitzers in travelling configuration. The chassis of the 2S1 is superficially similar to that of the PT-76 light amphibious tank but is in fact derived from the chassis of the MT-LB, although it is fitted with seven rather than six road wheels.

M109 Self-propelled gun

M185 155-mm howitzer
The long 155-mm howitzer has a distinctive smoke extractor approximately two-thirds of the way along the barrel. The semi-automatic breech block and hydro-pneumatic recoil system enable an astounding rate of fire of three rounds per minute to be attained over a short period. However the 4.3-kg (9.5-lb) shell is difficult to handle in the confined turret and crew fatigue reduces the practical rate of sustained fire to 45 rounds per hour. Furthermore, as each gun carries only 28 rounds of ammunition, replenishment soon becomes a problem. The gun can be elevated to +75° and has a maximum range of 18-24 km (11-15 miles), depending on the type of ammunition fired. It fires various HE rounds, smoke, illumination, mines and bomblets, CLGP and (during the years of the Cold War) binary chemical shells. A longer barrelled version was introduced on the M109A1 and increased the range by approximately 4500 m (14,764 ft).

Anti-armour capability
The artillery's job was made more difficult by the introduction of much improved tank armour during the later stages of the Cold War. Previously, a near miss from a 105-mm (4.1-in) Abbot self-propelled gun would have immobilised an enemy tank, but nothing less than a 155-mm gun could hope to have that effect against the T-64, T-72 or T-80 main battle tanks fielded by Warsaw Pact forces and their allies during the 1980s. However, the venerable but reliable United States' M109 howitzer adequately filled this role.

Gunner
In addition to the gunner, the turret contains the commander and three ammunition handlers.

M109A3 variant
The M109A3 model was not built as new, but was a depot-converted M109A1 with the 27 various mid-life improvements of the M109A2 model. As such, the A3 is effectively identical to the A2. However, whereas some A3s have three contact arm assemblies, all examples of the A2 are fitted with five contact assemblies.

Improved model
The M109A2 new production variant incorporated the various improvements of the M109A1 and also introduced a rear bustle rack at the rear of the cab. This addition allows for the carriage of an increased quantity of ammunition. Further enhancements include an all-weather ballistic shield over the panoramic telescope at the front of the turret and a counterbalanced travel lock. The M109A2's improvements also include the RAM (Reliability, Availability and Maintainability) kit and expanded safety features together with enhanced operational capabilities. An M140 alignment device is an optional feature for the M109A2.

0.5-in (12.7-mm) Browning M2 machine-gun
This is pintle-mounted on the front of the commander's cupola on the right-hand side of the turret. Its primary function is for anti-aircraft fire: if the commander finds himself engaging enemy infantry with it, the M109 is in serious trouble.

Hull and turret
Although the all-welded aluminium hull and turret provide the crew of the M109 with protection against small arms fire, they are of little use against shrapnel. In a Cold War confrontation, the comparatively short-ranged M109 would have been vulnerable to counter-battery fire in an artillery duel with its Soviet divisional level equivalent, the 2S3.

Rear access door
This has to remain open when in action because the turret of the M109 quickly fills with fumes despite the new fume extractors fitted on the M109A1. The M109A5 introduced an NBC system able to ventilate the turret so that the vehicle can fire while closed down. NBC equipment is also fitted to the M109A4.

M109 vs Gvozdika Cold War SP artillery

Well-used artillery causes more casualties to an enemy, and has a greater adverse effect on its will to fight, than any other weapon. No matter how capable the latest tanks and infantry weapons may be, neither can hope to bring about victory if the enemy can bring down accurate artillery fire on their positions. But if artillery is to carry out its prime role of disrupting, demoralising and destroying the enemy it must have sufficient range and power to bring down concentrated fire on enemy positions. The American M109 and the Soviet-designed 2S1 Gvozdika reveal two different approaches to self-propelled artillery design developed during the superpower stand-off of the Cold War.

A 2S1 is seen in action during the Yugoslavian conflict. The Gvozdika's 122-mm howitzer has a range of around 15300 m (16,732 yards) and the vehicle was designed to have the cross-country capability to maintain pace with Soviet motorised rifle regiments primarily equipped with the BMP series. The 2S1 is thus considerably lighter than the rival M109.

Armoured glacis
Estimated at between 14 and 20 mm (0.55 and 0.78 in) thick, the 2S1's armour is designed to protect the vehicle only from small arms fire and shell fragments. The anti-tank rounds stored in the turret are for emergencies only; the vehicle would stand little chance in a shooting match with an enemy tank.

Driver
The 2S1's driver is provided with a windscreen and sits to the left of the engine, which is accessible through a large hatch on the right hull front. The transmission is manual, with five forward and one reverse gears.

Engine
The 2S1 is powered by a V-8 water-cooled 224-kW (300-hp) diesel engine, the same powerplant that is used by the MT-LB. This gives a respectable power-to-weight ratio of 11.2 kW (15 hp) per tonne.

Polish 2S1s with their 122-mm howitzers in the elevated firing position. This weapon was developed from the D-30 towed howitzer. A double-baffle muzzle brake is located at the front of the hull; the bore evacuator is located midway along the tube. The 2S1 is also used in the direct-fire role against enemy armour, minefields and obstacles.

The 251 self-propelled gun had no direct NATO equivalent except perhaps for the British Abbot. Its most important role was to provide quick-response indirect fire ahead of advancing Soviet tanks. The 251 was built in large numbers, at least 10,000 units being completed by the early 1990s.

Gunner
The gunner uses the periscope forward of the commander's cupola to sight the gun for indirect fire. There is a sight for direct fire mounted to the right of the main armament. The gun is loaded by a fourth crew member seated to the right of the gun and he throws the empty shell cases out of the hatch.

Commander
The commander directs the operation of the vehicle in accordance with orders received from the CO of the artillery unit. The Soviet command system distributed the 2S1 at battalion level but this artillery would only support the unit to which it was attached. It was a rigid and potentially wasteful system.

NBC system
An air filter is fitted in the back of the turret and the 2S1 has an over-pressure system to keep out nuclear, biological or chemical contamination. In contrast with the American M109, the 2S1 was fitted with such equipment from the outset, a reflection of the high priority placed by Soviet doctrine on operations under NBC conditions. Warsaw Pact forces even undertook exercises using 'live' chemical or biological agents.

Tracks
The 2S1 normally travels on 400-mm (15.7-in) tracks but when operating in snow or over swampy areas it is fitted with special tracks 670 mm (26.4 in) wide, which reduce ground pressure. The 2S1 is amphibious and is propelled through the water by its tracks.

ASTROS II Artillery Saturation Rocket System

Based on its experience in the design, development and production of a variety of ground- and air-launched unguided rockets for the Brazilian armed forces, the Brazilian company of AVI-BRAS subsequently developed a much more effective artillery rocket system called **ASTROS II** (Artillery Saturation Rocket System).

Development of this was completed in the early 1980s with the first production systems being completed in the 1983 and since then large numbers have been produced for the home and export markets, especially the Middle East (Iraq, Qatar and Saudi Arabia) and more recently Asia (Malaysia). Iraq manufactured a version of the ASTROS II named **Sajeel**.

ASTROS II consists of two key elements, both of which are based on the same 6x6 cross-country truck chassis: these are the actual launcher and the ammunition resupply vehicle which is fitted with a crane for loading new rockets. Both of these are provided with fully armoured forward control cabs. There is also an optional command centre/fire-control system based on a similar or more compact 4x4 chassis.

The launcher for the unguided surface-to-surface rockets is mounted at the rear and can be fitted with various pods of different calibre rockets with the larger the calibre the greater the operational range.

The shortest rocket is the SS-30 with each launcher having 32 tubes with a stated maximum range of 30 km (18.6 miles). The next model is the SS-40 with a range of 35 km (21.7 miles) and 16 tubes. The largest rocket currently in production is the SS-60 with a maximum stated range of 60 km (37.3 miles) and four tubes. Development of the SS-80 is complete and this has a maximum range of 90 km (55.9 miles).

Warhead types

To meet different operational requirements, various types of warhead can be fitted including bomblet type to attack the vulnerable upper surfaces of armoured vehicles, mines or anti-airfield, for example. More recently it has been revealed that a winged version has been developed with a longer range. The latter is known as the ASTROS TM (Tactical Missile) and is understood to have a range of 150 km (93.2 miles) but has yet to enter production.

The rockets can be launched by the operator seated in the safety of the cab either singly or in ripples. The standard rockets are unguided and have solid propellant with wrap-around fins that unfold at the rear.

Although originally developed for surface-to-surface applications, the ASTROS II is now being marketed for coastal defence applications with the first customer being the Brazilian army. This system is used in conjunction with a vehicle-mounted radar system to detect surface craft before they are engaged by the ASTROS II rockets.

More recently it has been revealed that AVIBRAS is working on an **ASTROS III** system which will be based on a much larger 8x8 truck which in addition to carrying and launching the standard series of SS-30, SS-40, SS-60 and SS-80 rockets will also launch a new generation of rockets including the SS-150.

A Saudi Arabian ASTROS II system in a dug-in firing position during the 1990-91 Gulf War, in which both Iraqi and Saudi Arabian systems saw extensive use.

SPECIFICATION	
ASTROS II (SS-30 rocket)	**Rocket length:** 3.9 m (12 ft 10 in)
Crew: 3	**Rocket weight:** 68 kg (149.9 lb)
Chassis: 10000-kg (22,046-lb) Tectran AV-VBA 6x6 truck	**Maximum range:** 30 km (18.6 miles)
Calibre: 127 mm (5 in)	**Warhead types:** HE
No. of launch tubes: 32	

WS-1B Four-round artillery rocket system

NORINCO (China North Industries Corporation) have developed almost all of the surface-to-surface rocket systems used by the Peoples Liberation Army (PLA). In the past some of these have been very simple systems and as well as being procured by the PLA have also been exported in some quantities, especially to Middle East armies.

Some of the more recent sophisticated surface-to-surface rocket systems have bee developed by the China Precision Machinery Import and Export Corporation (CPMIEC) with one of the latest being the 302-mm (11.89-in) **WS-1B** (four-round) system. There was also an earlier 320-mm (12.59-in) system known as the **WS-1** but this is no longer marketed.

WS-1B is based on a locally manufactured Mercedes-Benz forward-control (6x6) truck chassis and to the rear of the cab there is a small pod for additional crew members.

Mounted at the very rear of the chassis is a launcher with four tubes each of which carries and launches one unguided rocket. To provide a more stable firing platform, four hydraulic stabilisers are lowered to the ground. Two of these are at the rear and the other two are located on each side to the rear of the cab.

Battery components

A typical WS-1B battery would consist of one command truck, six to nine rocket launcher trucks designated **HF-4** and a similar number of transport and loading trucks designated QY-88B. All of these are based on the same 6x6 chassis for logistical and training reasons.

Target information is relayed to the battery command truck which in turn provides this information to each launcher. The turntable mounted launcher pod has a traverse of 30° left and right with elevation limits from 0° to +60°.

The rockets have a solid propellant motor and can be fitted with two different types of warhead to suit the type of target being engaged. One warhead is of the high explosive type which is claimed to have an effective radius of at least 70 m (76 yards).

The second warhead carries over 450 sub-munitions to attack the vulnerable upper surfaces of armoured vehicles. Each sub-munition is fitted with a high explosive anti-tank (HEAT) type warhead which will penetrate up to 70 mm (2¾ in) of conventional steel armour. It is is also highly effective against soft-skinned vehicles and troops in the open.

Once the rockets have been launched the HF-4 launchers would normally rapidly move to avoid counter battery fire. In a safe and probably camouflaged area they would be reloaded by the QY-88B transport and loading truck using its onboard crane.

In recent years surface-to-surface rockets have been deployed by an increasing number of countries but they supplement rather than

The WS-1B system is a further development of the WS-1 that is understood to be in service with the PLA. and also based on a Mercedes 6x6 truck chassis.

replace conventional towed and self-propelled tube artillery. Surface-to-surface rocket systems such as the WS-1B are very much area weapons.

SPECIFICATION	
WS-1B	HE or SZB-1 submunition; effective lethal radius (ZDB-2) 70 m (76 yards)
Chassis: Mercedes-Benz 6x6 truck	
Calibre: 302 mm (11.89 in)	
No. of launch tubes: 4	**Warhead weights:** warhead 150 kg (331 lb); propellant 370 kg (816 lb); rocket motor 538 kg (1,186 lb)
Rocket length: 6.182 m (20 ft 4 in)	
Rocket weight: 708 kg (1,561 lb)	
Warhead types: ZDB-2 blast-type	

LARS Light Artillery Rocket System

The 110-mm (4.33-in) **Light Artillery Rocket System** (**LARS**) was developed by Wegmann (later Krauss-Maffei Wegmann) in the mid-1960s and accepted into West German army service in 1969. Designated **Artillerie Raketenwerfer 110 SF2** by the West German army, the type was issued on the scale of one battery of eight launchers per army division, each battery also having two 4x4 truck-mounted Swiss Contraves Fieldguard fire-control systems on 4x4 truck chassis and a resupply vehicle with 144 rockets.

Following upgrading to the **LARS II** standard, each launcher is now mounted on the rear of a 7000-kg (15,432-lb) MAN 6x6 truck chassis and consists of two side-by-side banks of 18 launcher tubes. The fin-stabilised solid propellant rockets can all be fired within 17.5 seconds, manual reloading taking approximately 15 minutes. The minimum and maximum ranges are 6 km (3.7 miles) and 14 km (8.7 miles) respectively. There are seven major types of warhead that can be fitted to the rocket, these including the DM-711 mine dispenser with five parachute-retarded AT2 anti-tank mines, the DM-21 HE-fragmentation (proximity fuze), and the DM-701 mine dispenser with eight AT1 anti-tank mines. Diehl and DM-28 training and practice warheads, DM-11 fragmentation (impact fuze), DM-39 radar target and DM-15 smoke warheads are further options.

Service

By the mid-1980s, a total of 209 LARS II launchers was in service with the West German army, and these were relegated to reserve units as the longer-range MLRS was phased into service during the late 1980s and early 1990s. At the beginning of the 21st century, LARS II was no longer in front-line German service, although units may be passed on to another NATO member.

SPECIFICATION	
LARS II	**No. of launcher tubes:** 36
Combat weight: 17480 kg (38,537 lb)	**Rocket length:** 2.263 m (7 ft 5 in)
Crew: 3	**Rocket weight:** 35 kg (77 lb)
Chassis: 7000-kg (15,432-lb) MAN 6x6 truck	**Warhead types:** HE fragmentation, submunition, smoke, practice, radar target
Calibre: 110 mm (4.33 in)	**Warhead weights:** 17.3 kg (38 lb)

Below left: The German army's Light Artillery Rocket System was upgraded from LARS to LARS II standard. The programme included a new fire-control system, additional rocket types and an increase in mobility by fitting the launcher to the MAN 6x6 chassis, the standard German army cross-country truck.

Below: Mounted on the cab of the MAN 6x6 truck of the LARS II system is a 7.62-mm (0.3-in) MG3 machine-gun with 360° traverse and elevation of +9° to +50°. The crew of three all sit in the unarmoured cab.

Valkiri Mk 1 Multiple artillery rocket system

Development of the 127-mm (5-in) **Valkiri Mk 1** started in 1977 as a counter to the Soviet 122-mm (4.8-in) BM-21 MRL and other long-range artillery pieces in service with neighbouring African countries. The first systems entered service in late 1981 with the South African army, and were deployed with artillery regiments in batteries of eight launchers that were tasked either to work on their own or with more conventional tube artillery to attack area targets such as guerrilla camps, troop or artillery concentrations, and soft-skinned vehicle convoys. The system consists of a 24-round launcher mounted on the rear hull of a 4x4 SAMIL truck chassis with overhead canopy rails so as to make it appear to be just a normal truck when travelling. The highly mobile Valkiri was ideally suited to mechanised

cross-border raids against SWAPO guerrilla bases and Angolan army units deep within Angola. A second 5-ton truck with 48 reload rounds is assigned to each Valkiri Mk 1. The full load of 24 rounds can be fired in 24 seconds, reloading taking about 10 minutes. The solid-propellant rocket is fitted with an HE fragmentation warhead filled with some 3,500 steel balls to give a lethal area of some 1500 m² (16,146 sq ft). The range can be varied from a minimum of 8 km (5 miles) to a maximum of 22 km (13.7 miles) depending upon which spoiler rings are fitted to the rocket body.

The launch signature of the Valkiri is minimal. This helped the system avoid counter-battery fire from the long-range Soviet-supplied artillery pieces of surrounding African states and guerrilla forces.

Above: Overhead canopy rails are fitted to the Valkiri Mk 1 launcher in order to camouflage the vehicle to appear as a normal South African army SAMIL 20 4x4 light truck. With the canopy down it is almost impossible to tell the difference.

SPECIFICATION	
Valkiri Mk 1	**Rocket length:** 2.68 m (8 ft 10 in)
Combat weight: 6440 kg (14,198 lb)	**Rocket weight:** 53 kg (117 lb)
Crew: 2	**Warhead type:** HE fragmentation with contact of proximity fuze; lethal area 1500 m² (16,146 sq ft)
Chassis: 2200-kg (4,850-lb) SAMIL 20 4x4 truck	**Maximum range:** 22 km (13.7 miles)
Calibre: 127 mm (5 in)	
No. of launcher tubes: 24	

BM-21 Grad Multiple-launch rocket system

As prime contractor for all Soviet and Russian multiple-launch rocket systems (MRLSs), the Splav Scientici Production Concern (now the Splav State Unitary Enterprise) designed the BM-21 Grad (hail) MLRS as a divisional-level *reaktivaya sistema zalpovogo ognya* (salvo fire rocket system) in the mid-1950s. Development was completed in 1958, and the weapon entered service in 1963. Each division's artillery component has a battalion of BM-21 equipments, its peacetime establishment of 12 systems increasing to 18 in time of war. The system is also found at army and front (army group) levels, where the unit is the regiment of three battalions each with 12 (18 in war) systems.

Principal roles

The primary divisional-level task of the BM-21 is support fire for the suppression of anti-tank missile, mortar and artillery positions, destruction of strong-points and elimination of any centres of resistance.

The BM-21 is based on the Ural-375D or, in its latest **BM-21-1 Grad** form, Ural-4360 6x6 truck with the launcher (four 10-tube banks) over the two rear axles in a position allowing 180° traverse (60° left and 120° right) and 55° elevation (0° to +55°). The vehicle is stabilised in firing position by the lowering of two stabilisers, and the rockets are fired individually or in rippled or full salvoes from a firing position in the cab or at the end of a 60-m (65-yard) cable. The discharge of 40 rockets takes 20 seconds, the launcher being reloaded in 7 minutes.

Each BM-21 comprises one BM-21 MLRS and one 9F37 resupply vehicle to bring up the required numbers of the M-21-OF rocket,

Above: The BM-21 was the standard MLRS used by Warsaw Pact countries. Production exceeded 2,000 units, and several countries, including China, Croatia, Egypt, India, Iran, Iraq, North Korea, Pakistan, Slovakia and Romania, have copied the system.

Right: Reloading of the BM-21 takes seven minutes as the rockets have to be slipped into the 40 tubes manually.

Below: With its good cross-country mobility and rugged reliability, the BM-21 is ideally suited to operations such as Afghanistan, where its high-trajectory fire allows the rockets to penetrate deep valleys.

Left: The multiple-launch rocket system first found favour with the USSR, which devoted much of its land warfare design capability to the development of weapons such as the BM-21.

Below: In northern Lebanon, a BM-21 of the Tawheed Islami is readied for movement as Syrian troops collect heavy arms belonging to leftist militias and Muslim fundamentalists after bloody fighting.

which has the manufacturing designation 9M22U. The basic rocket is roll-stabilised in flight by four spring-out tail fins, and has a diameter of 122 mm (4.8 in) and a length of 3.226 m (10 ft 7 in). The complete round weighs 77.5 kg (170.9 lb) and can carry HE fragmentation, smoke, incendiary and chemical warheads: the first and last weigh 19.4 and 19.3 kg (42.77 and 42.55 lb) respec-

tively. At a burn-out velocity of 690 m (2,264 ft) per second the rocket attains a maximum range of 20380 m (22,290 yards). Other rockets include the 66-kg (145.5-lb) 9M22M that is 2.87 m (9 ft 5 in) long and carries an 18.4-kg (40.56-lb) HE fragmentation warhead to 20000 m (21,875 yards), and the 48.5-kg (106.9-lb) 9M28 that is 1.905 m (6 ft 3 in) long and carries the standard

warhead types to 10800 m (11,810 yards).

In 1976 the Soviets introduced the 36-tube **BM-21 Grad-1** based on the MT-LB tracked chassis, for the six-launcher MLRS batteries of some tank and motorised rifle regiments. The system uses an updated rocket with a warhead of the HE fragmentation (pre-formed) or incendiary types.

The 6000-kg (13,123-lb)

BM-21 Grad-V is a light-weight system for parachute delivery, and comprises 12 tubes on the back of a GAZ-66B 4x4 truck. The rockets can be fired singly or in a rip-

pled salvo, and reloading takes five minutes. The **BM-21-P** is a single-tube launcher. Some 54 countries use the BM-21, which is still the subject of improvement.

Right: Based on a truck with 6x6 drive and a useful ground clearance figure, the BM-21 is admirably suited to European and Middle Eastern conditions.

SPECIFICATION

BM-21
Type: 40-tube multiple-launch rocket system
Crew: 6
Weight: 13700 kg (30,203 lb) fully loaded
Chassis: 4000-kg (8,818-lb) Ural-375D 6x6 truck
Dimensions: (travelling) length 7.35 m (24 ft 1 in); width 2.69 m (8 ft 10 in); height 2.85 m (9 ft 4 in)
Powerplant: one ZIL-375 water-cooled V-8 petrol engine developing 134 kW (180 hp) coupled to a

manual gearbox with five forward and one reverse gears
Performance: maximum road speed 80 km/h (50 mph); maximum range 1000 km (621 miles)
Fording: 1.5 m (4 ft 11 in)
Gradient: 60 per cent
Vertical obstacle: 0.65 m (2 ft 1½ in)
Trench: 0.875 m (2 ft 10½ in)
Rocket: 122-mm (4.8-in) type in different lengths with an option of several warheads including (9M218 rocket) 45 anti-tank submunitions

The BM-21 system's launcher unit can be elevated to 55° and traversed respectively 60° and 120° degrees to the left and right of the vehicle's centreline.

The MLRS can operate with only two crew, and it is theoretically possible for one man to fire and load the system alone. An overpressure system in the cab keeps the fumes out and a full NBC system is fitted.

Development of the MLRS

The long-range rocket, once a simple area-saturation weapon, has matured in recent years as an accurate means of delivering a host of submunitions. Leading the pack is the US with its excellent Multiple-Launch Rocket System.

Until the early 1970s, only the West Germans shared the enthusiasm of the Soviets for multiple rocket-launchers. On the Eastern Front in World War II both sides had supplemented their conventional artillery with massed rocket fire, enabling them to blast the enemy with a savage intensity. Multiple rocket-launchers were therefore ideal offensive weapons, able to deluge enemy defences immediately before an attack. They are ideal for the delivery of intense concentrations of smoke to conceal an advance, or chemical ammunition for instant saturation of a target area.

LARS system

These were the primary tasks of the Soviet multiple rocket-launchers, but NATO rockets had a different role as part of the alliance's comprehensive anti-tank plan. The West German LARS (Light Artillery Rocket System) is mounted on a MAN 6x6 truck chassis. A variety of munitions, including HE, smoke, incendiary, anti-vehicle and anti-armour, can be fired, often in a 'mixed-bag' assortment whose most impressive payload type is the AT1 anti-tank minelet. Although the LARS seemed very advanced when introduced in 1969, the evolution during the 1970s of a new generation of Soviet self-propelled artillery and the introduction of new types of tank armour soon made it obsolescent.

The 122-mm (4.8-in) 2S1 Gvozdika howitzer, introduced into Soviet tank and BMP-equipped regiments from 1974, could easily outrange the LARS, and the armour of the T-64 and T-72 tanks then entering service with the Group of Soviet Forces in Germany was such that the comparatively light 110-mm (4.33-in) LARS rocket would have had to score a nearly direct hit to inflict serious damage.

The need for a larger, longer-ranged and more accurate rocket was emphasised by a change in

An MLRS in action during Desert Storm in 1991. The US Army deployed over 230 launchers to the Gulf region in order to take part in the conflict, while the British Army deployed 16 launchers.

tactical thinking then taking place in NATO. Previously the alliance had concentrated its resources for the destruction of the enemy in the front line, but it now started to emphasise the importance of striking deeper into the enemy's rear to disrupt his command, control, communications and intelligence (C3I) network. Whereas low-flying fighter and ground-attack aircraft could deliver attacks 50 km (37 miles) and more behind the FEBA (Forward Edge of the Battle Area), they could not operate closer to the front line without sustaining severe losses from Soviet anti-aircraft systems. What NATO needed was thus a long-range rocket.

New-generation weapon

The result was the MLRS (Multiple-Launch Rocket System), which entered service with the US 1st Infantry Division (Mechanized) at Fort Riley, Kansas, in 1983. By the autumn of 1986 the US Army had 337 launchers operational, while the UK, France and West Germany had others on order.

Mounted on a tracked self-propelled loader-launcher vehicle (SPLL) based on the M2 Bradley chassis, MLRS has the mobility and speed to keep up with armoured units. Its ability to halt, fire 12 independently aimed rockets and withdraw, all in the space of 90 seconds, makes it a formidable weapon.

The MLRS is designed to deliver dual-role bomblets and anti-armour minelets, with other types following. The M77 bomblet is of the greatest use against unprotected soft-skinned vehicles, APCs and towed artillery. Some 644 such bomblets are packed into each M26 warhead, so each MLRS is capable of simultaneously discharging 7,728 bomblets over a given area.

Greater capability against tanks is offered by the AT2 warhead, which delivers seven dispensers each carrying four DM1399 anti-tank minelets. About 1000 m (1,095 yards) from the general target the main warhead disintegrates, releasing the dispensers that in turn drop their mines over a sizeable area.

Production of the MLRS is now an international effort, with the system manufactured by a European consortium as well as by Lockheed Martin, which bought Vought, the original contractor. The development of the M270 launcher and the weapons it fires (now including the Army Tactical Missile System, or ATACMS) continues for operators in 14 countries. The ATACMS, whose container-launcher occupies half of the Launcher Loader Module, carries 950 M74 dual-role bomblets to a range of more than 265 km (165 miles).

Left: US Army NBC-suited crew members with their M270 MLRS on exercise in West Germany. The Loader Launcher Module is traversed 90° from the centreline revealing the rocket tubes with their blow-off covers. Each loaded tube is a certified round. Designed for use in a European war, the main role of the MLRS would have been to rapidly lay down minefields in the path of advancing enemy armour. Using the AT2 anti-tank mine, MLRS could have sown 336 mines over an area 1000 x 400 m (1,094 x 437 yards) in one minute.

Below: An M270 MLRS and a reload vehicle at speed in the desert. With plenty of reload rockets, the MLRS is a devastating weapon in terms of payload weight delivered accurately onto a distant target. Based on a modified M2 Bradley chassis, MLRS has excellent cross-country mobility. Because it is so easy to detect its firing postion by its launch signature, the MLRS uses 'shoot and scoot' tactics: firing a rapid salvo and then driving away quickly before the enemy can bring down fire on its position. Early MLRs relied on massive salvoes to make up for the relative inaccuracy of individual rockets. The MLRS introduces much more accurate rockets with advanced sub-munition and shaped-charge warheads.

US Army M270 MLRS

Transportable in C-130, C-141 and C-5 transport aircraft, together with its support vehicles, the MLRS is currently a mainstay of the divisions of both the US Army and the Army National Guard. Under the 'Division '86' plan, 'heavy' armoured and mechanised divisions of the US Army were each allocated one battery (comprising three firing platoons each of three MLRS) and two batteries each with six M110 203-mm (8-in) self-propelled howitzers in a single mixed artillery battalion. By the first part of the 21st century, the US Army and ANG had received more than 500 M270 and improved M270A1 vehicles together with 450,000 or more tactical rockets and large numbers of resupply vehicles. Production and development continue.

BM-21 vs M270 MLRS

In World War II the artillery rocket was steadily developed as an area-saturation weapon of shorter range but considerably lower cost than conventional artillery. Since that time the rocket has matured with considerably greater range and accuracy, and the ability to carry warheads able to dispense guided as well as unguided submunitions. Moreover, it is now possible for multi-tube launchers to be carried by tracked as well as wheeled vehicles. In the process the rocket has come to bridge the tactical gap between artillery and guided missiles. It was the Soviet Union that introduced the MRL during World War II, and throughout the Cold War the USSR remained the world leader in their production and use.

BM-21 Grad multiple-launch rocket system

The Grad (hail) was developed in the mid-1950s as a divisional-level area-saturation weapon (a battalion of 12 launchers expanded to 18 launchers in time of war) with a launcher assembly of four 10-tube units on the back of a Ural-375D 6x6 truck to fire 122-mm (4.82-in) M-21-OF (9M22U) fin-stabilised rockets. The complete fire unit has a crew of six, and the 40-tube launcher can be loaded in seven minutes from a 9F37 ammunition supply vehicle. Once the vehicle has halted, its takes the crew 2 minutes 30 seconds to get the launcher into action, and the launcher is aligned with and ranged onto the target by training it (120° left and 60° right) and elevating it (0° to +55°). All 40 rockets can be fired in 20 seconds. The standard M-21-OF rocket weighs 77.5 kg (171 lb) with a warhead weighing about 19.4 kg (42.8 lb). Warhead types include HE-fragmentation, smoke, incendiary and, now out of service, chemical. The rocket has a direct-fire minimum range of 500 m (545 yards) and an indirect-fire maximum range of 20380 m (22,290 yards).

No protection

The cab of the Ural-375D launcher vehicle lacks any form of protection, so it is standard practice for the launcher unit to be trained so that neither the rockets nor their exhaust plumes pass over this structure. Before the rockets are fired, two stabilisers are lowered to the ground at the sides of the vehicle's rear to steady the launcher and thereby enhance accuracy. The rockets can be fired from either the cab or a remote-control unit connected to the vehicle by a 60-m (66-yard) cable, and the control unit allows the selection of single-tube, selective ripple or salvo fire.

Launcher vehicle

The BM-21 Grad system weighs 13700 kg (30,203 lb) fully loaded, and in travelling order is 7.35 m (24 ft 11⁄3 in) long. The vehicle is powered by a ZIL-375 water-cooled V-8 petrol engine developing 135 kW (181 hp) and coupled to a manual transmission with five forward and one reverse gears as well as a two-speed transfer case. The maximum road speed is 80 km/h (50 mph), and the fuel capacity of 360 litres (79.2 Imp gal) yields a road range of 1000 km (621 miles).

BM-21 in action

In service with ex-Soviet and former Warsaw Pact forces and the armies of many former Soviet allies in the Third World, the BM-21 remains a highly effective weapons system. It is cheap, sturdy and reliable and the Ural 4x4 chassis offers excellent cross-counry mobility. In African and low-intensity Middle East conflicts the moral effect of a multiple rocket salvo on half-trained or irregular troops has been outstanding. However, the BM-21 was originally designed for a European conflict, in which it would have been used to provide sudden shock firepower to support a brakthrough or to deluge NATO positions with chemical weapons.

M77 rocket

The M270 launcher of the MLRS carries 12 227-mm (8.94-in) rockets. The standard Phase I rocket has a length of 3.937 m (12 ft 11 in) and incorporates the M26 warhead with 644 M77 dual-role submunitions. The alternative Phase II rocket with the AT2 anti-tank warhead is 1.959 m (6 ft 4 in) long and its warhead carries seven dispensers each loaded with four DM1399 minelets. The XR-M77 extended-range rocket has a longer rocket motor and only 518 M77 submunitions, but at a weight of 296 kg (653 lb) can reach out to 45500 m (49,760 yards).

Phase I and Phase II developments

Whereas Phase I of the MLRS's development was based on a rocket carrying the M26 warhead loaded with 644 M77 Dual-Purpose Improved Conventional Munitions, Phase II development saw the introduction of the AT2 warhead optimised for the anti-tank role. Procured by Germany and the UK, this warhead carries 28 DM1399 dedicated anti-tank submunitions, and its weight of 108 kg (238 lb) reduces the rocket's weight to 258 kg (569 lb) for a maximum range of 40000 m (43,745 yards). The mines are deployed as the rocket overflies the target area at around 1200 m (3,935 ft), the efforts of two launcher loads creating a field measuring 2000 x 115 m (2,185 x 125 yards). Each mine can penetrate more than 140 mm (5.51 in) of belly armour, or rip off a track and cripple the suspension.

Launch tubes and resupply

The MLRS system's rockets are contained in fibreglass tubes within an aluminium six-pack structure. US Army MLRS batteries are supported by Oshkosh HEMTT 8x8 resupply trucks, each carrying four six-round launch pods each. In addition, each truck can tow a Heavy Expanded Mobility Ammunition Trailer (HEMAT) whcih can carry a further four full-loaded rocket pods. Other MLRS operators use different resupply vehicles, the British Army for example opting for the DROPS truck-trailer system based on the Leyland Medium Mobility Load Carrier (MMLC) truck.

Crew compartment

Though based on the chassis of the M2, the MLRS has an entirely revised structure above the upper lines of the tracks. Located at the front of the vehicle is the cab for the crew of three (driver, gunner and section chief), although the whole of the MLRS mission, including the reloading of the launcher, can in fact be accomplished by one person. The cab is fitted with aluminium armour and louvred windows to provide the crew with protection against small arms fire and shell splinters, an overpressure ventilation system prevents the ingress of rocket launch fumes, and there is also a filtration system to provide NBC protection. A Mk 19 40-mm grenade launcher can be mounted on the cab roof for local protection.

Lockheed Martin MLRS

The M270 Multiple-Launch Rocket System operated by the US and allies is based on the 'stretched' chassis of the M2 Bradley Infantry Fighting Vehicle adapted for the carriage of an elevating/traversing launcher for 12 M77 fin-stabilised rockets. These each weigh 306 kg (675 lb) and deliver 644 anti-tank/personnel submunitions to 31600 m (34,550 yards).

Lower hull and suspension

The lower hull of the MLRS is fabricated from aluminium. The tracks of the MLRS are of the single-pin type with replaceable rubber pads, and on each side the vehicle is carried by six dual rubber-tyred road wheels with torsion-bar-in-tube suspensions and shock absorbers for the first, second and sixth wheels. There are four track-return rollers, the drive sprocket is at the front and the idler is at the rear.

Launcher Loader Module

Mounted at the rear of the MLRS's hull is the Launcher Loader Module. This comprises the base, turret and cage, and includes the computerised fire-control system, the stabilisation reference package and position determining system, a launcher drive system, and a two-boom crane so that the crew can load and unload the launcher's 12 rocket tubes. The rockets are hermetically sealed in their tubes and have a shelf life of 10 years.

MLRs in action Long-range area devastation

From the later 1970s the artillery rocket evolved from a relatively simple and cheap method of saturating an area with high explosive or submunitions into an altogether more sophisticated weapon still optimised for the area attack role but offering much enhanced accuracy and thus the ability to deliver precision-attack weapons with great tactical flexibility than can be achieved by artillery at less cost that than of a larger guided weapon.

Surprisingly, it is only relatively recently that the West, and in particular the US, realised the importance of the MRL in modern warfare; but instead of learning direct from the Soviets their use of such weapons, most NATO nations which deploy the joint American-European Multiple-Launch Rocket System (MLRS) use it in place of conventional artillery pieces rather than as a supplement to them. As evidenced above, the launch singature of any MLR is considerable; thus the firing platform will stay back from the forward line of troops in order to conceal itself.

Left: Developed by AVIBRAS, the 70-mm Skyfire family of unguided rockets is unusual in that it has been developed for both airborne and land-based applications. The weapon is seen here in the surface-to-surface role, for which it is launched from a 36-tube launcher on the rear of a light truck. The ground-launched Skyfire rocket is powered by a solid-propellant motor and is fitted with warapround fins and a larger warhead than its SBAT-70 air-launched counterpart.

Right: Developed for the Brazilian army and export operators in the early 1980s, the ASTROS II system fires a single SS-60 rocket. The system's AV-LMU universal launcher can fire four types of unguided rocket: the 127-mm SS-30 (32 rounds per launcher), the 180-mm SS-40 (16 rounds), the 300-mm SS-60 (four rounds) and the extended-range 300-mm SS-80 (four rounds). These rockets are armed with a variety of warheads including cluster munition, dual-effect anti-armour/anti-personnel, high-explosive incendiary (HE-I), mine deployment and airfield denial with delayed action submunitions.

Right: The ASTROS II system had seen extensive combat use by Iraq during the war with Iran during the 1980s before going into action with both Iraqi and Saudi forces during the 1991 Gulf War. This Saudi Arabian system carries 127-mm SS-30 rockets.

Below: The standard MLRS rocket pod is also the transport and storage container and weighs 2308 kg (5,088 lb) with its six rockets. A rigid aluminium alloy frame holds the six glassfibre tubes, which are sealed front and rear by blow-off covers. A spent pod is removed and a fresh pod loaded by the M270's integral crane. This launcher is one of 55 in French service, equipping two regiments (24 MLRS each), the 12th and 74th. The latter operates as part of France's Rapid Reaction Force.

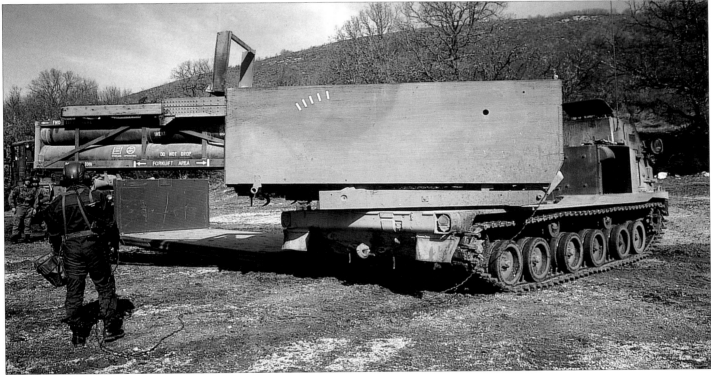

Right: MLR Afghan style. This Northern Alliance UAZ-469 light 4x4 utility vehicle carries in its payload section an extemporised tripod mounting for an aircraft rocket pod (a UB-16 unit for 16 57-mm weapons), allowing its use as a surface-to-surface weapon. Similar field conversions were conducted by Serbian forces during the wars in the former Yugoslavia.

122-mm RM-70 Artillery Rocket System

The **RM-70** artillery rocket system dates from the early 1970s. It was designed and built in Czechoslovakia.

In 1985 an updated version was introduced and an ammunition upgrade package is now available. The system is supported by ZTS Dubnica nad Vahom of Slovakia who maintain the system on a production as required basis.

The main feature of the RM-70 is its rapid reload system. Once all 40 122-mm (4.8 in) fin stabilised rockets have been fired, the launcher barrels can be aligned with a magazine pack of a further 40 rockets that are then mechanically inserted into the empty barrels. The entire reloading process can take less than a minute, far shorter than employing the usual manual reloading methods and enabling the RM-70 to deliver two rapid salvos, each complete salvo lasting between 18 to 22 seconds.

The RM-70 is carried on Tatra 8x8 trucks, originally a Tatra 813 with an armoured cab. After 1985 the improved Tatra 815 was introduced and the cab carrying the crew of four was left unarmoured. A dozer blade to clear obstacles is an optional add-on to both trucks.

The 122-mm rockets are essentially the same as those fired from the Soviet/Russian BM-21 Grad (Cherrystone) system, with a range of 20000 m (65,616 ft). By updating the rocket motors the latest versions of these rockets can extend

the maximum range up to 36000 m (118,110 ft). Warhead can vary from high explosive fragmentation to enhanced warheads with pre-formed fragments. Cargo warheads can also scatter small anti-tank mines.

RM-70 systems were once used by East Germany. In 1994 150 of these were passed to Greece. Export sales were also made to Angola, Ecuador, Rwanda and Zimbabwe.

Above: The RM-70 is seen here with its rocket launcher elevated and traversed. The Tatra vehicle is also available without an armoured cab.

Right: Despite being armoured, the outline of the cab betrays the Tatra 8x8 truck routes of the RM-70's carrying vehicle. Versions of the system are also available fitted with a dozer blade.

SPECIFICATION

RM-70
Crew: 4
Rocket calibre: 122 mm
Number of barrels: 40
Weight, complete system: 25300 kg (50, 705 lb)
Rocket weight, each: 66 kg (145 lb)

Warhead weight, each: 18.4 kg (40.5 lb)
Max range: 20000 m (36000 m/98,425 ft updated)
Vehicle length: 8.8 m (28 ft)
Vehicle width: 2.55 m (8.3 ft)
Vehicle height: 2.96 m

Iraqi Artillery Rocket Systems

Prior to Operation Iraqi Freedom the Iraqi armed forces fielded a remarkable array of artillery rocket systems. They included imported systems such as licence-produced **Brazilian Avibras Astros** rockets of various calibres (the **Sajeel** series) and large numbers of 122-mm (4.8-in) **BM-21 Grad** systems from Egypt and the former Soviet Union. In addition to these, several systems were developed locally, some of them with technical assistance from elsewhere.

One of these was a 107-mm (4-in) 12-barrel

A long way from its cold Russian home: an Iraqi Frog-7 system is seen here following the end of Operation Desert Storm. Saddam Hussein army used several foreign-artillery systems.

system virtually identical to the **Chinese Norinco 107-mm Type 63** and was almost certainly produced using Chinese technical assistance. Most of these 107-mm launchers were towed while others had the launchers mounted on tracked armoured carriers.

According to Iraqi sources the maximum range was 8000 m (26,246 ft) firing a 19 kg (41.8 lb) rocket.

Another locally copied system involves 122-mm rockets launched from various types of vehicle in salvos of up to 30 rockets. The source appears to have been the Egyptian **Sakr-36** with a range of 20000 m (65,616 ft) using a 66 kg (145 lb) rocket. Again, some of these 122-mm systems were mounted on tracked armoured carriers.

Abadeel

At one stage the former Yugoslavia used Iraqi funds to co-develop a 262-mm (10.3-in) system known in Iraq as the **Ababeel 50**, the Yugoslav version being known as the **M-87 Orkan**. The system involved 12 launcher barrels carried on a heavy track, each rocket having a weight of about 389 kg (850 lb) and a maximum range of 50000 m (164,041 ft). It appears that few of these systems were manufactured in Iraq and were used against Iran.

Frog

Another rather rare system was known as the **Ababeel 100** and appears to have been locally developed.

This involved four truck-mounted launch tubes. Few details are available although the range has been quoted as 100000 m (328,083 ft). Also available was the **Laith 90**, a 550-mm (21.6-in) calibre copy of the Soviet **Frog-7** series with a maximum range of 90000 m (295,275 ft). Several of these systems will have been destroyed during Operation Desert Storm and later during Operation Enduring Freedom.

SPECIFICATION	
T-90S	Kontakt ERA offering a total of 1220 mm equivalent against HEAT and 810 mm equivalent against APFSDS
Crew: 3	
Combat weight: 50 tonnes	**Armament:** 125-mm 2A46M smoothbore with 43 rounds; coaxial PKT 7.62-mm (0.3-in) MG; NSVT 12.7-mm (0.5-in) heavy AA MG on turret
Dimensions: length (with gun forward) 9.53 m (31 ft 3 in); length (hull) 6.86 m (22 ft 6 in); width 3.37 m (11 ft 1 in); height (overall) 2.23 m (7 ft 4 in)	
Armour: 520 mm on turret plus	

Roketsan Artillery Rocket System

Formed in 1988, Roketsan of Turkey manufacture rocket and missile technology for the Turkish armed forces. Among other products, Roketsan build the launch and flight motors for Stinger missiles under licence from Raytheon in the United States. Roketsan includes the companies MKEK, Aselsan, Kalekalip, STFA, Kutlutas and TSKGV.

Grad

Roketsan also build two artillery rocket systems, both of them based on designs originally produced elsewhere. A 107-mm (4.2-in) towed system is based on a Chinese design: the 107-mm **Type 63** while a 122-mm truck-carried system is based on the Soviet/Russian 122-mm (4.8 in) **Grad** (Cherrystone) system.

The Roketsan 107-mm towed system has 12 barrels and is known as the **T-107**. A complete salvo can be launched in from seven to nine seconds, each salvo delivering about 100 kg (220 lb) of explosive. The rockets involved are spin stabilised with warheads that can be either high explosive or with 2,800 steel balls packed around the explosive content to increase the lethal radius of each rocket to about 25 m (82 ft). The maximum range using standard rockets is 8500 m (27,887-ft), although an extended range rocket known as the **TR-107** can extend the range to 13000 m (42,650 ft).

The Roketsan 122-mm system is known as the T-122 and is normally carried on a locally-produced MAN 6x6 tactical truck chassis.

Rapid-fire

Rockets are launched from two elevating and traversing arrays of barrels at the rear of the vehicle, each array containing 2.03 m (6 ft 6 in) long barrels. All 40 rockets can be fired within 80 seconds. A completely loaded system with the truck, weighs 22200 kg (48,941 lb).

Balls of steel

The standard 122-mm rockets fired are essentially the same as those for the Russian Grad system and can be utilised with the T-122, the maximum range being 20000 m (65,616 ft).

Above: Roketsan rocket artillery system can be truck mounted on a MAN 6x6 chassis, although this 107-mm (4.2-in) system is based on a Chinese design and is seen here fitted onto a trailer.

Locally developed rockets can have warheads with up to 5,500 steel balls added to the explosive content. Also locally developed is the TRB-122 rocket with a range of 40000 m (131,233 ft) and the **TRK-122** capable of scattering 56 bomblets over 30000 m (98,425 ft).

SPECIFICATION	
T-107	**T-122**
Rocket calibre: 107 mm	**Rocket calibre:** 122 mm
Number of barrels: 12	**Number of barrels:** 2 x 20
Weight, complete system: 620 kg (1,366 lb)	**Weight, complete system:** 22200 kg (48,491 lb)
Rocket weight, each: 19.5 kg (43 lb)	**Rocket weight, each:** 66.6 kg (146.8 lb)
Warhead weight, each: 8.4 kg (18.5 lb)	**Warhead weight, each:** 18.4 kg (40.5 lb)
Max range: 8500 m (27,887 ft); 13,000 m (42,650 ft)	**Max range:** 20000 m (65,616 ft); 40000 m (131,233 ft)
Barrel length: 880 mm (34 in)	**Barrel length:** 3 m (9.8 ft)

Rheinmetall 20-mm Twin light AA gun

The **Rheinmetall 20-mm** light anti-aircraft gun mount was developed by the Rheinmetall company of Düsseldorf to meet the requirements of the West German ministry of defence. The mount is armed with two examples of the 20-mm MK 20 Rh 202 cannon, which at the time was the standard weapon in its class in the West German army: it was also installed in the Marder MICV in a two-man power-operated turret, arms the Wiesel 1 light air-portable armoured vehicle that has been produced for German airborne units, and is fitted in the two-man turret of the Luchs amphibious armoured car. The cannon is also installed on a single mount for various naval applications, and the Italians have installed the cannon in the turret of the Tipo 6616 armoured car.

Galileo sight

This lightweight twin 20-mm anti-aircraft gun system is carried on a two-wheel trailer that can be towed by a light vehicle such as a Unimog 4x4 truck. The gunner is seated at the rear of the mount and aims the twin cannon using an Italian Galileo P56 computing sight, which has an optical sight with x5 magnification, an electronic analogue computer for calculating the lead angles required to hit aerial targets, a joystick for elevation and traverse, and a panel for inserting target information.

Elevation and traverse are hydraulic, maximum traverse speed being 80° per second and maximum elevation speed 48° per second, power for these functions being provided by an air-

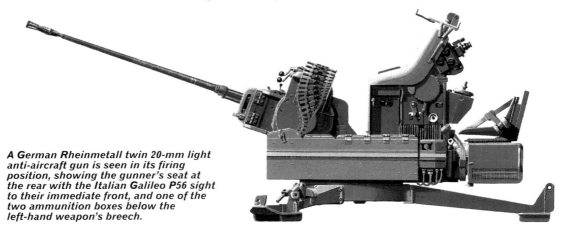

A German Rheinmetall twin 20-mm light anti-aircraft gun is seen in its firing position, showing the gunner's seat at the rear with the Italian Galileo P56 sight to their immediate front, and one of the two ammunition boxes below the left-hand weapon's breech.

cooled two-stroke petrol engine mounted under the gunner's seat.

The cannon are gas-operated and fully automatic, the gunner firing them via a foot-operated pedal that is fitted with a safety device. The gunner can select either single-shot or full automatic fire with one or two barrels. The cannon have a cyclic rate of fire of 2,000 rounds per barrel per minute, and each cannon is provided with an ammunition box containing 270 rounds of fixed ammunition, with another 10 rounds in the flexible feed system that connects the ammunition boxes with the gun. The types of ammunition that can be fired include armour-piercing discarding sabot-tracer (APDS-T), armour-piercing incendiary-tracer (API-T), high explosive incendiary (HEI), high explosive incendiary-tracer (HE-T), and various training rounds. The APDS-T has a muzzle velocity of 1150 m (3,773 ft) per second.

In the firing position the

weapon is supported on three outriggers. The system is essentially of the clear-weather type, although it can be integrated into an overall defence system. In addition to being used by the German armed forces it is operated by Argentina, Greece, Indonesia, Portugal and Turkey: the weapon was used by Argentina in the Falklands War of 1982 to defend Port Stanley airfield. The French air force uses the same twin mounting fitted with a Giat Industries M693(F2) 20-mm cannon under the designation **76T2** or **Cerbere**.

Norwegian model

To meet the requirements of the Norwegian armed forces, Hispano-Suiza and A/S Kongsberg Vappenfabrikk designed and built a single-mount anti-aircraft gun called the **FK 20-2** using the same 20-mm MK 20 Rh 202 cannon. The FK 20-2 is used by the German and Norwegian armies. The FK 20-2 can also be used to engage ground targets.

SPECIFICATION	
Rheinmetall 20-mm mounting	travelling 2.075 m (6 ft 9¾ in)
Calibre: 20 mm (0.79 in)	**Elevation:** -3.5° to +81.6°
Weights: travelling 2160 kg (4,762 lb) and firing 1640 kg (3,616 lb)	**Traverse:** 360°
	Ranges: maximum horizontal 6000 m (6,560 yards); maximum vertical 4500 m (14,765 ft); effective vertical 2000 m (6,560 ft)
Dimensions: length travelling 5.035 m (16 ft 6¼ in); width travelling 2.36 m (7 ft 9 in); height	
	Crew: 4-5 (but only 1 on mount)

The FK 20-2 is in effect the single-barrel counterpart of the twin-barrel Rheinmetall mount, and uses exactly the same MK 20 Rh 202 cannon, a well-proved weapon firing a wide range of ammunition types.

Breda 40L70 Field Mounting 40-mm twin light AA gun

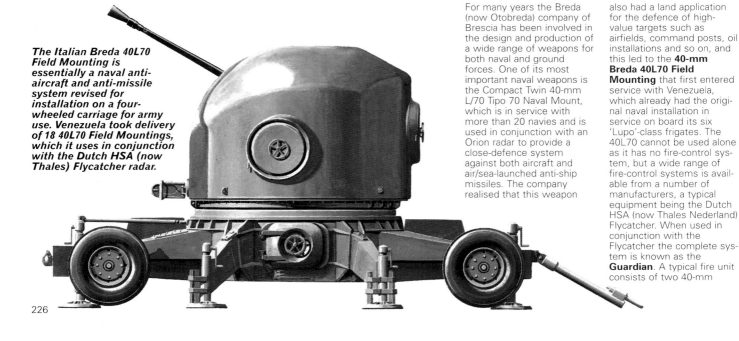

The Italian Breda 40L70 Field Mounting is essentially a naval anti-aircraft and anti-missile system revised for installation on a four-wheeled carriage for army use. Venezuela took delivery of 18 40L70 Field Mountings, which it uses in conjunction with the Dutch HSA (now Thales) Flycatcher radar.

For many years the Breda (now Otobreda) company of Brescia has been involved in the design and production of a wide range of weapons for both naval and ground forces. One of its most important naval weapons is the Compact Twin 40-mm L/70 Tipo 70 Naval Mount, which is in service with more than 20 navies and is used in conjunction with an Orion radar to provide a close-defence system against both aircraft and air/sea-launched anti-ship missiles. The company realised that this weapon

also had a land application for the defence of high-value targets such as airfields, command posts, oil installations and so on, and this led to the **40-mm Breda 40L70 Field Mounting** that first entered service with Venezuela, which already had the original naval installation in service on board its six 'Lupo'-class frigates. The 40L70 cannot be used alone as it has no fire-control system, but a wide range of fire-control systems is available from a number of manufacturers, a typical equipment being the Dutch HSA (now Thales Nederland) Flycatcher. When used in conjunction with the Flycatcher the complete system is known as the **Guardian**. A typical fire unit consists of two 40-mm

40L70 mounts, one Flycatcher fire-control system, and generators.

The twin 40-mm 40L70 mount is essentially the standard naval turret installed on a four-wheel carriage. In the firing position the system is supported on six jacks that are adjustable to suit the different ground conditions: one jack is located at each end of the carriage, and the other four are placed two on each side on outriggers.

Ammunition types

Turret traverse and weapon elevation are electrically powered at a maximum traverse speed of 90° per second. The mount has two 40-mm Bofors L/70 guns, which have a cyclic rate of fire of 300 rounds per barrel per minute. The ammunition is identical to that used in the famous Bofors L/70 anti-aircraft gun and includes proximity-fused pre-fragmented high explosive (PFHE), high-capacity high explosive (HCHE), high explosive-tracer (HE-T), armour-piercing capped-tracer (APC-T) and target practice (TP). To engage aerial targets such as helicopters, aircraft and missiles, the PFHE round would be used as it produces over 2,400 fragments of which some 600 are tungsten pellets, which can penetrate 14 mm (0.55 in) of aluminium.

A total of 444 rounds of 40-mm ammunition (carried in four-round clips) is carried in the turret, and the empty cartridge cases are ejected outside the forward part of the turret. When firing, the turret is unmanned, being controlled by the operator in the fire-control centre. For many years Breda has been producing the 40-mm Bofors L/70 anti-aircraft gun (including the towed version) under licence. To increase the rate of fire of its particular model Breda designed an automatic feeding device, and this boosts the cyclic rate of fire from 240 to 300 rounds per minute, with 144 ready-use rounds carried.

More recently Breda developed to the prototype stage a twin 30-mm towed anti-aircraft gun using a German weapon, the 30-mm Mauser Model F. This provides a cyclic rate of fire of 800 rounds per gun per minute, and each gun has 250 rounds of ready-use ammunition. The system is fitted with the Italian Galileo P75D optronic fire-control system and an on-carriage power unit.

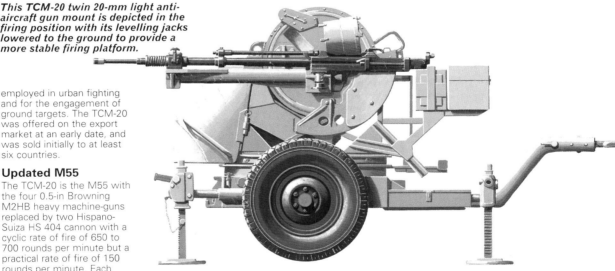

When the 40L70 weapon is firing no crewmembers are present as the guns are aimed and fired by remote control using the Flycatcher fire-control system.

SPECIFICATION	
40-mm Breda 40L70	3.2 m (10 ft 6 in); height travelling
Calibre: 40 mm (1.57 in)	3.65 m (11 ft 11¾ in)
Weights: travelling without	**Elevation:** -13° to +85°
ammunition 9900 kg (21,826 lb) and	**Traverse:** 360°
travelling with ammunition	**Ranges:** maximum horizontal
10966 kg (24,176 lb)	12500 m (13,670 yards); maximum
Dimensions: length travelling	vertical 8700 m (28,545 ft);
8.05 m (26 ft 5 in); width travelling	effective vertical 4000 m (13,125 ft)

RAMTA TCM-20 20-mm twin light AA gun

For many years the Israeli military used the American M55 trailer-mounted 0.5-in (12.7-mm) quadruple light anti-aircraft gun mount, but realised that this had only a very short range. The RAMTA Structures and Systems Division of Israel Aircraft Industries then modernised the system as the **RAMTA TCM-20** with two 20-mm cannon to meet the requirements of the Israeli Air Defence Command. After trials with prototype systems, the type was accepted for service in time to be used in combat during the 1970 'War of Attrition', when it is claimed to have shot down 10 aircraft in 10 engagements. It was also used during the Yom Kippur War of 1973, when it is credited with shooting down some 60 per cent of the Arab aircraft downed by Israeli air defences, the remaining 40 per cent being shot down by HAWK SAMs and other anti-aircraft guns. In Israel's 1982 invasion of Lebanon, the TCM-20 was used not only to shoot down Syrian aircraft and helicopters, but was also

This TCM-20 twin 20-mm light anti-aircraft gun mount is depicted in the firing position with its levelling jacks lowered to the ground to provide a more stable firing platform.

employed in urban fighting and for the engagement of ground targets. The TCM-20 was offered on the export market at an early date, and was sold initially to at least six countries.

Updated M55

The TCM-20 is the M55 with the four 0.5-in Browning M2HB heavy machine-guns replaced by two Hispano-Suiza HS 404 cannon with a cyclic rate of fire of 650 to 700 rounds per minute but a practical rate of fire of 150 rounds per minute. Each barrel has a quick-change drum magazine that holds 60 rounds of ready-use ammunition. The gunner aims the cannon with an M18 reflex sight. Mount traverse and weapon elevation are electric, with onboard power provided by two 12-volt batteries mounted at

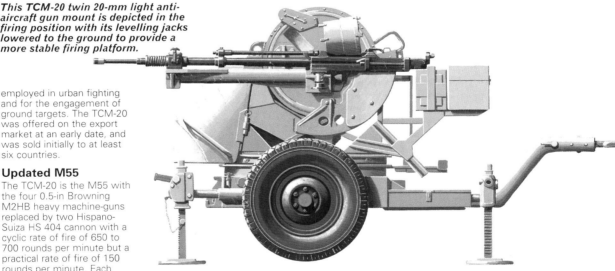

the rear of the carriage; the batteries are kept charged by an auxiliary power unit. In the firing position the wheels are normally removed and the carriage is supported on three jacks.

The basic mount is normally towed by any 4x4 light vehicle, although Israel has also used a self-propelled model based on the M3 series halftrack. There is no provision for all-weather fire control, although warning of the exact direction of

Towed and self-propelled versions of the TCM-20 were developed. The latter was mounted on the rear of an M3 series halftrack. The system was used for the first time during the 'War of Attrition' in 1970.

approach by enemy aircraft can be given by an Elta EL/M-2106 point-defence alerting radar.

Larger cannon

At a later date RAMTA developed a new system, the **TCM Mk 3**, basically modelled on the original TCM but capable of being fitted with a variety of different weapons in the 20-mm to 25-mm class, including

the 23-mm cannon used in the Soviet ZU-23 towed and ZSU-23-4 self-propelled anti-aircraft gun systems. In addition to the same M18 optical sight as installed on the original TCM-20, the TCM Mk 3 was offered with a Starlight sight with x4 magnification for night operations, and a fire-control system including a laser rangefinder and computerised sight system.

SPECIFICATION	
TCM-20	**Elevation:** -10° to +90°
Calibre: 20 mm (0.79 in)	**Traverse:** 360°
Weight: travelling 1350 kg	**Ranges:** maximum horizontal
(2,976 lb)	5700 m (6,235 yards); maximum
Dimensions: length travelling	vertical 4500 m (14,765 ft);
3.27 m (10 ft 8¾ in); width	effective vertical 1200 m (3,935 ft)
travelling 1.7 m (5 ft 7 in); height	**Crew:** 4 (only 1 on the mount)
travelling 1.63 m (5 ft 4¼ in)	

20-mm Tarasque Light anti-aircraft gun

One of the features of the French 20-mm Tarasque light anti-aircraft gun is that it can be towed by a light vehicle such as the M201 (4x4). The 20-mm M693 cannon has dual-feed, so enabling the gunner to change from one type of ammunition to another to engage different types of target.

Taking its name from a fiercesomely enormous six-legged French Dragon, the **20-mm Tarasque light anti-aircraft gun** entered service with the French army in 1982 under the designation **Type 53T2**. It is armed with the 20-mm M693 cannon (the standard weapon of its type in the French army), which is also installed in the AMX-1 OP mechanised infantry combat vehicle and the AMX-30 main battle tank. The South African Army uses the gun on its Ratel 20 Infantry Fighting Vehicle. The gun is built under licence by LIW, a division of Denel in South Africa. The weapon is also in service in Senegal and Djibouti.

The Tarasque light anti-aircraft gun is carried on a two-wheeled carriage that can be towed by a light 4x4 vehicle such as the M201 or Land Rover. Its light weight also means that it can be transported slung beneath a helicopter.

One-man operation

The weapon can be brought into action by two men in about 15 seconds: on arrival at the selected firing position the locking pin retaining the rear foot is removed and the mount slewed through 90° to place the other two feet in contact with the ground; the carriage is then removed and the mount supported on the three feet. Only one man is required to operate the Tarasque gun, the other two men acting as ammunition handlers or aircraft spotters. The gunner is seated on the left side of the mount and moves in elevation with the 20-mm cannon. Elevation and traverse are hydraulic, though manual controls are provided for emergency use. These controls can include a hand-operated hydraulic pump and also handwheels. One handwheel will give 10° of traverse, while the elevation of another handwheel will give 6° of elevation. When powered by the motor, the gun's maximum traverse speed is 40° per second and maximum elevation speed is 80° per second. The gunner is able to select either automatic or single-shot firing modes, via the hydraulic firing mechanism which is selected by the gunner's right foot.

The 20-mm M693 is a dual-feed cannon and has a cyclic rate of fire of 740 rounds per minute, The gunner fires the cannon by pressing down his right foot, and can fire single aimed shots or bursts. A total of 140 rounds of ready-use ammunition is carried, of which 100 are normally high explosive (HE) or high explosive incendiary (HEI) for engaging aerial targets, and 40 of Armour-Piercing Discarding Sabot (APDS) for engaging armoured targets. Practice Tracer (French designation OXT) and Practice Inert (French designation OX) can also be used. The APDS round will penetrate 20-mm (0.79-in) of armour at an incidence of 0° at a range of 1000 m (1,094 yards). As well as being able to engage aerial targets, the gun has the residual capability to hit against personnel and light armoured vehicles in the ground role.

Sight magnification

The gunner has an M348 anti-aircraft day sight with a magnification of x1 and a ground-to-ground sight with a magnification of x5.

The Tarasque can also be installed, less its carriage, in the rear of cross-country vehicles such as the TRM 2000 4x4 truck; this gives the weapon greater cross-country mobility as well as enabling it to open fire as soon as the vehicle comes to a halt.

It must be noted that the weapon is an exclusively clear weather system, and it lacks any all-weather fire control system.

A GIAT 20-mm Tarasque light anti-aircraft gun baking in the desert sun is seen here with its crew of three, the gunner located towards the right of the group. Note the M348 day sight being used by the gunner. The other two troops can be seen in their role as surrogate anti-aircraft fire controllers.

SPECIFICATION	
Tarasque	1.70 m (5 ft 6 in)
Calibre: 20 mm (0.79 in)	**Elevation:** +83°/-8°
Weights: travelling with	**Traverse:** 360°
ammunition 840 kg (1,852 lb); firing	**Ranges:** maximum horizontal
with ammunition 660 kg (1,455 lb)	2000 m (6,562 ft); maximum vertical
Dimensions: length travelling	4500 m (14,764 ft); effective
4.15 m (13 ft 7 in); width travelling	vertical 2000 m (6,562 ft)
1.90 m (6 ft 2 in); height travelling	**Crew:** 3 (1 on mount)

23-mm ZU-23 Light anti-aircraft gun

For many years after the end of World War II the standard light anti-aircraft gun of the Soviet army was the ZPU series of 14.5-mm (0.57-in) weapons using the Vladimirov KPV heavy machine-gun, which even today is installed in turrets mounted on a number of Soviet armoured vehicles including the BRDM-2, BTR-60PB and OT-64. There are three basic models of the ZPU, the ZIPU-1, ZPU-2

A Soviet-built 23-mm ZU-23 light anti-aircraft gun of the East German army is seen in the firing position, showing the box of 50 rounds of ready-use ammunition for each barrel. The ZU-23 has been seen in Afghanistan mounted on the rear of cross-country trucks to protect vehicle convoys.

Although no longer in large-scale use with the Soviet Union, the twin 23-mm ZU-23-2 light anti-aircraft gun system is still highly effective, and a number were used against American forces during the invasion of Grenada.

and ZIPU-4, the numeral referring to the number of barrels. Although withdrawn from front-line service with the Russian army some years ago, the ZPU series remains in service with over 50 countries around the world.

In the 1960s the ZPU series was replaced in the Soviet army by the **ZU-23-2** twin 23-mm towed anti-aircraft gun system, which is no longer in front-line use, having been replaced by surface-to-air missiles. Twin-barrelled versions of the weapon are designated as the ZU-23-2, while single barrel versions are known by the designation of **ZU-23**. However, the weapon is still used by 60 countries, including China, Bulgaria, Egypt, Iran and Poland. The weapon was encountered by United States forces during their invasion of Grenada in October 1983, when ZU-23-2 and ZPU series light anti-aircraft guns downed a number of American helicopters. In Afghanistan the Soviets mounted a number of ZU-23 guns on the rear of trucks to provide suppressive ground-to-ground fire when convoys were ambushed by guerrillas.

The ZU-23-2 was normally towed by a light vehicle such as the 4x4 GAZ-69, the Soviet equivalent of the Land Rover. The carriage has two rubber-tyred road wheels in the firing position; these wheels are raised off the ground and the carriage is supported on three screw-type levelling jacks. Each of the 23-mm barrels is provided with a flash suppressor, and a handle is mounted on top of each barrel to enable it to be changed quickly. Each barrel has a box of 50 rounds of ready-use ammunition, and a cyclic rate of fire of 800 to 1,000 rounds per minute is possible; the practical rate of fire is 200 rounds per minute.

Two types of fixed ammunition are fired by the ZU-23, namely armour-piercing incendiary-tracer (API-T) and high explosive incendiary-tracer (HEI-T), the former being used to engage armoured vehicles and the latter to engage aircraft. Both projectiles have a muzzle velocity of 970 m (3,182ft) per second, and the API-T projectile will penetrate 25 mm (0.98 in) of armour at a range of 500 m (547 yards). The mounting has no provision for off carriage fire control. The 23-mm cannon of the ZU-23 are also used in the famous 23-mm ZSU-23-4 self-propelled anti-aircraft gun system, although in this application the weapons are water-cooled to enable a higher rate of fire to be achieved.

ZU-23M1
An upgrade programme for the ZU-23-2 has been planned, redesignating the weapon the **ZU-23M1**. This would see a pod of two fire-and-forget missiles, perhaps KBM Igla (SA-18 'Grail') weapons, being installed above the left-hand gun barrel. The missiles could be used to engage targets some distance from the weapon, while the gun itself could be used against shorter range targets. An IFF system and fire-control system may also be fitted.

57-mm S-60 Anti-aircraft gun

The **57-mm (2.24-in) S-60** anti-aircraft gun entered service with the Soviet army after World War II as the replacement for the 37-mm M1939 light anti-aircraft gun which was the Soviet equivalent of the famous Bofors 40-mm L/60 weapon used in large numbers by the US and British armies during the war. Until very recently each tank division and motorised rifle division in the Soviet army had an anti-aircraft regiment equipped with the S-60. Each regiment had four batteries each with six guns, each battery having two three-gun platoons. Each battery had a SON-9/SON-9A 'Fire Can' fire-control radar, while at regimental HQ were two 'Flat Face' target-acquisition radars. More recently the 'Flap Wheel' radar has been used with the S-60 system.

The S-60 is still used by some 45 countries, especially in Africa, the Middle East and the Far East, and it featured in the inventory of most Warsaw Pact countries. The S-60 can be towed by a variety of vehicles including 6x6 trucks such as the Ural-37513 or the AT-L light tracked artillery tractors. The weapon can engage anti-aircraft targets with its wheels in contact with the ground, but it is much more accurate with its wheels raised off the ground and the carriage supported by four screw jacks. Optical sights are fitted for the engagement of both ground and aerial targets.

Four modes
Four operational modes are available: firstly, manual with the crew operating handwheels for elevation and traverse; secondly, power-assisted with the handwheels operated by the crews but assisted by a servo motor; thirdly, remotely-controlled by a Puazo series director and zero indicator; and fourthly fully automatic and remotely controlled by a director and zero indicator, plus radar. Ammunition is loaded in four-round clips, one clip being in the feed tray to the left of the breech and another clip on the mount itself. Three types of ammunition can be fired by the S-60, all of which have a muzzle velocity of 1000 m (3,281 ft) per second: two types of fragmentation tracer (FRAG-T) and armour-piercing capped-tracers (APC-T). These will penetrate 96 mm (3.78 in) of armour at 1000 m (3,028 ft). The S-60 has a cyclic rate of fire up to 120 rounds per minute (rpm) and a practical rate of fire of 70 rpm.

For many years the 57-mm S-60 was one of the standard towed anti-aircraft guns of the Soviet army and was issued on the scale of 24 guns per division. This S-60 is of the Egyptian army and is in the travelling position, being towed by a 6x6 truck. It was replaced by the SA-8 surface-to-air missile.

Above: The 57-mm S-60 anti-aircraft gun is highly effective when used together with the PUAZO-6160 director and the SON-9/SON-9A radar, which is called 'Fire Can' by NATO. In the 1980s Iraq was using the S-60 together with a low-light-level television system to engage Iranian aircraft.

Bofors 40-mm L/70 Anti-aircraft gun

In 1930 Bofors developed a 40-mm towed anti-aircraft gun that in only a few years became world famous. This had a 60-calibre barrel (resulting in the standard appellation Bofors 40-mm L/60) and had a cyclic rate of fire of 120 rounds per minute. The weapon was widely used in World War II, and was made in many countries including the US (as the M1), UK (Mk 1), Hungary, Italy and Poland.

After the end of World War II Bofors developed a much-improved 40-mm gun, which entered service in 1951 as the **Bofors 40-mm L/70**. In addition to having a longer 70-calibre barrel for a higher muzzle velocity for greater penetrative effect and shorter time to target, the new weapon had a cyclic rate increased to 300 rounds per minute, the latter achieved by ramming the new round during run-out and ejecting the empty cartridge cases forward of the mount toward the end of recoil. Two models were initially offered as the **L/70 Model A** and **L/70 Model B**. The Model A relied on an external source for power while the Model B had its own generator mounted toward the carriage's front.

Gun crew

The basic L/70 has a six-man crew, of whom four are on the carriage at all times: the elevation and traverse layers are seated one on each side of the mount, while two ammunition feeders are placed one on each side at the rear. Ammunition is fed to the weapon in four-round clips, and a tray above the

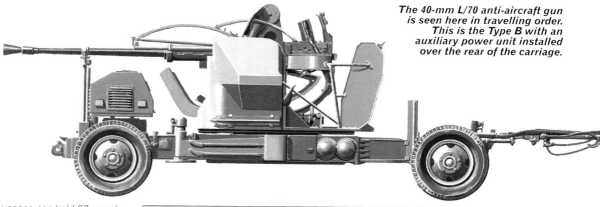

The 40-mm L/70 anti-aircraft gun is seen here in travelling order. This is the Type B with an auxiliary power unit installed over the rear of the carriage.

weapon can hold 26 rounds of ready-use ammunition. At the rear of the mount, one on each side, are ready-use racks that hold 96 rounds of ammunition.

Weapon elevation and mount traverse are electro-hydraulic, with manual controls for emergency use. Maximum elevation speed is 45° per second and maximum traverse speed is 85° per second.

Ammunition options

Ammunition development is a continuous process at Bofors, and five basic rounds are available. All the ammunition is of the fixed type, and comprises prefragmented HE (PFHE), high-capacity HE (HCHE), HE-tracer (HE-T), armour-piercing capped-tracer (APC-T). In more recent years Bofors and other companies have produced more advanced types of ammunition, and though intended primarily for more modern versions of the 40-mm Bofors gun, some of these ammunition types can

Seen in one of its more advanced forms with radar, the 40-mm L/70 gun has a cyclic rate of 300 rounds per minute, reduced to something below this figure by the need to hand-load the ammunition stay.

Above and below: The Bofors PFHE (Pre-Fragmented HE) projectile is one of the more advanced types, with the fuse at the front and the explosive content at the rear of the projectile inside a ring of fragments.

be used with the L/70 weapon.

In the firing position the wheels of the carriage supporting the L/70 weapon are raised clear of the ground and the carriage is supported on four jacks, one at each end of the carriage and one on each side on outriggers, to provide maximum stability in the firing mode.

The L/70 has been made under licence in a number of countries including the UK, Germany, India, Italy, the Netherlands and Spain. The

complete L/70 equipment is usually towed by a 4x4 or 6x6 truck that also carries the crew and a supply of ready-use ammunition. Despite the fact that in some of the more advanced countries – for example Germany and the UK – it has been replaced by short-range SAMs such as the Rapier and Roland systems, the L/70 gun nevertheless remains a useful weapon when combined in batteries with an up-to-date fire-control system (usually with

radar for the earliest possible target detection and often with an optronic director for continued operability in electronically degraded conditions). Another aspect of the L/70 weapon in modern land warfare conditions is that, as a result of its ammunition options, it retains a useful capability against vehicles of several types up to and including light armoured fighting vehicles, and in sea warfare conditions against landing craft and fast attack craft.

This 40-mm L/70 gun is fitted with a system to measure the muzzle velocity and so allow an off-carriage system to generate a more accurate solution to the fire-control problem.

SPECIFICATION	
40-mm L/70 Type A	
Calibre: 40 mm (1.57 in)	**Muzzle velocity:** 1005-1030 m (3,297-3,379 ft) per second
Weight: travelling 4800 kg (10,582 lb)	**Range:** maximum horizontal 12500 m (13,670 yards); maximum
Dimensions: (travelling) length 7.29 m (23 ft 11 in); width 2.25 m (7 ft 4.6 in); height 2.35 m (7 ft 8¼ in)	vertical 8700 m (28,545 ft); effective vertical 4000 m (13,125 ft)
Elevation: -4° to +90°	**Cyclic rate of fire:** 240-300 rounds per minute
Traverse: 360°	**Crew:** 6 (2 on mount)

Oerlikon 20-mm GAI-DO1 Light anti-aircraft gun

Best known as a product of Oerlikon-Bührle but now supported by Oerlikon Contraves, as the company (now a component of the Rheinmetall group) is currently known, the **Oerlikon GAI-D01** twin 20-mm gun mount was designed in the early 1970s as the **Hispano-Suiza HSS 666A** and became available for delivery in 1978. The equipment has succeeded in bridging the tactical gap between the short range and comparatively low volume of fire provided by single-barrel 20-mm weapons and the greater range and higher volume of fire generated by heavier equipments such as the twin 35-mm GDF-002. The equipment is borne on a twin-wheel carriage weighing 470 kg (1,036 lb) and fitted with an adjustable towing eye, and can be brought into action by its five-man crew within one minute of halting.

Wankel engine

Though intended primarily for AA use, the mounting can also be deployed for a number of other battlefield roles. The two guns are gas-operated KAD-B (originally HS 820-SL) cannon: these each weigh 68 kg (150 lb), and comprise a KAD-B16 (originally HS 820-SL7° D2)

An Oerlikon 20-mm GAI-D01 twin light anti-aircraft gun in firing position. Mounted outboard of each of the 20-mm cannon is a box of 120 rounds of ready-use ammunition. The gunner aims the weapon using an Italian Galileo P56 sighting and an aiming unit containing an analogue computer.

on the left with left-hand belt feed and a KAD-B17 (originally HS 820-SL7° D3) on the right with right-hand belt feed, in each case from a box magazine that weighs 68 kg complete with 120 rounds. The gunner has multiple fire options, including single shot, rapid single shot, burst or sustained fire. The mounting is controlled hydraulically (with a manual reversionary system for emergency use), power for this system being provided by a 5.15-kW (6.9-hp) NSU-Wankel rotary engine located under the gunner's adjustable seat. In powered mode the mounting has a traverse rate of 80° per sec-

ond, while the cannon has an elevation rate which is 48° per second.

The gunner aims with the aid of an Officine Galileo P56 sight. This is an Italian-designed system intended for use in clear weather only, and is based on a solid-state analogue computer, monocular optical sight with x5 magnification and an objective prism capable of movement between -7° and +85° for use against ground and air targets, and a panel on which the gunner manually inputs target data. In a typical surface-to-air engagement the gunner must first acquire the target visually (there being an option for the gunner to have been warned by radio

from a higher-level target-detection system such as the Contraves Italiana LPD-20 radar), and then enter into the computer, by means of the left of the sight unit, estimated values for the target's speed between 216 and 1260 km/h (134 and 783 mph) and crossing point distance between 100 and 1000 m (110 and 1,095 yards). This crossing point distance at which the gunner's line of sight intersects the target's line of flight at right angles (the shortest possible interception range). The gunner then starts to track the target with his mechanical sight, before shifting to the optical sight and tracking the target until the aiming

point and target nose coincide. The gunner then presses down his control column, allowing the computer to process traverse and elevation angle corrections with the previously calculated super-elevation angle to produce a requirement for total lead, this automatically being fed into the fire-control system in the form of adjustment of the lead mark in the sight. So long as the gunner keeps his sight centred on the target, he thus has every chance of securing a hit.

Ground targets

For a ground target the gunner has merely to enter a figure for range between 100 and 2500 m (110 and 2,735 yards), the target then being engaged with single-shot or short-burst fire.

The ammunition comprises five operational (AP-T, HEI, HEI-T, SAPHEI and SAPHEI-T) types, each weighing just under 0.34 kg (12 oz), and practice types. Production has now ceased in Switzerland although it is thought to be continuing in Turkey, where MKEK builds the weapon for the Turkish army. The GAI-DO1 is also in service with several countries which include Bolivia and Guatemala.

This Oerlikon GAI-D01 twin 20-mm light anti-aircraft gun in the firing position shows the Wankel engine under the gunner's seat. This is a clear-weather system, although a radar such as the Contraves LPD-20 could be used to provide early warning to a number of guns.

SPECIFICATION	
GAI-D01	**Muzzle velocity:** 1100-1150 m (3,609-3,773 ft) per second
Calibre: 20 mm (0.79 in)	**Range:** maximum horizontal 5700 m (6,235 yards); effective horizontal 2200 m (2,405 yards); maximum vertical 4500 m (14,765 ft); effective vertical 1500 m (4,920 ft)
Weights: (with ammunition) travelling 1800 kg (3,968 lb); firing 1330 kg (2,932 lb)	
Dimensions: (travelling) length 4.59 m (15 ft 0.7 in); width 1.86 m (6 ft 1.2 in); height 2.34 m (7 ft 8.1 in)	**Cyclic rate of fire:** 1,000 rounds per minute per barrel
Elevation: -3° to +81°	**Crew:** 5 (1 on mount)
Traverse: 360°	

M53/59 Twin 30-mm self-propelled AA gun mounting

It was once widely believed that the USSR forced other Warsaw Pact countries either to purchase Soviet equipment or manufacture it under licence. In fact some of the Warsaw Pact countries had their own flourishing defence industries, one such being Czechoslovakia which, in the late 1970s, developed a 152-mm (6-in) self-propelled gun on an 8x8 Tatra truck chassis. In the 1950s Czechoslovakia developed and placed in production the **M53/59** twin 30-mm self-propelled anti-aircraft gun system, and this is known to have entered service with Cuba, Guinea, Libya and Yugoslavia in addition to the Czechoslovak army. In some Czechoslovak units, however, the M53/59 was soon replaced by the ZSU-23-4 SPAAG, which is a much more effective system.

The M53/59 was used by the Czechoslovak army in place of the Soviet ZSU-57-2 SPAAG, and consisted essentially of the Praga V3S 6x6 3-tonne truck chassis fitted with an armoured cab and a twin M53 30-mm AA gun system at the rear.

Vehicle layout

The engine was at the front of the vehicle, which was provided with full armour protection from shell splinters and small arms fire. The cab was to the immediate rear of the engine with the driver seated on the left and the commander on the right; the latter had a hemispherical Plexiglass cupola in the cab roof for all-round observation. Both crew members were provided with side doors and vision slits, while to their immediate front was a windscreen covered by an

Dating from the 1950s, the M53/59 was a clear-weather system. Four of the crew sat in the armoured cab, with the twin 30-mm mount operated hydraulically. No infra-red night vision lights were carried, nor was there any NBC protection.

armoured shutter in combat. To the rear of the commander and driver were the two ammunition members, who sat facing the rear.

The twin 30-mm mount had hydraulic power traverse through 360°; the weapons elevated from -10° to +85°. The cyclic rate of fire was 450 to 500 rounds per gun per minute, while the practical rate of fire (conditioned by ammunition supply) was 150 rounds per gun per minute. The basic towed 30-mm M53 was fed with clips of 10 rounds, whereas the M53/59 had a 50-round vertical magazine for each gas-operated cannon. It was estimated that between 600 and 800 rounds of 30-mm ammunition of two types (API and HEI) were carried. The API (armour-piercing incendiary) projectile could penetrate 55 mm (2.16 in) of armour at a range of 500 m (546 yards) and was used mainly against vehicles, while the HEI (high explosive incendiary) round was

used against aerial targets. Both had a muzzle velocity of 1000 m (3,280 ft) per second. Effective anti-aircraft range was estimated at 3000 m (3,280 yards) and maximum vertical range at 6300 m (20,670 ft).

Cross-country ability

Apart from its limitation of having been a clear-weather system without radar or optronic fire-control capability, the M53/59 also lacked cross-country mobility when operating with fully-tracked vehicles such as tanks and armoured personnel carriers, and had neither NBC protec-

Above: The relative age of the M53/59 was evidenced by the lack of protection offered for its gunners, and its lack of cross-country mobility that would have hampered operations with tracked vehicles.

SPECIFICATION	
M53/59	water-cooled 6-cylinder diesel developing 82 kW (110 hp)
Crew: 6	**Performance:** maximum road speed 60 km/h (37 mph); maximum range 500 km (311 miles)
Weight: 10300 kg (22,707 lb)	
Dimensions: length 6.92 m (22 ft 8 in); width 2.35 m (7 ft 9 in); height (without magazines) 2.585 m (8 ft 6 in)	
	Gradient: 60 per cent
	Vertical obstacle: 0.46 m (18 in)
Powerplant: one Tatra T 912-2	**Trench:** 0.69 m (2 ft 3 in)

tion nor infra-red night-vision sights. An unusual feature of the M53/59 was that the

complete mount could be removed from the chassis and placed on the ground.

Type 63 Twin 37-mm self-propelled AA gun mounting

The USSR supplied China with considerable amounts of military equipment in the 1950s and 1960s before relations between the two countries were temporarily broken off. To meet its needs for a self-propelled anti-aircraft gun system, China used the T-34 series tank chassis with its turret replaced by a new open-topped turret armed with twin 37-mm anti-aircraft guns; this gun was already in service with the Chinese army, mounted on a four-wheeled carriage. The chassis of the **Type 63** was identical to that of the tank with the driver at the front left and bow machine-gunner to his right, though it was probable that the bow machine-gun was removed. The turret was in the centre of the hull with the engine and transmission at the rear.

By modern standards, the Type 63 was a weapon of decidedly limited tactical capability. Mounted on an essentially unmodified T-34 tank hull, the turret had no provision for radar fire control, and the optically sighted weapons were traversed and elevated manually.

This Type 63 was supplied to North Vietnam, from whom it was captured by the US forces during the Vietnam War. It was a simple clear-weather system.

The Christie-type suspension had five dual rubber-tyred road wheels, with the drive sprocket at the rear and idler at the front; there were no track-return rollers as the top section of the track rested on the upper part of the road wheels.

The twin 37-mm cannon were recoil operated and had a cyclic rate of fire of 160 to 189 rounds per minute, but practical rate of fire per barrel was 80 rounds a minute. Weapon elevation and turret traverse were manual, which would have been a major tactical drawback in the engagement of aircraft flying at low level and high speed. Only optical sights were fitted, with no provision at all for radar fire-control. The ammunition was fed to each weapon in clips of five rounds, some ready-use ammunition being stowed inside the turret with the bulk of the ammunition stowed externally in panniers on each side of the hull.

Ammunition types

Two basic types of ammunition were fired, FRAG-T (fragmentation with tracer) being used against aerial targets and AP-T (armour-piercing with tracer) being used against armoured targets such as light tanks. Both projectiles had a muzzle velocity of 880 m (2,887 ft) per second, and the AP-T round could penetrate 37 mm (1.46 in) of armour at a range of 1000 m (1,095 yards) or 46 mm (1.81 in) of armour at 500 m (547 yards), penetration being improved at shorter ranges because of the projectile's higher velocity. Effective anti-aircraft range was 3000 m (3,280 yards), and maximum vertical range was 6700 m (21,980 ft).

Vietnamese service

The Type 63 was supplied to the North Vietnamese, from whom one piece of equipment was subsequently captured by the South Vietnamese and sent to the US for evaluation at the Aberdeen Proving Ground, where it is now on display at the Ordnance Corps museum. As far as it is known China was not supplied with any ZSU-57-2 or ZSU-23-4 self-propelled anti-aircraft guns by the USSR, although China has been producing its own tanks, armoured personnel carriers, towed artillery and rocket launchers for many years.

After the Type 63 had been in service for some time, the Chinese developed improved SPAAGs with twin 57-mm, 37-mm and 35-mm guns. The 31-tonne Type 80 with two 57-mm guns and optical fire-control was basically similar to the ZSU-57-2 but used the hull of the Type 69 tank, and was produced only in very limited numbers. The 35-tonne Type 88 had two 37-mm cannon in a fully enclosed turret on the Type 69 tank chassis and also carried a radar-based fire-control system, but did not enter production. The Type 90-II has two 35-mm cannon based on the Oerlikon GDF weapon.

SPECIFICATION

Type 63	V-12 diesel developing 373 kW
Crew: 6	(500 hp)
Weight: 32000 kg (70,547 lb)	**Performance:** maximum road
Dimensions: length (guns forward)	speed 55 km/h (34 mph); maximum
7.53 m (24 ft 8 in) and (hull) 6.432 m	range 300 km (186 miles)
(21 ft 1 in); width 3.27 m (10 ft 9 in);	**Gradient:** 60 per cent
height 2.995 m (9 ft 10 in)	**Vertical obstacle:** 0.73 m (29 in)
Powerplant: one water-cooled	**Trench:** 2.5 m (8 ft 2 in)

BTR-152A Twin 14.5-mm self-propelled AA gun mounting

While the ZSU-57-2 twin 57-mm SPAAG was the first purpose-built weapon of its type to be introduced into the Soviet army in large numbers during the post-war period, the **BTR-152A** 6x6 and BTR-40A 4x4 vehicles had entered service some years earlier. In both cases these were essentially armoured personnel carrier chassis with the twin 14.5-mm (0.57-in) KPV heavy machine-guns (normally towed) turret-mounted in the troop compartment at the rear of the hull. The turret is designated the ZPTU-2 and can be traversed through 360°, the weapons being able to elevate -5° to +80°. The KPV machine-gun is also fitted in a number of Soviet armoured vehicles, including the BRDM-2 4x4 amphibious scout car and the BTR-60PB and BTR-70 8x8 armoured personnel carriers. It was also installed as the co-axial and anti-aircraft weapon of the T-10M heavy tank, which is no longer even in reserve service with what is now the CIS. There are also three versions of the towed KPV heavy anti-aircraft machine-gun: the ZPU-1 single, ZPU-2 twin and ZPU-4 quadruple mounts. In the Warsaw Pact most of the towed ZPUs were replaced by the 23-mm ZU-23 anti-aircraft cannon, and the BTR-152A and BTR-40A both remain in service

The BTR-152A has seen operational service in Vietnam and the Middle East in both the AA and fire-support roles.

only outside what was the Warsaw Pact.

Rate of fire

The KPV heavy machine-gun has a cyclic rate of fire of 600 rounds per minute per barrel, but its practical rate of fire is 150 rounds per minute per barrel. The method of operation is gas-assisted short recoil. The barrel is air-cooled, is fitted with a flash eliminator and a handle for carrying out quick changes, and is chromium-plated internally to reduce barrel wear. Two types of ammunition, API and HEI-T, are fired. The armour-piercing incendiary round is used mainly against armoured vehicles and will penetrate 32 mm (1.25 in) of armour at a range of 500 m (547 yards). The HE incendiary with tracer round is used against aircraft. Only optical sights are fitted, there being no provision for radar fire-control. This limits the system's capability to clear-weather operations only. The lack of power traverse and elevation also limits the system's capability to engage fast-moving targets at low level.

In addition to being used in its originally designed anti-aircraft role in the Middle East and Vietnam, the system has also been used in the ground fire-support role, in which its high rate of fire has proved most useful. During fighting in the Lebanon in the summer of 1982 the Israeli army captured a number of BTR-152 APCs with the more effective twin 23-mm ZU-23 cannon mounted in the rear, but as far as is known this was a local modification.

One of the more interesting local modifications carried out by Egypt on the BTR-152 was the installation of the Czechoslovak quadruple 12.7-mm (0.5-in) M53 machine-gun mounting in the rear of the vehicle. The weapon has a lower cyclic rate of fire than the KPV and also a shorter effective range.

SPECIFICATION

BTR-152A	cooled 6-cylinder petrol engine
Crew: 4	developing 82 kW (110 hp)
Weight: 9600 kg (21,164 lb)	**Performance:** maximum road
Dimensions: length 6.83 m (22 ft	speed 65 km/h (40 mph); maximum
5 in); width 2.32 m (7 ft 7 in);	range 780 km (485 miles)
height (overall) 2.7 m (9 ft 2 in)	**Vertical obstacle:** 0.6 m (24 in)
Powerplant: one ZIL-123 water-	**Trench:** 0.69 m (2 ft 3 in)

ZSU-57-2 Self-propelled AA gun

Late production ZSU-57-2s were fitted with a more sophisticated sighting system, identified by two small ports in the forward upper portion of the turret front. The system was built in China as the Type 80.

The **ZSU-57-2** was introduced in November 1957. It was the first post-war Soviet self-propelled anti-aircraft gun to be introduced on a large scale.

In the ZSU-57-2 designation ZSU means that the equipment is a self-propelled anti-aircraft gun system, 57 is for the calibre of the weapons (57-mm) and 2 is for the number of guns.

The chassis of the ZSU-57-2 was a variant of that used on the T-54 MBT with thinner armour protection and one road wheel less on each side, though the length of track on the ground remains identical. The chassis was of all-welded steel construction, with the driver at the front left, the other five crew members in the open-topped turret in the centre of the hull, and the engine and transmission at the rear. Suspension was of the torsion-bar type with the drive sprocket at the rear and the idler at the front; there were four road wheels but no track-return rollers. As the ZSU-57-2 was lighter than the T-54 tank on which it was based, it had a higher

power-to-weight ratio of 18.56 hp/ton and a lower ground pressure. To extend its operating range to 595 km (370 miles), long-range fuel tanks could be fitted at the rear of the hull.

Ammunition

The guns fired the same ammunition and had the same performance as the widely used 57-mm S-60 towed anti-aircraft gun system. The cannon were power-operated from -5° to +85° at 20° per second, with turret traverse through 360° at a speed of 30° per second; manual controls were provided for emergency use.

Each gun had a cyclic rate of fire of 106 to 120 rounds per minute, though the practical rate of fire was 70 rounds per minute.

Ammunition was fed to each weapon in clips of four rounds, the empty cartridge cases and clips being deposited onto a conveyor belt under the weapon. This ran to the turret rear and dropped the empty cartridge cases and clips into the large wire basket mounted externally at the turret rear.

The following types of fixed ammunition were fired: FRAG-T (fragmentation-tracer) and APC-T (armour piercing capped-tracer). The former was used mainly against aerial targets while the latter, which could penetrate 96 mm (3.78-in) of armour at a range of 1000 m (3,281 ft), was used against ground targets such as tanks and APCs. Effective anti-aircraft range was 4000 m

(13,123 ft) with a maximum vertical range of 8800 m (28,870 ft). Maximum horizontal range was 12000 m (39,370 ft), although fire control was characteristically a major problem at such long ranges.

Widely deployed by the Soviet Union, the vehicle was ultimately replaced in all front line units by the ZSU-23-4 self-propelled

anti-aircraft gun system. It also saw service with the armed forces of Algeria, Angola, Bulgaria, Cuba, East Germany, Egypt, Ethiopia, Finland, Hungary, Iran, Iraq, North Korea, Poland, Romania, Syria and Yugoslavia. In 1982 the Syrian army made extensive use of the ZSU-57-2 in the ground-support role during fighting in Lebanon.

SPECIFICATION	
ZSU-57-2	diesel developing 388 kW (520 hp)
Crew: 6	**Performance:** maximum road
Weight: 28100 kg (61,949 lb)	speed 50 km/h (31 mph); maximum
Dimensions: length 8.48 m	range 420 km (260 miles); gradient
(27 ft 10 in); length (hull) 6.22 m	60 per cent; vertical obstacle
(20 ft 5 in); width 3.27 m	0.80 m (2 ft 1/2 in); trench 2.70 m
(10 ft 9 in); height 2.75 m (9 ft)	(2 ft 8 in)
Powerplant: one Model V-54 V-12	

ZSU-23-4 Self-propelled AA gun

The **ZSU-23-4** was developed in the 1960s as the replacement for the 57-mm ZSU-57-2 self-propelled anti-aircraft gun system. Although the ZSU-23-4's 23-mm cannon has a shorter range than the earlier

The most recent Shilka variant is the ZSU-23-4M4, with large ammunition panniers on the turret sides, a digital computer and improved 'Gun Dish' radar.

weapon, the system is much more effective as it has a radar fire-control system and a much higher rate of fire.

Export operators

After being introduced

into the Soviet army on a large scale it was exported to almost every country that received Soviet military equipment, including Afghanistan, Algeria, Angola, Bulgaria, Cuba, Czechoslovakia, East Germany, Egypt, Ethiopia, Hungary, India, Iran, Iraq, Jordan, Libya, Mozambique, Nigeria, North Korea, North

A veteran of successive Middle East wars, the Shilka was put to use by the Soviets in Afghanistan in both the anti-aircraft and anti-ground-target roles.

Yemen, Peru, Poland, Romania, Somalia, South Yemen, Syria, Vietnam and Yugoslavia. In addition to seeing extensive action during the conflict in Vietnam, the ZSU-23-4 also proved to be one of the most effective systems during the 1973 Middle East war. Soviet-supplied missiles, such as the SA-6 'Gainful', forced Israeli aircraft to fly at low altitude, where they encountered the ZSU-23-4 and the SA-7 man-portable missiles. In the

Soviet army, where the system was known as the Shilka, the ZSU-23-4 was issued on the scale of 16 systems per division and normally operated in pairs.

The chassis of the ZSU-23-4 is very similar to that of the SA-6 'Gainful' SAM system, and uses automotive components of the PT-76 amphibious light tank family. It is of all-welded steel construction with a maximum thickness of 15 mm (0.6 in) at the

*The **ZSU**-23-4 has a capability to both acquire and track low-flying aircraft targets, with an effective **AA** range of 2500 m (8,202 ft). It can also fire on the move because of its integrated radar/gun stabilisation system.*

front and 10 mm (0.4 in) over the remainder of the vehicle including the turret, and this provides protection only against small arms fire and shell splinters. The driver is seated at the front of the hull on the left with the turret in the centre and engine and transmission at the rear. Suspension is of the torsion-bar type and consists of six single rubber-tyred road wheels with the drive sprocket at the rear and idler at the front. A gas turbine is installed in the rear to provide power for the turret and other systems while the main engine is not running.

Crew positions

The commander, search radar operator/gunner and range-finding number are all seated in the large flat turret. Main armament consists of four AZP-23 23-mm gas-operated cannon

with a cyclic rate of fire of 800 to 1000 rounds per minute per barrel. These weapons have an elevation of +85° and a depression of -4° in a turret capable of traversing through 360°. Turret traverse and weapon elevation are powered, manual controls being provided for emergency use. The gunner can select 3/5-, 5/10- or 50-round bursts, and the cannon have an effective anti-aircraft range of 2500 m (8,202 ft) and a similar range in the ground-target role. Each cannon has 500

rounds of ready-use ammunition; the two types normally fired are API-T (armoured-piercing incendiary-tracer) and HEI-T (high-explosive incendiary-tracer). The ZSU-23-4 has a fire-control system that includes a radar scanner mounted on the turret rear, sights and a fire-control computer. Targets can be engaged while the vehicle is travelling across country, but where possible the ZSU-23-4 will stop to provide a more stable firing platform.

SPECIFICATION

ZSU-23-4
Crew: 4
Weight: 19000 kg (41,888 lb)
Dimensions: length 6.54 m (21 ft 5 in); width 2.95 m (9 ft 8 in); height (without radar) 2.25 m (7 ft 4 in)
Powerplant: one V-6R diesel

developing 210 kW (280 hp)
Performance: maximum road speed 44 km/h (27 mph); maximum road range 260 km (162 miles); gradient 60 per cent; vertical obstacle 1.10 m (3 ft 7 in); trench 2.80 m (9 ft 2 in)

2S6 Tunguska Integrated Air Defence System

Introduced in 1990, the **2S6 Tunguska Integrated Air Defence System (IADS)** was developed as a follow-on to the successful ZSU-23-4 Shilka. The Tunguska, however, combines heavier-calibre 30-mm cannon with 9M311 (SA-19 'Grison') surface-to-air missiles. Both weapons systems employ a common radar-computer suite. The 2S6 was designed to provide low-level air defence for motorised infantry and armour units, offering protection from air attack against low-flying 'surprise' targets, including hovering helicopters, RPVs and cruise missiles. Tunguska is capable of engaging aerial targets before they are within the effective range of their own weapons. Targets can be engaged (with cannon) whilst the vehicle is on the move.

Platform

A lightweight armoured tracked vehicle with a 360° rotary armoured turret, the Tunguska is based on the chassis of the intermediate-weight GM-352M. The hull accomodates a driver's compartment, turbo-diesel engine and 50-kW (67-hp) turbine, power transmission, electrical equipment, power supply system, gyroscopic equipment, turret traverse hydraulic drive, internal communications systems, NBC protection systems, life sup-

port and fire-fighting equipment, and optical devices. Hydro-pneumatic suspension allows for changing road clearance, ensuring a high level of cross-country ability.

The 'Hot Shot' radar system comprises separate tracking radar (pedestal-mounted at the front of the turret) and acquisition/designation radar (at the rear of the turret). Information provided by the radar is sent to a digital computer, which in turn determines the control and firing commands for the weapons. Radar detection range is 18 km (11 miles), whilst tracking range is 16 km (10 miles).

Missiles

Eight 9M311 surface-to-air missiles are carried in sealed containers either side of the turret, re-loaded in clips of two missiles by a transloader vehicle; complete reload time (for gun ammunition and missiles) is 16 minutes. Two additional missiles can be carried within the vehicle itself. These weapons have semi-automatic radar command to line of sight guidance, and are armed with 9-kg (19-lb 12-oz) FRAG/HE warheads. With a speed of 900 m per second (2,953 ft per second), the 9M311 can engage targets flying at speeds of up to 500 m per second (1,640 ft per second) at ranges of between

Despite retaining the 30-mm calibre weapons of the BMP-2, the cannon used in the 2S6 are much longer, and mounted in pairs with the right weapon being located slightly to the rear of the left gun. Maximum vertical range is 5000 m (16,404 ft), with an effective range against aerial targets of approximately 3000 m (9,843 ft).

2500 m and 10000 m (8,202 ft and 32,808 ft).

Two 30-mm twin-barrel 2A38M automatic cannon (similar weapons to those used by the BMP-2 and Ka-50 attack helicopter) have an elevation/depression of +80°/-6°. Ammunition comprises of 1,904 rounds of AP-T, FRAG-T and HE-I ammunition, despatched at a rate of fire of 5,000 rounds per minute. Tunguska guns have a maximum effective range of 4000 m (13,123 ft), and a minimum effective range of 200 m (656 ft), although they can also be employed to engage 'soft' ground tar-

gets. Maximum effective altitude for engagement is 3000 m (9,843 ft), with a minimum effective altitude of around 10 m (33 ft). The cannon are capable of engaging targets moving at speeds of up to 700 m

(2,297 ft) per second, and again the system can be used against targets moving at up to 500 m (1,640 ft) per second. Current Tunguska operators comprise Russia and Belarus, and the Indian Army.

Missile armament for the Tunguska comprises the SA-19 'Grison', known in Russia as the 9M311, which has a launch weight of 30 kg (66 lb). Manufactured by KBP, which previously specialised in anti-tank missiles, the system itself is named 2K22 Treugolnik.

SPECIFICATION

2S6 TUNGUSKA
Crew: 4
Powerplant: one 552-kW (740-hp) V-64-4 V-12 turbo-diesel
Maximum road speed: 65 km/h (40 mph)
Combat weight: 34000 kg

(74,956 lb)
Length: 7.93 m (26 ft)
Width: 3.24 m (10 ft 7 1/4 in)
Height: 4.02 m (13 ft 2 in)
Armament: 2 x 30-mm 2A38M cannon, 8 x 9M311 (SA-19 'Grison') SAMs

M42 Twin 40-mm self-propelled AA gun

During the latter half of World War II the United States developed a series of tracked vehicles (the Light Combat Team) which included the M24 Chaffee light tank, M37 105-mm howitzer motor carriage, M41 155-mm howitzer motor carriage and M19 twin 40-mm self-propelled anti-aircraft gun system.

After the end of the war and with the advent of the Korean conflict, a new family of light vehicles was developed, this included a light tank called the M41 (or Walker Bulldog) while an anti-aircraft gun system, which had the same automotive components but a different hull, was designated **M42**, and more commonly known as the **Duster**. The turret of the M42 is the same as that of the earlier M19, though in the former it was mounted in the centre of the hull and in the latter it is at the rear of the hull. The M42, whose development designation was **T141**, was in

production from 1951 to 1956 and about 3,700 were built, the majority by the Cadillac Motor Car Division of the General Motors Corporation at the Cleveland Tank Plant. Late production equipments are designated **M42A1**, the major difference being the fuel injection system for the engine. One of the main drawbacks of the M42, along with other members of this family, is its use of a petrol engine, which results in a very short operating range. The M42 is still used by Greece, Guatemala, Jordan, Lebanon, Taiwan, Thailand, Turkey and Venezuela. It was used successfully in Vietnam by both the US and South Vietnamese armies, although its primary role was in the ground-support fire role rather than the air-defence role for which it was originally designed.

The hull and turret of the M42 are of all-welded steel construction. The comman-

der and driver are seated in the front of the vehicle, the turret with the other four crew members is located in the centre, and the engine and transmission are installed at the rear. The interior also features a carbon-dioxide fire-suppression system. Suspension is of the well-tried torsion-bar type, and consists of five dual rubber-tyred road wheels, with the drive sprocket at the rear

Based on the M41 light tank, the M42 was essentially a clear-weather weapon, being optically sighted. The final US Army examples were phased out in 1990-91.

and idler at the front. There are also three track-return rollers.

The turret and weapons are power operated; the turret can be traversed through 360° at 40° per second, and the guns can be elevated from -3° to +85° at a speed of 25° per second. Manual controls are provided for emergency use. A total of 480 rounds of ammunition is carried, and the guns have a practical rate of fire of 120 rounds per minute per barrel with an effective anti-aircraft range of 5000 m (16,404 ft). The gunner can select single shots or full automatic fire, and the four types of ammu-

nition carried are APT (armour piercing tracer), HET (high explosive tracer), HEI-T (high explosive incendiary-tracer) and TPT (target practice tracer). A 0.3-in (7.62-mm) M60 or M1919A4 machine-gun is mounted externally on the left rear of the turret for local defence, 1,750 rounds of ammunition being stored in the vehicle.

Essentially a clear-weather platform, the M42's fire-control system includes an M38 computing sight, M24 reflex sight and a speed ring sight. Efforts were made to fit a radar fire-control system, but this idea was eventually dropped.

M42s of the 60th Artillery are seen in action on the Cambodian border in August 1967. The 40-mm HEI-T (High-Explosive Incendiary-Tracer) shells were deadly against troops in the open or against field fortifications.

SPECIFICATION	
M42	petrol engine developing 373 kW
Crew: 6	(500 bhp)
Combat weight: 22452 kg	**Performance:** maximum road
(49,394 lb)	speed 72.4 km/h (45 mph);
Dimensions: length (guns forward)	maximum range 161 km (100 miles)
6.37 m (20 ft 10 in); length (hull)	**Gradient:** 60 per cent
5.82 m (91 ft 1 in); width 3.23 m	**Vertical obstacle:** 0.71 m
(10 ft 7 in); height 2.85 m (9 ft 4 in)	(2 ft 4 in)
Powerplant: one Continental	**Trench:** 1.83 m (6 ft)
AOS-895-3 6-cylinder air-cooled	

M163 Vulcan 20-mm self-propelled AA gun

In the early 1960s Rock Island Arsenal developed two 20-mm Vulcan air defence systems. The self-propelled model was based on a modified M113 APC chassis and was designated **XM163** (the chassis being the **XM741**) while the towed model was the **XM167**. These were subsequently accepted for service as the **M163** and **M167** respectively. The former was produced by the General Electric Company of Burlington, Vermont, and was soon deployed to South Vietnam, where it was widely used in the ground fire-support role. In the US Army the M163 was deployed in composite battalions, each of which had two batteries each with 12 Chaparral SAM launchers and two batteries each with 12 M163s. The towed M167

was used mainly by the air-mobile and air-assault divisions. The M163 is used by Israel, Jordan, Morocco, Portugal, Saudi Arabia, Sudan, Thailand and Yemen. The M163 was retired from US military service in 1994, after seeing service in the ground-support role during Desert Storm.

M163 detail

The M163 consists of a standard M113 chassis on top of which has been mounted an electrically-operated turret fitted with a 20-mm six-barrelled M61-series cannon, a US Navy Mk 20 lead-computing sight, and an EMTECH range-only radar located on the right side of the turret. The turret can be traversed through 360° at a speed of 60° per second. Manual controls are provided in case of power failure. The

20-mm cannon, which is a development of the weapon originally designed for the Lockheed F-104 Starfighter in the 1950s and still fitted in

The M163 Vulcan consists of a 20-mm Gatling-type cannon mounted upon an M113 APC chassis. The gunner can select rates of fire of 1,000 or 3,000 rounds per minute for use against ground or airborne targets, and can select bursts of 10, 30, 60 or 100 rounds.

M163
Crew: 4
Combat weight: 12310 kg (27,139 lb)
Dimensions: length 4.86 m (15 ft 11 in); width 2.85 m (9 ft 4 in); height (overall) 2.74 m (8 ft 11 in); height (hull top) 1.83 m (6 ft)

Powerplant: one Detroit Diesel 6V-53 6-cylinder diesel developing 160 kW (215 bhp)
Performance: maximum road speed 67 km/h (42 mph); maximum range 483 km (300 miles)
Gradient: 60 per cent
Vertical obstacle: 0.61 m (2 ft)
Trench: 1.68 m (5 ft 6 in)

The M163's massive short-range firepower was shown to advantage in Vietnam, where it dealt with Viet Cong ambushers after its introduction in 1968.

Towards the end of its career, the PIVADS upgrade gave the M163 a modified fire-control system and its effective range was increased to 2600 m (8,530 ft).

aircraft such as the Lockheed Martin F-22 Raptor, has two rates of fire in this application: 1,000 and 3,000 rounds per minute. The former is normally used for engagement of ground targets, while the higher rate of fire is used against aerial targets. The gunner can select 10-, 30-, 60- or 100-round bursts, and 1,100 rounds of ready-use ammunition are carried, with a further 1,000 rounds in reserve.

Ammunition types

Ammunition types that can be fired include APT, TP (target practice), HEI, TPT and HEI-T. All have a muzzle velocity of 1030 m (3,380 ft) per second. Maximum effective range in the anti-aircraft role is 1600 m (5,249 ft) and in the ground role 3000 m (9,843 ft).

Between 1984-88, several of the original Vulcan systems (both towed and self-propelled versions) were upgraded under the Product

Improved Vulcan Air Defence System (PIVADS) programme. PIVADS included the installation of a new digital fire control system and radar suite, together with a new Mk 149 Armour Piercing Discarding Sabot (APDS) round which increased the Vulcan's effective range to 2600 m (8,530 ft). However, by the early 1980s it seemed that the M163 would eventually be outclassed by the Mi-24P 'Hind-F' attack helicopter and by the eventual deployment of the Mi-28 'Havoc'. Both of these aircraft featured weapons systems consisting

of Shturm (AT-6 'Spiral') anti-tank missiles and powerful cannon. The US Army Air Defence Artillery replaced

both its M163 Vulcans and M167 towed guns with HMMWVs fitted with FIM-92C Stinger SAMs.

M247 Sgt York Advanced twin 40-mm self-propelled AA gun

Since the late 1960s, the only self-propelled anti-aircraft gun system in front-line service with the US Army has been the M163 20-mm Vulcan system, which had a relatively short range and was not considered to be very accurate. In January 1978, after studying a number of proposals from industry, the United States Armament Research and Development Command issued two competitive contracts for the development of a self-propelled anti-aircraft gun system on a modified M48A5 tank chassis under the designation **Division Air Defense Gun** (**DIVAD**) system. General Dynamics, Pomona Division, entered a system that used twin 35-mm Oerlikon cannon while Ford Aerospace and Communications Corporation entered a system that used twin 40-mm L/70 Bofors guns. In the towed configuration some of the latter were

already operated by a number of NATO countries.

Sgt York selected

Both entries in the competition had a comprehensive fire control system that included both surveillance and tracking radars designed to engage both aircraft and helicopters. Following evaluation of the two systems, the Ford Aerospace and Communications model was selected for production in May 1981 and was later designated as the **M247 Sgt York**. The M247 was an M48A5 tank chassis with a new turret mounted in the centre of the hull. The driver was seated at the front of the hull, and the engine and transmission were at the rear. Suspension was of the torsion-bar type, and consisted of six dual rubber-tyred wheels, with the idler at the front and drive sprocket at the rear; there were five

The M247 was to carry HEPD ammunition for engaging close-in and ground targets, and PFPX rounds for engaging aircraft at longer range.

track-return rollers. Two radars were mounted on the turret, the circular tracking radar on the left and the flat search radar at the rear; both of these could be folded down to reduce the overall height of the vehicle.

The gunner was seated on the left of the turret and the commander on the right and each member was provided with a hatch cover. The gunner had a roof-mounted sight incorporating a laser rangefinder, while the commander had a panoramic roof-mounted periscope and fixed periscopes. The fire-control system was fully automatic with manual override. The twin 40-mm cannon had powered elevation in a turret capable of traverse through 360°. Each gun was provided with its own magazine, and 502 rounds of ammunition were carried. Two types of ammunition were developed for

Although based on a tank rather than an APC chassis, the Sgt York was incapable of keeping pace with modern armour.

DIVAD, namely HEPD (high explosive point detonating) and PFPX (pre-fragmented proximity fused). However, Sgt York proved to be a highly expensive white elephant. The project experienced problems inte-

grating 'off the shelf' military technology; the M247's chassis also proved unable to keep pace with the faster M1 tank. In December 1986, after 50 prototypes had been built, the project was terminated at substantial cost.

M247 Sgt York
Crew: 3
Combat weight: 54430 kg (119,996 lb)
Dimensions: length 7.67 m (25 ft 2 in); length (hull) 7.12 m (23 ft 4 in); width 3.63 m (11 ft 11 in); height (radar up) 4.61 m (15 ft 2 in); height (to roof of turret) 3.42 m (11 ft 3 in)

Powerplant: one Teledyne Continental AVDS-1790-2D diesel engine developing 559 kW (750 hp)
Performance: maximum road speed 48 km/h (30 mph); maximum range 500 km (311 miles)
Gradient: 60 per cent
Vertical obstacle: 0.914 m (3 ft)
Trench: 2.59 m (8 ft 6 in)

Panhard M3/VDA Twin 20-mm self-propelled AA gun

The Panhard AML 4x4 light armoured car has been one of the most successful vehicles of its type designed since World War II. To operate with this vehicle Panhard also developed a 4x4 APC that uses 95 per cent of the automotive components (for example the engine, transmission and suspension) from the original armoured car. This vehicle is the M3, and has also proved to be highly successful and since production started in the early 1970s more than 1,200 M3 and related Buffalo APCs have been built for export to more than 30 countries.

The anti-aircraft member of the family is the **Panhard M3/VDA (Véhicule de Défense Antiaérienne)** and entered production in 1975. The VDA is a standard M3 APC on whose hull top is mounted a DETEXIS turret with two 20-mm anti-aircraft cannon. The turret itself was designed by Hispano-Suiza with Galileo of Italy providing the sight, Oerlikon the 20-mm cannon and Electronique Serge Dassault the radar; the last was the prime contractor for the turret before it was delivered to Panhard for installation on the chassis.

Service

The M3/VDA is known to have entered service with the Ivory Coast, Niger and Abu Dhabi, and the turret can also be fitted without difficulty to other tracked and wheeled chassis such as the Renault VAB, SIBMAS, Panhard ERC and Engesa EE-11 Urutu 6x6 wheeled vehicles and also on the Alvis Spartan, Steyr and, more recently, AMX-13 VCI fully tracked vehicles.

The M3/VDA has a crew of three with the commander at the front, gunner in the turret located on the centre of the hull, and the commander at the rear. The turret has fully powered traverse through 360° at the rate of 60° per second, and the guns can be elevated between -5° and +85° at the rate of 90° per second. Mounted on the turret rear is a radar antenna rotating at some 40 rpm. Carrying out both surveillance and tracking functions, the RA-20 radar can track up to four targets simultaneously, information being relayed to a screen at the commander's position. The gunner has a P56T sight with magnifications of x5 and x12 for the engagement of aerial targets, a ground sight and six periscopes for all-round observation. The 20-mm cannon are mounted externally, one on each side of the turret, the gunner having the option of selecting either or both cannon. The gunner can also select single-shot, burst

The M3/VDA is a version of the successful Panhard M3 APC, armed with two 20-mm Oerlikon cannon. It is powered by a 4-cylinder air-cooled petrol engine.

or fully automatic fire. Two cyclic rates of fire are available, namely 200 or 1,000 rounds per minute, the latter being used for the anti-aircraft role. Each cannon is provided with 300 rounds of ready-use ammunition, and additional ammunition can be carried in the hull. A 7.62-mm (0.3-in) machine-gun is normally fitted for local protection, and there are two electrically operated forward-firing smoke dischargers on each side of the turret. To provide a steadier firing platform, four stabilisers are lowered to the ground hydraulically before the equipment starts firing, although in an emergency the guns can be fired at the lower cyclic rate of fire without the stabilisers in position.

SPECIFICATION	
Panhard M3/VDA	engine delivering 67.1 kW (90 hp)
Crew: 3	**Performance:** maximum road
Weight: 7200 kg (15,873 lb)	speed 90 km/h (56 mph); maximum
Dimensions: length 4.45 m (17 ft	range 1000 km (621 miles)
5 in); width 2.4 m (7 ft 11 in);	**Gradient:** 60 per cent
height 2.995 m (9 ft 11 in)	**Vertical obstacle:** 0.3 m (12 in)
excluding the radar	**Trench:** 0.8 m (2 ft 7 in) with one
Powerplant: one Panhard Model 4	channel or 3.1 m (10 ft 2 in) with
HD air-cooled four-cylinder petrol	four channels

Four stabilisers are lowered automatically before full-rate fire is opened, although the guns can be fired at a lower rate before the stabilisers have been lowered.

AMX-13 DCA Twin 30-mm self-propelled AA gun

In the 1950s prototypes of a number of self-propelled anti-aircraft gun systems were designed and built to meet the requirements of the French army, but it was not until the late 1960s that one of these was considered sufficiently developed to enter production. This was designated as the **AMX-13 DCA (Défense Contre Avions)** and was essentially an AMX-13 chassis fitted with a cast steel turret mounted on the hull at the rear. Prime contractor for the turret was SAMM, with Thomson-CSF responsible for the radar and its associated electronics, and the Swiss company Hispano-Suiza (later Oerlikon-Bührle) for the weapons and ammunition.

Sixty AMX-13 DCA equipments were built for the French army, with final deliveries in 1969, remaining in service into the later 1980s. The AMX-13 DCA was to have been followed into French service by the VADAR twin 20-mm system on the VAB wheeled chassis, but this was cancelled on economy grounds.

Potent cannon

The main armament of the AMX-13 DCA comprised two 30-mm HSS-831A (later KCB) cannon capable of elevation between -5° and +85° in a turret capable of traversing through 360°. The maximum rates of powered elevation and traverse were 45° and 80° per second respectively. Each cannon had 300 rounds of ready-use ammunition, and the gunner could select single-shot, five or 15-round burst or fully automatic fire. The empty cartridge cases were ejected from the turret together with the links. In the anti-aircraft role the weapons had a maximum effective range of 3500 m (3,830 yards), and also possessed a very useful secondary capability against ground targets.

Mounted at the turret rear

Entering service with the French army in 1969, the AMX-13 DCA comprised a twin 30-mm Hispano-Suiza (later Oerlikon-Bührle) cannon system mounted on an AMX-13 light chassis with the antenna for the Oeil Noir 1 (black eye 1) radar mounted at the rear of the turret. A total of 60 such AMX-13 DCA equipments was delivered to the French army.

Right: Pursuing a line of development from the original DCA turret through the Saudi AMX-30 SA and the Dragon, Thomson-CSF developed the SABRE turret. Armed with two 30-mm cannon, the system was trialled on a Steyr APC, but was also tested on the hulls of the Chieftain MBT and Marder MICV.

Below: As a private venture, the DCA turret was mounted on the chassis of the AMX-30 MBT, but found no buyers. A version with an improved turret was sold to Saudi Arabia, and by 1984 the last of 53 examples ordered had been delivered.

was the antenna for the Oeil Noir 1 (black eye 1) coherent pulse-Doppler radar, and this could be retracted into the turret bustle when not required. Although the cannon was normally aimed with the aid of the radar system (providing search and ranging functions), the anti-aircraft sight, a sight was also provided for the engagement of ground targets. Mounted on each side of the turret was a bank of three electrically operated smoke dischargers.

AMX-30 chassis
In the 1960s the same turret was also fitted to the chassis of the AMX-30 MBT, but the combination was not adopted by the French army as this service was already ordering the Roland SAM system on the AMX-30 chassis. However, to provide close-in defence to its Thomson-CSF/Matra Shahine mobile surface-to-air missile systems, Saudi

Arabia ordered 53 examples of a more up-to-date version of this turret on the AMX-30 chassis, and by 1984 all of these equipments had been delivered. This is called the **AMX-30 SA**, and its turret is fitted with the more powerful Thomson-CSF Oeil Vert (green eye) radar as well as improved electronics. Thomson-CSF also developed with SAMM the **SABRE** turret, which was for trials purposes installed on a number of chassis such

as those of the Chieftain MBT, Marder MICV and Steyr-Daimler-Puch APC.

This turret also had twin 30-mm cannon but a more capable fire-control system.

SPECIFICATION	
AMX-13 DCA	petrol engine delivering 186 kW (250 hp)
Crew: 3	**Performance:** maximum road speed 60 km/h (37 mph); maximum range 300 km (186 miles)
Weight: 17200 kg (37,919 lb)	
Dimensions: length 5.4 m (17 ft 11 in); width 2.5 m (8 ft 2 in); height 3.8 m (12 ft 6 in) or 3 m (9 ft 10 in) with the antenna up or down	**Gradient:** 60 per cent
	Vertical obstacle: 0.65 m (2 ft 2 in)
Powerplant: one SOFAM Modele 8Gxb water-cooled eight-cylinder	**Trench:** 1.7 m (5 ft 7 in)

Dragon Twin 30-mm self-propelled AA gun

Given the ever rising cost of defence equipment, there has been an increasing trend since the 1960s, especially in Europe, for the co-operative development of weapon systems. For example, the 155-mm (6-in) FH-70 howitzer was developed by Germany, Italy and the UK, with production undertaken in all three countries. A similar type of development took place on a private-venture basis to create the **Dragon** twin 30-mm SPAAG.

Development
The hull was developed by Thyssen-Henschel, while the turret and its associated fire-control system were developed by SAMM and the Electronics Systems Division of Thomson-CSF. The chassis was similar to that of the Marder MICV and TAM medium tank, and as such was of all-welded steel construction providing the crew with protection from small arms fire and shell splinters. The driver was seated at the front left with the engine to his right, the turret was located in the centre, and the reserve ammunition supply was at the rear of the hull. The Dragon retained the power-operated ramp in the rear of the hull to provide quick access to the reserve ammunition supply. The torsion-bar suspension consisted of six dual rubber-

tyred road wheels, with the drive sprocket at the front and the idler at the rear, and there were three track-return rollers. The upper part of the track was covered by a rubber skirt that helped to keep the dust down. The Dragon could be fitted with additional fuel tanks at the hull rear to increase the operating range by some 67 per cent to a maximum of 1000 km (621 miles).

Core of the system
The all-welded steel turret had the commander seated on the left and the gunner on the right. Mounted at the turret's rear was the Oeil Vert (green eye) radar that undertook both the surveillance and tracking functions. When not required, the radar was retracted into the turret bustle. Both the commander and gunner were provided with sights for the engagement of ground targets, as well as periscopes for observation purposes.

The turret had fully powered traverse through 360° at the rate of 35° per second, and the twin 30-mm cannon could be elevated from -8° to +85° at the rate of 30° per second. Turret traverse and weapon elevation were both hydraulic, with manual controls for emergency use. The gunner could select bursts of one to five rounds, or a burst of 15 rounds for the

Mounted on a Marder-type chassis, the Dragon system was equipped with the Oeil Vert (green eye) radar used on the Saudi AMX-30 SA vehicle.

weapons, which had a maximum effective AA range of 3000 m (3,280 yards). They could also be used against ground targets firing SAPHEI (semi-armour-piercing high explosive incendiary) ammunition to penetrate the thin armour of APCs before exploding inside the vehicle.

The Dragon SPAAG first ran in prototype form in 1979 and in definitive form for the export market during 1981, but failed to find a buyer. Further development of the turret by Thomson-CSF has resulted in the SABRE turret which was fit-

ted for trials purposes onto the British Chieftain MBT and Austrian Steyr APC

chassis, and was proposed for the French AMX-10RC 6x6 armoured car.

SPECIFICATION	
Dragon	cooled six-cylinder diesel delivering 536 kW (720 hp)
Crew: 3	**Performance:** maximum road speed 72 km/h (45 mph); maximum range 600 km (373 miles)
Weight: 31000 kg (68,342 lb)	
Dimensions: length 6.775 m (22 ft 3 in); width 3.12 m (10 ft 3 in); height 4.195 m (13 ft 11 in) with the antenna up	**Gradient:** 65 per cent
	Vertical obstacle: 1 m (3 ft 3 in)
Powerplant: one MTU liquid-	**Trench:** 2.5 m (8 ft 2 in)

ZSU-23-4 Shilka SPAAG

The ZSU-23-4 Shilka - Drill, was developed in the late 1950s by the Astrov KB design team as a replacement for the open-topped 57-mm ZSU-57-2 Self Propelled Anti-Aircraft Gun (SPAAG). It was first seen by Western observers in 1965 in the November Revolution parade held in Red Square. Though with the Group of Soviet Forces in Germany it was a potent threat to NATO aircraft on the Central Front, it was in 1973 that it demonstrated its lethality. Following the Egyptian crossing of the Suez Canal in October and co-ordinated attack by Syrian forces against Israel, the Israeli air force attempted to buy time for the Army flying ground attack missions. Its pilots encountered a very effective layered defence developed by the Soviet Union. If aircraft attempted to evade Surface to Air Missiles (SAMs) by approaching at low altitude the ZSU-23-4 radar would pick them up, track and then the crew could engage them. The Shilka SPAAG accounted for 30% of the aircraft lost by the Israelis during the 1973 war.

The ZSU (Zenitnaia Samokhodnaia Ustanovka) used the AZP-23M cannon that was entering service as a twin-barrelled towed mount. Four guns mounted in a closed turret with an acquisition and tracking radar and fire control computer. The cannon could be elevated to +80° and depressed to -4° and were gas operated producing a phenomenal rate of fire of between 800 and 1,000 rounds a minute. To avoid overheating, the crew engaged targets with one or two of the cannon and fired in bursts ranging from five to 30 rounds per barrel.

Above: Shilkas on the prowl. These weapons were usually assigned to motor rifle and tank regiments in groups of four, with pairs of guns providing a protective umbrella for each of the two first-echelon battalions. In low air threat environments they were used against ground targets.

Though the turret was powered, it could be operated manually by either the commander or the gunner and the guns could also be laid without using the folding RPK-2 J-band 'Gun Dish' radar. The radar had a panoramic search range of up to 20 km (12.43 miles) and a tracking mode of 18 km. (11.18 miles). If the radar was jammed or detected an incoming missile it automatically shut down but the gunner could continue to engage targets manually. The guns could be laid while the vehicle was moving at speeds of 25 km/h (15.53 mph) though this halved the accuracy. The vehicle could also fire when on an incline of 10°.

During the Soviet intervention in Afghanistan the ZSU-23-4 had its radar removed and ammunition capacity increased from 2,000 rounds to 4,000 and was fitted with additional night vision equipment. Thus modified it was used in a ground-to-ground role protecting convoys and key points.

The chassis was also used for the PRU Mobile Reconnaissance and Control Post that mounted a 'Dog Ear' radar and was used to provide target information for AA guns and missiles.

Production of the ZSU-23-4 ran from 1965 to 1983, in which time between 6,000 and 7,000 vehicles were built.

It was widely exported and among its biggest users were Syria with 400, Algeria with 210 and Libya with 250. The Iraqis had over 200 but many of these were lost in the 1991 war. The Shilka is now being replaced by the 2S6 that has a 30-mm cannon and missile combination.

Left: Egyptian Shilkas on parade. This potent weapon was exported to most Soviet client states in eastern Europe and the Middle East. In Egyptian hands it proved an extremely effective anti-aircraft system, much to the discomfort of the overconfident Israeli Air Force.

ZSU versus Gepard Radar-guided firepower in action

Both ZSU-23/4 and Gepard have proved, in their own ways, to be very successful vehicles. Although Gepard has never been used in combat, unlike the ZSU-23/4, which saw action in numerous Arab/Israeli wars and in Afghanistan, it has proved itself in other ways, and as a result is a popular export vehicle. The ZSU relies on a high rate of relatively inaccurate firepower to achieve its aim, whereas Gepard fires a smaller number of much heavier rounds with greater accuracy. However, it is a classic example of western technology being far more expensive than its Soviet-era Russian contemporary. It poses a serious question: is it better to maintain a large quantity of simple but cheap weaponry rather than a few much more costly but deadly systems?

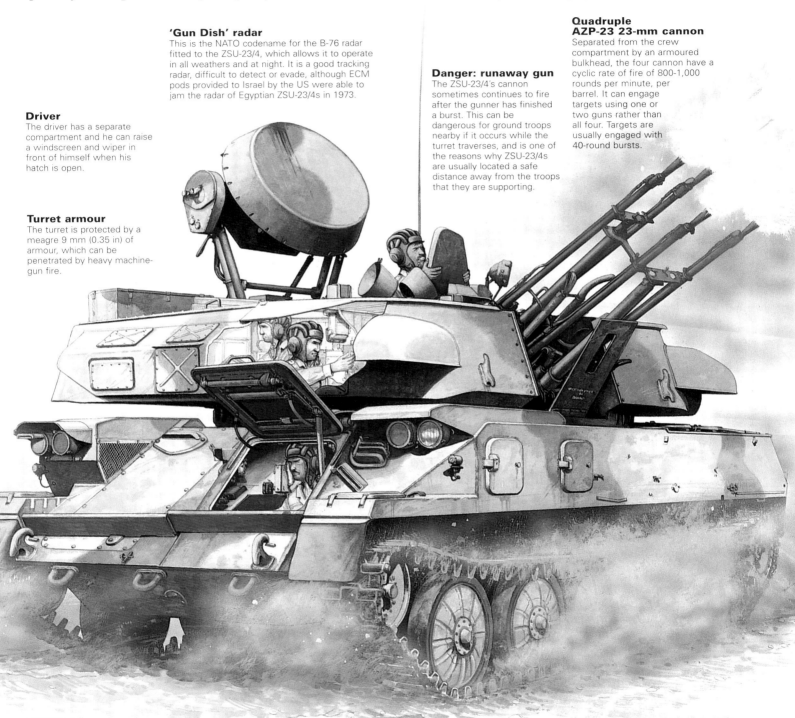

'Gun Dish' radar
This is the NATO codename for the B-76 radar fitted to the ZSU-23/4, which allows it to operate in all weathers and at night. It is a good tracking radar, difficult to detect or evade, although ECM pods provided to Israel by the US were able to jam the radar of Egyptian ZSU-23/4s in 1973.

Danger: runaway gun
The ZSU-23/4's cannon sometimes continues to fire after the gunner has finished a burst. This can be dangerous for ground troops nearby if it occurs while the turret traverses, and is one of the reasons why ZSU-23/4s are usually located a safe distance away from the troops that they are supporting.

Quadruple AZP-23 23-mm cannon
Separated from the crew compartment by an armoured bulkhead, the four cannon have a cyclic rate of fire of 800-1,000 rounds per minute, per barrel. It can engage targets using one or two guns rather than all four. Targets are usually engaged with 40-round bursts.

Driver
The driver has a separate compartment and he can raise a windscreen and wiper in front of himself when his hatch is open.

Turret armour
The turret is protected by a meagre 9 mm (0.35 in) of armour, which can be penetrated by heavy machine-gun fire.

Ammunition
The ZSU-23/4's 23-mm (0.9-in) ammunition comes in belts of 500 rounds with one armour-piercing to every three high-explosive rounds. Both have a tracer base. The AP round can penetrate 25 mm (0.97 in) of armour at 500 metres and 19 mm (0.7 in) at 1,000 metres. Each ZSU-23/4 carries 2,000 rounds in 40 boxes of 500, and supply trucks follow about 1 km (0.621 miles) behind with another 3,000 rounds for each vehicle.

Chassis
Similar to that of the PT-76 light tank, the chassis of the ZSU-23/4 has an overpressure NBC system but, surprisingly, is not amphibious. It crosses rivers on GSP ferries and can fire while afloat.

Hull armour protection
The ZSU-23/4 has only 15 mm (0.6 in) of armour on its hull front, sloped at 55°, and 15 mm (0.6 in) of armour on the hull sides. This protects the hull from small-arms fire and shell splinters but is easily penetrated by anti-tank rockets and cannon.

SPAAGs Briefing Close-range air defence

World War II showed that armoured columns are horribly vulnerable to air attack. During the war, most armies developed mobile air defences, which usually consisted of fast-firing guns mounted on some kind of armoured chassis. After the war, missiles became the primary defensive system, but the gun was still popular for point defence. Modern gun systems began to emerge in the 1960s. Mounting several fast-firing cannon firing explosive rounds at high velocity, the gun system was transformed by the addition of tracking and fire control radar, which enabled the guns to engage fast-flying, low-level targets in all weathers and at all times of day or night. The Soviet ZSU-23-4 and the German Gepard represent two contrasting solutions to the same problem.

Officially described as a Flugabwehrkanonenpanzer (Air defense cannon tank), the Gepard is based on the chassis of the Leopard 1 main battle tank. The vehicle is fitted with a fire control system, all-weather tracking and acquisition sensors and powerful automatic guns. It was developed to protect key installations, combat units and troops on the move, as well as on the battlefield.

Modern anti-aircraft weapons have come a long way from the relatively primitive systems in use during World War II. Weapons like the Gepard have accurate, fast-firing guns that are directed by sophisticated radar and optronic systems.

The tracking radar mounted on the front of the Gepard's turret has a range of 13 km (8.08 miles). The radar system is designed to pick out moving targets even amid the clutter of ground returns, and the fire control system uses the data to aim the guns.

The search radar mounted on the rear of the Gepard's turret also has a range of 15 km (9.32 miles). The radar system is designed to pick out moving targets even amid the clutter of ground returns, and the fire control system uses the data to aim the guns. The radar provides 360° scanning, and can track multiple targets simultaneously.

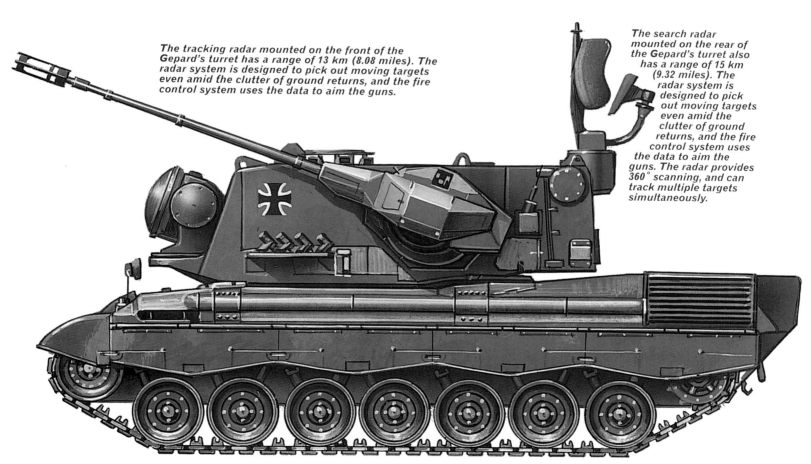

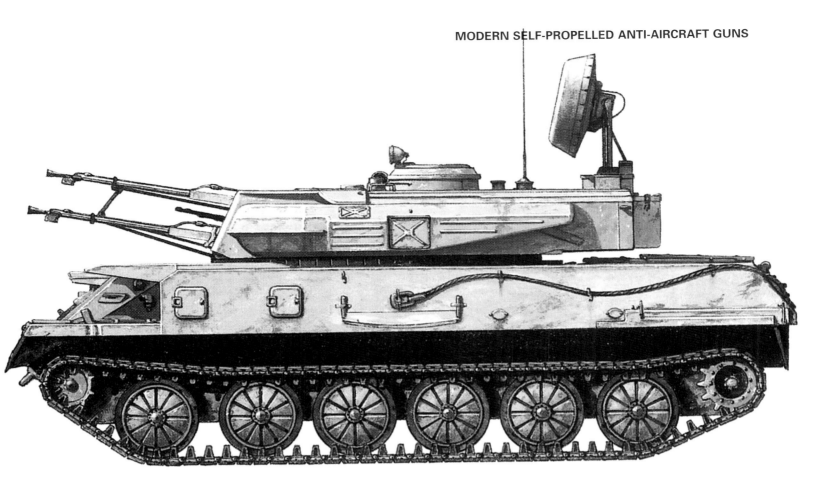

Above: The ZSU-23-4 is designed for the same mission as the Gepard, but is a much lighter vehicle. Its four 23-mm cannons are individually smaller than the guns on the German vehicle, but they fire a much higher number of shells.

Above: The ZSU, nicknamed the 'Zoo' by its potential American opponents, carries four water-cooled AZP-23 cannons with a theoretical firing rate of up to 4,000 rounds per minute (800-1,000 rpm per barrel). However, firing at that rate would soon melt the barrels, so the guns are fired in bursts of up to 30 rounds each.

Right: The Gepard is fitted with a two-man electric power-operated turret armed with twin Oerlikon KDA 35-mm guns which are equipped with an automatic belt feed. The rate of fire provided by the two barrels is 1,100 rounds per minute – slower than the ZSU, but the shells fired are more than twice as heavy.

SPECIFICATION

ZSU-23-4 Self-Propelled Anti-Aircraft Gun
Crew: Four
Dimensions: length 6.54 m (21 ft 5 in); height 2.25 m (7 ft 5 in); width 2.95 m (9 ft 8 in); combat weight 20.5 tonnes
Armour: maximum thickness 9.2 mm hull, 8.3 mm turret
Performance: maximum road speed: 50km/h (31 mph); cruising range (on roads) 450 km (280 miles); fording 1.0 m (3 ft 6 in)
Armament: 4x23mm water-cooled AZP-23 cannons, traverses 360 degrees; maximum effective range (vertical) 3,000 m (9,843 ft); rate of fire maximum 800-1000 rds/min/barrel, sustained 30 rds/barrel/burst
Type of ammunition: API-T, HEI-T, Frag-HE-T
Basic Load: 2,000 rds
Electronics: fire control
Gun Dish: radar and optical-mechanical sight, infrared system for commander and driver
NBC Protection: air filtration and overpressure system, radiation detection and warning system

Gepard Self-Propelled Anti-Aircraft Gun
Crew: four
Dimensions: length (guns pointing forward) 7.68 m (25 ft 3 in); height (with search radar lowered) 3.29 m (10ft 9 in); width (with track skirts) 3.71 m (12 ft 2 in); combat weight 47.5 tonnes
Performance: maximum road speed: 65 km/h (41 mph); cruising range (on roads) 550 km (280 miles)
Armament: 2x35-mm belt-fed KDA cannon traverses 360 degrees; maximum effective range (vertical) over 4,000 m (13,120 ft); rate of fire maximum 1100 rds/min/barrel usually fired in bursts of up to 50
Type of ammunition: API-T, HEI-T,Frag-HE-T
Basic Load: 320 rds
Electronics: digital fire control computer; IFF system
Sighting: S-band search radar, Ku-band tracking radar, periscopic optical sight with x1.5 to x6 magnification
NBC Protection: air filtration and overpressure system, radiation detection and warning system

ZSU versus Gepard Radar-guided firepower in action

Cannon
The twin 35-mm Oerlikon KDA used by the Gepard can fire at a rate of 550 rounds per minute. The projectiles have a muzzle velocity of 1175 m/s (2,600 mph). The guns are externally mounted, reducing the risk to the crew of an ammunition explosion. The KDA can fire both high-explosive and armour-piercing high-explosive against aerial targets. It has a special AP round for use against ground targets such as bunkers and light armoured vehicles.

Tracking radar
Once a target is acquired and coded hostile by the search radar, the tracking radar will pick up the target. Its function is to bring the guns into line for the correct elevation and aim-off.

Crew
The crew of three is made up of a driver in the hull and the commander and gunner in the turret. Both can operate the guns and have similar gun controls. It is the commander's job to acquire and identify targets. The gunner will then take over the shoot while the commander looks for another target.

Driver
The driver's cab is self-contained with no access to the turret. Communication is achieved by an internal intercom. The vehicle is steered by motorbike-type handlebars, rather than two separate sticks as found on older MBTs. Gepard has a fully automatic four-speed gearbox. It has the ability to execute a complete pivot on one spot: one track is driven forward, the other backwards, thus rotating the vehicle about its own axis.

Optical sights

For operating closed down, the commander and operator are provided with x1 vision ports for general observation. In addition there are optical tracking devices which provided x1.5 or x6 magnification. They are fully stabilised and can be used in periods when radar may not be used. They can also be used for multiple target engagements and for taking on ground targets that may try to hide in radar cover.

Search radar

Gepard, unlike its Soviet counterpart, uses two radars: one for target search and acquisition, and the other for target tracking. The search radar has a range of 15 km (9.3 miles) and operates in the S-band. It has a choice of six operating frequencies, which are controlled by the operator. The IFF (Identification Friend or Foe) system is built in and automatic.

Hull

As the Gepard shares the same hull as the Leopard 1 Main Battle Tank, it has excellent cross-country ability due to the independently mounted suspension units for each road wheel. Since Gepard is not expected to be in direct combat, some of the frontal armour has been reduced to save weight.

Engine

The same liquid-cooled 10-cylinder V-engine as is found on the Leopard MBT powers Gepard. It provides 610 kW (830 hp) of power, giving the Gepard a power-to-weight ration of 18:1. The vehicle can travel at a maximum speed of 65 km/h (40 mph) and has a battle range of 550 km (330 miles).

Gepard Twin 35-mm self-propelled AA gun

When the West German army was formed in the 1950s, it was supplied with some 500 M42 twin 40-mm self-propelled anti-aircraft gun systems by the US. The M42's 40-mm guns possessed good range but the vehicle lacked any onboard fire-control system. From the late 1960s various projects were initiated for the development of a new SPAAG, but these all came to nothing. In 1966 contracts were issued for the development of a SPAAG based on the chassis of the Leopard 1 MBT which had recently entered production for the West Germany army, and after the completion of systems with twin 30-mm and 35-mm cannon, the latter was selected for full-scale development.

Construction
The prime contractor for the twin 35-mm system was Contraves of Switzerland, and after the construction of additional prototypes, this system was selected for service with the West German army as the **Flakpanzer Gepard**. The first production vehicle was completed in 1976 and final deliveries were made in 1970. Some 420 Gepards were built for the West German army, 55 for the Belgian army and 95 for the Dutch army. The last differed from the Belgian and West German vehicles in that the turret was fitted with a Dutch Hollandse Signaalapparaten surveillance and tracking radar with moving-target indication and other minor differences. The turret could also have been installed on other chassis such as those of the Swiss Pz 68 MBT and Italian OTO Melara OF-40, and at one time Saudi Arabia expressed an interest in acquiring up to 100 of a modernised version of this turret fitted to the chassis of the Leopard 2 MBT.

The chassis of the Gepard is similar to that of the Leopard 1 but with thinner armour protection for the hull. The driver is at the front of the hull on the right, with the auxiliary power unit to his left; the turret is in the centre; the engine and transmission are at the rear. The suspension is of the torsion-bar type, and on each side consists of seven dual rubber-tyred road wheels, with the idler at front and the drive sprocket at the rear; there are two track-return rollers.

Created for the defence of major armoured formations against air attack, the Gepard offers the same level of battlefield mobility as the Leopard 1 MBT, the chassis of which it inherited, albeit with decreased levels of armour prootection.

The search radar is mounted at the turret rear and can be folded down if required, while the tracking radar is on the front of the turret.

Type KDA cannon
Mounted externally on each side of the turret is a 35-mm Oerlikon Type KDA cannon with a cyclic rate of fire of 550 rounds per minute. This weapon is provided with 310 rounds of ready-use AA ammunition and 20 rounds of APDS-T (Armour-Piercing Discarding Sabot – Tracer) for the engagement of ground targets. In addition to the APDS-T ammunition, HEI (HE Incendiary), HEI-T (HE Incendiary – Tracer), practice and SAPHEI-T (Semi-Armour-Piercing HE Incendiary – Tracer) ammunition is available. In addition to the tracking and surveillance radars the Gepard has a comprehensive fire-control system, onboard land navigation system, sights for engaging surface as well as air targets, and an NBC system. Some of the West German Gepards have been fitted with a Siemens laser rangefinder.

The Gepard's 35-mm cannon are controlled via a capable fire-control system drawing data from vehicle-mounted sensors that include surveillance and tracking radars on the rear and front of the turret.

SPECIFICATION	
Crew: 3	Ca M500 V-10 liquid-cooled diesel developing 619 kW (830 hp)
Weight: 47.3 tonnes	**Performance:** maximum road speed 65 km/h (40 mph); maximum road range 550 km (342 miles)
Dimensions: length (guns forward) 7.73 m (25 ft 4 in); length (hull) 6.85 m (22 ft 6 in); width 3.37 m (11 ft 1 in); height (radar elevated) 4.03 m (13 ft 3 in); height (periscopes) 3.01 m (9 ft 11 in)	**Gradient:** 60 per cent **Vertical obstacle:** 1.15 m (3 ft 9 in)
Powerplant: one MTU MB 838	**Trench:** 3 m (9 ft 10 in)

Wildcat Twin 35-mm self-propelled AA gun

Krauss-Maffei of Munich built all of the Gepard twin 35-mm self-propelled anti-aircraft guns on a modified Leopard 1 chassis delivered to the Belgian, West German and Dutch armies. The company realised, however, that although this was a highly effective system for European armies, it was too heavy, complex and costly for many potential export customers. The company therefore decided to develop a complete family of SPAAG systems that would be able to meet the requirements of almost every customer.

Given its experience with the Transportpanzer 1 6x6 cross-country vehicle, already in production for the West German army, the company decided to use automotive components of this vehicle in a new hull which could be fitted with a turret armed with twin 30-mm cannon. Six different fire-control options were offered, these ranging from the V1 clear-weather system with optical tracking via the V3 with radar target detection and automatic target tracking, up to the V6 with an all-weather fire-control system and automatic target tracking. Two prototypes were built with the V3 fire-control system, one on the original 6x6 chassis and the other on the MOWAG Shark 8x8 chassis.

The basic layout of the

The Wildcat was a brave but ultimately fruitless private-venture attempt to create an affordable yet capable AA gun system offering a good level of cross-country mobility.

Wildcat, as the system was designated, was the same in all versions, with the driver and radio operator/gunner in the front, the turret in the centre, and engine and transmission at the rear. The suspension consisted of axles with coil springs and hydraulic shock absorbers to provide good cross-country ride. The steering was power-assisted on the front four wheels, and run-flat tyres could be fitted.

External weapons

The turret was fitted with two 30-mm Mauser MK 30-F cannon installed as one external weapon on each side of the turret, each cannon having 250 rounds of ready-use ammunition. The cannon had a cyclic rate of fire of 800 rounds per minute and could fire three types of ammunition, namely APDS (Armour-Piercing Discarding Sabot), HEI (HE Incendiary) and TP (Target Practice).

A typical target engagement would have taken place in the following manner. The radar operator/gunner monitored his radar scope on a constant basis, and once an aircraft had been spotted by the radar and appeared on his scope, the operator had then to determine whether or not it was hostile. If the target was confirmed by IFF as hostile, the periscope traversed onto the target's bearing and then searched for the target in elevation. The laser rangefinder then started to feed information to the computer, whereupon the turret and guns were trained on the target, the cannon opening fire as soon as the target was in range. At the same time the computer would have been updated with new information should a second burst be required to destroy the target. In addition to the anti-aircraft/anti-helicopter role, with a range of about 3000 m (3,280 yards), the weapons could also be used to engage ground targets.

A later development of

The Wildcat was an interesting attempt to create a tactically effective but comparatively low-cost self-propelled AA gun system through the installation of a moderately advanced yet affordable weapon/sensor turret on a wheeled chassis.

this interesting weapon system's evolution was the possible replacement of the twin 30-mm cannon by short-range missiles such as the American General Dynamics Stinger or British Shorts Blowpipe/Javelin.

In the event the Wildcat did not enter production.

SPECIFICATION	
Wildcat (1st prototype)	liquid-cooled turbocharged
Crew: 3	8-cylinder diesel developing
Weight: 18500 kg (40,785 lb)	239 kW (320 hp)
Dimensions: length 6.88 m (22 ft	**Performance:** maximum road
7 in); width 2.98 m (9 ft 9 in); height	speed 80 km/h (50 mph); maximum
(radar down) 2.74 m (9 ft)	range 600 km (373 km)
Powerplant: one Mercedes-Benz	**Gradient:** 60 per cent

OTOMATIC 76.2-mm self-propelled AA gun

The **OTOMATIC** 76.2-mm (3-in) self-propelled anti-aircraft/anti-helicopter system was developed by OTO Melara of La Spezia as a private venture specifically for the export market. It consisted basically of a modified OF-40 MBT chassis fitted with a new all-welded turret armed with a 76.2-mm (3-in) L/62 automatic gun developed from the naval weapon of the same calibre and used by many navies around the world, and also manufactured in Japan, Spain and the US. The unique feature of the OTOMATIC compared with the many other comparable systems on offer at the time was the fact that it was designed specifically to engage and destroy attack helicopters before they themselves could approach to missile-firing range. Most self-propelled anti-aircraft and anti-helicopter systems are armed with cannon in the calibre bracket between 30 and 40 mm, and therefore have a maximum effective range of between 3000 and 4000 m (3,280 and 4,375 yards), providing them with an engagement only marginally adequate for the successful engagement of the target before it reaches missile-release range. Later

generations of air-launched missiles, as typified by the AGM-114 Hellfire, offered extended range capability as well as a fire-and-forget capability. The availability of this type of weapon opened the way for the attack helicopter to stand off and attack tank formations without any danger of being destroyed by smaller-calibre self-propelled anti-aircraft gun systems.

Gun mounting

The 76.2-mm gun of the OTOMATIC was mounted in a turret with powered traverse, and the weapon had maximum elevation of +60° and a depression of -5°. Some 100 rounds of fixed ammunition were carried, of which 70 rounds were in the turret and the remaining 30 in the hull; 25 of these rounds were held in the automatic loading system for immediate use. For the engagement of aerial targets the weapon would fire HE or pre-formed fragmentation projectiles with either a point detonating or proximity fuse, while for the engagement of ground targets an APFSDS (Armour-Piercing Fin-Stabilised Discarding Sabot) projectile would be fired.

The OTOMATIC anti-aircraft gun system offered exceptional capabilities in terms of target-engagement range and projectile lethality, but failed to find a buyer in a market dominated with multiple installations of smaller-calibre weapons.

According to the OTO Melara company, targets could have been destroyed at a maximum range of at least 6000 m (6,560 yards), a closely controlled six-round burst being considered sufficient for most targets. An advanced and very comprehensive fire-control system was installed to ensure timely target detection and tracking as well as extremely accurate laying of the 76.2-mm gun, and this fire-control system included a search radar with its antenna mounted on an arm above the rear of the turret and a tracking radar with its antenna on the roof of the turret just forward of the search radar's antenna arm. The tracking radar was complemented by a co-axial optronic tracker for continued system operability in

the event that the tracking radar was knocked out or was degraded in performance by electronic countermeasures, and there was also an optical fire-control system for the engagement of ground targets. Both of the antennae were designed to retract when not being used.

Mounted on each side of the turret was a bank of three electrically operated smoke dischargers, while provision was made for the installation of a 7.62-mm (0.3-in) machine-gun on the turret roof to provide a measure of local protection.

Prototypes

Two prototypes of the OTOMATIC were completed, the first of these finishing its initial firing and stabilisation trials in January

1987, and the second prototype had been finished by September of the same year. OTO Melara offered the system for installation on the hulls of vehicles able to accept the 15000-kg (33,068-lb) weight of the turret, the two most likely candidates being MBTs such as the Leopard 1 to create a variant that would have been known as the **HEFAS76-L1**, and self-propelled artillery systems such as the Palmaria. In the event OTO Melara found no purchasers for its system, which was offered on the market for several years.

Major sub-contractors included SMA, which supplied the search and tracking radars, and Officine Galileo, which supplied the optronic and all-weather fire-control system.

SPECIFICATION	
OTOMATIC	(1,000-hp) liquid-cooled four-stroke
Crew: 4	supercharged diesel
Weight: 46 tonnes	**Performance:** maximum road
Dimensions: length (gun forward)	speed 60 km/h (37 mph); maximum
9.64 m (31 ft 7 in); length (hull)	road range 500 km (311 miles)
7.27 m (23 ft 10 in); width 3.35 m	**Fording:** 1.2 m (3 ft 11 in)
(11 ft); height (turret top) 3.15 m	**Gradient:** 60 per cent
(10 ft 4 in)	**Vertical obstacle:** 1.15 m (3 ft 9 in)
Powerplant: one 746-kW	**Trench:** 3 m (9 ft 10 in)

Escorter 35 series Twin 35-mm self-propelled AA guns

For many years the Swiss-based company Oerlikon-Bührle (now Oerlikon-Contraves), with subsidiaries in Italy and the UK, produced the world's largest range of towed anti-aircraft guns including the highly successful GDF series of 35-mm weapons, of which more than 1,500 have been manufactured. It also designed the armament and weapons used in Germany's Gepard self-propelled twin 35-mm anti-aircraft gun system.

Developed for the task of defending rear-area targets such as airbases, factories, ports and command centres, the GDF-D03 comprised two 35-mm KDF cannon mounted on the HYKA cross-country truck chassis, and was equipped with a fire-control system including a laser rangefinder and a Contraves radar.

Potential demand

The company also realised that there could also be a demand for a highly mobile twin 35-mm system to defend rear-area targets such as airports, command centres and factories, and that such a system, unlike the Gepard, would not need to be based on a MBT chassis. The result has been the **Escorter 35** series of twin 35-mm anti-aircraft gun systems, announced in the 1980s but not successful in finding any buyers. Two chassis were offered, one tracked and the other wheeled. The tracked chassis was a version of the M528 tracked cargo carrier (lengthened by an additional road wheel on each side), itself a member of the American M113 series of tracked armoured vehicle of which more than 74,000 have been produced to date by the FMC Corporation

(now United Defense) for the home and export markets. The wheeled system was based on the chassis of the HYKA cross-country vehicle and offered a higher road speed and greater operational range than the tracked version, although it was some 3.5 tonnes heavier.

Fire-control systems

In each case two fire-control systems were offered: the **GDF-C02** (tracked) and the **GDF-D02** (wheeled) systems had a day/night fire-control system developed by Contraves and including a laser rangefinder, while the **MF-C03** (tracked) and **MF-D03** (wheeled) systems were similar apart from the

addition of an Italian Contraves search radar that has a maximum range of some 23 km (14 miles). For most applications a customer would probably order one vehicle fitted with the radar to every three without the radar, the former then supplying target information to the others.

All versions were fitted with a power-operated turret armed with twin 35-mm MF cannon and 430 rounds of ready-use ammunition. Each cannon had a cyclic rate of fire of 600 rounds per minute. The 35-mm cannon's effective range was about 3500 m (3,830 yards), and the ammunition types included HEI (high-explosive

SPECIFICATION	
MF-C03	delivering 160 kW (215 hp)
Crew: 3	**Performance:** maximum road
Weight: 18000 kg (39,683 lb)	speed 45 km/h (28 mph); maximum
Dimensions: length 6.7 m (22 ft);	road range 480 km (297 miles)
width 2.813 m (9 ft 3 in); height	**Gradient:** 60 per cent
4 m (13 ft 2 in)	**Vertical obstacle:** 0.609 m (2 ft)
Powerplant: one GMC 6V-53T	**Trench:** 1.8 m (5 ft 11 in)
water-cooled 6-cylinder diesel	

incendiary), HEI-T (high-explosive incendiary-tracer), SAPHEI-T (semi-armour-piercing high-explosive incendiary-tracer), APDS-T (armour-piercing discarding sabot-tracer) and practice. The APDS-T round was designed for use against ground targets such as light tanks and armoured person-

nel carriers, and could penetrate 40 mm (1.6 in) of armour at 60° at a range of 1000 m (1,095 yards).

In both systems the crew compartment was at the front of the vehicle with the turret at the rear, and had a three-man crew comprising the vehicle commander, gunner and driver.

CV 9040 AAV 40-mm self-propelled AA gun

To provide a highly mobile air-defence capability for the Swedish army's mechanised forces, the Swedish Defence Matériel Administration selected a further development of the Combat Vehicle 90 family.

This is called the **CV 9040 Anti-Aircraft Vehicle**, or **Lvkv 90**, by the Swedish army. Development began in the late 1980s. The first prototypes were completed in 1991, and there followed extensive user trials.

The main production run of 27 CV 9040 AAVs was completed in the late 1990s, and this is the only self-propelled anti-aircraft gun (SPAAG) currently in service

with the Swedish army.

The baseline CV 9040 infantry combat vehicle (ICV) has been built in large numbers for the Swedish army, with what is now Alvis Hägglunds responsible for the chassis and Bofors Defence for the turret and 40-mm weapon system.

In appearance the CV 9040 AAV is similar to the CV 9040 ICV but the former has a crew of six and its weapon system is optimised for the engagement of tactical fixed- and rotary-wing aircraft. The CV 9040 AAV has a crew of six in the form of the driver seated in the front of the vehicle, vehicle

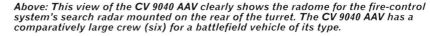

Above: This view of the CV 9040 AAV clearly shows the radome for the fire-control system's search radar mounted on the rear of the turret. The CV 9040 AAV has a comparatively large crew (six) for a battlefield vehicle of its type.

Left: The CV 9040 AAV's gun is a further development of the world famous 40-mm L/70 towed air-defence system firing more advanced ammunition including the 3P programmable round. There is also an AP round for engaging light AFVs.

The CV 9040 AAV combines a well-proven chassis with the latest version of Bofors 40-mm gun in a turret carrying radar and a laser rangefinder.

SPECIFICATION	
CV 9040 AAV	to an Allison X-300 transmission
Crew: 6	**Performance:** maximum road
Weight: 23000 kg (50,705 lb)	speed 70 km/h (43.5 mph);
Dimensions: length 6.71 m (22 ft);	maximum range 600 km (373 miles)
width 3.192 m (10 ft 5¼ in); height	**Gradient:** 60 per cent
2.3 m (7 ft 6½ in) without radar	**Fording:** 1 m (3 ft 3 in)
Powerplant: one Scania DS 14	**Vertical obstacle:** 1 m (3 ft 3 in)
diesel delivering 410 kW (550 hp)	**Trench:** 2 m (6 ft 5 in)

Below: The French-supplied TRS 2620 search radar uses an antenna in a retractable radome mounted on the back of the CV 9040 AAV's turret. The complete turret is also available for use on other vehicles.

commander and gunner in the turret and the other three crew members in the hull rear. These are the radar operator, plotter and the air defence combat commander, of whom the last is in overall control of the platform's air-defence elements.

Mounted in the middle of the roof is the two-person turret armed with a Bofors Defence 40-mm L/70 anti-aircraft gun. Ammunition is fed from below, and the empty cartridge cases are ejected from the turret roof. Mounted on the turret rear is a Thales TRS 2620 search

radar, which provides target information to the crew seated in the vehicle rear.

The gunner is provided with a roof-mounted optical/thermal sighting system, which also includes a laser rangefinder to feed range information to the fire-control computer.

Tridon 40-mm self-propelled AA gun

The Bofors Defence 40-mm L/70 towed anti-aircraft gun system was developed shortly after the end of World War II for the Swedish army, but was adopted by many countries all over the world. The main drawback of the gun in its basic towed form is its lack of mobility, the time needed for it to go into and come out of action, and its relatively high manpower requirements.

Private venture

Some years ago Bofors Defence started working as a private venture on the **Tridon** 40-mm self-propelled anti-aircraft gun (SPAAG). This was essentially a modified Volvo 6x6 cross-country chassis fitted at the front with an armour-protected crew cab, and over the rear the complete upper part of the Bofors Defence 40-mm L/70 towed AA gun system.

In this application the 40-mm L/70 mount was upgraded in a number of aspects, including the installation of new all-electric gun control equipment and an LVS sighting system.

When the equipment had been deployed in its firing position, stabilisers were lowered to the ground to create a more stable firing platform. On the first version the weapon was still aimed and fired with the crew on the gun mount. However, the projected Phase III developed also featured a passive sensor package.

The standard Bofors 40-mm L/70 was normally

towed by a truck which also carried the crew and ammunition, with another truck needed for the generator and fire-control system.

Not only did Tridon have greater cross-country mobility than the towed version, but it could also come into action much more quickly and required a crew of only five personnel.

The Swedish Defence Matériel Administration awarded Bofors Defence a development contract for the further enhancement of the

Tridon's capabilities for the Swedish coastal artillery. In the end the whole programme was cancelled, however, as the Swedish coastal artillery arm was disbanded.

Had the programme gone ahead, the Swedish coastal artillery Karelin 120-mm (4.7-in) towed artillery systems would have been mounted on similar Volvo 6x6 chassis for rapid deployment anywhere in Sweden, the associated Tridon systems providing protection.

The Tridon was very much a mix of old and new, and as such was better suited to the protection of coastal defences than battlefield operations. With a maximum road speed of 70 km/h, however, Tridon offered good mobility and deployment without tank transporters.

SPECIFICATION	
Tridon	diesel delivering 190 kW (255 hp)
Crew: 6	to an M 5 HP 500 transmission
Weight: 23500 kg (51,808 lb)	**Performance:** maximum road
Dimensions: length 11.5 m (37 ft	speed 70 km/h (43.5 mph);
8¾ in); width 3.1 m (10 ft 2 in);	maximum range 300 km (186 miles)
height 3.5 m (11 ft 6 in)	**Gradient:** 60 per cent
Powerplant: one Volvo 6-cylinder	**Fording:** 1 m (3 ft 3 in)

Glossary

AA: anti-aircraft

AFV: armoured fighting vehicle

AP: armour piercing

APCR: armoured piercing cored round, ammunition with a hard core (usually tungsten)

APDS: armour piercing discarding sabot

BREECH: the closed end of the barrel (also used to measure its length)

CALIBRE: the inside diameter of the barrel (also used to measure its length)

EFFECTIVE CEILING: the highest altitude (of an approaching aircraft) to which a AA gun can fire for 30 seconds before it reaches maximum elevation

EFFECTIVE RANGE: the furthest distance a weapon can be accurately aimed

ELEVATION: the amount a gun can be move vertically

FLASH SUPPRESSOR: a device that minimises the visible flash from the gun when fired

HE: high explosive

HESH: high explosive shaped head, ammunition with a shaped charge warhead

MG: machine gun

MUZZLE: the front, open end of the barrel

MUZZLE BRAKE: a device that directs exhaust gases backwards to help counteract recoil

PENETRATION (OF ARMOUR): given in the form AA/BBB/C, where AA is the thickness of armour penetrated in millimetres; BBB is the range at which it occurred; and C is the slope of the armour. Thus, $75/1000/30°$ means that the shot penetrated 75mm (2.95in) of armour at 1000 metres range, striking at an angle of 30° to the target face.

RECOIL: the force that drives a gun backwards when fired

RIFLED (BARREL): a barrel with spiral grooves that make the shell spin, for greater accuracy.

SABOT: a protective sleeve that fits round a (usually finned) shell fired from a smoothbore gun

SHAPED (CHARGE): explosive that is shaped or becomes shaped on impact in a way that gives it maximum destructive value when it burns

SHRAPNEL: ammunition that, when it explodes, spreads small pieces of hot metal in all directions, most effective against infantry.

SMOOTHBORE: a barrel that does not have rifled grooves

TRAVERSE: the amount a barrel can be moved horizontally

Index

Page numbers in italics refer to illustrations and captions. The following abbreviations are used in sub-headings: **AA** anti-aircraft; **SP** self-propelled; **SRBM** short range ballistic missile. The calibre of weapons is only given where it is necessary for differentiation purposes.

ammunition, gliding 24
AMX-13 DCA SP AA guns 238-9, *238*, *239*
anti-aircraft cannons
Bofors 142-3, *143*
Oerlikon 142, *142*
Type 98 141, *141*
anti-aircraft guns
Bofors L/70 230, *230*
Bordkanone 109
Breda Modello 35 DP 140-1, *140*, *141*
Flak 41 116, *116*, 140, *140*, 148, *148*
Flak 88 113, *113*
German 16
heavy
Bofors Model 1929 152, *152*
Bofors Model 1930 152
Cannone da 75/46 C.A. modello 34 150, *150*
Cannone da 90/53 151, *151*
Flak 40 149, *149*
M1 *18*, 157, *157*
M2 157, *157*
M3 156, *156*
Model 1939 152-3, *152*
Model 1944 152-3
Ordnance QF 3in 153, *153*
Ordnance QF 3.7in 154-5, *154*
Ordnance QF 4.5in Mk II 155, *155*
Schneider mle 1936 150, *150*
Type 88 151, *151*
light
Breda 40L70 226-7, *226*, *227*
Flak 30 135, *135*
Flak 38 *16*, 17, *17*, 136, *136*, 148
Flak 39 148-9, *149*
Flak 43 137
Flakvierling 38 136, *136*
Flakzwilling 43 137, *138*
Hotchkiss Mle 1938 134, *134*
Hotchkiss Mle 1939 134
Hotchkiss Mle 1940 134
M1A2 145, *145*
Maxson Mount 144-5, *144*, *145*
Polsten 144, *144*
RAMTA TCM-20 227, *227*
Rheinmetall Twin 226,

226
Tarasque 228, *228*
ZU-23 228-9, *228*, *229*
medium
Flak 18 116, *116*, 136-7, 146, 147, *147*
Flak 36 *136*, 137, *137*, 146, *146*
Flak 37 137, 146, *146*
Schneider Mle 1930 134-5, *134*
Oerlikon GAI-DO1 231, *231*
range-finding *19*
S-60 229, *229*
self-propelled
AMX-13 DCA 238-9, *238*, *239*
BTR-40A 22
BTR-152A 233, *233*
CV 9040 AAV 248-9, *248*, *249*
development 28-9
Dragon 239, *239*
Escorter 35 series 248, *248*
Gepard *28*, 29, *242*, 243, *243*, 244-5, 246, *246*
M42 Duster 236, *236*
M53/59 232, *232*
M163 Vulcan 236-7, *236*, *237*
M247 Sgt York *28*, 29, 237, *237*
Möbelwagen 138, *138*
Ostwind 139, *139*
OTOMATIC 247, *247*
Panhard M3/VDA 238, *238*
SdKfz 7/2 139, *139*
Tridon 249, *249*
2S6 Tunguska IADS 235, *235*
2S6M Tunguska *22*, 23
Type 63 232-3, *232*, *233*
Vulcan 29
Wildcat 29, *29*, 246-7, *246*, *247*
Wirbelwind 138, *138*
ZSU-23-4 Shilka *22*, 23, *23*, *28*, 29, 240, *240*, 241, 243, *243*
ZSU-57-2 22-3, *23*, 29, 234, *234*
ZSU-57-4 234-5, *234*, *235*
shells *18*
anti-aircraft rockets
3in 130, *130*
2in 130, *130*
anti-ballistic missile (ABM)

systems 21
anti-tank guns
see also tank destroyers
Böhler Model 35 118, *118*
lePak 41 111, *111*
M3A1 122, *122*
M5 122, *122*
M1932 120
M1936 121, *121*
M1938 120
M1942 121, *121*
Model 1937 120
Model 1942 120, *120*
Ordnance QF 2pdr 106, *106*
Ordnance QF 6pdr 106-7, *106*, *107*
Ordnance QF 17pdr 107, *107*
Ordnance QF 25pdr 67
Pak 35/36 108, *108*
Pak 38 108-9, *108*
Pak 40 109, *109*
Pak 41 111, *111*
Pak 43 110, *110*
Pak 43/41 110, 112, *112*
Pak 88 113, *113*, 114-15, 116-17
SA mle 1937 123, *123*
SA-L mle 1934 123, *123*
SA-L mle 1937 123
self-propelled
ASU-85 166-7, *166*, *167*
M56 Scorpion 170-1, *170*, *171*
Skoda kanon P.U.V. vz 36 118-19, *118*, *119*
sPzB 41 111, *111*
T-12/MT-12 196, *196*
taper-bore 111
2A45M Sprut-B 196, *196*
Type 1 119, *119*
armoured cars, light, T17
Staghound 29
armoured trains
British 88, *88*
German 88, *88*
Soviet 89, *89*
Armscor G5 towed gun-howitzers 185, *185*
Army 20cm rockets 126, *126*
AS90 SP gun-howitzers 200-1, *201*
assault guns
ASU-57 166, *166*
Sturmgeschütz III 98-9, *98*, *99*
Sturmtiger 97, *97*
ASTROS II rocket systems 27, 214, *214*, *222*, *223*

ASU-57 assault guns 166, *166*
ASU-85 SP anti-tank guns 166-7, *166*, *167*

Bandkanon 1A SP guns 202, *202*
Battalion Gun Type 92 58, *58*
'Big Bertha' howitzers 44, *44*
Bishop SP gun-howitzers 103, *103*
BL 8in howitzers 48, *48*
Mk VI 48
Mk VII 48
BL 9.2in siege howitzers 48
Mk I 48
Mk II 48
BL 12in siege howitzers 49
Mk I 49
Mk II 49
Mk IV 49
rail mounted 49
BL 15in siege howitzers 49, *49*
BL 26cwt field howitzers 47, *47*
BL 60pdr long-range guns *46*, 47
Mk I 46
Mk II 47
Mk III *46*
BL Mk 1, 3 & 5 rail howitzers 90-1, *90*, *91*
Blue Water SRBM 178, *178*
BM-21 Grad rocket systems 216-17, *216*, *217*, 220
Bofors
cannons 142-3, *143*
FH-77A towed howitzers 184-5, *184*
L/70 AA guns 230, *230*
Model 1929 heavy AA guns 152, *152*
Model 1930 heavy AA guns 152
Model 1934 mountain howitzers 59, *59*
Böhler Model 35 anti-tank guns 118, *118*
Bordkanone AA guns 109
Breda
40L70 light AA guns 226-7, *226*, *227*
Modello 35 DP AA guns 140-1, *140*, *141*
Brummbär SP howitzers 96-7, *96*, *97*
BTR-40A AA artillery 22
BTR-152A SP AA guns 233, *233*

Calliope rocket launchers 132-3, *133*

Cannone da 75/27 field guns
modello 06 56, *56*
modello 11 34, *34*, 56, *56*

Cannone da 75/32 modello 37
field guns 57, *57*

Cannone da 75/46 C.A.
modello 34 heavy AA guns
150, *150*

Cannone da 90/53 heavy AA
guns 151, *151*

Canon de 75mle 1897 field
guns 31, *50*
captured 50
development of 30-1, 50
recoil mechanism 31, *31*
variants 31, 50

Canon de 105 court mle 1935
B howitzers 51, *51*

Canon de 105mle 1913
Schneider field guns 31, *31*,
50-1, *51*

Canon de 194 GPF SP heavy
guns 41, *41*

Canon de 220 L mle 1917
Schneider heavy guns 38-9,
38

Canon de 240 L mle 84/17 St
Chamond heavy guns 39, *39*

Canon de 240 Modèle 93/96
rail guns 82, *82*

Canon de 320 Modèle 70/93
rail guns 82-3, *82*

Canon de 320 T 17 rail guns
83, *83*

CITEFA Model 77 towed
howitzers 180, *180*

coastal defence guns
Kanone 18 72-3, *72*
Kanone 39 73, *73*

coastal defence howitzers,
28cm 43, *43*

computer control, rockets 27

Congreve rockets 14

Crusader SP howitzers 207,
207

CV 9040 AAV SP AA guns 248-9, *248*, *249*

D-20/M1955 gun-howitzers
163, *163*

D-30 towed howitzers 194,
194

Doher SP guns 165

Dragon SP AA guns 239, *239*

Duster SP AA guns 236, *236*

Ehrhardt 15pdr field guns 32,
32

El Alamain, Battle of 66-7, *112*

English Electric Blue Water
SRBM 178, *178*

Escorter 35 series SP AA guns
248, *248*

Excaliber, XM987 projectiles 24

Falklands campaign 188, *188*

FH-70 towed howitzers 184,
184

FH-77A towed howitzers 184-5, *184*

FH2000 towed gun-howitzers
183, *183*

field artillery
decline of 9
mobility 24-5
shrapnel 9, 36

field guns
Cannone da 75/27 34, *34*,
56, *56*
Cannone da 75/32 modello
37 57, *57*
Canon de 75mle 1897 30-1,
31, 50, *50*
Canon de 105mle 1913
Schneider 31, *31*, 50-1, *51*
Ehrhardt 15pdr 32, *32*
FK 16 *32*, 33
FK 16 nA 53, *53*
FK 40 109
FK 96 32-3, *32*, *33*
heavy
Kanone 18 72-3, *72*
Kanone 39 73, *73*
Kanone 16 42, *42*
Kanone 18 71, *71*
Kanone 18/40 71, *71*
leFK 18 53, *53*
M-46 162, *162*
medium, 5.5in 159, *159*
Model 00/02 34-5, *35*
Model 1910 35, *35*
Model 1910/30 76
Model 1936 13, 60, *60*
Model 1939 60-1
Model 1942 60, *60*, 61
Ordnance
QF 13pdr 36, *36*
QF 15pdr 36-7, *36*, *37*
QF 18pdr 37, *37*
Type 38 (Improved) 58, *58*

field howitzers
Battalion Gun Type 92 58,
58
BL 26cwt 47, *47*
M2A1 69, *69*
Model 1938 (M-10) 76-7, *77*
Model 1943 77
obice da 75/18 modello 35
56-7, *56*, *57*
Ordnance QF 46, *46*
sFH 18 72, *72*
Skoda
Modell 14 30, *30*
Modell 14/16 30, *30*
vz 37 (K4) 70, *70*
Type 64 77

fire control
data 18
radar 18-19

Firestone Corporal SRBM 178,
178

5.5in medium field guns 159,
159

FK 16 field guns *32*, 33

FK 16 nA field guns 53, *53*

FK 40 field guns 109

FK 96 field guns 32-3, *32*, *33*

Flak 18 medium AA guns 116,
116, 118, *118*, 136-7, 146,
147, *147*

Flak 30 light AA guns 135, *135*

Flak 36 medium AA guns *136*,
137, *137*, 146, *146*

Flak 37 medium AA guns 137,
146, *146*

Flak 38 light AA guns 16, 17,
17, 136, *136*, 148

Flak 39 light AA guns 148-9,
149

Flak 40 heavy AA guns 149,
149

Flak 41 AA guns 116, *116*, 140,
140, 148, *148*

Flak 43 light AA guns 137

Flak 88 AA guns 113, *113*

Flakvierling 38 light AA guns
136, *136*

Flakzwilling 43 light AA guns
137, *138*

flying bombs, V-1 18, *19*

fortifications, linear and ring 10

forward observers, uses of *10*

40L70 light AA guns 226-7,
226, 227

FROG series SRBM 176, *176*,
224, 225

G5 SP artillery systems 25, *25*

G5 towed gun-howitzers 185,
185

G6 SP artillery systems 24, 25

G6 SP gun-howitzers 203, *203*

GADES (Gun Air Defense
Effectiveness Study) 29

GCT/155 AUF1 SP guns 204,
204

Gepard SP AA guns 28, 29,
242, 243, *243*, 244-5, 246,
246

German Army
AA guns 16
Flakregiment, organisation
16-17
howitzer tactics 13

GHN-45 towed gun-howitzers
181, *181*

Giat LG1 light guns *24*, 25

guided projectiles, Krasnopol-M
196-7, *196*

Gun Air Defense Effectiveness
Study (GADES) 29

gun ranging, forward observers
10

gun-howitzers
see also howitzers
D-20/M1955 163, *163*
H M.1 11
introduction 10-11, 12-13
'Little David' 11
Model 137 11
Model 1910/34 76
Model 1931 11, *13*

Model 1937 76

Ordnance QF 25pdr 12-13,
13, 68, *68*
Mk 1 66, 68
Mk 2 *62-3*, 63, *64-5*, 66-8, *66*, 68

S-23/M1955 163, *163*

self-propelled
AS90 200-1, *201*
Bishop 103, *103*
G6 203, *203*
M7 Priest 104, *104*
Sexton 102, *102*
2S3/M1973 Akatsiya 199,
199
2S5 199, *199*
ZTS vz 77 Dana 203, *203*

towed
Armscor G5 185, *185*
FH2000 183, *183*
GHN-45 181, *181*
Soltam M-68 182-3, *182*,
183
Soltam M-71 183
Type 59-1 181
Type 66 181
Type 83 181
Type 85 181
Type 89 181, *181*

guns
see also field guns; gun-howitzers

assault
ASU-57 166, *166*
Sturmgeschütz III 98-9,
98, *99*
Sturmtiger 97, *97*

barrels 12

heavy
Canon de 220 L mle
1917 Schneider 38-9, *38*
Canon de 240 L mle
84/17 St Chamond 39,
39
M1 'Long Tom' 80, *80*
M1A1 80
M2 80
M40 80
M59 80
and howitzers 12-13
K18 *12*

light
Giat LG1 *24*, 25
L118 186-7, *186-7*
L118A1 189, *189*, *190*,
191, *191*
Royal Ordnance 25

Lightweight Experimental
Ordnance 25, *25*

long-range
BL 60pdr 46-7, *46*, *47*
lange Kanone in
Schiessgerüst 'Paris
Gun' 45, *45*

medium, Mk 2 78, *78*

propellants 12

range 12

self-propelled

Bandkanon 1A 202, *202*
Canon de 194 GPF 41, *41*
Doher 165
FV433 Abbot 200, *200*
GCT/155 AUF1 204, *204*
ISU-122 101, *101*
ISU-152 101, *101*
L33 165, *165*
M-50 165, *165*
M40 105, *105*
M107 171, *171*
M280 sur chenilles 41, *41*
Mk 61 164, *164*
Mk F3 164-5, *164*, *165*
Romach 165
Semovente da 149/40 92, *92*
SU-76 100, *100*
towed
  A36 195, *195*
  TR 182, *182*
ultra-heavy
  HM.1 74
  Kanone 3 74
  Kanone 4 74
uses 12
Gvozdika/M1974 SP howitzers 198, *198*, 212-13

H M.1 gun-howitzers 11
Hades SRBM 172
Hatf/Shadoz SRBM *172*, 173
heavy AA guns
  Bofors Model 1929 152, *152*
  Bofors Model 1930 152
  Cannone da 75/46 C.A. modello 34 150, *150*
  Cannone da 90/53 151, *151*
  Flak 40 149, *149*
  M1 157, *157*
  M2 157, *157*
  M3 *18*, 156, *156*
  Model 1939 152-3, *152*
  Model 1944 152-3
  Ordnance
    QF 3in 153, *153*
    QF 3.7in 154-5, *154*
    QF 4.5in Mk II 155, *155*
  Schneider mle 1936 150, *150*
  Type 88 151, *151*
heavy field guns
  Kanone 18 72-3, *72*
  Kanone 39 73, *73*
heavy guns
  see also self-propelled heavy guns
  Canon de 220 L mle 1917 Schneider 38-9, *38*
  Canon de 240 L mle 84/17 St Chamond 39, *39*
  M1 'Long Tom' 80, *80*
  M1A1 80
  M2 80
  M40 80
  M59 80

heavy howitzers
  Kanone 18 74, *74*
  Kanone Mörser 18 74
  M1 79, *79*, 81, *81*
  M43 81
  M115 81
  Model 1931 77, *77*
  Mortier de 280mle 14/16 Schneider 40, *40*
  Mortier de 370 Filloux 40-1, *40*, *41*
  Obice da 210/22 modello 35 75, *75*
  Skoda
    220mm 70-1, *70*
    Model 1911 38, *38*
    Model 1914 38
    Model 1916 Barbara 38
    Model 1917 38
Hedgehog rocket launcher 14, *14*
high explosives shells 9
HM.1 ultra-heavy guns 74
HMG siege rail guns 91, *91*
Holt tractors *9*
Honest John SRBM 20, 179, *179*
Hotchkiss
  Mle 1938 light AA guns 134, *134*
  Mle 1939 light AA guns 134
  Mle 1940 light AA guns 134
howitzers
  see also gun-howitzers
  barrels 12
  BL 8in 48, *48*
  British 7.2in *10*
  Canon de 105 court mle 1935 B 51, *51*
  coastal defence, 28cm 43, *43*
  effectiveness 9, 10
  field
    Battalion Gun Type 92 58, *58*
    BL 26cwt 47, *47*
    M2A1 69, *69*
    Model 1938 (M-10) 76-7, *77*
    Model 1943 77
    obice da 75/18 modello 35 56-7, *56*, *57*
    Ordnance QF 4.5in 46, *46*
    sFH 18 72, *72*
    Skoda Modell 14 30, *39*
    Skoda Modell 14/16 30, *30*
    Skoda vz 37 (K4) 70, *70*
    Type 64 77
  German
    30.6cm/12in *9*
    105mm/4.13in *12*
    150mm/5.9in *13*
  German Army, tactics 13 and guns 12-13
  heavy
    Kanone 18 74, *74*

Kanone Mörser 18 74
M1 79, *79*, 81, *81*
M43 81
M115 81
Model 1931 77, *77*
Mortier de 280mle 14/16 Schneider 40, *40*
Mortier de 370 Filloux 40-1, *40*, *41*
Obice da 210/22 modello 35 75, *75*
Skoda 220mm 70-1, *70*
Skoda Model 1911 38, *38*
Skoda Model 1914 38
Skoda Model 1916 Barbara 38
Skoda Model 1917 38
infantry, schwere
  Infantriegeschutz 33 54, *54*
light
  Infantry Mk II 68, *68*
  leFH 18(M) 55, *55*
  M1A1 Pack 69, *69*
M-56 197, *197*
M-Gerät 'Big Bertha' 44, *44*
M1 'Long Tom' 11, *11*
M2A1 13
M102 *12*
Mks I-V & 6 79, *79*
mountain, Bofors Model 1934 59, *59*
pack, OTO-Malera modella 56 158-9, *158*, *159*
rail, BL Mk 1, 3 & 5 90-1, *90*, *91*
Russian 6in/152mm *8*
self-propelled
  Brummbär 96-7, *96*, *97*
  Crusader 207, *207*
  Hummel 94-5, *94*, *95*
  Karl series 96, *96*
  M37 168
  M44 168, *168*
  M52 168-9, *168*, *169*
  M109 series 206, *206*, 208, *208*, 209, *209*, 210-11
  M110 206-7, *207*
  Palmaria 202, *202*
  PzH 2000 201, *201*
  sIG 33 auf Geschützwagen 93, *93*
  Slammer 204, *204*
  2S1 Gvozdika/M1974 198, *198*
  Type 4 HO-RO 93
  Type 75 205, *205*
  Type 97 93-4, *93*, *94*
  Waffentrager 95, *95*
  Wespe 94, *94*
siege
  9.2in/234mm *8*
  28cm 43, *43*
  BL 9.2in 48, *48*
  BL 12in 49, *49*
  BL 15in 49, *49*

Skoda
  kanon vz 14 52-3, *52*
  kanon vz 14/19 53
  kanon vz 30 52, *52*
towed
  Bofors FH-77A 184-5, *184*
  CITEFA Model 77 180, *180*
  D-30 194, *194*
  FH-70 184, *184*
  M101 160, *160*
  M101A1 160
  M114 161, *161*
  M119A1 193, *193*
  M198 192, *192*
  M777 193, *193*
  Modèle 50 158, *158*
uses 12
Hummel SP howitzers 94-5, *94*, *95*

infantry howitzers, schwere
  Infantriegeschutz 33 54, *54*
Infantry Mk II light howitzers 68, *68*
Intermediate Nuclear Forces (INF) treaty 20
ISU-122 SP guns 101, *101*
ISU-152 SP guns 101, *101*

Jericho 1 SRBM 173

K4 field howitzers 70, *70*
K4 ultra-heavy guns 74
K16 guns 42, *42*
K18 field guns 71, *71*, 72-3, *72*
K18 guns *12*
K18/40 field guns 71, *71*
K39 heavy field guns 73, *73*
Kanone 3 ultra-heavy guns 74
Kanone 4 ultra-heavy guns 74
Kanone 16 field guns 42, *42*
Kanone 18 field guns 71, *71*
Kanone 18 heavy field guns 72-3, *72*
Kanone 18 heavy howitzers 74, *74*
Kanone 18/40 field guns 71, *71*
Kanone 39 heavy field guns 73, *73*
Kanone (E) 'Schwere Gustav' rail guns 86-7, *86-7*
Kanone Mörser 18 heavy howitzers 74
Kanonen 5 (E) rail guns 85, *85*
Kanonen 12 (E) experimental rail guns 84-5, *84*, *85*
Kanonen (E) 15cm rail guns 84, *84*
Kanonen (E) 17cm rail guns 84, *84*
Karl series SP howitzers 96, *96*
Katyusha series rocket launchers 127-9, *129*
King's Troop, Royal Artillery 36
Krasnopol-M guided projectiles 196-7, *196*

L 13 S 31, *31*, 50-1, *51*
L 17 S 38-9, *38*
L33 SP guns 165, *165*
L118 light guns 186-7, *186-7*
L118A1 light guns 189, *189*, *190*, 191, *191*
Lance SRBM *21*
Land Mattress rocket launchers 15, *15*, 131, *131*
Land Rover tractors 186, *186*, *191*
lange Kanone in Schiessgerüst, 'Paris Gun 45, *45*
LARS II rocket systems 215, *215*
LARS rocket systems, development 218
leFH 18(M) light howitzers 55, *55*
leFK 18 field guns 53, *53*
lePak 41 anti-tank guns 111, *111*
light AA guns
  Breda 40L70 226-7, *226*, *227*
  Flak 30 135, *135*
  Flak 38 *16*, 17, *17*, 136, *136*, 148
  Flak 39 148-9, *149*
  Flak 43 137
  Flakvierling 38 136, *136*
  Flakzwilling 43 137, *138*
  Hotchkiss Mle 1938 134, *134*
  Hotchkiss Mle 1939 134
  Hotchkiss Mle 1940 134
  M1A2 145, *145*
  Maxson Mount 144-5, *144*, *145*
  Polsten 144, *144*
  RAMTA TCM-20 227, *227*
  Rheinmetall Twin 226, *226*
  Tarasque 228, *228*
  ZU-23 228-9, *228*, *229*
light armoured cars, T17 Staghound *29*
light guns
  Giat LG1 *24*, 25
  L118 186-7, *186-7*
  L118A1 189, *189*, *190*, 191, *191*
  Royal Ordnance 105mm 25
light howitzers
  Infantry Mk II 68, *68*
  leFH 18(M) 55, *55*
  M1A1 Pack 69, *69*
Lightweight Experimental Ordnance 25, *25*
LILO rockets 131, *131*
'Little David' gun-howitzer 11
'Long Tom'M1 howitzer/gun 11, *11*, 80, *80*
long-range counter-bombardment guns 10
long-range guns
  BL 60pdr 46-7, *46*, *47*
  'Paris Gun' 45, *45*

M-8 rockets 127, *127*
M-10 field howitzers 76-7, *77*
M-13 rockets 128-9, *128*, *129*
M-30 rockets 127, *127*
M-31 rockets 127
M-46 field guns 162, *162*
M-50 SP guns 165, *165*
M-56 howitzers 197, *197*
M-68 towed gun-howitzers 182-3, *182*, *183*
M-71 towed gun-howitzers 183
M-Gerät 'Big Bertha' howitzers 44, *44*
M1 heavy AA guns *18*, 157, *157*
M1 heavy howitzers 79, *79*, 81, *81*
M1 'Long Tom' 155mm howitzer 11, *11*
M1 'Long Tom' heavy guns 80, *80*
M1A1 heavy guns 80
M1A1 Pack light howitzers 69, *69*
M1A2 light AA guns 145, *145*
M2 heavy AA guns 157, *157*
M2 heavy guns 80
M2A1 field howitzers 13, 69, *69*
M3 heavy AA guns 156, *156*
M3/VDA SP AA guns 238, *238*
M3A1 anti-tank guns 122, *122*
M5 anti-tank guns 122, *122*
M7 Priest SP gun-howitzers 104, *104*
M8 rockets *14*, 15, *15*, 132, *132*
M16 rockets *132*, 133
M37 SP howitzers 168
M40 heavy guns 80
M40 SP guns 105, *105*
M42 Duster SP AA guns 236, *236*
M43 heavy howitzers 81
M44 self-propelled howitzers 168, *168*
M50 Ontos tank destroyers 170, *170*
M52 SP howitzers 168-9, *168*, *169*
M53 SP artillery 169, *169*
M53/59 SP AA guns 232, *232*
M55 SP artillery 169, *169*
M56 Scorpion SP anti-tank guns 170-1, *170*, *171*
M59 heavy guns 80
M101 towed howitzers 160, *160*
M101A1 towed howitzers 160
M102 howitzer *12*
M102 towed howitzers 160-1, *160*
M107 SP guns 171, *171*
M109 SP howitzers 206, *206*, 208, *208*, 209, *209*, 210-11 and 2S1 Gvozdika *212-13*
M109A1 SP howitzers 206, 208

M109A2 SP howitzers 206, 208, *211*
M109A3 SP howitzers 206, *210*
M109A3G SP howitzers *209*
M109A4 SP howitzers 206, 208
M109A5 SP howitzers 206, 208
M109A6 Paladin SP howitzers 206, 208
M110 SP howitzers 206-7, *207*
M114 towed howitzers 161, *161*
M115 heavy howitzers 81
M119A1 towed howitzers 193, *193*
M163 Vulcan SP AA guns 236-7, *236*, *237*
M198 towed howitzers 192, *192*
M247 Sgt York SP AA guns *28*, 29, 237, *237*
M270 MLRS *219*, 221
M280 sur chenilles SP heavy guns 41, *41*
M777 towed howitzers 193, *193*
M1932 anti-tank guns 120
M1936 anti-tank guns 121, *121*
M1938 anti-tank guns 120
M1942 anti-tank guns 121, *121*
Maxson Mount light AA guns 144-5, *144*, *145*
medium AA guns
  Flak 18 116, *116*, 118, *118*, 136-7, 146, 147, *147*
  Flak 36 *136*, 137, *137*, 146, *146*
  Flak 37 137, 146, *146*
  Schneider Mle 1930 134-5, *134*
medium field guns, 5.5in 159, *159*
medium guns, Mk 2 78, *78*
Mk 2 medium guns 78, *78*
Mk 10 & Mk 13 rail guns 90, *90*
Mk 61 SP guns 164, *164*
Mk F3 SP guns 164-5, *164*, *165*
Mks I-V & 6 howitzers 79, *79*
MLRS rockets 26, *26*
Möbelwagen SP AA guns 138, *138*
Model 00/02 field guns 34-5, *35*
Model 35 anti-tank guns 118, *118*
Model 137 gun-howitzers 11
Model 1910 field guns 35, *35*
Model 1910/30 field guns 76
Model 1910/34 gun-howitzers 76
Model 1929 heavy AA guns 152, *152*
Model 1930 heavy AA guns 152

Model 1931 gun-howitzers 11, *13*
Model 1931 heavy howitzers 77, *77*
Model 1934 mountain howitzers 59, *59*
Model 1936 field guns 13, 60, *60*
Model 1937 anti-tank guns 120
Model 1937 gun-howitzers 76
Model 1938 (M-10) field howitzers 76-7, *77*
Model 1939 field guns 60-1
Model 1939 heavy AA guns 152-3, *152*
Model 1942 anti-tank guns 120, *120*
Model 1942 field guns 60-1, *60*, *61*
Model 1943 field howitzers 77
Model 1944 heavy AA guns 152-3
Modèle 50 towed howitzers 158, *158*
Modèle 1912 rail guns 83, *83*
Modello 35 DP AA guns 140-1, *140*, *141*
Mortier de 280mle 14/16 Schneider heavy howitzers 40, *40*
Mortier de 370 Filloux heavy howitzers 40-1, *40*, *41*
mountain howitzers, Bofors Model 1934 59, *59*
muzzle brakes 55, *55*
  25pdr gun-howitzers 68

Nebelwerfer 41 rocket launchers 124, 125
Nebelwerfer 42 rocket launchers 125, 126

Obice da 75/18 modello 35 field howitzers 56-7, *56*, *57*
Obice da 210/22 modello 35 heavy howitzers 75, *75*
Oerlikon
  AA cannons 142, *142*
  GAI-DO1 AA guns 231, *231*
Ordnance
  QF 2pdr anti-tank guns 106, *106*
  QF 3in heavy AA guns 153, *153*
  QF 3.7in heavy AA guns 154-5, *154*
  QF 4.5in field howitzers 46, *46*
  QF 4.5in Mk II heavy AA guns 155, *155*
  QF 6pdr anti-tank guns 106-7, *106*, *107*
  QF 13pdr field guns 36, *36*
  QF 15pdr field guns 36-7, *36*, *37*
  QF 17pdr anti-tank guns 107, *107*
  QF 18pdr field guns 37, *37*

Mk I 37, *37*
Mk IV 37
QF 25pdr gun-howitzers 12-13, *13*, *66*, *67*, 68, *68*
  anti-tank role 67
  muzzle brakes 68
  Mk 1 *66*, 68
  Mk 2 *64*, *65*, 68
Ostwind SP AA guns 139, *139*
OTO-Malera modella 56 pack howitzers 158-9, *158*, *159*
OTOMATIC SP AA guns 247, *247*

pack howitzers, OTO-Malera modella 56 158-9, *158*, *159*
Pak 35/36 anti-tank guns 108, *108*
Pak 38 anti-tank guns 108-9, *108*
Pak 40 anti-tank guns 109, *109*
Pak 41 anti-tank guns 111, *111*
Pak 43 anti-tank guns 110, *110*
Pak 43/41 anti-tank guns 110
Pak 88 anti-tank guns 113, *113*, *114-15*
  AA role 113, 114, 116, *116-17*
  development of 117
  rail guns 116
  range 115
  shortcomings 115
  variants 114
Paladin SP howitzers 206, 208
Palmaria SP howitzers 202, *202*
Panhard M3/VDA SP AA guns 238, *238*
'Paris Gun, lange Kanone in Schiessgerüst 45, *45*
Pluton SRBM 20, 172, *172*
PLZ45 SP artillery 205
Polsten light AA guns 144, *144*
Prithvi SRBM 172-3, *173*
projectiles
  guided, Krasnopol-M 196-7, *196*
  SP artillery systems 25
propellants, rockets 26-7
PzH 2000 SP artillery systems *24*, 25
PzH 2000 SP howitzers 201, *201*

quick-fire artillery 8
  trench warfare 8

radar, fire control 18-19
rail guns
  Canon de 240 Modèle 93/96 82, *82*
  Canon de 320 Modèle 70/93 82-3, *82*
  Canon de 320 T 17 83, *83*
  Kanone (E) 'Schwere Gustav' 86-7, *86-7*
  Kanonen 5 (E) 85, *85*
  Kanonen 12 (E)

experimental 84-5, *84*, *85*
  Kanonen (E) 15cm 84, *84*
  Kanonen (E) 17cm 84, *84*
  Mk 10 & Mk 13 90, *90*
  Modèle 1912 83, *83*
  Pak 88 anti-tank guns 116
  Schiffskanone L/45 'Max' *8*
  siege, HMG 91, *91*
rail howitzers, BL Mk 1, 3 & 5 90-1, *90*, *91*
RAMTA TCM-20 light AA guns 227, *227*
range-finding, anti-aircraft guns 19
rangefinders, wide-base 18, *19*
Rheinmetall Twin light AA guns 226, *226*
RM-70 rocket systems 224, *224*
rocket launchers
  see also rocket systems
  Katyusha series 127-9, *129*
  Land Mattress 15, *15*, 131, *131*
  M270 MLRS *219*, *221*
  Nebelwerfer 41 124, 125
  Nebelwerfer 42 125, 126
  T27 132, *133*
  T32 Calliope 132-3, *133*
  T66 133
  Type 4 126
rocket systems
  see also rocket launchers
  ASTROS II *27*, 214, *214*, *222*, *223*
  BM-21 Grad 216-17, *216*, *217*, *220*
  LARS, development 218
  LARS II 215, *215*
  RM-70 224, *224*
  Rocketsan 225, *225*
  Valkiri
    Mark I 215, *215*
    Mark II *26*
  WS-1B 214, *214*
rockets
  accuracy 14
  anti-aircraft
    2in 130, *130*
    3in 130, *130*
    Army 20cm 126, *126*
  computer control 27
  Congreve 14
  Hedgehog 14, *14*
  LILO 131, *131*
  M-8 127, *127*
  M-13 128-9, *128*, *129*
  M-30 127, *127*
  M-31 127
  M8 *14*, 15, *15*, 132, *132*
  M16 *132*, 133
  MLRS *26*, *26*
  propellants 26-7
  rail launched 14
  Skyfire *222*
  stabilisation
    fins 15
    spin 15

warheads 27
Wurfgranate 41 124
Wurfgranate 42 15cm 124, *124*
Wurfgranate 42 21cm 124-5, *124*, *125*
Wurfkörpfer 42 126, *126*
Wurfkörpfer Spreng 125, *125*
Rocketsan rocket systems 225, *225*
Romach SP guns 165
Royal Marine Artillery crews 49
Royal Ordnance light guns 25

S-23/M1955 gun-howitzers 163, *163*
S-60 AA guns 229, *229*
SA mle 1937 anti-tank guns 123, *123*
SA-L mle 1934 anti-tank guns 123, *123*
SA-L mle 1937 anti-tank guns 123
Schiffskanone L/45 'Max' rail guns *8*
Schlieffen Plan 44
Schneider
  Mle 1930 medium AA guns 134-5, *134*
  Mle 1936 heavy AA guns 150, *150*
'Schwere Gustav' rail guns 86-7, *86-7*
schwere Infantriegeschutz 33 infantry howitzers 54, *54*
Scud-A SRBM 20, 174, *174*, *175*
Scud-B SRBM 20, 174
Scud-C SRBM 174
SdKfz 7/2 SP AA guns 139, *139*
self-propelled AA guns
  AMX-13 DCA 238-9, *238*, *239*
  BTR-152A 233, *233*
  CV 9040 AAV 248-9, *248*, *249*
  development 28-9
  Dragon 239, *239*
  Escorter 35 series 248, *248*
  Gepard *28*, 29, *242*, 243, *243*, *244-5*, 246, *246*
  M42 Duster 236, *236*
  M53/59 232, *232*
  M163 Vulcan 236-7, *236*, *237*
  M247 Sgt York *28*, 29, 237, *237*
  Möbelwagen 138, *138*
  Ostwind 139, *139*
  OTOMATIC 247, *247*
  Panhard M3/VDA 238, *238*
  SdKfz 7/2 139, *139*
  Tridon 249, *249*
  2S6 Tunguska IADS 235, *235*
  Type 63 232-3, *232*, *233*

Vulcan *29*
Wildcat 29, *29*, 246-7, *246*, *247*
Wirbelwind 138, *138*
ZSU-23-4 Shilka 240, *240*, *241*, 243, *243*
ZSU-57-2 22-3, *23*, 29, 234, *234*
ZSU-57-4 234-5, *234*, *235*
self-propelled anti-tank guns
  ASU-85 166-7, *166*, *167*
  M56 Scorpion 170-1, *170*, *171*
self-propelled artillery
  M53 169, *169*
  M55 169, *169*
  PLZ45 205
  2S19/MSTA-S 198, *198*
  Type 54-1 205
  Type 83 205, *205*
  Type 85 205
self-propelled artillery systems
  G5 25, *25*
  G6 *24*, 25
  Giat Caesar 25
  projectiles 25
  PzH 2000 *24*, 25
self-propelled gun-howitzers
  AS90 200-1, *201*
  Bishop 103, *103*
  G6 203, *203*
  M7 Priest 104, *104*
  Sexton 102, *102*
  2S3/M1973 Akatsiya 199, *199*
  2S5 199, *199*
  ZTS vz 77 Dana 203, *203*
self-propelled guns
  Bandkanon 1A 202, *202*
  Canon de 194 GPF 41, *41*
  Doher 165
  FV433 Abbot 200, *200*
  GCT/155 AUF1 204, *204*
  ISU-122 101, *101*
  ISU-152 101, *101*
  L33 165, *165*
  M-50 165, *165*
  M40 105, *105*
  M107 171, *171*
  M280 sur chenilles 41, *41*
  Mk 61 164, *164*
  Mk F3 164-5, *164*, *165*
  Romach 165
  Semovente da 149/40 92, *92*
  SU-76 100, *100*
self-propelled howitzers
  Brummbär 96-7, *96*, *97*
  Crusader 207, *207*
  Hummel 94-5, *94*, *95*
  Karl series 96, *96*
  M37 168
  M44 168, *168*
  M52 168-9, *168*, *169*
  M109 series 206, *206*, 208, *208*, 209, *209*, *210-11*
  M110 206-7, *207*
  Palmaria 202, *202*

PzH 2000 201, *201*
sIG 33 auf Geschützwagen 93, *93*
Slammer 204, *204*
2S1 Gvozdika/M1974 198, *198*
Type 4 HO-RO 93
Type 75 205, *205*
Type 97 93-4, *93*, *94*
Waffentrager 95, *95*
Wespe 94, *94*
Semovente da 149/40 SP guns 92, *92*
Sexton SP gun-howitzers 102, *102*
sFH 18 field howitzers 72, *72*
Sgt York SP AA guns 28, 29, 237, *237*
shell scandal 46
short-range ballistic missiles 20, *20*
  advantages 21
  English Electric Blue Water 178, *178*
  Firestone Corporal 178, *178*
  FROG series 176, *176*
  Hades 172
  Hatf/Shadoz *172*, 173
  Honest John 20, 179, *179*
  Jericho 1 173
  Lance *21*
  nuclear capability 20
  Pluton *20*, 172, *172*
  Prithvi 172-3, *173*
  Sperry Sergeant 179, *179*
  SS-1b Scud-A 20, 174, *174*, *175*
  SS-1c Scud-B 20, 174
  SS-1d Scud-C 174
  SS-12 Scaleboard 175, *175*
  SS-20 Saber 177, *177*
  SS-21 Scarab 177, *177*
  SS-23 Spider 177, *177*
  Transport-Erector-Launchers 20, *21*, 172
shrapnel
  types of 36
  uses of 9
siege howitzers
  9.2in/234mm *8*
  28cm 43, *43*
  BL 9.2in 48, *48*
  BL 12in 49, *49*
  BL 15in 49, *49*
siege rail guns, HMG 91, *91*
sIG 33 auf Geschützwagen self-propelled howitzers 93, *93*
sights, wire *18*
Skoda
  heavy howitzers 70-1, *70*
  kanon P.U.V. vz 36 anti-tank guns 118-19, *118*, *119*
  kanon vz 14 howitzers 52-3, *52*
  kanon vz 14/19 howitzers 53
  kanon vz 30 howitzers 52, *52*

Model 14 field howitzers 30, *39*
Model 14/16 field howitzers 30, *30*
Model 1911 heavy howitzers 38, *38*
Model 1914 heavy howitzers 38
Model 1916 Barbara heavy howitzers 38
Model 1917 heavy howitzers 38
vz 37 (K4) field howitzers 70, *70*
Skyfire rockets *222*
Slammer SP howitzers 204, *204*
soixante-quinze *see* Canon de 75mle 1897 field guns
Soltam
  M-68 towed gun-howitzers 182-3, *182*, *183*
  M-71 towed gun-howitzers 183
Sperry Sergeant SRBM 179, *179*
sPzB 41 anti-tank guns 111, *111*
SRBM *see* short range ballistic missiles
SS-1b Scud-A SRBM 20, 174, *174*, *175*
SS-1c Scud-B SRBM 20, 174
SS-1d Scud-C SRBM 174
SS-12 Scaleboard SRBM 175, *175*
SS-20 Saber SRBM 177, *177*
SS-21 Scarab SRBM 177, *177*
SS-23 Spider SRBM 177, *177*
Sturmgeschütz III assault guns 98-9, *98*, *99*
Sturmtiger assault guns 97, *97*
SU-76 SP guns 100, *100*
SU-100 tank destroyers 167, *167*

T-12/MT-12 anti-tank guns 196, *196*
T17 Staghound light armoured cars *29*
T27 rocket launchers 132, *133*
T32 Calliope rocket launchers 132-3, *133*
T66 rocket launchers 133
tank destroyers
  M50 Ontos 170, *170*
  SU-100 167, *167*
tanks, Sherman, rocket launchers *14*
taper-bore anti-tank guns 111
Tarasque light AA guns 228, *228*
TCM-20 light AA guns 227, *227*
TEL (Transport-Erector-Launchers) 20
3in AA rockets 130, *130*
towed gun-howitzers

Armscor G5 185, *185*
FH2000 183, *183*
GHN-45 181, *181*
Soltam
  M-68 182-3, *182*, *183*
  M-71 183
Type 59-1 181
Type 66 181
Type 83 181
Type 85 181
Type 89 181, *181*
towed guns
  TR 182, *182*
  A36 195, *195*
towed howitzers
  Bofors FH-77A 184-5, *184*
  CITEFA Model 77 180, *180*
  D-30 194, *194*
  FH-70 184, *184*
  M101 160, *160*
  M101A1 160
  M102 160-1, *160*
  M114 161, *161*
  M119A1 193, *193*
  M198 192, *192*
  M777 193, *193*
  Modèle 50 158, *158*
TR towed guns 182, *182*
Transport-Erector-Launchers (TEL) 20, *21*
trench warfare, quick-fire artillery 8
Tridon SP AA guns 249, *249*
25-pdr *see* Ordnance QF 25pdr
2A36 towed guns 195, *195*
2A45M Sprut-B anti-tank guns 196, *196*
2in AA rockets 130, *130*
2S1 Gvozdika/M1974 SP howitzers 198, *198*, *212-13* and M109 *212-13*
2S3/M1973 Akatsiya SP gun-howitzers 199, *199*
2S5 SP gun-howitzers 199, *199*
2S6 Tunguska IADS SP AA guns 235, *235*
2S6M Tunguska AA artillery *22*, 23
2S19/MSTA-S self-propelled artillery 198, *198*
Type 1 anti-tank guns 119, *119*
Type 4 HO-RO SP howitzers 93
Type 4 rocket launchers 126
Type 38 (Improved) field guns 58, *58*
Type 54-1 SP artillery 205
Type 59-1 towed gun-howitzers 181
Type 63 SP AA guns 232-3, *232*, *233*
Type 64 field howitzers 77
Type 66 towed gun-howitzers 181
Type 75 SP howitzers 205, *205*
Type 83 SP artillery 205, *205*
Type 83 towed gun-howitzers 181
Type 85 SP artillery 205

Type 85 towed gun-howitzers 181
Type 88 heavy AA guns 151, *151*
Type 89 towed gun-howitzers 181, *181*
Type 97 SP howitzers 93-4, *93*, *94*
Type 98 AA cannons 141, *141*

ultra-heavy guns
  HM.1 74
  Kanone 3 74
  Kanone 4 74

V-1 flying bombs 18, *19*
V-2 missiles 20
Valkiri rocket systems
  Mk I 215, *215*
  Mk II *26*
Vulcan SP AA guns 29, *29*, 236-7, *236*, *237*

Waffentrager SP howitzers 95, *95*
warheads, rockets 27
Wespe SP howitzers 94, *94*
Wildcat SP AA guns 29, *29*, 246-7, *246*, *247*
Wirbelwind SP AA guns 138, *138*
WS-1B rocket systems 214, *214*
Wurfgranate 41 rockets 124
Wurfgranate 42 rockets
  15cm 124, *124*
  21cm 124-5, *124*, *125*
Wurfkörpfer 42 rockets 126, *126*
Wurfkörpfer Spreng rockets 125, *125*

XM987 Excaliber projectiles 24

ZSU-23-4 Shilka SP AA guns *22*, 23, *23*, *28*, 29, 240, *240*, 241, 243, *243*
ZSU-57-2 SP AA guns 22-3, *23*, 29, 234, *234*
ZSU-57-4 SP AA guns 234-5, *234*, *235*
ZTS vz 77 Dana SP gun-howitzers 203, *203*
ZU-23 light AA guns 228-9, *228*, *229*